S0-AIO-820

Annals of Mathematics Studies

Number 57

ANNALS OF MATHEMATICS STUDIES

Edited by Robert C. Gunning, John C. Moore, and Marston Morse

1. Algebraic Theory of Numbers, *by* HERMANN WEYL
3. Consistency of the Continuum Hypothesis, *by* KURT GÖDEL
11. Introduction to Nonlinear Mechanics, *by* N. KRYLOFF *and* N. BOGOLIUBOFF
20. Contributions to the Theory of Nonlinear Oscillations, Vol. I, *edited by* S. LEFSCHETZ
21. Functional Operators, Vol. 1, *by* JOHN VON NEUMANN
24. Contributions to the Theory of Games, Vol. I, *edited by* H. W. KUHN *and* A. W. TUCKER
25. Contributions to Fourier Analysis, *edited by* A. ZYGMUND, W. TRANSUE, M. MORSE, A. P. CALDERON, *and* S. BOCHNER
28. Contributions to the Theory of Games, Vol. II, *edited by* H. W. KUHN *and* A. W. TUCKER
30. Contributions to the Theory of Riemann Surfaces, *edited by* L. AHLFORS *et al.*
33. Contributions to the Theory of Partial Differential Equations, *edited by* L. BERS, S. BOCHNER, *and* F. JOHN
34. Automata Studies, *edited by* C. E. SHANNON *and* J. MCCARTHY
38. Linear Inequalities and Related Systems, *edited by* H. W. KUHN *and* A. W. TUCKER
39. Contributions to the Theory of Games, Vol. III, *edited by* M. DRESHER, A. W. TUCKER *and* P. WOLFE
40. Contributions to the Theory of Games, Vol. IV, *edited by* R. DUNCAN LUCE *and* A. W. TUCKER
41. Contributions to the Theory of Nonlinear Oscillations, Vol. IV, *edited by* S. LEFSCHETZ
42. Lectures on Fourier Integrals, *by* S. BOCHNER
43. Ramification Theoretic Methods in Algebraic Geometry, *by* S. ABHYANKAR
44. Stationary Processes and Prediction Theory, *by* H. FURSTENBERG
45. Contributions to the Theory of Nonlinear Oscillations, Vol. V, *edited by* L. CESARI, J. LASALLE, *and* S. LEFSCHETZ
46. Seminar on Transformation Groups, *by* A. BOREL *et al.*
47. Theory of Formal Systems, *by* R. SMULLYAN
48. Lectures on Modular Forms, *by* R. C. GUNNING
49. Composition Methods in Homotopy Groups of Spheres, *by* H. TODA
50. Cohomology Operations, *lectures by* N. E. STEENROD, *written and revised by* D. B. A. EPSTEIN
51. Morse Theory, *by* J. W. MILNOR
52. Advances in Game Theory, *edited by* M. DRESHER, L. SHAPLEY, *and* A. W. TUCKER
53. Flows on Homogeneous Spaces, *by* L. AUSLANDER, L. GREEN, F. HAHN, *et al.*
54. Elementary Differential Topology, *by* J. R. MUNKRES
55. Degrees of Unsolvability, *by* G. E. SACKS
56. Knot Groups, *by* L. P. NEUWIRTH
57. Seminar on the Atiyah-Singer Index Theorem, *by* R. S. PALAIS
58. Continuous Model Theory, *by* C. C. CHANG *and* H. J. KEISLER
59. Lectures on Curves on an Algebraic Surface, *by* DAVID MUMFORD
60. Topology Seminar, Wisconsin, 1965, *edited by* R. H. BING *and* R. J. BEAN

SEMINAR ON THE ATIYAH-SINGER INDEX THEOREM

BY

Richard S. Palais

WITH CONTRIBUTIONS BY

M. F. ATIYAH
A. BOREL
E. E. FLOYD
R. T. SEELEY
W. SHIH
R. SOLOVAY

PRINCETON, NEW JERSEY
PRINCETON UNIVERSITY PRESS
1965

L.C. CARD: 65-17157

Second Printing 1966

PRINTED IN THE UNITED STATES OF AMERICA

CONTENTS

PREFACE ix

CHAPTER: STATEMENT OF THE THEOREM

OUTLINE OF THE PROOF, by A. Borel. 1

§1. The index theorem 1
§2. The topological index 4
§3. The analytical index 6
§4. Appendix. 9

CHAPTER II: REVIEW OF K-THEORY, by R. Solovay 13

§1. K(X) a finite CW-complex 13
§2. The Chern character 14
§3. The difference construction 15
§4. L-theory 18
§5. Products in L-theory. 20

CHAPTER III: THE TOPOLOGICAL INDEX OF AN OPERATOR ASSOCIATED

TO A G-STRUCTURE, by R. Solovay. 27

CHAPTER IV: DIFFERENTIAL OPERATORS ON VECTOR BUNDLES, by R.S. Palais 51

§1. Notation 51
§2. Jet bundles 55
§3. Differential operators and their symbols. 61
§4. Hermitian bundles and adjoint operators 69
§5. Green's forms 73
§6. Some classical differential operators 75
§7. Whitney sums 79
§8. Tensor products 81
§9. Connections and covariant derivatives 84
§10. Spin structures and Dirac operators 91

CHAPTER V: ANALYTICAL INDICES OF SOME CONCRETE OPERATORS, by
M. Solovay 95

§1. Review of Hodge theory. 95
§2. The Euler Characteristic 96
§3. The Hirzebruch signature theorem 98
§4. Odd-dimensional manifolds 103

CHAPTER VI: REVIEW OF FUNCTIONAL ANALYSIS, by R.S. Palais 107

CHAPTER VII: FREDHOLM OPERATORS, by R. S. Palais 119

CONTENTS

CHAPTER VIII: CHAINS OF HILBERTIAN SPACES, by R. S. Palais 125

§1. Chains 125
§2. Quadratic interpolation of pairs of hilbert spaces 131
§3. Quadratic interpolation of chains 139
§4. Scales and the chains $\{\ell^2_k(\mathbf{Z}^n, V)\}$ 141

CHAPTER IX: THE DISCRETE SOBOLEV CHAIN OF A VECTOR BUNDLE, by R. S. Palais 147

§1. The spaces $C^k(\xi)$ 147
§2. The hilbert space $H^0(\xi)$ 148
§3. The spaces $H^k(\xi)$ 149

CHAPTER X: THE CONTINUOUS SOBOLEV CHAIN OF A VECTOR BUNDLE, by R. S. Palais 155

§1. Continuous Sobolev chains 155
§2. The chains $\{H^k(T^n, V)\}$ 156
§3. An extension theorem 162
§4. The Rellich, Sobolev, and restriction theorems 164

CHAPTER XI: THE SEELEY ALGEBRA, by R. S. Palais 175

CHAPTER XII: HOMOTOPY INVARIANCE OF THE INDEX, by R. S. Palais . . . 185

CHAPTER XIII: WHITNEY SUMS, by R. S. Palais 191

§1. Direct sums of chains of hilbertian spaces 191
§2. The Sobolev chain of a Whitney sum 192
§3. Behaviour of Smbl_k with respect to Whitney sums 193
§4. Behaviour of Int_k and σ_k under Whitney sums 193
§5. Behaviour of the index under Whitney sums 194

CHAPTER XIV: TENSOR PRODUCTS, by R. S. Palais 197

§1. Tensor products of chains of hilbertian spaces 197
§2. The Sobolev chain of a tensor product of bundles 201
§3. The # operation 206
§4. The property (S6) of the Seeley Algebra 209
§5. Multiplicativity of the index 210

CHAPTER XV: DEFINITION OF i_a AND i_t ON $K(M)$, by R. M. Solovay. 215

§1. Definition of the analytical index on $K(B(M), S(M))$ 215
§2. Multiplicative properties of i_t 217
§3. Proof of Lemma 1 222
§4. Definition of i_t and i_a on $K(M)$ 223
§5. Summary of the properties of i_a and i_t on $K(M)$ 226
§6. Multiplicative properties of i on $K(X)$ 228
§7. Direct check that $i_a = i_t$ in some special cases 232

CONTENTS

CHAPTER XVI: CONSTRUCTION OF Int_k; by R. S. Palais and R. T. Seeley 235

§1. The Fourier Transform 235
§2. Calderón-Zygmund operators. 243
§3. Calderón-Zygmund operators for a compact manifold 259
§4. Calderón-Zygmund operators for vector bundles 266
§5. Definition and properties of $\mathrm{Int}_r(\xi, \eta)$. 270
§6. An element of $\mathrm{Int}_0(S^1)$ with analytical index -1 272
§7. The topological index of the operator of §6 275
§8. Sign conventions 281

CHAPTER XVII: COBORDISM INVARIANCE OF THE ANALYTICAL INDEX, by R. S. Palais and R. T. Seeley 285

CHAPTER XVIII: BORDISM GROUPS OF BUNDLES, by E. E. Floyd. 303

§1. Introductory remarks. 303
§2. Computation of $\Omega_k(X) \otimes \mathbf{Q}$ 306
§3. The bordism ring of bundles 307

CHAPTER XIX: THE INDEX THEOREM: APPLICATIONS, by R. M. Solovay . . 313

§1. Proof of the index theorem. 313
§2. An alternative formulation of the index theorem 315
§3. The non-orientable case of Theorem 2 318
§4. The Riemann-Roch-Hirzebruch theorem 324
§5. Generalities on integrality theorems. 326
§6. The integrality theorems. 329

APPENDIX I: THE INDEX THEOREM FOR MANIFOLDS WITH BOUNDARY, by M. F. Atiyah. 337

§1. Ellipticity for manifolds with boundary 338
§2. The difference element $[\sigma(d, b)]$ 346
§3. Comments on the proof 350

APPENDIX II: NON STABLE CHARACTERISTIC CLASSES AND THE TOPOLOGICAL INDEX OF CLASSICAL ELLIPTIC OPERATORS, by W. Shih . . 353

§1. Characteristic classes. 353
§2. τ-homomorphism 360
§3. The character of classical elliptic operators 362

PREFACE

The Index Theorem is a striking and central result in a rapidly developing field of research which may be described as the study of the relation between analytic and topological invariants of a certain class of linear maps between sections of differentiable vector bundles (the class of integro-differential, or pseudo-differential operators). The field is not really new and has several classical results, for example the Hodge theory of harmonic forms and the Hirzebruch formulation of the Riemann-Roch theorem, both of which are in fact closely related to the Index Theorem. Moreover, since the Index Theorem there have been other notable results discovered by Atiyah, Bott, Singer and others. To mention only two there is a mod 2 "index" defined for elliptic operators on real bundles with self adjoint symbols, which in certain cases seems to be related to the Arf invariant of a manifold, and there has been a remarkable generalization of the Lefschetz fixed point formula, which already has had important applications to the theory of h-cobordism and to the study of the fixed points of periodic transformations.

This book consists mainly of slightly revised notes of a seminar held at the Institute for Advanced Study in 1963-64 upon the initiative of A. Borel. Exceptions are Chapters XVI and XVII and the Appendix by M. Atiyah which were written somewhat later.

Aside from going through the details of the proof of the Index Theorem, the major emphasis of the seminar was placed on developing the topological and analytical machinery associated with integro-differential operators. On the topological side the agreement was to assume a reasonable degree of sophistication. Thus, the basic facts concerning K-theory and characteristic classes are reviewed rather than proved and the emphasis is on showing how, with these tools, elliptic operators give rise to cohomology classes and on studying the properties of these classes. On the analytical side, it was decided to start more or less *ab initio*. The reason for this somewhat unbalanced exposition is in part due to the predelictions of the organizers of the seminar, but also in part it is due to the fact that while most of the algebraic topology involved is covered in complete detail in easily accessible published papers, much of the analysis is quite recent, and the published versions often refer explicitly only to the case of trivial bundles over domains in Euclidean space.

I would like to thank the many persons who attended the seminar lectures and whose suggestions lead to a smoother presentation. In particular the section on jet bundles in Chapter IV was considerably improved by A. Vasquez and L. Charlap, and a suggestion by M. Kneser led to a smoother version of the section on Fredholm operators (Chapter VII).

I would also like to express my great appreciation to F. Browder, E. Nelson and E. Stein for their constant and invaluable advice while I was writing my part of these notes.

Finally, a very careful reading of the entire manuscript by W. Shih led to the elimination of a great number of misprints and other errors. For this I am sure he has the readers thanks as well as mine.

Richard S. Palais
Brandeis University
January, 1965

CHAPTER I

STATEMENT OF THE THEOREM

OUTLINE OF THE PROOF

A. Borel

As an introduction to the subject matter of this seminar, this lecture gives the statement and a rough description of the proof of the index theorem. More details on the proofs of the results stated and on the concepts discussed here will be found in the subsequent lectures.

Manifolds are compact, smooth (i.e., C^∞), orientable and *oriented*, consist of connected components of the same dimension, and, unless otherwise stated, have no boundary. Complex vector bundles will usually be denoted by the same letter as their total spaces. E_x denotes the fibre at a point x of a bundle E and $C^\infty(E)$ the space of smooth cross sections of a smooth complex vector bundle E over a manifold.

§1. The index theorem

1. Let X be a manifold, E, F smooth complex vector bundles on X. A differential operator d from E to F is a linear map $d: C^\infty(E) \to C^\infty(F)$ which is given locally by a matrix of ordinary (i.e., scalar) differential operators. More precisely, let U be the domain of definition of a local chart, $x_1, \ldots, x_n$ ($n = \dim X$) local coordinates, $C^\infty(U)$ the space of complex valued C^∞-functions on U, and choose sections of E and F over U which at each point $x \in U$ form a basis of E_x and F_x. Then d defines a map $C^\infty(U)^p \to C^\infty(U)^q$ ($p = \dim E_x$, $q = \dim F_x$ ($x \in U$)) given by a matrix $P(x, d) = (P(x, \partial/\partial x_1, \ldots, \partial/\partial x_n)_{ij})$ ($1 \leq i \leq p$; $1 \leq j \leq q$), where $P_{ij} \in C^\infty(U)[\partial/\partial x_1, \ldots, \partial/\partial x_n]$. The order r of

d is the maximum of the degrees of the P_{ij} in the partial derivatives. The characteristic matrix $\mathbf{Q}(x, \xi)$ of d at x is obtained from P by taking the terms of degree r, substituting indeterminates ξ_i for the partial derivatives $\partial/\partial x_i$, and multiplying by $(-1)^{r/2}$. To each cotangent vector $\xi_1 dx + \cdots + \xi_n dx_n$, there is then associated a $p \times q$ matrix $\mathbf{Q}(x, \xi)$ with complex coefficients. The system is elliptic if $p = q$ and if this matrix is invertible for all $\xi \neq 0$ and for all $x \in X$. Under those circumstances, it is known that ker d and coker $d = C^{\infty}(F)/\mathrm{Im}\, d$ are finite dimensional; the difference of their dimensions is the *index of* d. In order to distinguish it from another index, to be defined below, we shall call this the *analytical index* of d and denote it by $i_a(d)$. Thus

(1) $$i_a(d) = \dim \ker d - \dim \operatorname{coker} d \quad .$$

It is known that $i_a(d)$ is invariant under deformations of d, and this led Gelfand to ask whether it could be expressed in terms of topological data. The index theorem provides a positive answer to that question. In order to formulate it, a mixed rational cohomology class $\mathrm{ch}\, d \in H^*(X; \mathbf{Q})$, depending on the symbol of d (see section 2, below), is introduced. Let moreover $\mathcal{T}(X)$ be the Todd class or the complexified tangent bundle of X. It is obtained by considering the product of formal power series

$$-x_i^2(1-e^{-x_i})^{-1} \cdot (1-e^{x_i})^{-1} \quad ,$$

where the x_i $(i = 1, \ldots, s \geq \dim X/2)$ are indeterminates, expressing it as a formal sum of homogeneous polynomials, which are then symmetric in the x_i^2, writing these as polynomials in the elementary symmetric functions in the x_i^2's, and then replacing the j-th symmetric function by the j-th Pontrjagin class of X $(j = 1, 2, \ldots)$. The *topological index* $i_t(d)$ is then defined as

(2) $$i_t(d) = (\mathrm{ch}\, d \cdot \mathcal{T}(X))[X] \qquad (n = \dim X) \quad ,$$

where the right hand side stands for the value of the n-dimensional component of $\mathrm{ch}\, d.\ \mathcal{T}(X)$ on the fundamental cycle of X. We have then the

THEOREM (Atiyah-Singer). Let d be an elliptic operator on the manifold X. Then $i_a(d) = i_t(d)$.

This is not the most general form of the theorem. Atiyah and Singer have extended it: (a) to elliptic complexes, i.e., sequences of operators whose symbols form an exact sequence, but this can easily be reduced to the case of one operator; (b) to a wider class of operators; this is quite important for the proof, and will be dealt with at length in this seminar; (c) to boundary value problems; this will probably not be touched upon here, for lack of time and material. [See however, Appendix I, by M. Atiyah.] A fourth generalization, which would include Grothendieck's version of the Riemann-Roch theorem over $\mathbf{C}$, is contemplated but, as far as I know, has not yet been carried out.

The proof falls naturally into two parts: a topological one, which investigates the properties of $i_t(d)$, and an analytical one, concerned with $i_a(d)$. The former one also gives the motivation for the latter one, and here we shall summarize it first. Before doing that, however, we give some more details on ch d.

2. *The definition of* ch d. Let X be a finite CW-complex. The Grothendieck group $K(X)$ of X is the quotient of the free commutative group generated by the isomorphism classes of complex vector bundles on X by the subgroup generated by the elements $E - E' - E''$ where $0 \to E'' \to E \to E' \to 0$ is an exact sequence. If a base point $x \in X$ has been chosen, then $\tilde{K}(X)$ is the kernel of the homomorphism $K(X) \to \mathbf{Z}$ which assigns to each bundle E the dimension of E_x. If Y is a closed subcomplex of X, the relative Grothendieck group $K(X, Y)$ is by definition $\tilde{K}(X/Y)$, where X/Y means X with Y pinched to a point, which is then taken as base point.

Let now X be again a manifold. Let $B(X)$ (resp. $S(X)$) be the unit ball (resp. unit sphere) bundle of the cotangent bundle $T^*(X)$, with respect to some Riemannian metric, and $\pi: B(X) \to X$ the natural projection. It is known that, via cup product, $H^*(B(X), S(X))$ (any ring of coefficients) is a free module over $H^*(X)$, with a canonical generator U of degree $n = \dim X$, whence the existence of an isomorphism $\varphi_*: H^*(B(X),$
$\varphi_*: H^*(B(X), S(X)) \to H^*(X)$, the Thom isomorphism, which decreases dimensions by n, the inverse of $a \mapsto a \cup U (a \in H^*(X))$.

Let $d: C^\infty(E) \to C^\infty(F)$ be a differential operator of order r on X. It is well-known that the matrix $Q(x, \xi)$, which was defined above using local coordinates, has in fact an intrinsic meaning and associates to each $\xi \in T^*(X)_x$ a linear map of E_x into F_x. This linear map depends of course smoothly on x, ξ, whence a homomorphism $\sigma_r(d): \pi^*E \to \pi^*F$ of the bundles on $B(X)$ lifted from E and F via π, to be called the *symbol* of d. Ellipticity means that $\sigma_r(d)$, restricted to $S(X)$, is an isomorphism. In that case, one can associate to $(\pi^*E, \pi^*F, \sigma_r(d)|S(X))$ a difference element $[\sigma_r(d)] \in K(B(X), S(X))$ (see [2]). Then ch d is defined by

$$\text{ch } d = (-1)^{n(n+1)/2} \varphi_* \text{ch}[\sigma_r(d)] \quad , \tag{3}$$

where $\text{ch}[\sigma_r(d)] \in H^*(B(X), S(X); \mathbf{Q})$ is the Chern character of $[\sigma_r(d)]$.

§2. The topological index

The right hand side of (3) makes sense for any element $a \in K(B(X), S(X))$ regardless of whether it comes from an elliptic operator or not, and therefore so does i_t. The topological index may thus be viewed as a function on $K(B(X), S(X))$; it is a homomorphism of the latter into $\mathbf{Q}$, whose main properties are the following:

3. *Multiplicativity under* $\otimes$. Let X, X' be two manifolds. There is then a pairing

$$K(B(X), S(X)) \times K(B(X'), S(X')) \to K(B(X \times X'), S(X \times X'))$$

to be called a tensor product, and we have

$$i_t(a \otimes b) = i_t(a) \cdot i_t(b) \quad (a \in K(B(X), S(X)), \ b \in K(B(X'), S(X')). \tag{4}$$

Briefly, $a \otimes b$ is defined as follows. Choose bundles E, F on $B(X)$, E', F' on $B(X')$ and isomorphisms $\sigma: E \to F$, $\sigma': E' \to F'$ on $S(X)$ and $S(X')$ respectively, such that a and b are the corresponding difference elements, which is always possible. On $X \times Y$, the tensor product

$$0 \to E \otimes E' \to E \otimes F' + E' \otimes F \to E' \otimes F' \to 0$$

of the complexes $0 \to E \xrightarrow{\sigma} F \to 0$, $0 \to E' \xrightarrow{\sigma'} F' \to 0$, is easily seen to be an exact sequence on $S(X \times Y)$. The corresponding difference element [2] is then $a \otimes b$.

4. Let X be even dimensional. As we shall see later, there exists on X an elliptic differential system D_0, whose topological index is the L-genus of X, and whose analytical index is zero if $\dim X \equiv 2 \bmod 4$, equal to the index of X if $\dim X \equiv 0 \bmod 4$. Let $\chi_0 = [\sigma(D_0)]$.

On the other hand, $K(B(X), S(X))$ is a module over $K(X)$. We may therefore define i_t also on $K(X)$ by putting

$$(5) \qquad i_t(X, V) = i_t(V \cdot \chi_0), \quad (V \in K(X)) \quad .$$

This is a homomorphism of $K(X)$ into $\mathbf{Q}$. The subgroup $K(X) \quad \chi_0$ is of finite index in $K(B(X), S(X))$, and therefore i_t is completely determined by its values on this subgroup. The function i_t on $K(X)$ has the following properties:

(a) $i_t(X + Y, a + b) = i_t(X, a) + i_t(Y, b)$,

$$i_t(X, a \oplus b) = i_t(X, a) + i_t(X, b)$$

where $+$ is disjoint sum, $\oplus$ Whitney sum.

(b) $i_t(X \times Y, a \otimes b) = i_t(X, a) \cdot i_t(Y, b)$

(c) $i_t(X, a) = 0$ if $(X, a) \sim 0$, i.e., if there exists a manifold Y with boundary $X = \partial Y$, and an element $a' \in K(Y)$ whose restriction to X is equal to a.

(d) $i_t(P_{2n}(\mathbf{C})), 1) = 1$, $i_t(S^{2m}, V_m) = 2^m$, where V_m, 1 form a system of generators of $K(S^{2m})$.

5. Finally, a *uniqueness theorem* asserts that there is only one real valued function on the groups $K(X)$, X running through the even-dimensional manifolds, which satisfies (a) to (d).

This is in fact a consequence of a cobordism theorem. Let Σ be the set of isomorphism classes of objects $[X, a]$, where X is an even-dimensional manifold and $a \in K(X)$. let A be the set of equivalence classes in Σ under the relation: $[X, a] \sim [X', a']$ if there exists a manifold Y with $\partial Y = X - X'$ and an element $b \in K(Y)$ whose restriction to X (resp. X') is equal to a (resp. a'). The set A may be given a ring structure, with addition and multiplication defined by means of disjoint sum and tensor product, respectively. Moreover, the set A_1 of classes of elements [X, a], with a of virtual dimension one, is a subring. It may be shown that $A_1 \otimes \mathbf{Q}$ is a ring of polynomials over the classes of the elements which occur in (d) above. Now a real valued function on Σ satisfying (a), (b), (c) may be thought of as a homomorphism of $A \otimes \mathbf{Q}$ into $\mathbf{R}$. It follows rather directly from the structure theorem on $A_1 \otimes \mathbf{Q}$ just mentioned that such a function is completely determined by its values on the above elements.

§3. The analytical index

The uniqueness theorem above suggests naturally to try to consider i_a as a function on K(B(X), S(X)) and prove that it has the same properties as i_t. This will be possible if the two following assertions are true

(i) if d, d' are elliptic operators whose symbols define the same element of K(B(X), S(X)), then $i_a(d) = i_a(d')$;

(ii) every element of K(B(X), S(X)) is the class of a symbol of an elliptic operator.

In (i), the assumption means that the symbols are homotopic. On the other hand, homotopic operators have the same analytical index, therefore (i) will be a consequence of

(iii) a homotopy between symbols can be "raised" to a homotopy between elliptic operators.

It appears that (ii), (iii) are not true in general for differential elliptic operators. This has led one to consider a wider class of elliptic operators, for which both i_a and i_t are still defined, in which there are enough elements to fulfill (ii), (iii), and to prove the index theorem for these operators. This brings us to the first topic of the analytical part of the proof:

6. *The Seeley algebra* $\mathrm{Int}_r(E, F)$ *of operators of order* $\leq r$ [5]. In order to give a rough idea of what these operators are, we recall

first some facts on operators on $\mathbf{R}^n$, using the standard multiplicative notation: $\alpha = (\alpha_1, \ldots, \alpha_n)$, $(\alpha_i \geq 0, \alpha_i \in \mathbf{Z})$, $|\alpha| = \Sigma\,\alpha_i$, $D^\alpha = \partial^{|\alpha|}/\partial x_1^{\alpha_1} \ldots \partial x_n^{\alpha_n}$, $\xi^\alpha = \xi_1^{\alpha_1} \ldots \xi_n^{\alpha_n}$. We put also $|\xi|^2 = \Sigma\,\xi_i^2$, and denote by $\mathfrak{F}$ the Fourier transform $f \to \hat{f}$ where $\hat{f}(\xi) = (2\pi)^{-n/2} \int f(x) e^{i(x,\xi)} dx$.

The Riesz operator R^α is $\mathfrak{F}^{-1} \circ (\xi/|\xi|)^\alpha \circ \mathfrak{F}$, where, of course, the middle factor stands for the multiplication by $(\xi/|\xi|)^\alpha$. To a finite linear combination $A = \Sigma_\alpha\, a_\alpha(x) R^\alpha$ of Riesz operators, with coefficients in the space $B^\infty = B^\infty(\mathbf{R}^n)$ of C^∞-functions all of whose partial derivatives are bounded, we associate the symbol $\sigma(A) = \Sigma\, a_\alpha(x)(\xi/|\xi|)^\alpha$, which may be viewed as a function on $\mathbf{R}^n \times S^{n-1}$. The symbol map $A \to \sigma(A)$ is injective, and extends by continuity (in suitable topologies) to a 1-1 map of a certain class of operators of $H^\infty(\mathbf{R}^n)$ to $H^\infty(\mathbf{R}^n)$, (where $H^\infty(\mathbf{R}^n)$ is the space of functions all of whose partial derivatives are square integrable), to be called B^∞ singular integral operators of order zero, onto the space of functions on $\mathbf{R}^n \times S^{n-1}$, all of whose derivatives are bounded. A B^∞ operator of order r is then a product $B = A\Lambda^r$, where A is of order zero, and $\Lambda = \mathfrak{F}^{-1} \circ (1 + |\xi|^2)^{1/2} \circ \mathfrak{F}$ is the square root of $1 + \Delta$, (Δ being the Laplacian). The symbol $\sigma_r(B)$ is then $\sigma(A) \cdot |\xi|^r$.

These operators, modulo operators of lower order, include the differential operators $D = \Sigma_{|\alpha|=r}\, a_\alpha(x) D^\alpha$ of order r, with coefficients in B^∞, because, since $D^\alpha = \mathfrak{F}^{-1} \circ (-i\xi)^\alpha \circ \mathfrak{F}$, we may write $D = (\Sigma\, a_\alpha(x) R^\alpha) \cdot (-i\Lambda_0)^r$, where $\Lambda_0 = \mathfrak{F}^{-1} \circ |\xi| \circ \mathfrak{F}$ is the "square root" of Δ, and it can be shown that $\Lambda^r - \Lambda_0^r$ is of order $\leq r-2$.

Let now X be a manifold, E, F smooth complex vector bundles on X. A linear map $A: C^\infty(E) \to C^\infty(F)$ belongs to $\mathrm{Int}_r(E, F)$ if:

(1) for $\varphi, \psi \in C^\infty(X)$ with disjoint supports, $\varphi A \psi$ is of order $\leq r-1$;

(2) for $\varphi, \psi \in C^\infty(X)$ with supports in some coordinate neighborhood U, over which sections of E, F are chosen as in section 1, $\varphi A \psi$ is given, modulo operators of order $\leq r-1$, by a matrix (A_{ij}) of B^∞ operators of order r.

The matrix $(\sigma_r(A_{ij}))$ of the symbols is shown to have an intrinsic meaning, and associates to every $\xi \in T^*(X)_x - 0$ $(x \in U)$ a linear transformation of E_x into F_x, whence a homomorphism $\sigma_r(A): \pi^*E \to \pi^*F$, defined on $S(X)$, the *symbol of* A. The operator A is elliptic of order r if it is in $\mathrm{Int}_r(E, F)$ and if $\sigma_r(A)$ is an isomorphism. The set of such operators is denoted $\mathrm{Ell}_r(E, F)$. If $A \in \mathrm{Ell}_r(E, F)$, then, using $\sigma_r(A)$, the cohomology class ch A and the topological index $i_t(A)$ are defined as in the case of differential operators. Moreover, it can be shown that ker A, coker A are finite dimensional, so that $i_a(A)$ is again defined, and that (ii), (iii) are true. Consequently i_a may now be viewed as a function on $K(B(X), S(X))$ and the next steps of the proof consist in showing that it has the same properties as i_t, namely:

7. *Multiplicativity*. One wants to know: if A, B, C, are elliptic operators on X, Y and $X \times Y$ such that $[\sigma(A)] \cdot [\sigma(B)] = [\sigma(C)]$, in the sense of the pairing of §2, section 3, then $i_a(A) \cdot i_a(B) = i_a(C)$. This will be proved by making use of a pairing of operators: $(A,B) \mapsto A \# B$ which is suggested by the construction underlying section 3 above. This, however, meets with some technical difficulties since $A \# B$ is not in general an integro-differential operator. It will nevertheless be a limit of such operators and this will allow one to keep track of symbols and indices.

8. If X is even-dimensional, and V a bundle on X, we define

$$i_a(X, V) = i_a(V \cdot x_0) \quad ,$$

where the right hand side stands for the analytical index of any operator with symbol belonging to $V \cdot x_0$. In fact, using a connection on V and the operator D_0 mentioned in 4, we may find a differential operator with that symbol. One then has to prove that (a) to (d) in section 4 are true with i_t replaced by i_a. This is fairly standard, except, however, for (c), which is one of the main parts of the whole proof.

The index theorem for even-dimensional manifolds then follows from 4, 5 and 8. In order to extend it to odd-dimensional manifolds, we need the following statement:

9. *There exists on the circle* S^1 *an elliptic operator* E_0, *from the trivial bundle to the trivial bundle, with* $i_a(E_0) = i_t(E_0) \neq 0$, which, together with the multiplicativity properties 3, 7, allows one to reduce the odd-dimensional case to the even-dimensional one by multiplying with E_0.

10. The analytical index is an integer by definition. Since every element of $K(B(X), S(X))$ is the class of a symbol of an elliptic operator in the Seeley algebra, the main theorem for these operators implies the

COROLLARY. Let X be a manifold, and $\alpha \in K(B(X), S(X))$. Then the topological index of α is an integer.

As we shall see, this yields all the integrality theorems pertaining to the Todd genus or the $\hat{A}$-genus.

§4. Appendix

The order of exposition in the sequel does not coincide with the one adopted in the previous outline. In order to orient the reader, we make here some comments on the contents of the different chapters.

Chapters II to X give some background material both for the topological and the analytical parts. In conformity with the purpose of this seminar, the treatment of the latter one is practically self-contained, omitting only proofs of some quite standard facts, while much is taken for granted on the topological side. Chapter II reviews briefly K-theory, Chern characters, and shows that $K(X, Y)$ may be defined as the set of equivalence classes of suitable sequences of vector bundles. Chapter III describes a method to compute the topological index when the bundles underlying the differential operator and the tangent bundle to the base manifold are associated in a suitable way to a given principal bundle.

Chapter IV introduces some basic material on differential operators: definition, symbols, the jet bundle exact sequence, adjoints, Green operators, some classical differential operators.

Chapter V defines the differential operator leading to the index of a manifold and checks the index theorem in some special cases.

Chapters VI to X review some notions and results in functional analysis: in particular bounded operators on Banach spaces with finite dimensional kernel and cokernel (to be called Fredholm operators) the Sobolev spaces H^k, the Sobolev inequality, and Rellich's theorem.

The Seeley algebra is introduced axiomatically in XI, by means of five conditions, the existence proof being postponed to XVI. Chapters XII, XIII, XIV, and part of XV are devoted to the main properties of the Seeley algebra: regularity properties of elliptic operators (XI), homotopy invariance of i_a (XII), (this is (i) of §3; property (ii) is essentially built in the axioms, so that its validity is really part of the existence proof), behaviour under Whitney sums (XIII); and the multiplicativity property 7 above, which is dealt with with the help of the sixth condition imposed on the Seeley algebra (XIV).

Chapter XV proves that both i_t and i_a satisfy the condition conditions (a), (b), (d) of 4, and that i_t also verifies (c). The proof that (c) also is true for i_a is much harder and is given in XVII.

Chapter XVI proves the existence of the Seeley algebra of integro-differential operators, with the properties postulated in XI and XIV. The method finally adopted in these Notes is different from that of [5], after which the above summary was patterned. This turned out to be more convenient for a self-contained exposition. Chapter XVI also contains the construction of an elliptic scalar operator on the circle with both indices equal to -1, comments on the sign conventions made in defining i_a and i_t, and historical remarks on singular integral operators.

Chapter XVIII is topological, and gives the proof of the uniqueness theorem in Section 5 of 1, using the main results of Thom's cobordism theory.

How the results of Chapters XI to XVIII yield a proof of the index theorem is briefly recapitulated in Chapter XIX, which also contains an extension to the non-orientable case, further remarks on the theorem, and some of the main applications (the Riemann-Roch theorem, the Hirzebruch index theorem, various integrality theorems of algebraic topology).

Appendix I is devoted to the index theorem on manifolds with boundary. It gives the precise statement, and discusses the notions underlying it; but the proof is only briefly sketched. Finally, there is an appendix by Weishu Shih, pertaining to Chapter III, which treats in a more general setting, characteristic classes and the topological index of differential operators associated to G-structures.

REFERENCES

[1] M. F. Atiyah, "The index of elliptic operators on compact manifolds," Sem. Bourbaki, Mai 1963, Exp. 253.

[2] M. F. Atiyah and F. Hirzebruch, "Analytic cycles on complex manifolds," Topology 1 (1962), pp. 25-46.

[3] M. F. Atiyah and I. M. Singer, "The index of elliptic operators on compact manifolds," Bull. A. M. S. 69 (1963), pp. 422-433.

[4] R. T. Seeley, "Singular integrals on compact manifolds," Amer. J. M. 81 (1959), pp. 658-690.

[5] R. T. Seeley, Integro-differential operators on vector bundles, Trans. A.M.S. 117 (1965), pp. 167-204.

CHAPTER II

REVIEW OF K-THEORY

Robert Solovay

§1. Let X be a finite CW-complex. One defines an abelian group, $K(X)$, as follows. The generators will be the equivalence classes, $\{\xi\}$, of complex vector bundles over X. (If X is not connected, one allows the dimensions of the fibers of ξ to differ on different connectedness components of X.) For each short exact sequence of vector bundles,

$$(E) \quad 0 \to \xi' \to \xi \to \xi'' \to 0 \quad ,$$

there is a relation, $\{\xi\} = \{\xi'\} + \{\xi''\}$, in $K(X)$.

The tensor product of vector bundles makes $K(X)$ into a commutative ring: $\{\xi\} \cdot \{\eta\} = \{\xi \otimes \eta\}$. A mapping $f\colon Y \to X$ induces (through the pull-back of vector bundles) a map $f^!\colon K(X) \to K(Y)\colon f^!(\{\xi\}) = \{f^*\xi\}$.

Let x be a point. Then $\dim\colon K(\{x\}) \cong \mathbf{Z}$ is defined by $\dim(\{\xi\}) = \dim \xi$. If X is a space with basepoint x, we put $\widetilde{K}(X) = \text{kernel } (K(X) \to K(\{x\}))$.

If (X, Y) is a finite CW-pair, we let X/Y be the space obtained by collapsing Y to a point $\{Y\}$ which we take as the basepoint for X/Y. (If $Y = \emptyset$, X/Y is the disjoint union of X with a basepoint.) The relative group, $K(X, Y)$, is by definition $\widetilde{K}(X/Y)$.

In [1], Atiyah and Hirzebruch have shown that one can define "cohomology groups"

$$K^i(X, Y) \qquad (i \in \mathbf{Z}_2) \quad .$$

which satisfy all the Eilenberg-Steenrod axioms (modified for $\mathbf{Z}_2$-grading) except for the dimension axiom, and such that

$$K^0(X, Y) = K(X, Y) \quad .$$

The exact sequence in cohomology reduces to an exact hexagon:

$$\begin{array}{ccccc} & K^0(X, Y) & \longrightarrow & K^0(X) & \\ {\scriptstyle\delta}\nearrow & & & & \searrow \\ K^1(Y) & & & & K^0(Y) \\ \nwarrow & & & & \swarrow{\scriptstyle\delta} \\ & K^1(X) & \longleftarrow & K^1(X, Y) & \end{array}$$

(The construction of this cohomology theory uses the Bott periodicity theorem.)

Moreover, the ring structure on $K(X, Y)$ extends to an anti-commutative ring structure on $K^*(X, Y)$:

$$K^i(X, Y) \cdot K^j(X, Y) \subset K^{i+j}(X, Y) \quad .$$

§2. The Chern Character.

If X is a topological space, $H^{**}(X, A)$ is the direct product $\prod_{j \geq 0} H^j(X, A)$. Let ξ be an n-dimensional complex vector bundle over X with total Chern class (rational coefficients)

$$c(\xi) = 1 + c_1(\xi) + \cdots + c_n(\xi) \quad .$$

Following Borel and Serre, one considers $c_i(\xi)$ as the $i^{\underline{th}}$ elementary symmetric function in the indeterminants $x_1, \ldots, x_n$:

$$c(\xi) = \prod_{i=1}^{n} (1+x_i) \quad .$$

Then by definition, $ch(\xi) \in H^{**}(X, \mathbf{Q})$ is

$$\sum_{i=1}^{n} e^{x_i} \quad .$$

Of course, if X is finite dimensional, $H^*(X) = H^{**}(X)$ and

$$ch(\xi) \in H^*(X, \mathbf{Q}) \quad .$$

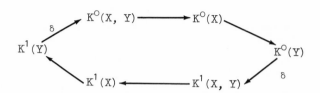

The map ch extends to a ring homomorphism

$$ch: K^*(X, Y) \to H^{**}(X, Y; \mathbf{Q}) \quad .$$

If we give $H^{**}(X, Y; \mathbf{Q})$ the $\mathbf{Z}_2$-grading:

$$H^{**} = H^+ \oplus H^-$$

(where $H^+ = \prod_{i \equiv 0(2)} H^i$ and $H^- = \prod_{i \equiv 1(2)} H^i$), then ch is compatible with the $\mathbf{Z}_2$-gradings and commutes with the coboundary homomorphism, δ.

If (X, Y) is a finite CW-pair, then $K^*(X, Y)$ is finitely generated and

$$ch \otimes 1_{\mathbf{Q}}: K^*(X, Y) \otimes \mathbf{Q} \cong H^*(X, Y; \mathbf{Q})$$

is an isomorphism. $K^*(X, Y)$ admits a natural graded module structure over $K^*(X)$ which is compatible, via ch, with the module structure of $H^*(X, Y; \mathbf{Q})$ over $H^*(X; \mathbf{Q})$.

The Bott periodicity theorem entails the following description of $\widetilde{K}^*(S^m)$:

The map $ch: \widetilde{K}^*(S^m) \to H^m(S^m, \mathbf{Q})$ is a monomorphism with image the subgroup of integral elements, $H^m(S^m, \mathbf{Z})$.

§3. The Difference Construction. (After [2]).

3.1. Suppose that (X, Y) is a finite CW-pair, that E and F are vector bundles over X and that

$$\alpha: E|Y \cong F|Y$$

is an isomorphism of the restrictions of E and F to Y. Then the difference element

$$d(E, F, \alpha) \in K(X, Y)$$

is defined as follows:

Let $A \subset X \times I$ be

$$X \times \{0\} \cup Y \times I \cup X \times \{1\} \quad .$$

Thus $X \times I/A \cong S^1(X/Y)$ ($S^1(X)$ is the reduced suspension of X.) Put

$$A_0 = X \times \{0\} \cup Y \times (0, 1)$$

and

$$A_1 = X \times \{1\} \cup Y \times (0, 1)$$

and let $f_i\colon A_i \to X$ be the restriction of the projection map $X \times I \to X$. Define a bundle ξ over A as follows: on A_0, ξ is $f_0^*(F)$; on A_1, ξ is $f_1^*(E)$; on $A_0 \cap A_1$ we identify $f_0^*(F)$ with $f_1^*(E)$ using α. Let $d(E, F, \alpha)$ be the image of $\{\xi\}$ under the composition

$$K^0(A) \to K^1(X \times I, A) \cong \tilde{K}^1(S^1(X/Y)) \cong K^0(X, Y) \quad .$$

3.2. The following lemma gives the principal properties of the difference construction.

LEMMA 1:

(i) For a map $f\colon (X', Y') \to (X, Y)$ we have

$$d(f^*E, f^*F, f^*\alpha) = f^! d(E, F, \alpha) \ .$$

(ii) $d(E, F, \alpha)$ depends only on the homotopy class of α.

(iii) For $Y = \emptyset$ we have $d(E, F, \alpha) = E - F$.

(iv) For the natural map $f^!\colon K(X, Y) \to K(X)$, we have

$$f^!(d(E, F, \alpha)) = E - F \ .$$

(v) The element $d(E, F, \alpha) = 0$ if and only if there is a vector bundle G on X such that the isomorphism

$$\alpha \oplus 1_G\colon (E \oplus G)|Y \cong (F \oplus G)|Y$$

extends to an isomorphism of $E \oplus G$ with $F \oplus G$ defined on the whole of X.

(vi) $d(E \oplus E', F \oplus F', \alpha) = d(E, F, \alpha) + d(E', F', \alpha')$.

(vii) $d(F, E, \alpha^{-1}) = -d(E, F, \alpha)$.

(viii) If G is a vector bundle over X then

$$d(G \otimes E, G \otimes F, 1_G \otimes \alpha) = G \cdot d(E, F, \alpha) \ .$$

(ix) Suppose that $\alpha\colon E|Y \cong E'|Y$ and $\alpha'\colon E'|Y \cong E''|Y$. Then

$$d(E, E''), \alpha' \circ \alpha) = d(E, E', \alpha) + d(E', E'', \alpha').$$

PROOF: (i)–(iv) and (vi)–(viii) are proved in [2].

PROOF of (v): First suppose that there is a bundle G on X and an isomorphism

$$\sigma: E \oplus G \cong F \oplus G$$

extending $\alpha \oplus 1_G$. If $f: (X, Y) \to (X, X)$, then

$$d(E \oplus G, F \oplus G, \alpha \oplus 1_G) = f^! d(E \oplus G, F \oplus G, \sigma) = 0$$

(since $K(X, X) = 0$). By (vi),

$$0 = d(E \oplus G, F \oplus G, \alpha \oplus 1_G) = d(E, F, \alpha) + d(G, G, 1_G|Y) \quad .$$

But $d(G, G, 1_G|Y) = f^! d(G, G, 1_G) = 0$. This establishes the sufficiency. Suppose now that $d(E, F, \alpha) = 0$. Select G of high dimension such that $E \oplus G \cong X \times \mathbf{C}^N$. Replacing (E, F, α) by $(E \oplus G, F \oplus G, \alpha \oplus 1_G)$, we may assume that E is the trivial bundle $X \times \mathbf{C}^N$, that α is a trivialization

$$\alpha: F|Y \cong Y \times \mathbf{C}^N \quad ,$$

and that N is large compared to $\dim X$. By means of α, we identify the fibers of $F|Y$ with one another. The result of this collapsing process is a bundle $\widetilde{F}$ over X/Y; if $p: X \to X/Y$ is the natural map, then $p^*\widetilde{F} = F$. Let $\widetilde{E} = X/Y \times \mathbf{C}^N$ and let $\widetilde{\alpha}$ be the map of $\widetilde{E}|\{Y\} \cong \widetilde{F}|\{Y\}$ induced by α. We have $p^! d(\widetilde{E}, \widetilde{F}, \widetilde{\alpha}) = d(E, F, \alpha) = 0$. But

$$p^!: \widetilde{K}(X/Y) \to K(X, Y)$$

is bijective, and the natural map $\widetilde{K}(X/Y) \to K(X/Y)$ is injective. Thus $\widetilde{F} = \widetilde{E}$ in $K(X/Y)$. Since $\dim \widetilde{F}$ is large compared to $\dim X \geq \dim X/Y$, $\widetilde{F} = \widetilde{E} = X/Y \times \mathbf{C}^N$. If we identify $\widetilde{F}$ with $\widetilde{E}$ so that $\widetilde{\alpha}$ becomes the identity, then $F = p^*\widetilde{F}$ is identified with $E = p^*\widetilde{E}$ so that $\alpha = p^*\widetilde{\alpha}$ becomes $1_E|Y$ (which manifestly extends to X). To sum up: if G is of high dimension, and $E \oplus G \cong X \times \mathbf{C}^N$, then $\alpha \oplus 1_G$ extends to an isomorphism $\sigma: E \oplus G \cong F \oplus G$.

PROOF of (ix): By (v) and (vii) there is a bundle F over X and an isomorphism

$$\phi: E \oplus E' \oplus F \cong E' \oplus E \oplus F$$

extending $\alpha \oplus \alpha^{-1} \oplus 1_F$.

One has a commutative diagram:

$$\begin{array}{ccc} E \oplus E' \oplus F & \xrightarrow{\alpha \oplus \alpha' \oplus 1_F} & E' \oplus E'' \oplus F \\ \downarrow \phi & & \downarrow 1 \\ E' \oplus E \oplus F & \xrightarrow{1_{E'} \oplus \alpha'\alpha \oplus 1_F} & E' \oplus E'' \oplus F \end{array}$$

of isomorphisms over Y in which the vertical maps extend to isomorphisms over X. Put $\eta_1 = d(E \oplus E' \oplus F, E' \oplus E'' \oplus F, \alpha \oplus \alpha' \oplus 1_F)$ and $\eta_2 = d(E' \oplus E \oplus F, E' \oplus E'' \oplus F, 1_{E'} \oplus \alpha'\alpha \oplus 1_F)$. From the diagram and (i), we get $\eta_1 = \eta_2$. But $\eta_1 = d(E, E', \alpha) + d(E', E'', \alpha')$ by (v) and (vi), and $\eta_2 = d(E, E'', \alpha' \circ \alpha)$ for the same reasons. The proof of (ix) is complete.

§4. L-Theory

We are going to give a Grothendieck type definition of the relative groups $K(X, Y)$. Let (X, Y) be a finite CW-pair. We define $\mathcal{E}_1(X, Y)$ to be the set of all triples,

$$\tilde{E} = (E_0, E_1, \sigma) \quad ,$$

such that E_0 and E_1 are complex vector bundles over X, and σ is an isomorphism of $E_0|Y$ with $E_1|Y$. The addition of triples is defined using the Whitney sum.

A triple, $\tilde{E}$, of the form

$$(E_0, E_0, 1_{E_0}|Y)$$

is said to be elementary. Note that if $\tilde{E}$ is elementary, it lies in the image of the map $\{\mathcal{E}(X, X) \to \mathcal{E}(X, Y)\}$.

Two triples $\tilde{E}, \tilde{E}' \in \mathcal{E}(X, Y)$ are called equivalent if there are elementary triples $\tilde{P}$ and $\tilde{Q}$ such that there is an isomorphism

$$\tilde{E} \oplus \tilde{P} \cong \tilde{E}' \oplus \tilde{Q} \quad .$$

(An isomorphism of the triples $\tilde{E}'$ and $\tilde{E}''$ is a pair of isomorphisms

$$E_0' \longrightarrow E_0'', \quad E_1' \longrightarrow E_1''$$

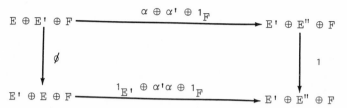

defined over X, such that, over Y, the diagram

$$\begin{array}{ccc} E_0' & \xrightarrow{\sigma'} & E_1' \\ \downarrow & & \downarrow \\ E_0'' & \xrightarrow{\sigma''} & E_1'' \end{array}$$

is commutative.)

DEFINITION: $L_1(X, Y)$ is the set of equivalence classes of $\mathcal{E}_1(X, Y)$, under the equivalence relation just defined. $L_1(X, Y)$ is, a priori, an abelian semigroup with respect to Whitney sum. We put $L_1(X) = L_1(X, \emptyset)$.

$L_1(X, Y)$ is a contravariant functor of the pair (X, Y). We define a natural transformation

$$\chi\colon\ L_1(X, Y) \to K(X, Y)$$

as follows: If $\tilde{E} \in \mathcal{E}_1(X, Y)$ represents the element $[\tilde{E}]$ of $L_1(X, Y)$, then $\chi([\tilde{E}]) = d(E_0, E_1, \sigma)$. Using Lemma 1 of Section 3, one checks that χ is well-defined and additive. Moreover, if $Y = \emptyset$, $\chi([\tilde{E}])$ is just

$$E_0 - E_1 \quad .$$

The main result of this paragraph is

THEOREM 2. The map $\chi\colon\ L_1(X, Y) \to K(X, Y)$ is an isomorphism.

PROOF. We first show that χ is surjective. Since $K(X, Y) \cong K(X/Y, \{Y\})$, we may assume that Y is a point:

$$\begin{array}{ccc} L_1(X, Y) & \longleftarrow & L_1(X/Y, \{Y\}) \\ \downarrow & & \downarrow \\ K(X, Y) & \cong & K(X/Y, \{Y\}) \end{array}$$

So let $\alpha \in K(X, \{x\})$. The image of α in $K(X)$ may be written as $E - E'$ where $\dim E_x = \dim E_x'$. Let $\sigma\colon\ E_x \cong E_x'$. Then

$$\tilde{E} = (E, E', \sigma)$$

lies in $\mathcal{E}_1(X, \{x\})$ and $\chi([\tilde{E}])$ goes to $E - E'$ under the natural map

(1) $$K(X, \{x\}) \to K(X) \quad .$$

Since (1) is 1-1, $\chi([\tilde{E}]) = \alpha$. Thus χ is surjective.

Lemma 1 (v) of Section 3 shows that χ has kernel zero. By Lemma 1 (vi) and (vii), it follows that χ is injective. This completes the proof.

§5. Products in L-Theory.

Let (X_i, Y_i) be a finite CW-pair $(i = 1, 2)$. We put

(2) $$X = X_1 \times X_2; \quad Y = X_1 \times Y_2 \cup Y_1 \times X_2 \quad .$$

(X, Y) is the Cartesian product of the pairs (X_1, Y_1) and (X_2, Y_2). In K-theory, there is a cross-product

(3) $$K(X_1, Y_1) \otimes K(X_2, Y_2) \to K(X, Y) \quad ,$$

$\alpha \otimes \beta \to \alpha \times \beta$; for $Y_1 = Y_2 = \emptyset$, this is induced from the external tensor product of vector bundles: if E_i is a complex vector bundle over X_i, $(i = 1, 2)$, then $E_1 \hat{\otimes} E_2$ is the vector bundle

$$\pi_1{}^*E_1 \otimes \pi_2{}^*E_2$$

on $X_1 \times X_2$, and $[E_1] \times [E_2] = [E_1 \hat{\otimes} E_2]$.

In studying the multiplicative properties of the topological index, one needs a description of (3) in terms of the "Grothendieck group" definition of $K(X, Y)$. We shall define, for each integer r, a pairing

(4) $$\psi_r\colon \; L_1(X_1, Y_1) \otimes L_1(X_2, Y_2) \to L_1(X, Y)$$

which corresponds to (3) via the isomorphism $\chi\colon \; L_1 \to K$ of Section 4. (The dependence on r is not deep, but it's useful for the application.)

The definition of (4) will be preceded by some preliminary material. First, let X be compact, and let E be a complex vector bundle over X. Recall that a *hermitian structure* on E consists of a positive definite inner product, $(\ ,\ )_x$, on each fibre, E_x, of E; the inner product should depend continuously on $x \in X$. It is known that E has hermitian structures; moreover, any two hermitian structures on E

are homotopic. (The proof is a "partition of unity" argument.)

Now let E and F be hermitian bundles over X (that is, bundles with designated hermitian structures) and let θ: $E \to F$ be a bundle map. The *adjoint* of θ,

$$\theta^*: \ F \to E \quad ,$$

is given by the formula $\theta^*(x) = [\theta(x)]^*$ (for all $x \in X$); here $\theta(x)$: $E_x \to F_x$ is the map of fibres induced by θ.

We shall also need the following lemma:

LEMMA 3. Let (X, Y) be a finite CW-pair. Let [E, F, σ] lie in $\mathscr{E}_1(X, Y)$. Then there is a bundle map $\tilde{\sigma}$: $E \to F$ whose restriction to Y is σ. If $\tilde{\sigma}$ and $\tilde{\sigma}'$ are two such extensions, then $\tilde{\sigma}$ is homotopic to $\tilde{\sigma}'$ by a homotopy constant on Y.

PROOF. This is clear since bundle maps of E into F are in natural 1-1 correspondence with continuous cross-sections of the vector bundle Hom(E, F).

Suppose now that we are given triples $\tilde{T}_i \in \mathscr{E}_1(X_i, Y_i)$, $(i = 1, 2)$;

$$\tilde{T}_i = [E_i, F_i, \sigma_i] \quad .$$

Our task is to define $\psi_r([\tilde{T}_1] \otimes [\tilde{T}_2])$. We first choose hermitian structures for the bundles E_1, F_1, E_2, and F_2. We also select bundle maps

$$\tilde{\sigma}_i: \ E \to F$$

extending σ_i. (Cf. Lemma 3.)

We define complex vector bundles E, F over X by:

$$(5) \qquad \begin{aligned} E &= E_1 \hat{\otimes} E_2 \oplus F_1 \hat{\otimes} F_2 \\ F &= F_1 \otimes E_2 \oplus E_1 \otimes F_2 \end{aligned}$$

Define the bundle map $\tilde{\sigma}_1 \# \tilde{\sigma}_2$: $E \to F$ by the matrix:

$$(6)\qquad \begin{pmatrix} \tilde\sigma_1 \hat\otimes 1_{E_2} & (-1)^{r+1}\, 1_{F_1} \hat\otimes \tilde\sigma_2^* \\ 1_{E_1} \hat\otimes \tilde\sigma_2 & (-1)^r\, \tilde\sigma_1^* \hat\otimes 1_{F_2} \end{pmatrix}$$

LEMMA 4. The restriction of $\tilde\sigma_1 \# \tilde\sigma_2$ to Y $(= X_1 \times Y_2 \cup Y_1 \times X_2)$ is an isomorphism:

$$\tilde\sigma_1 \# \tilde\sigma_2 | Y\colon\; E|Y \cong F|Y \quad .$$

PROOF. We show first that $\dim E_y = \dim F_y$ for $y \in Y$. Say $y = (y_1, y_2)$. Then an easy computation shows that (5) implies:

$$(7)\qquad (\dim E_{1,y_1} - \dim F_{1,y_1}) \cdot (\dim E_{2,y_2} - \dim F_{2,y_2}) = \dim E_y - \dim F_y \quad .$$

Since $y \in Y$, either $y_1 \in Y_1$ or $y_2 \in Y_2$. If $y_1 \in Y_1$, the first factor of (7)'s left-hand side is zero. In fact, $\tilde\sigma_1(y_1) = \sigma_1(y_1)$ is an isomorphism of E_{1,y_1} with F_{1,y_1}. It follows that the right-hand side of (7) is zero. The discussion if $y_2 \in Y_2$ is similar.

Since $\dim E_y = \dim F_y$, to prove $\tilde\sigma_1 \# \tilde\sigma_2(y)$ is an isomorphism, it suffices to prove that it is 1-1. To show this, we compute $(\tilde\sigma_1 \# \tilde\sigma_2)^*(\sigma_1 \# \sigma_2)(y)$ and verify that it is an isomorphism. This suffices

We first compute the matrix of the adjoint $(\tilde\sigma_1 \# \tilde\sigma_2)^*$. This is done by reflecting the matrix of $\tilde\sigma_1 \# \tilde\sigma_2$ along the main diagonal and taking the adjoint of each entry. Thus $(\tilde\sigma_1 \# \tilde\sigma_2)^*$ has the matrix:

$$\begin{pmatrix} \tilde\sigma_1^* \hat\otimes 1_{E_2} & 1_{E_1} \hat\otimes \tilde\sigma_2^* \\ (-1)^{r+1}\, 1_{F_1} \hat\otimes \tilde\sigma_2 & (-1)^r\, \tilde\sigma_1 \hat\otimes 1_{F_2} \end{pmatrix}$$

It follows that $(\tilde\sigma_1 \# \tilde\sigma_2)^*(\tilde\sigma_1 \# \tilde\sigma_2)$ has the matrix:

$$\begin{pmatrix} \tilde\sigma_1^*\tilde\sigma_1 \hat\otimes 1_{E_2} + 1_{E_1} \hat\otimes \tilde\sigma_2^*\tilde\sigma_2 & \bigcirc \\ \bigcirc & 1_{F_1} \hat\otimes \tilde\sigma_2\, \tilde\sigma_2^* + \tilde\sigma_1\, \tilde\sigma_1^* \hat\otimes 1_{F_2} \end{pmatrix}$$

This is clearly a strictly positive endomorphism of $E_{(x_1,x_2)}$ at each (x_1, x_2) of X where at least one of the maps $\tilde{\sigma}_1(x_1)$ and $\tilde{\sigma}_2(x_2)$ is an isomorphism. In particular, $(\tilde{\sigma}_1 \# \tilde{\sigma}_2)^*(\tilde{\sigma}_1 \# \tilde{\sigma}_2)(y)$ is a bijection for each $y \in Y$. In fact, if $y = (y_1, y_2)$, then for some i, we have $y_i \in Y_i$, so $\tilde{\sigma}_i(y_i) = \tilde{\sigma}_i(y_i)$ is a bijection. As remarked earlier, this completes the proof.

LEMMA 5. The homotopy class of the isomorphism $\sigma_1 \# \sigma_2 | Y$ does not depend on the choices made. Thus we get a natural pairing

$$\psi_r^!: \mathscr{E}_1(X_1, Y_1) \times \mathscr{E}_1(X_2, Y_2) \to L(X, Y) \quad . \tag{8}$$

(A representative for $\psi_r^!(\tilde{T}_1, \tilde{T}_2)$ is $[E, F, \tilde{\sigma}_1 \# \tilde{\sigma}_2 | Y]$.)

PROOF By Lemma 3 and the remarks preceding it, the choices of hermitian structures and of extensions $\tilde{\sigma}_i$ are unique up to a homotopy. So the first sentence of the lemma is clear. To prove $\psi_r^!$ well-defined, it suffices to show $\chi\psi_r^!$ is well-defined (sence χ: $L_1 \cong K_2$). But $\chi\psi_r^!(\tilde{T}_1, \tilde{T}_2) = d(E, F, \tilde{\sigma}_1 \# \tilde{\sigma}_2 | Y)$. By Lemma 1, (ii), $d(E, F, \tilde{\sigma}_1 \# \tilde{\sigma}_2 | Y)$ depends only on the homotopy class of the isomorphism $\tilde{\sigma}_1 \# \tilde{\sigma}_2 | Y$. In view of the first sentence of the lemma, we are done.

LEMMA 6. The map $\psi_r^!$ of Lemma 5 passes to quotients to define the pairing of (4):

$$\psi_r: L_1(X_1, Y_1) \otimes L_1(X_2, Y_2) \to L_1(X, Y) \quad .$$

PROOF. The map $\psi_r^!$ is clearly bilinear. Moreover, if the triples $\tilde{T}_i$, $\tilde{T}_i'$ in $\mathscr{E}_1(X_i, Y_i)$ are isomorphic (for $i = 1, 2$), we clearly have

$$\psi_r^!(\tilde{T}_1, \tilde{T}_2) = \psi_r^!(\tilde{T}_1', \tilde{T}_2') \quad .$$

Thus it suffices to show the following: if either $\tilde{T}_1$ or $\tilde{T}_2$ is an elementary triple, then $\psi_r^!(\tilde{T}_1, \tilde{T}_2) = 0$. Suppose, for example, that $\tilde{T}_1 \in \mathscr{E}_1(X_1, Y_1)$ is elementary. We observed previously that $\tilde{T}_1$ is then in the image of $\{\mathscr{E}_1(X_1, X_1) \to \mathscr{E}_1(X_1, Y_1)\}$. In view of the commutative diagram

$$\begin{array}{ccc} \mathscr{E}_1(X_1, X_1) \times \mathscr{E}_1(X_2, Y_2) & \xrightarrow{\psi_r'} & L_1(X, X) \\ \downarrow & & \downarrow \\ \mathscr{E}_1(X_1, Y_1) \times \mathscr{E}_2(X_2, Y_2) & \xrightarrow{\psi_r'} & L_1(X, Y) \end{array} \quad ,$$

where the vertical maps are induced by inclusions, the element $\psi_r'(\tilde{T}_1, \tilde{T}_2)$ lies in the image of the map $\{L_1(X, X) \to L_1(X, Y)\}$. Since $L_1(X, X) \cong K(X, X) = 0$, we have $\psi_r'(\tilde{T}_1, \tilde{T}_2) = 0$. The proof is complete.

LEMMA 7. The map $\chi\colon L_1 \to K$ is multiplicative. In other words, the following diagram is commutative:

(9)
$$\begin{array}{ccc} L_1(X_1, Y_1) \otimes L_1(X_2, Y_2) & \xrightarrow{\psi_r} & L_1(X, Y) \\ \Big\downarrow \chi \times \chi & & \Big\downarrow \chi \\ K(X_1, Y_1) \otimes K(X_2, Y_2) & \xrightarrow{\times} & K(X, Y) \end{array}$$

PROOF. Let $\tilde{T}_i$ be an element of $\mathscr{E}_1(X_i, Y_i)$; $\tilde{T}_i = [E_i, F_i, \sigma_i]$ Let $\tilde{T} = [E, F, \tilde{\sigma}_1 \# \tilde{\sigma}_2|Y]$. We have to show that

$$\chi([\tilde{T}]) = \chi([\tilde{T}_1]) \times \chi([\tilde{T}_2]) \quad .$$

The proof will rely heavily on the fact that the pairings ψ_r and $\times$ are natural in the variables (X_1, Y_1) and (X_2, Y_2).

CASE 1. $Y_1 = Y_2 = \emptyset$

$$\chi([\tilde{T}_1]) = [E_i] - [F_i], \text{ by Lemma 1 (iii)} \ .$$

The K-theory cross-product comes from the external tensor product. Thus, for example,

$$[E_1] \times [E_2] = [E_1 \hat{\otimes} E_2] \quad .$$

It follows that $\chi([\tilde{T}_1]) \times \chi([\tilde{T}_2]) = ([E_1] - [F_1]) \times ([E_2] - [F_2]) = [E_1 \hat{\otimes} E_2] + [F_1 \hat{\otimes} F_2] - [E_1 \hat{\otimes} F_2] - [F_1 \hat{\otimes} E_2] =$ (cf. (5)) $= [E] - [F] = \chi([\tilde{T}])$.

q.e.d.

CASE 2. Y_1 and Y_2 are points $\{y_1\}$ and $\{y_2\}$.

According to [1, §1.4–1.5] the maps

$$K(X_i, \{y_i\}) \to K(X_i, \emptyset)$$

and

$$K(X_1 \times X_2, X_1 \times \{y_2\} \cup \{y_1\} \times X_2) \to K(X_1 \times X_2, \emptyset)$$

are injective. Thus Case 2 follows from Case 1, by means of the diagram

$$\begin{array}{ccc} (X_1, \{y_1\}) \times (X_2, \{y_2\}) & \to & (X_1 \times X_2, X_1 \times \{y_2\} \cup \{y_1\} \times X_2) \\ \downarrow & & \downarrow \\ (X_1, \emptyset) \times (X_2, \emptyset) & \longrightarrow & (X_1 \times X_2, \emptyset) \end{array} .$$

(One uses the fact that χ is a natural transformation.)

CASE 3. Y_1 and Y_2 are arbitrary.

By the excision axiom, the maps

$$K(X_i, Y_i) \longleftarrow K(X_i/Y_i, \{Y_i\})$$

and

$$K(X_1 \times X_2, X_1 \times Y_2 \cup Y_1 \times X_2) \leftarrow K(X_1/Y_1 \times X_2/Y_2, X_1 \times \{Y_2\} \cup \{Y_1\} \times X_2)$$

are bijections. Thus Case 3 follows, by naturality, from Case 2 and the fact that $\chi\colon L_1 \to K$ is an isomorphism.

We may summarize what we have proved as follows:

THEOREM 8. For $i = 1, 2$, let (X_i, Y_i) be a finite CW-pair. Let (X, Y) be the Cartesian product of these pairs (cf. (2)). Let $\alpha_i \in K(X_i, Y_i)$. We suppose that

$$\alpha_i = d(E_i, F_i, \tilde{\sigma}_i | Y) \quad ;$$

here E_i and F_i are complex vector bundles over X_i, and $\tilde{\sigma}_i\colon E_i \to F_i$ is a bundle map whose restriction to Y_i is an isomorphism. Define bundles E and F over X by (5) and define the bundle map

$$\tilde{\sigma}_1 \# \tilde{\sigma}_2\colon \; E \to F$$

by (6). Then $\tilde{\sigma}_1 \# \tilde{\sigma}_2 | Y$ is an isomorphism and

$$d(E,\ F,\ \tilde{\sigma}_1 \ \#\ \tilde{\sigma}_2 | Y) \ = \ \alpha_1 \times \alpha_2 \quad (\text{in } K(X,\ Y)).$$

REFERENCES

[1] M. F. Atiyah and F. Hirzebruch, Vector Bundles and Homogeneous Spaces, Proc. Symp. Pure Math., 3. Differential Geometry, Amer. Math. Soc. (1961), pp. 7-38.

[2] _______, Analytic Cycles on Complex Manifolds, Topology 1 (1962) pp. 25-46.

CHAPTER III

THE TOPOLOGICAL INDEX OF AN OPERATOR ASSOCIATED TO A G-STRUCTURE

Robert Solovay

1.0. We recall the basic facts about the Thom isomorphism. Let E be an oriented vector bundle, of dimension n, over the paracompact space X. We suppose that the structural group of E has been reduced to $SO(n)$. We may then define $B(E)$ and $S(E)$ to be the unit ball bundle and unit sphere bundle associated to E: $S(E) \subset B(E) \subset E$. Let π denote the projection in any of these bundles. If $x \in X$, let E_x be the fibre of E over x. The orientation of E determines canonical generators

$$U_x \in H^n(B(E_x), S(E_x); \mathbf{Q}) \quad ,$$

for each x. Let

$$j_x: \ ((B(E_x), S(E_x)) \to (B(E), S(E))$$

be the inclusion map. According to Thom, there is a unique class

$$U \in H^n(B(E), S(E); \mathbf{Q})$$

(the Thom class of E) such that $j_x^*(U) = U_x$, for all x. The Thom isomorphism

$$\varphi_*: \ H^\ell(X; \mathbf{Q}) \cong H^{n+\ell}(B(E), S(E); \mathbf{Q})$$

is given by the formula

$$(1) \qquad \varphi_*(a) = \pi^* a \cup U \qquad (\pi: \ B(E) \to X) \quad .$$

(The groups $H^j(B(E), S(E); \mathbf{Q})$ are zero for $j < n$.)

Let $i: (B(E), \emptyset) \to (B(E), S(E))$ be the inclusion map. Then the Euler class of E,

$$\chi(E) \in H^n(X, \mathbf{Q}) \quad ,$$

is related to U by the formula

$$\pi^*(\chi(E)) = i^*(U) \quad . \tag{2}$$

1.1. All manifolds considered in this lecture will be closed, oriented, and *even-dimensional*. Let X be a manifold of dimension 2ℓ. Let $T^*(X)$ be the cotangent bundle of X. Let $B(X)$ and $S(X)$ be the associated ball and sphere bundles of $T^*(X)$, with respect to some Riemannian structure on X. The projection of $T^*(X)$ onto X and its restrictions to $B(X)$ and $S(X)$ shall be denoted by π. The orientation of X induces an orientation of $T^*(X)$. Therefore, as discussed in 1.0, we have a Thom isomorphism

$$\varphi_*: H^*(X, \mathbf{Q}) \cong H^*(B(X), S(X); \mathbf{Q}) \quad .$$

1.2. Let $\alpha \in K(B(X), S(X))$. Then we put

$$\mathrm{ch}(D_\alpha) = (-1)^\ell \varphi_*^{-1} \mathrm{ch}(\alpha) \quad . \tag{3}$$

(Thus $\mathrm{ch}(D_\alpha) \in H^*(X)$.) In order to motivate this definition we shall recall briefly the definition of $\mathrm{ch}(D)$.

Let E and F be complex vector bundles over X. Let $C^\infty(E)$ (resp. $C^\infty(F)$) denote the set of C^∞ cross-sections of E (resp. F). Let

$$D: C^\infty(E) \to C^\infty(F)$$

be an elliptic operator. D might be a differential operator, as discussed in Lecture IV, or more generally, an integro-differential operator à la Seeley. In any case the symbol

$$\sigma(D) \in \mathrm{Hom}(\pi^* E, \pi^* F) \qquad (\pi: B(X) \to X)$$

is defined. The condition that D is elliptic is just that $\sigma(D) | S(X)$ be an isomorphism. Thus, using the difference construction discussed in Lecture

II, we can define $\gamma(D) \in K(B(X), S(X))$:

$$\gamma(D) = d(\pi^* E, \pi^* F; \sigma(D)|S(X)) \quad .$$

By definition

$$\mathrm{ch}(D) = (-1)^{\ell} \varphi_*^{-1} \mathrm{ch}(\gamma(D)) \quad .$$

It is clear that this depends only on $\gamma(D)$, and in (3) we have defined $\mathrm{ch}(D_\alpha)$ as if D_α were an elliptic operator with $\gamma(D_\alpha) = \alpha$. In point of fact, there always is an elliptic integro-differential operator D_α (to which the index theorem will apply), such that $\gamma(D_\alpha) = \alpha$.

§2. G-Structures on Manifolds

2.0. Let G be a compact Lie group. A *real G-module* is a real vector space, M, together with a representation

$$\lambda: \; G \to \mathrm{Aut}_{\mathbf{R}}(M) \quad .$$

There is an analogous notion of a *complex G-module*. An oriented real G-module, M, is a real G-module whose underlying vector space is oriented, and such that the operations of G on M are orientation preserving. If M and N are, for example, complex G-modules then the vector spaces

$$M^*, \; \Lambda^* M, \; \text{and} \; \mathrm{Hom}_{\mathbf{C}}(M, N)$$

are also G-modules, in an obvious way.

2.1. A G-structure on the manifold X consists of the following: (1) An oriented real G-module, V; (2) A principal G-bundle, P, over X; (3) An orientation preserving isomorphism

$$\psi: \; P \times_G V \cong T(X) \quad .$$

(T(X) is, of course, the tangent bundle of X.)

For example, if G is SO(n), and V is R^n (with the usual action of SO(n) on it) then a G-structure on X is just a Riemannian structure on X.

If M is a G-module, then the vector bundle

$$P \times_G M$$

is associated with the G-structure on X. For example, let $G = SO(n)$, $V = \mathbf{R}^n$, as above and let

$$M = \Lambda^k(V^*) \quad .$$

Then $P \times_G M$ is just the bundle of real valued exterior differential k-forms on X.

2.2. Let B_G be a classifying space for G, and let E_G be the universal principal G-bundle over B_G. Let $f\colon X \to B_G$ be a classifying map for the principal G-bundle P; we shall call f a classifying map for the G-structure on X. If M is any G-module, we put $\widetilde{M} = E_G \times_G M$. Thus $\widetilde{M}$ is the vector bundle on the universal example corresponding to M. We have a canonical isomorphism

$$T(X) \cong f^*\widetilde{V} \quad . \tag{4}$$

2.3. If X is a manifold with a G-structure, then one can construct elements $\alpha \in K(B(X), S(X))$ which are *associated to the G-structure* in the following way:

Let M and N be complex G-modules. Let $\pi\colon B(V^*) \to B_G$ be the projection map. We suppose that there is an isomorphism

$$\widetilde{\sigma}\colon \pi^*\widetilde{M}|S(\widetilde{V}^*) \cong \pi^*\widetilde{N}|S(\widetilde{V}^*) \quad . \tag{5}$$

The difference construction yields an element

$$\gamma \in K(B(\widetilde{V}^*), S(\widetilde{V}^*)) \quad :$$

$\gamma = d(\pi^*\widetilde{M}, \pi^*\widetilde{N}, \widetilde{\sigma})$.† Let $\widetilde{f}\colon (B(X), S(X)) \to (B(\widetilde{V}), S(\widetilde{V}))$ be the map induced by f. (Cf. (4).) Then we put

$$\alpha = \widetilde{f}^! \gamma \quad .$$

† In Lecture II, K-theory was discussed only for the category of finite CW-pairs. Therefore, strictly speaking, we should work with N-universal classifying space, $B_{G,N}$, and then let N tend to infinity. (The spaces $B_{G,N}$ can be finite CW-complexes.) However, we shall continue to speak only of B_G.

2.4. Let $\alpha \in K(B(X), S(X))$ be associated to the G-structure on X. We are going to show eventually how to find an explicit formula for $ch(D_\alpha)$ for various concrete α. The following theorem is a first step in that direction.

THEOREM 1. Let X be a manifold of dimension 2ℓ. Suppose that X has a G-structure with classifying map $f\colon X \to B_G$. Let $\alpha \in K(B(X), S(X))$ be associated to the G-structure. We suppose that α is constructed from M, N, and $\tilde{\sigma}$ as discussed above. We suppose also that the rational Euler class $\chi(\tilde{V}^*) \in H^*(B_G, \mathbf{Q})$ is non-zero. Then

$$ch(\tilde{M}) - ch(\tilde{N})$$

is divisible by $\chi(\tilde{V}^*)$, and

$$ch(D_\alpha) = f^{**}\left((-1)^\ell \frac{ch(\tilde{M}) - ch(\tilde{N})}{\chi(\tilde{V}^*)}\right) \quad . \tag{6}$$

REMARK 1: According to Borel, the ring $H^*(B_G, \mathbf{Q})$ has no divisors of zero. (Cf. [1].) Thus the right hand side of (6) is well-defined.

REMARK 2: The right hand side of (6) depends only on M and N and not on the isomorphism $\tilde{\sigma}$. Therefore, the same is true of $ch(D_\alpha)$.

PROOF of Theorem 1. Let $\gamma = d(\pi^*\tilde{M}, \pi^*\tilde{N}, \tilde{\sigma})$. Since ch and the Thom isomorphism are natural,

$$\begin{aligned} ch(D_\alpha) = (-1)^\ell \varphi_*^{-1} ch(\alpha) &= (-1)^\ell \varphi_*^{-1} ch(\tilde{f}^! \gamma) \\ &= (-1)^\ell f^{**}(\varphi_*^{-1} ch(\gamma)) \quad . \end{aligned}$$

Thus it suffices to show that

$$\chi(\tilde{V}^*) \cup \varphi_*^{-1} ch(\gamma) = ch(\tilde{M}) - ch(\tilde{N}) \quad . \tag{7}$$

Let $i\colon (B(\tilde{V}^*), \emptyset) \to (B(\tilde{V}^*), S(\tilde{V}^*))$ be the inclusion map. Consider the diagram

$$\begin{array}{ccc}
K(B(\widetilde{V}^*),\ S(\widetilde{V}^*)) & \xrightarrow{\quad i^! \quad} & K(B(\widetilde{V}),\ \emptyset) \\
\downarrow \mathrm{ch} & & \downarrow \mathrm{ch} \\
H^{**}(B(\widetilde{V}^*),\ S(\widetilde{V}^*);\ \mathbf{Q}) & \xrightarrow{\quad i^{**} \quad} & H^{**}(B(\widetilde{V}),\ \emptyset;\ \mathbf{Q}) \\
\cong \uparrow \varphi_* & & \cong \uparrow \pi^{**} \\
H^{**}(B_G,\ \mathbf{Q}) & \xrightarrow{\quad \cup\, \chi(\widetilde{V}^*) \quad} & H^{**}(B_G,\ \mathbf{Q})
\end{array} .$$

Since ch is natural, the upper square is commutative. (We recall that $H^{**}(X) = \prod_{i \geq 0} H^i(X)$.) The commutativity of the lower square follows from (1) and (2) of 1.0. Since the diagram is commutative,

(8) $$\varphi_*^{-1}(\mathrm{ch}(\gamma)) \cup \chi(\widetilde{V}^*) = (\pi^{**})^{-1}(\mathrm{ch}(i^!(\gamma)) \quad .$$

Since $\gamma = d(\pi^* \widetilde{M}, \pi^* \widetilde{N}, \widetilde{\sigma})$,

$$i^!(\gamma) = \pi^* \widetilde{M} - \pi^* \widetilde{N}$$

(by II Lemma 1 (iv)) so the right hand side of (8) is just $\mathrm{ch}\, \widetilde{M} - \mathrm{ch}\, \widetilde{N}$. The proof is complete.

§3. Review of the Borel-Hirzebruch Formalism (after [2]).

3.1. Let T^r be a torus of dimension r:

$$T^r = S^1 \times \cdots \times S^1 \qquad (r \text{ times}) \quad .$$

Then the classifying space, B_T, is the Cartesian product of r copies of infinite-dimensional complex projective space $CP(\infty)$:

$$B_T = CP(\infty) \times \cdots \times CP(\infty) \quad .$$

Therefore we have

$$H^*(B_T, \mathbf{Q}) \cong \mathbf{Q}[x_1, \ldots, x_r]$$

and

$$H^{**}(B_T, \mathbf{Q}) \cong \mathbf{Q}\{x_1, \ldots, x_r\}$$ (= the ring of formal power series)

where $x_i \in H^2(B_T, \mathbf{Q})$.

3.2. Now let G be a compact Lie group, and let T be a maximal torus of G. The inclusion map of T in G determines a map of classifying spaces

$$\rho\colon\ B_T \to B_G$$

(well-defined up to homotopy).

The Weyl group, $W(G, T)$, is the group of automorphisms of T which extend to inner automorphisms of G. The Weyl group acts on the cohomology ring, $H^*(B_T, \mathbf{Q})$, (since it consists of automorphisms of T). We can now state Borel's description of $H^*(B_G, \mathbf{Q})$.

THEOREM 2. The map

$$\rho^*\colon\ H^*(B_G, \mathbf{Q}) \to H^*(B_T, \mathbf{Q})$$

is injective. The image consists of those elements y in $H^*(B_T, \mathbf{Q})$ which are invariant under the action of the Weyl group of G. (I.e., $g \cdot y = y$ for all $g \in W(G, T)$.)

We shall frequently identify $H^*(B_G, \mathbf{Q})$ with its image in $H^*(B_T, \mathbf{Q})$ under ρ.

3.3. Let S^1 be the group of reals mod 1: $S^1 = \mathbf{R}/\mathbf{Z}$. One has, for any torus T, canonical isomorphisms

$$\mu\colon\ \mathrm{Hom}(T, S^1) \to H^1(T, \mathbf{Z})$$

and

$$\upsilon\colon\ \mathrm{Hom}(T, S^1) \to H^2(B_T, \mathbf{Z})$$

which we shall treat in the future as identifications. They may be described as follows: Let $\sigma \in H^1(S^1, \mathbf{Z})$ be the canonical generator. Then $\mu(h) = h^*\sigma$. To describe υ, we identify temporarily the groups S^1 and $U(1)$ via the map

$$s \to e^{2\pi i s} \qquad (s \in S^1) \quad .$$

A homomorphism $h\colon\ T \to S^1$ gives rise to a principal $U(1)$-bundle, ξ_h, on B_T. We put

$$\upsilon(h) = c_1(\xi_h) \quad .$$

3.4. Let G be a compact Lie group, T a maximal torus of G, M a G-module, and E_G the universal principal G-bundle over B_G. Recall that $\widetilde{M} = E_G \times_G M$ is the vector bundle over B_G corresponding to M. We shall now recall the Borel-Hirzebruch description of the characteristic classes of $\widetilde{M}$.

CASE 1: M is a complex G-module (of dimension n). We consider M as a T-module. Then M is the direct sum of irreducible T-modules of dimension one: $M = M_1 \oplus \cdots \oplus M_n$. On M_j, T acts by

$$t \cdot m = e^{2\pi i \omega_j(t)} \cdot m \qquad (m \in M_j) \quad ,$$

where $\omega_j \in \mathrm{Hom}(T, S^1)$. The ω_i are called the weights of the G-module M. The set of weights does not depend on the particular decomposition of M into irreducible T-modules (by the Jordan-Holder theorem).

Now consider the ω_i as elements of $H^2(B_T, \mathbf{Q})$ (as discussed in 3.3), and identify $H^*(B_G, \mathbf{Q})$ with a subring of $H^*(B_T, \mathbf{Q})$ as in 3.2. Then the following formulas are valid:

$$(9) \qquad 1 + c_1(\widetilde{M}) + \cdots + c_n(\widetilde{M}) = \prod_{i=1}^{n} (1 + \omega_i)$$

$$(10) \qquad ch(\widetilde{M}) = \sum_{i=1}^{n} e^{\omega_i} \quad .$$

REMARK 1: Formula (9) says that $c_i(\widetilde{M})$ is the ith elementary symmetric function in the weights of M.

REMARK 2: Let $\lambda\colon G \to \mathrm{Aut}_{\mathbf{C}}(M)$ describe the action of G on M. The classical character, $ch(\lambda)$, is a complex valued function on G: $ch(\lambda)(g) = \mathrm{Trace}\,(\lambda(g))$. On T we have the identity

$$ch(\lambda)(t) = \sum_{j=1}^{n} e^{2\pi i \omega_j(t)}$$

which bears a close resemblance to (10). If we know the classical character of M (on T), we can write down immediately the expression for $ch(\widetilde{M})$.

CASE 2 (2'): M is a real G-module of dimension $2n$ $(2n+1)$.

Now, as a T-module, M splits into the direct sum of n two-dimensional T-modules:

(11) $$M = M_1 \oplus \cdots \oplus M_n \quad .$$

((11') $$M = M_1 \oplus \cdots \oplus M_n \oplus R^1 \quad ,$$

and T acts trivially on R^1).

We give M a G-invariant metric. Then with respect to an orthonarmal basis of M_j, the action of $t \in T$ is described by a matrix

$$\begin{pmatrix} \cos 2\pi\omega_j(t) & -\sin 2\pi\omega_j(t) \\ \sin 2\pi\omega_j(t) & \cos 2\pi\omega_j(t) \end{pmatrix}$$

where $\omega_j \in \mathrm{Hom}(T, S^1)$. The ω_j's are called the weights of M. The element ω_j depends on the orientation of the basis in M_j; if we change the orientation in M_j, ω_j is replaced by $-\omega_j$.

The Pontrjagin classes of the real vector bundle, $\widetilde{M}$, are given by the formula

(12) $$1 + p_1(\widetilde{M}) + \cdots + p_n(\widetilde{M}) = \prod_{i=1}^{n} (1 + \omega_i^2) \quad .$$

Thus $p_i(\widetilde{M})$ is the ith elementary symmetric function of the elements $\omega_1^2, \ldots, \omega_n^2$.

CASE 3: M is an oriented real G-module of dimension $2n$.

In this case, the bundle $\widetilde{M}$ is oriented. In defining the weights of M, we now choose orientations in the M_i's so that M receives its given orientation (cf. (11)). Then the Euler class of $\widetilde{M}$ is given by

(13) $$\chi(\widetilde{M}) = \prod_{i=1}^{n} \omega_i \quad .$$

3.5. PROPOSITION. (a) Let M^n be a complex G-module with weights $\omega_1, \ldots, \omega_n$. Then the complex conjugate G-module $\bar{M}$ has weights $-\omega_1, \ldots, -\omega_n$. (If $\bar{M} = \{\bar{m} \mid m \in M\}$, then $\lambda\bar{m} = \overline{\bar{\lambda}m}$, $\bar{m}_1 + \bar{m}_2 = \overline{m_1 + m_2}$, $g\cdot\bar{m} = \overline{gm}$.)

(b) Let M^n be a complex G-module with weights $\omega_1, \ldots,$

ω_n. Let M' be the underlying real oriented G-module of M. Then the weights of M' are $\omega_1, \dots, \omega_n$.

(c) Let M be a real G-module of dimension m. Let $\omega_1, \dots, \omega_n$ be the weights of M $(n = [m/2])$. Then the weights of $M \otimes C$ as a complex G-module are $\pm\omega_1, \dots, \pm\omega_n$ (if $m = 2n$), and $\pm\omega_1, \dots, \pm\omega_n, 0$ (if $m = 2n+1$).

PROOF. (Sketch) We may assume $G = T$, and then that M is either a one-dimensional complex vector space or a two-dimensional real one. The result now follows from the definition of the weights of a G-module.

3.7. Using Formula (13) for the Euler class, Theorem 1 may be rephrased as follows:

THEOREM 3. Let $X^{2\ell}$ be a manifold with a G-structure, $f\colon X \to B_G$ the classifying map for the G-structure, and V the oriented real G-module such that

$$T(X) \cong f^*\widetilde{V} \quad .$$

Let $\omega_1, \dots, \omega_\ell$ be the weights of V. Then if $\alpha \in K(B(X), S(X))$ is associated to the G-structure, and M and N are as in 2.3, then

$$\mathrm{ch}(D_\alpha) = f^{**}\left(\frac{\mathrm{ch}(\widetilde{M}) - \mathrm{ch}(\widetilde{N})}{\prod_j (-\omega_j)} \right) \quad .$$

3.8. Notation for $H^*(B_T, \mathbf{Q})$.

CASE 1: $G = U(n)$.

Let $\mathbf{C}^n$ be a $U(n)$-module in the obvious way. Let

$$(*) \qquad \mathbf{C}^n = \mathbf{C} \oplus \cdots \oplus \mathbf{C} \quad (n \text{ times})$$

be the tautological direct sum decomposition. Then the standard maximal torus, T, of $U(N)$ consists of those $g \in U(n)$ which map each direct summand of (*) into iself. Let $x_1, \dots, x_n$ be the weights of $\mathbf{C}^n$ as a

G-module (relative to the decomposition (*)). Then

$$H^*(B_T, \mathbf{Q}) = \mathbf{Q}[x_1, \ldots, x_n] \quad .$$

Moreover, if we identify $H^*(B_{U(n)}, \mathbf{Q})$ with a subring of $H^*(B_T, \mathbf{Q})$ then (by (9)) we have the following formula for the universal Chern classes:

$$1 + c_1 + \cdots + c_n = \prod_{j=1}^{n} (1 + x_j) \quad .$$

CASE 2: $G = SO(2n)$.

Let $\mathbf{R}^{2n}$ be an $SO(2n)$-module in the obvious way, and let

(**) $$\mathbf{R}^{2n} = \mathbf{R}^2 \oplus \cdots \oplus \mathbf{R}^2 \quad .$$

The standard maximal torus, T, of $SO(2n)$ consists of those $g \in SO(2n)$ which map each factor of (**) into itself. Each copy of $\mathbf{R}^2$ is oriented, so the weights of $\mathbf{R}^{2n}$ as a $SO(2n)$-module are well defined. Let the weights be $y_1, \ldots, y_n$. Then from (12) and (13) we get the following formulae for the universal Pontrjagin classes and the universal Euler class respectively:

$$1 + p_1 + \cdots + p_n = \prod_{i=1}^{n} (1 + y_i^2)$$

$$\chi = \prod_{i=1}^{n} y_i \quad .$$

3.9. We have stated the Borel-Hirzebruch results as results about the characteristic classes of vector bundles over B_G. By naturality, the results have implications for bundles over arbitrary spaces. We shall now illustrate this by an example.

Let ξ be a complex vector bundle over X. One introduces a formal factorization

$$1 + c_1(\xi) + \cdots + c_n(\xi) = \prod_{i=1}^{n} (1 + x_i) \quad .$$

Then each formal power series in $x_1, \ldots, x_n$ which is symmetric in $x_1, \ldots, x_n$ may be viewed as a power series in $c_1(\xi), \ldots, c_n(\xi)$ and thus as an element of $H^{**}(X, \mathbf{Q})$. In particular, we have

$$\mathcal{T}(\xi) = \prod_i \frac{x_i}{1-e^{-x_i}} .$$

Now let η^n be a real vector bundle over X. We view the Pontrjagin classes of η as the elementary symmetric functions in y_1^2, ..., y_n^2. Put

$$\mathcal{T}(\eta) = \mathcal{T}(\eta \otimes \mathbf{C}) .$$

(Since $\eta \otimes \mathbf{C}$ is complex, the right hand side has already been defined.)

PROPOSITION.
$$\mathcal{T}(\eta) = \prod_{j=1}^{n} \frac{y_i}{1-e^{-y_i}} \cdot \frac{-y_i}{1-e^{y_i}} .$$

PROOF. We first show the following: Let M be a complex G-module of dimension m (G a compact Lie group). Let $\widetilde{M} = E_G \times_G M$ be the complex vector on B_G associated to M. Let $\omega_1, \ldots, \omega_m$ be the weights of M. Then

$$\mathcal{T}(\widetilde{M}) = \prod_{i=1}^{m} \left(\frac{\omega_i}{1-e^{-\omega_i}} \right) . \tag{14}$$

PROOF of (14). Let $x_1, \ldots, x_m$ be indeterminates, and let $\sigma_1, \ldots, \sigma_m$ be the elementary symmetric functions in $x_1, \ldots, x_m$. We view $\mathbf{Q}[\sigma_1, \ldots, \sigma_m]$ as a graded algebra in which σ_i has grading $2i$.

Then for certain polynomials $T_k(\sigma_1, \ldots, \sigma_n)$, we have a formal identity:

$$\sum_{k=0}^{\infty} T_k(\sigma_1, \ldots, \sigma_m) = \prod_{i=1}^{m} \frac{x_i}{1-e^{-x_i}} \tag{15}$$

and $T_k(\sigma_1, \ldots, \sigma_m)$ has grading $2k$ in $\mathbf{Q}[\sigma_1, \ldots, \sigma_m]$. Then the definition of $\mathcal{T}(\xi)$ amounts to:

$$\mathcal{T}(\xi) = \sum_{k=0}^{\infty} T_k(c_1(\xi), \ldots, c_m(\xi)) .$$

In particular,

$$\mathcal{T}(\widetilde{M}) = \sum_{k=0}^{\infty} T_k(c_1(\widetilde{M}), \ldots, c_m(\widetilde{M})) . \tag{16}$$

But substituting $\omega_1, \ldots, \omega_m$ in (15), and using the fact that $\sigma_i(\omega_1, \ldots, \omega_m) = c_i(\widetilde{M})$ (by (9)), we get

$$(17) \qquad \sum_{k=0}^{\infty} T_k(c_1(\widetilde{M}), \ldots, c_m(\widetilde{M})) = \prod_{i=1}^{m} \frac{\omega_i}{1-e^{-\omega_i}} .$$

But (16) and (17) yield (14).

By naturality it suffices to prove the proposition when $X = B_{SO(n)}$, $M = \mathbf{R}^n$, and $\eta = \widetilde{M}$.. Let the weights be $y_1, \ldots, y_k$ $(k = [n/2])$. Then $\eta \otimes \mathbf{C} = \widetilde{M \otimes \mathbf{C}}$. By Proposition 3.5(c), $M \otimes \mathbf{C}$ has weights $\pm y_1, \ldots, \pm y_k$, and possibly 0. Since $x/(1-e^{-x})$ has constant term 1, $0/(1-e^{-0})$, appropriately interpreted, is 1. Thus by (14),

$$(18) \qquad \mathscr{T}(\widetilde{M} \otimes \mathbf{C}) = \prod_{i=1}^{k} \frac{y_i}{1-e^{-y_i}} \frac{-y_i}{1-e^{y_i}} .$$

Here the y_i are elements of $H^2(B_T, \mathbf{Q})$. However, by (12), $\prod_{i=1}^{k}(1+y_i^2) = 1 + p_1 + \cdots + p_K$. Thus the proposition is valid in the universal example, $\eta = \widetilde{M}$. (Cf. the proof of (14).) The proof is complete.

§4. An Application to ch(D).

If M and N are complex vector spaces, we let Iso(M, N) denote the set of isomorphisms of M with N.

Let G be a compact Lie group, V a real G-module, and M and N complex G-modules. Suppose that

$$\sigma: \; S(V^*) \to \mathrm{Iso}(M, N)$$

is a G-equivariant map. Then if P is a principal G-bundle, with base space X,

$$(19) \qquad E = P \times_G M, \qquad F = P \times_G N, \quad \text{and} \quad T = P \times_G V ,$$

then σ gives rise to a map

$$\sigma_P: \; \pi^* E \cong \pi^* F$$

where $\pi: S(T^*) \to X$ is the projection. Moreover, σ_P is natural with respect to bundle maps.

Now specialize to the case when X is a manifold with a G-structure, and P and V are the principal bundle and real oriented G-module associated to that structure: $P \times_G V \cong T(X)$. Let E and F be defined by (19). Let

$$D: \; C^\infty(E) \to C^\infty(F)$$

be an elliptic operator such that

$$\sigma(D) = \sigma_P \quad .$$

Then ch(D) *may be computed using Theorems* 1 *and* 3. In fact, let $\gamma(D) \in K(B(X), S(X))$ be

$$d(\pi^* E, \pi^* F, \sigma_P) \qquad (\pi: \; B(X) \to X) \quad .$$

Then $\gamma(D) = f^!(\pi \; \widetilde{M}, \pi \; \widetilde{N}, \sigma_{E_G})$ (by the naturality of σ_P in the variable P) so that $\gamma(D)$ is associated to the G-structure on X (in the sense of 2.3). To sum up: if $X^{2\ell}$ is a manifold with a G-structure,

$$D: \; C^\infty(E) \to C^\infty(F)$$

is an elliptic operator whose symbol, $\sigma(D)$, is given by a "universal formula" (i.e., $\sigma(D) = \sigma_P$), then $ch(D) = f^{**}((-1)^\ell \, ch(\widetilde{M}) - ch(\widetilde{N})/\chi(\widetilde{V}^*))$. Thus ch(D) can be computed from just the G-modules M, N, and V. In Lecture IV, we shall see that each of the classical elliptic operators is of this type. In the next paragraphs we shall compute the topological indices of such operators.

§5. The Euler Class and the Todd Class.

5.0. PROPOSITION. Let M be a complex G-module with weights $\omega_1, \ldots, \omega_n$. Then

$$\sum_{i=0}^{n} (-1)^i \, ch(\Lambda^i(\widetilde{M})) = \prod_{i=1}^{n} (1 - e^{\omega_i}) \quad .$$

PROOF. Let $e_1, \ldots, e_n$ be a basis for M such that

$$t \cdot e_j = e^{2\pi i \omega_j(t)} \, e_j \qquad (t \in T, \;\; 1 \leq j \leq n) \quad .$$

Then $\{e_{i_1} \wedge \cdots \wedge e_{i_k} \mid 1 \le i_1 < i_2 < \cdots < i_k \le n\}$ is a basis for $\dot{\Lambda}^k M$ and

$$t \cdot e_{i_1} \wedge \cdots \wedge e_{i_k} = \exp(2\pi i(\omega_{i_1} + \cdots + \omega_{i_k}(t)) \cdot e_{i_1} \wedge \cdots \wedge e_{i_k} .$$

Thus the weights of $\Lambda^k M$ are

$$\{\omega_{i_1} + \cdots + \omega_{i_k} \mid 1 \le i_1 < i_2 < \cdots < i_k \le n\} .$$

By (10) $$\sum_{j=0}^{n} (-1)^j \operatorname{ch}(\dot{\Lambda}^i(M)) = \sum_{j=0}^{n} \sum_{0 \le i_1 < \cdots < i_j \le n} (-1)^j e^{\omega_{i_1} + \cdots + \omega_{i_j}}$$

$$= \prod_{i=1}^{n} (1 - e^{\omega_i}) .$$

5.1. Let $G = SO(2n)$, and let V be $\mathbf{R}^{2n}$. In this case, a manifold, X, with a G-structure is just an oriented Riemannian manifold.

PROPOSITION. Let X^{2n} be an oriented Riemannian manifold, and let $D\colon C^\infty(\sum_{k\equiv 0(2)} \Lambda^k(T^*(X)) \otimes \mathbf{C}) \to C^\infty(\sum_{k\equiv 1(2)} \Lambda^k(T^*(X)) \otimes \mathbf{C})$ be elliptic. We suppose that the symbol of D arises from a universal construction (cf. §4). Then the topological index, $i_t(D)$, is

$$\chi(X)\,[X] .$$

($\chi(X)$ is the Euler class of the tangent bundle of X.)

PROOF. Put $V = \mathbf{R}^{2n}$, $M = \sum_{k\equiv 0(2)} \Lambda^k(V^* \otimes \mathbf{C})$, $N = \sum_{k\equiv 1(2)} \Lambda^k(V^* \otimes \mathbf{C})$. Note that V^* is isomorphic to V as G-module (under $x \to (x, \cdot)$, where $(\, , \,)$ is the Euclidean inner product).

Let the weights of V as a real G-module be $y_1, \ldots, y_n$. By Proposition 3.5(c), and the remark just made, $V^* \otimes \mathbf{C}$ has the weights $\pm y_1, \ldots, \pm y_n$. Thus by Proposition 5.1,

$$\operatorname{ch}(\tilde{M}) - \operatorname{ch}(\tilde{N}) = \prod_{i=1}^{n} (1 - e^{y_i})(1 - e^{-y_i}) .$$

According to §4 we may apply Theorem 3 to D and get

$$ch(D) = \prod_{i=1}^{n} (1 - e^{y_i})(1 - e^{-y_i})/-y_i \quad .$$

Recall that

$$\mathscr{T}(X) = \prod_{i=1}^{n} \frac{y_i \cdot -y_i}{(1 - e^{y_i})(1 - e^{-y_i})} \quad .$$

Thus $ch(D)\mathscr{T}(X) = \prod_{i=1}^{n} y_i = \chi(X)$ (by 3.8 Case 2).

Thus $i_t(D) = ch(D)\mathscr{T}(X)\ [X] = \chi(X)\ [X]$.

5.2. Now let $G = U(m) \times U(n)$, $V = \mathbf{C}^m$, $W = \mathbf{C}^n$. We let G act on V by the projection $U(m) \times U(m) \to U(m)$, and on W by the projection $U(m) \times U(n) \to U(n)$.

Let X be a manifold with a G-structure, and let P be the principal G-bundle of X. Then

$$T(X) \cong P \times_G V$$

is, in a natural way, a complex vector bundle with a hermitian inner product on its fibers. Thus X is a hermitian almost complex manifold in a canonical way. In addition, $\eta = P \times_G W$ is a hermitian complex vector bundle on X. Conversely, if X is a hermitian almost complex manifold and η is a hermitian complex vector bundle, then X has a canonical G-structure inducing the given hermitian almost complex structure on X and such that $P \times_G W$ is canonically isomorphic to η.

Now put

$$M = \sum_{k \equiv 0(2)} \Lambda^k(\bar{V}^*) \otimes W$$

and let

$$N = \sum_{k \equiv 1(2)} \Lambda^k(\bar{V}^*) \otimes W \quad .$$

We write $\mathscr{T}(X)$ for the Todd class of the complex vector bundle T(X), and $\mathscr{T}(X_r)$ for the Todd class of the underlying real bundle.

PROPOSITION. Let G be as above, X a manifold with a G-structure, and let $E = P \times_G M$, $F = P \times_G N$, $\eta = P \times_G W$. Suppose that

$$D: \quad C^\infty(E) \to C^\infty(F)$$

is elliptic and that the symbol of D arises from a universal construction. Then

$$i_t(D) = ch(\eta)\mathscr{T}(X)\,[X] \quad .$$

PROOF. Let the weights of V as a complex G-module be $x_1, \ldots, x_m$. By Proposition 3.5(b), the underlying oriented real G-module of V, V_r, also has as weights $x_1, \ldots, x_m$. Let $(\,,\,)$ be the standard hermitian inner product on $\mathbf{C}^m$. Then $x \to (\,, x)$ sets up an isomorphism of G-modules

$$\bar{V} \cong V^* \quad .$$

Thus $\bar{V}^* \cong \bar{\bar{V}} = V$ as a G-module. We can now apply Proposition 5.1 and get

$$ch(\widetilde{M}) - ch(\widetilde{N}) = ch(\widetilde{W}) \prod_{i=1}^{m} (1 - e^{x_i}) \quad .$$

By Theorem 3 (cf. §4),

$$ch(D) = f^{**}(ch(\widetilde{W}) \prod_{i=1}^{m} (1 - e^{x_i})/(-x_i)) \quad ,$$

where $f: X \to B_G$ is the classifying map. We next compute $\mathscr{T}(X_r)$:

If X_r is the underlying real C^∞-manifold of X,

$$T(X_r) \cong f^*(\widetilde{V}_r) \quad .$$

But V_r has as weights, $x_1, \ldots, x_m$. It follows that

$$\mathscr{T}(X_r) = f^{**}\Big(\prod_{i=1}^{m} \frac{x_i}{1-e^{-x_i}} \; \frac{-x_i}{1-e^{x_i}} \Big)$$

(by Proposition 3.9).

Now $\eta = f^*\widetilde{W}$, and $c_1(X), \ldots, c_m(X)$ are the elementary symmetric functions in $f^*x_1, \ldots, f^*x_n$. (Of course, $f^*x_1, \ldots, f^*x_m$ do not exist!) Thus

$$\mathrm{ch}(D)\mathscr{T}(X_r) = f^{**}\left(\mathrm{ch}(\widetilde{W}) \prod_{i=1}^{m} \frac{x_i}{1-e^{-x_i}}\right) = \mathrm{ch}(\eta)\mathscr{T}(X) \quad ,$$

and

$$i_t(D) = \mathrm{ch}(\eta)\mathscr{T}(X)\,[X]$$

q.e.d.

§6. The L-Genus

6.1. Let V^n be an oriented real vector space equipped with an inner product, $\langle\ \rangle$. We recall that there is an isomorphism

$$*\colon\ \Lambda^k(V) \cong \Lambda^{n-k}(V)$$

defined as follows:

$\Lambda^k(V)$ has a natural inner product characterized by the identity

$$\langle e_1 \wedge \dots \wedge e_k;\ f_1 \wedge \dots \wedge f_k \rangle = \det|\langle e_i, f_j \rangle| \quad .$$

If $e_1, \dots, e_n$ is an oriented orthonormal basis, we put

$$\det(e_1 \wedge \dots \wedge e_n) = 1 \quad .$$

The map det extends by linearity to a canonical isomrophism $\Lambda^n(V) \cong \mathbf{R}$. Then $*$ is defined by the identity

(20) $$\langle a, b \rangle = \det(a \wedge *b) \qquad (a, b \in \Lambda^k(V)) \quad .$$

If $e_1, \dots, e_k, \dots, e_n$ form an oriented orthonormal basis of V, then

(21) $$*(e_1 \wedge \dots \wedge e_k) = e_{k+1} \wedge \dots \wedge e_n \quad .$$

From this it is easy to deduce that $*^2 = (-1)^{k(n-k)}$ on $\Lambda^k(V)$. If $\dim V$ is even, which we shall always assume, then

(22) $$*^2 = (-1)^k \qquad \text{on} \qquad \Lambda^k(V) \quad .$$

Now let V have dimension 2ℓ, and let

$$\alpha\colon\ \Lambda^*(V) \otimes \mathbf{C} \to \Lambda^*(V) \otimes \mathbf{C}$$

be equal to

$$i^{k(k-1)+\ell} *$$

on $\Lambda^k(V)$. An easy computation, using (22), shows that

$$\alpha^2 = 1 \quad .$$

Thus we get a direct sum decomposition

$$\Lambda^*(V) \otimes C = \Lambda_+(V) \oplus \Lambda_-(V)$$

where $\Lambda_\pm$ is the eigenspace of α for the eigenvalue ± 1. Note that the spaces $\Lambda_\pm$ are complex vector spaces.

If E is a 2ℓ-dimensional oriented vector bundle, we can define α in the fibers of $\Lambda^*(E) \otimes \mathbf{C}$, thereby getting a direct sum decomposition:

$$\Lambda^*(E) \otimes C = \Lambda_+(E) \oplus \Lambda_-(E) \quad .$$

The following proposition will be proved at the end of this section.

PROPOSITION 6.1. Let V be $\mathbf{R}^{2n}$ considered as a real oriented $SO(2n)$-module. Then if $\tilde{V}$ is the bundle over $B_{SO(2n)}$ corresponding to V, we have

$$ch(\Lambda_+(\tilde{V})) - ch(\Lambda_-(\tilde{V})) = \prod_{i=1}^{n} (e^{-y_i} - e^{y_i})$$

where we identify $H^*(B_{SO(2n)})$ with a subgroup of $H^*(B_T)$, and let $y_1, \ldots, y_n$ be the weights of V.

PROPOSITION 6.2. Let X be a Riemannian manifold, and let

$$D: \; C^\infty(\Lambda_+(T^*(X)) \to C^\infty(\Lambda_-(T^*(X)))$$

be an elliptic operator whose symbol arises from a universal construction. Then

$$i_t(D) = \prod_i y_i/\tanh y_i \; [X]$$

where the Pontrjagin classes are viewed as the elementary symmetric function in the y_i^2 .

REMARK. $y/\tanh y$ is even and therefore is given by a power series in $\mathbf{Q}\{y^2\}$.

PROOF. We put $M = \Lambda_+(V)$, and $N = \Lambda_-(V)$; applying Theorem 3 and Proposition 6.1, we get

$$\mathrm{ch}(D) = \prod_{i=1}^{n} \frac{e^{-y_i} - e^{y_i}}{-y_i} .$$

$$\mathrm{ch}(D)\mathcal{T}(X) = \prod_{i=1}^{n} \frac{e^{-y_i} - e^{y_i}}{-y_i} \frac{y_i}{1-e^{-y_i}} \frac{-y_i}{1-e^{y_i}}$$

$$= \prod_{i=1}^{n} y_i\left(\frac{e^{-y_i} - e^{y_i}}{(1-e^{y_i})(1-e^{-y_i})} \right) .$$

We now use the identity

$$\frac{U^{-1} - U}{(1-U)(1-U^{-1})} = \frac{1 - U^2}{(1-U)(U-1)} = \frac{1+U}{U-1} = \frac{U^{1/2} + U^{-1/2}}{U^{1/2} - U^{-1/2}}$$

to get

$$\mathrm{ch}(D)\mathcal{T}(X) = \prod_i y_i \frac{\cosh y_i/2}{\sinh y_i/2} = \prod_i y_i/\tanh(y_i/2) .$$

Thus $i_t(D) = \mathrm{ch}(D)\mathcal{T}(X)\,[X] = \prod_i y_i/\tanh(y_i/2)\,[X]$. If we replace y_i by $2y_i$, the term in grading $2k$ will be multiplied by 2^k. Thus the top-dimensional term is multiplied by 2^n, and we have

$$2^n\, i_t(D) = \prod_{i=1}^{n} 2y_i/\tanh y_i\,[X]$$

or equivalently,

$$i_t(D) = \prod_i y_i/\tanh y_i\,[X] . \tag{23}$$

REMARK. The right hand side of (23) is just the Hirzebruch L-genus of X.

PROOF of Proposition 6.1.

1. Let V and W be even-dimensional vector spaces. Let $a \in \Lambda^k(V)$, $b \in \Lambda^\ell(W)$. Then the formula

$$(24) \qquad *_{V \oplus W}(a \wedge b) = (-1)^{k\ell} *_V(a) \wedge *_W(b)$$

follows easily from the definition of $*$ (cf. 20)). A routine computation now shows that

$$\alpha_{V \oplus W}(a \wedge b) = \alpha_V(a) \wedge \alpha_W(b) \quad .$$

From this it follows that

$$(25) \qquad \begin{aligned} \Lambda_+(V \oplus W) &= (\Lambda_+(V) \otimes \Lambda_+(W)) \oplus (\Lambda_-(V) \otimes \Lambda_-(W)) \\ \Lambda_-(V \oplus W) &= (\Lambda_-(V) \otimes \Lambda_+(W)) \oplus (\Lambda_+(V) \otimes \Lambda_-(W)) \quad . \end{aligned}$$

2. Let $p\colon B_T \to B_G$ be the map of classifying spaces induced by the inclusion, i, of T in G. Then by the definition of p, there is a map $\lambda\colon E_T \to E_G$ such that

$$\lambda(x \cdot t) = \lambda(x) \cdot t \quad (\text{for } x \in E_T \text{ and } t \in T)$$

and the diagram

$$\begin{array}{ccc} E_T & \xrightarrow{\lambda} & E_G \\ \Big\downarrow{\scriptstyle\pi} & & \Big\downarrow{\scriptstyle\pi} \\ B_T & \xrightarrow{p} & B_G \end{array}$$

is commutative.

Let M be a G-module, M' the underlying T-module. The map $\lambda \times 1_M\colon E_T \times M \to E_G \times M$ passes to quotients to define a bundle map of $\widetilde{M}' \to \widetilde{M}$ inducing p on base-spaces. Thus, $\widetilde{M}' = p^*\widetilde{M}$.

3. Since the map $p^*\colon H^*(B_G, \mathbf{Q}) \to H^*(B_T, \mathbf{Q})$ is a monomorphism, it suffices in view of 2, to show

$$\mathrm{ch}(\Lambda_+(\mathbf{R}^{2n})^\sim) - \mathrm{ch}(\Lambda_-(\mathbf{R}^{2n})^\sim) = \prod_i (e^{-y_i} - e^{y_i})$$

where $\mathbf{R}^{2n}$ is considered as a T-module.

4. Recall that if G is a compact Lie group, $R(G)$ is the free abelian group generated by the irreducible G-modules. An arbitrary G-module, M, splits into the direct sum of irreducible G-modules: $M = M_1 \oplus \cdots \oplus M_n$, and one defines $[M] \in R(G)$ as $\Sigma_i [M_i]$. The tensor product of G-modules makes $R(G)$ into a commutative ring: the representation ring of G.

The map

$$ch: R(G) \to H^{**}(B_G, Q) \quad ,$$

defined by

$$ch([M]) = ch(\widetilde{M})$$

is a ring homomorphism.

5. We return to the T-module R^{2n}. This splits into irreducible T-modules:

$$\mathbf{R}^{2n} = \mathbf{R}^2 \oplus \cdots \oplus \mathbf{R}^2 \quad .$$

Let V_i be the ith copy of $\mathbf{R}^2$ considered as a T-module. From (25) we get the following equation in $R(T)$:

$$[\Lambda_+(\mathbf{R}^{2n})] - [\Lambda_-(\mathbf{R}^{2n})] = \prod_{i=1}^{n} ([\Lambda_+(V_i)] - [\Lambda_-(V_i)]) \quad .$$

Taking ch of both sides,

$$(26) \quad ch(\Lambda_+(\mathbf{R}^{2n})^\sim) - ch(\Lambda_-(\mathbf{R}^{2n})^\sim) = \prod_{i=1}^{n} (ch(\Lambda_+(V_i)^\sim) - ch(\Lambda_-(V_i)^\sim) \quad .$$

6. The Euler class of V_i is y_i. Thus Proposition 6.1 will follow from (26) and the following:

LEMMA. Let V be an oriented 2-dimension real vector bundle. vector bundle. Then if y is the Euler class of V,

$$ch(\Lambda_+(V)) - ch(\Lambda_-(V)) = e^{-y_i} - e^{y_i} \quad .$$

PROOF. By naturality, we may assume V is the universal oriented $\mathbf{R}^2$-bundle over $B_{SO(2)}$.

If e_1, e_2 is the usual basis in $\mathbf{R}^2$,

$$*e_1 = e_2, \quad *e_2 = -e_1, \quad *1 = e_1 \wedge e_2, \quad *(e_1 \wedge e_2) = 1 .$$

Thus a basis for Λ_+ is $1 + i(e_1 \wedge e_2)$ and $e_1 + ie_2$; a basis for Λ_- is $1 - i(e_1 \wedge e_2)$ and $e_1 - ie_2$.

If $y\colon SO(2) \to S^1$ is the standard weight, then y sends the matrix

$$\begin{pmatrix} \cos 2\pi\theta & -\sin 2\pi\theta \\ \sin 2\pi\theta & \cos 2\pi\theta \end{pmatrix}$$

into θ. (Here $\theta \in S^1$.)

Let $[X]$ denote the 1-dimensional subspace spanned by x. Then the $SO(2)$-modules $[1 \pm i(e_1 \wedge e_2)]$ have weight 0, and the modules $[e_1 \pm ie_2]$ have weights $\mp y$ respectively. The Lemma now results from (10).

REFERENCES

[1] A. Borel, Sur la cohomologie des espaces fibrés principaux et des espaces homogènes de groupes de Lie compacts, Ann. of Math., 57(1953), pp. 115-207.

[2] A. Borel and F. Hirzebruch, Characteristic classes and homogeneous spaces I, Amer. J. Math., 80(1958), pp. 458-538.

CHAPTER IV

DIFFERENTIAL OPERATORS ON VECTOR BUNDLES

Richard S. Palais

§1. Notation

M will denote a paracompact C^∞ manifold, possibly with boundary, $C^\infty(M, \mathbf{C})$ the ring of complex valued C^∞ functions on M, $C^\infty(M, \mathbf{R})$ the subring of real valued functions. $V(M)$ will denote the additive category of C^∞ complex vector bundles over M. Objects of $V(M)$ will usually be denoted by ξ, η, ζ and we will generally use the same symbol to denote a vector bundle and its total space. The fiber of ξ at x will be denoted by ξ_x. We denote by C^∞ the additive functor from $V(M)$ to the category of complex vector spaces which assigns to ξ the vector space $C^\infty(\xi)$ of C^∞ cross-sections of ξ and to $F \in \mathrm{Hom}(\xi, \eta)$ the induced map $F_*\colon C^\infty(\xi) \to C^\infty(\eta)$ defined by $F_*(f)(x) = F(f(x))$ (an element of $\mathrm{Hom}(\xi, \eta)$ is of course a C^∞ map of ξ into η which for each $x \in M$ maps ξ_x linearly into η_x). $C_c^\infty(\xi)$ will denote the subspace of $C^\infty(\xi)$ consisting of sections with compact support and $C_0^\infty(\xi)$ the subspace of $C_c^\infty(\xi)$ consisting of sections whose supports are compact and disjoint from ∂M. We note that $C^\infty(\xi)$ is a $C^\infty(M, \mathbf{C})$ module, that $C_c^\infty(\xi)$ and $C_0^\infty(\xi)$ are submodules, that F_* is a module homomorphism, and that F_* maps $C_c^\infty(\xi)$ into $C_c^\infty(\eta)$ and maps $C_0^\infty(\xi)$ into $C_0^\infty(\eta)$.

We denote by L the functor from $V(M) \times V(M)$ to $V(M)$ which assigns to (ξ, η) the bundle $L(\xi, \eta)$ whose fiber $L(\xi, \eta)_x$ at x is the complex vector space $L(\xi_x, \eta_x)$ of linear maps of ξ_x into η_x. If $T \in \mathrm{Hom}(\xi, \eta)$ then $\bar{T}(x) = T|\xi_x \in L(\xi, \eta)_x$ and the bundle structure of $L(\xi, \eta)$ is uniquely characterized by the property that $\bar{T} \in C^\infty(L(\xi, \eta))$. Then $T \to \bar{T}$ is a natural equivalence of the functors Hom and $C^\infty L$ which we regard as an identification, i.e., $\mathrm{Hom} = C^\infty L$.

If W is a finite dimensional complex vector space then $W_M \in V(M)$ will denote the product bundle $M \times W$ and we will use the symbold $C^\infty(W_M)$ and $C^\infty(M, W)$ interchangeably. If $\xi \in V(M)$ its dual bundle is $\xi^* = L(\xi, \mathbf{C}_M)$. Similarly if γ is a C^∞ real vector bundle then γ^* will denote the dual real bundle.

If $M = M_1 \times \cdots \times M_k$ and $\xi^i \in V(M_i)$ then $\xi^1 \otimes \cdots \otimes \xi^k$ is a bundle over M whose fiber at $x = (x_1, \ldots, x_k)$ is $\xi^1_{x_1} \otimes \cdots \otimes \xi^k_{x_k}$. If $f^i \in C^\infty(\xi^i)$ we define $f^1 \otimes \cdots \otimes f^k$, a function on M, by $(f^1 \otimes \cdots \otimes f^k)(x) = f^1(x_1) \otimes \cdots \otimes f^k(x_k)$. The bundle structure of $\xi^1 \otimes \cdots \otimes \xi^k$ is characterized by the property that $f^1 \otimes \cdots \otimes f^k \in C^\infty(\xi^1 \otimes \cdots \otimes \xi^k)$ wherever $f^i \in C^\infty(\xi^i)$.

If $\xi^i \in V(M)$ $i = 1, \ldots, k$ we define $\xi^1 \hat{\otimes} \cdots \hat{\otimes} \xi^k \in V(M)$ by $\xi^1 \hat{\otimes} \cdots \hat{\otimes} \xi^k = \Delta^*(\xi^1 \otimes \cdots \otimes \xi^k)$, where $\Delta\colon M \to M \times \cdots \times M$ is the diagonal map, $x \to (x, \ldots, x)$. If $\xi^i = \xi (i = 1, \ldots, k)$ we write $\xi^1 \hat{\otimes} \cdots \hat{\otimes} \xi^k = \otimes^k \xi$. If π is a permutation of the set $\{1, \ldots, k\}$ then π induces a bundle morphism, also denoted by π of $\otimes^k \xi$ into itself characterized by $\pi(v_1 \otimes \cdots \otimes v_k) = v_{\pi(1)} \otimes \cdots \otimes v_{\pi(k)}$. The set of elements of $\otimes^k \xi$ left fixed by all such π is denoted by $S^k(\xi)$, the $k^{\underline{th}}$ symmetric tensor product of ξ. There is a canonical projection $S^{(k)} \in \mathrm{Hom}(\otimes^k \xi, S^k(\xi))$, namely $\frac{1}{k!} \Sigma\, \pi$, where the sum is over all $k!$ permutations of $\{1, \ldots, k\}$. We will also use $S^{(k)}$ to denote the projection $S^{(k)} \hat{\otimes}\, \mathrm{id}$ of $\otimes^k \xi \hat{\otimes} \eta$ onto $S^k(\xi) \hat{\otimes} \eta$.

We note that the above tensor and symmetric tensor products are of course also defined for C^∞ real bundles.

Let γ be a C^∞ real bundle over M. For each $\xi \in V(M)$ and non-negative integer k we define $L^k(\gamma, \xi)$ to be a C^∞ complex vector bundle over M whose fiber at x is the space $L^k(\gamma_x, \xi_x)$ of k linear (over $\mathbf{R}$) maps of $(\gamma_x)^k$ into ξ_x (we define $L^0(\gamma_x, \xi_x) = \xi_x$), and having the obvious bundle structure. We define $L^k_s(\gamma, \xi)$ to be the subbundle whose fiber at x is the space $L^k_s(\gamma_x, \xi_x)$ of symmetric k-linear maps of $(\gamma_x)^k$ into ξ_x. If $f \in L^k_s(\gamma_x, \xi_x)$ there is an associated map $\check{f}\colon \gamma_x \to \xi_x$, defined by $\check{f}(v) = f(v, \ldots, v)$ i.e., $\check{f} = f \circ \Delta$ where

Δ: $\gamma_x \to (\gamma_x)^k$ is the diagonal map. The image of the map $f \to \check{f}$ is easily identified, it is the space $P^{(k)}(\gamma_x, \xi_x)$ of homogeneous polynomial maps of degree k of γ_x into ξ_x. [If $e_1, \ldots, e_n$ is a basis for γ_x then $P^{(k)}(\gamma_x, \xi_x)$ consists of all maps of the form

$$\Big(\sum_{i=1}^{n} x_i e_i\Big) \to \Big(\sum_{\alpha} x_1^{\alpha_1} \cdots x_n^{\alpha_n}\Big) y_\alpha$$

where the sum is over all n-tuple of non-negative integers $\alpha = (\alpha_1, \ldots, \alpha_n)$ such that $\Sigma_{i=1}^{n} \alpha_i = k$, and the y_α are the elements of ξ_x]. The map $f \to \check{f}$ is an isomorphism of $L_s^k(\gamma_x, \xi_x)$ with $P^{(k)}(\gamma_x, \xi_x)$, the inverse map is called polarization. It follows that $L_s^k(\gamma, \xi)$ is naturally equivalent to $P^{(k)}(\gamma, \xi)$, the bundle whose fiber at x is $P^{(k)}(\gamma_x, \xi_x)$.

There is a canonical identification of $\otimes^k \gamma^* \hat{\otimes} \xi$ with $L^k(\gamma, \xi)$, characterized by the property that $(v_1 \otimes \cdots \otimes v_k) \otimes e$ in $\otimes^k \gamma_x \hat{\otimes} \xi_x$ corresponds to the map $(w_1, \ldots, w_k) \to v_1(w_1) \cdots v_k(w_k)e$ in $L^k(\gamma_x, \xi_x)$. Under this identification the sub-bundle $S^k(\gamma^*) \hat{\otimes} \xi$ of $\otimes^k \gamma^* \hat{\otimes} \xi$ is identified with the sub-bundle $L_s^k(\gamma, \xi)$ of $L^k(\gamma, \xi)$. In particular if $v \in \gamma_x^*$ and $e \in \xi_x$ then $(v \otimes \cdots \otimes v) \otimes e$ is in $S^k(\gamma_x^*) \otimes \xi_x$ and the corresponding element of $L_s^k(\gamma_x, \xi_x)$, namely

$$(w_1, \ldots, w_k) \to v(w_1) \cdots v(w_k)e$$

will be denoted by $S^k(v) \otimes e$.

Note that we how have three naturally equivalent bundles

$$S^k(\gamma^*) \hat{\otimes} \xi \approx L_s^k(\gamma, \xi) \approx P^{(k)}(\gamma, \xi) \quad .$$

In general we will find it convenient to "prefer" $L_s^k(\gamma, \xi)$ (some choice has to be made) however, it will be convenient to pass back and forth between these various ways of looking at the same thing and we shall often do so tacitly.

We denote the tangent bundle of M by $T(M)$, its dual bundle $T(M)^*$, the cotangent bundle of M, by $T^*(M)$ and we denote by $T'(M)$ the bundle $T^*(M)$ with the zero section removed; so elements of $T'(M)$ are pairs (v, x) where $x \in M$ and v is a non-zero linear functional on the tangent space to M at x, and the projection π: $T'(M) \to M$ is given by $\pi(v, x) = x$. Then $\pi^*(\xi)$ is a vector bundle over $T'(M)$ whose fiber at (v, x) is ξ_x, so $\mathrm{Hom}(\pi^*\xi, \pi^*\eta)$ consists of functions σ with domain $T'(M)$ such that $\sigma(v, x)$ is a linear map of ξ_x into η_x. For each real number k we define a linear subspace $\mathrm{Smbl}_k(\xi, \eta)$ of $\mathrm{Hom}(\pi^*\xi, \pi^*\eta)$ by

$$\mathrm{Smbl}_k(\xi, \eta) = \{\sigma \in \mathrm{Hom}(\pi^*\xi, \pi^*\eta) \mid \sigma(\rho v, x) = \rho^k\sigma(v, x) \text{ if } \rho > 0\} .$$

If k is a non-negative integer then we define a subspace $\mathrm{Smbl}_k^d(\xi, \eta)$ of $\mathrm{Smbl}_k(\xi, \eta)$ by

$$\mathrm{Smbl}_k^d(\xi, \eta) = C^\infty(P^{(k)}(T^*(M), L(\xi, \eta))$$

or, to be precise, an element σ of $\mathrm{Hom}(\pi^*\xi, \pi^*\eta)$ belongs to $\mathrm{Smbl}_k^d(\xi, \eta)$ if and only if for each $x \in M$ there is a homogeneous polynomial map f_x of degree k from $T^*(M)_x$ into $L(\xi_x, \eta_x)$ such that $\sigma(v, x) = f_x(v)$.

There is a canonical isomorphism

$$\lambda_k\colon \mathrm{Hom}(L_s^k(T(M), \xi), \eta) \approx \mathrm{Smbl}_k^d(\xi, \eta)$$

defined by

$$\lambda_k(F)(v, x)e = F(S^k(v) \otimes e) .$$

We leave it to the reader to verify that λ_k is the composition of the following sequence of canonical isomorphisms:

$$\begin{aligned}\mathrm{Hom}(L_s^k(T(M), \xi), \eta) &\approx C^\infty(L(S^k(T^*(M)) \mathbin{\hat\otimes} \xi, \eta))\\ &\approx C^\infty((S^k(T^*(M)) \mathbin{\hat\otimes} \xi)^* \mathbin{\hat\otimes} \eta)\\ &\approx C^\infty(S^k(T(M)) \mathbin{\hat\otimes} (\xi^* \mathbin{\hat\otimes} \eta))\\ &\approx C^\infty(P^{(k)}(T^*(M), L(\xi, \eta)) .\end{aligned}$$

The inverse inverse isomorphism to λ_k will be denoted by $\sigma \mapsto \tilde\sigma$. Thus if $\sigma \in \mathrm{Smbl}_k^d(\xi, \eta)$ then $\tilde\sigma \in \mathrm{Hom}(L_s^k(T(M), \xi), \eta)$ is characterized by $\tilde\sigma(S^k(v) \otimes e) = \sigma(v, x)e$.

Let V and W be respectively real and complex vector spaces of finite dimension and let $f\colon V \to W$ be a C^∞ map. Then for each $x \in V$ the differential of f at x is the element df_x of $L(V, W)$ defined by $df_x(v) = \lim 1/t(f(x+tv) - f(x))$ and $x \to df_x$ is a C^∞ map $df\colon V \to L(V, W$

called the first differential of f. Making the canonical identification $L(V, L^{k-1}(V, W)) \approx L^k(V, W)$ we get inductively a sequence of C^∞ maps $d^k f = d(d^{k-1} f)\colon V \to L^k(V, W)$ and by a standard result of advanced calculus (the "equality of cross-derivatives") we have in fact $d^k f\colon V \to L^k_s(V, W)$. If $e = (e_1, \ldots, e_n)$ is a base for V and we let $x_1, \ldots, x_n$ be the dual base for V^* (a C^∞ coordinate system for V) then

$$d^k f_x(e_{i_1} \ldots e_{i_k}) = \frac{\partial^k f}{\partial x_{i_1} \ldots \partial x_{i_k}}(x) .$$

If $\alpha = (\alpha_1, \ldots, \alpha_n)$ is an "n-multi index", i.e., an n-tuple of non-negative integers, we will put $|\alpha| = \alpha_1 + \cdots + \alpha_n$ and $\alpha! = \alpha_1! \cdots \alpha_n!$, and $\binom{|\alpha|}{\alpha} = \frac{|\alpha|!}{\alpha!}$. If $x = (x_1, \ldots, x_n)$ is an n-tuple of complex numbers $x^\alpha = x_1^{\alpha_1} \cdots x_n^{\alpha_n}$ and we write D^α for the differential operator $\partial^{|\alpha|}/\partial x_1^{\alpha_1} \cdots \partial x_n^{\alpha_n}$. If $e = (e_1, \ldots, e_n)$ is any n-tuple then $e^{(\alpha)}$ is the $|\alpha|$-tuple

$$\left(e_1^{(\alpha_1)} \ldots e_n^{(\alpha_n)} \right)$$

where $e_i^{(\alpha_i)}$ is the α_i-tuple $(e_i, \ldots, e_i)$. Thus for example the relation above of $d^k f_x$ to the partial derivatives of f becomes $d^{|\alpha|} f_x(e^{(\alpha)}) = D^\alpha f(x)$ and Taylor's Theorem is

$$f(x+v) = \sum_{m=0}^{k} \frac{1}{m!} d^m f_x(v^{(m)}) + R_{k+1}(x)(v^{(k+1)})$$

$$= \sum_{|\alpha| \le k} \frac{1}{\alpha!} D^\alpha f(x) v^\alpha + \sum_{|\alpha|=k+1} R_\alpha(x) v^\alpha$$

where $R_{k+1}\colon V \to L_s^{k+1}(V, W)$ and $R_\alpha\colon V \to W$ are C^∞ maps.

§2. Jet bundles

Given $p \in M$ we denote by $I_p(M)$, or simply I_p, the ideal in $C^\infty(M, \mathbf{C})$ of functions vanishing at p. If ξ is a C^∞ complex vector bundle over M we define

$$Z_p^k(\xi) = I_p^{k+1}(p) \cdot C^\infty(\xi)$$

and the complex vector space of k-jets of ξ at p, denoted by $J^k(\xi)_p$, is defined as

$$J^k(\xi)_p = C^\infty(\xi)/Z_p^k(\xi)$$

The canonical linear map of $C^\infty(\xi)$ into $J^k(\xi)_p$ is denoted by $f \mapsto j_k(f)_p$ and $j_k(f)_p$ is called the k-jet of f at p.

LEMMA 1. There is a unique linear map $d_p^k \colon I_p^k \to L_s^k(T(M)_p, \mathbf{C})$ such that if $X^1, \ldots, X^k$ are k vector fields on M and $f \in I_p^k$ then

$$d_p^k f(X_p^1, \ldots, X_p^k) = [(X^1X^2 \ldots X^k)f](p) \quad .$$

Moreover the sequence

$$0 \to I_p^{k+1} \to I_p^k \xrightarrow{d_p^k} L_s^k(T(M)_p, \mathbf{C}) \to 0$$

Is exact.

PROOF. For $k = 1$ the theorem is obvious and $d_p^1 f = df_p$. We assume inductively that the lemma holds for integers less than k. Let $f \in I_p^k$, so that by the inductive hypothesis $d_p^{k-1} f = 0$, and let $X^1, \ldots, X^k$ be C^∞ vector fields on M. Then

$$\begin{aligned}[(X^1 \ldots X^iX^{i+1} \ldots X^k)f](p) &- ([X^1 \ldots X^{i-1}X^{i+1}X^iX^{i+2} \ldots X^k)f](p) \\ &= [(X^1 \ldots X^{i-1}[X^i, X^{i+1}]X^{i+2} \ldots X^k)f](p) \\ &= d_p^{k-1}f(X_p^1 \ldots X_p^{i-1}, [X^i, X^{i+1}]_p, X^{i+2} \ldots X^k) = \end{aligned}$$

In other words $[(X^1 \ldots X^k)f](p)$ is symmetric in $X^1, \ldots, X^k$. In particular since $[(X^1 \ldots X^k)f](p) = X_p^1[(X^2 \ldots X^k)f]$ depends on X^1 only through its value, X_p^1, at p and is linear in X_p^1 it follows that $[(X^1 \ldots X^k)f](p)$ depends on X^i only through its value X_p^i at p and is linear in X_p^i. This proves the existence of $d_p^k f$ and uniqueness is clear, as in the linearity of $d_p^k \colon I_k^p \to L_s^k(T(M)_p, \mathbf{C})$. Next note that if $g_1, \ldots, g_{k+1}$ are in I_p and X is a C^∞ vector field on M then $X(g_1 \ldots g_k) = \Sigma g_1 \ldots (Xg_i) \ldots g_{k+1} \in I_p^k$ i.e., $f \mapsto Xf$ maps I_p^{k+1} into I_p^k. By induction if $f \in I_p^{k+1}$ then $(X^1 \ldots X^k)f \in \dot{I}_p$ i.e., $[(X^1 \ldots X^k)f](p) = d_p^k f(X_p^1 \ldots X_p^k) = 0$ which proves that $I_p^{k+1} \subseteq \ker d_p^k$.

Let $e = (e_1, \ldots, e_n)$ be a basis for $T(M)_p$, $(e_1^*, \ldots, e_n^*)$ the dual basis and let $X_1, \ldots, X_n \in C^\infty(M, \mathbf{R})$ satisfy $X_i(p) = 0$ and $(dX_i)_p = e_i^*$. If $f \in C^\infty(M, \mathbf{C})$ then by Taylor's Theorem $f = \sum_{|\alpha| \leq k} (\frac{1}{\alpha!} D^\alpha f(p))X^\alpha + g$

where $g \in I_p^{k+1}$ and where the notation is that introduced at the end of §1. If $f \in I_p^k$ then $D^\alpha f(p) = d_p^{|\alpha|} f((\frac{\partial}{\partial x_i})^{(\alpha)}) = 0$ if $|\alpha| < k$ so

$f = \sum_{|\alpha|=k} \left(\frac{1}{\alpha!} D^\alpha f(p)\right)X^\alpha + g$. Then $d_p^k f\left((\frac{\partial}{\partial x_i})_p^{(\alpha)}\right) = D^\alpha f(p)$, since if

$|\alpha| = |\beta| = k$ then $(D^\beta X^\alpha)(p) = 0$ if $\beta \neq \alpha$ and is $\alpha!$ if $\alpha = \beta$. Hence if $f \in \ker d_p^k$ then $D^\alpha(p) = 0$ for $|\alpha| = k$ so $f = g \in I_p^{k+1}$, i.e., $\ker d_p^k \subseteq I_p^{k+1}$. Finally given $a \in L_s^k(T(M)_p, \mathbf{C})$ let

$$f = \sum_{|\alpha|=k} \frac{1}{\alpha!} a(e^{(\alpha)})X^\alpha$$

Then $f \in I_p^k$ and $d_p^k f(e^{(\alpha)}) = (D^\alpha f)(p) = a(e^{(\alpha)})$ so $d_p^k f = a$ which proved that $d_p^k\colon I_p^k \to L_s^k(T(M)_p, \mathbf{C})$ is surjective.

q.e.d.

Remark. The case $k = 2$ of this lemma is of course well-known. If $f \in I_p^2$, i.e., if $df_p = 0$, then $d_p^2 f$ is called the Hessian of f at p.

LEMMA 2. If $g \in I_p(M)$ and $dg_p = v$ then $d_p^k g^k = k!S^k(v)$.

PROOF. Let $X^1, \ldots, X^k$ be C^∞ vector fields. Then $X^1 g^k = k(X^1 g)g^{k-1}$ and

$$X^2X^1 g = k(k-1)(X^1g)(X^2g)g^{k-2} + k(X_2X_1g)g^{k-1}$$

$$= k(k-1)(X^1g)(X^2g)g^{k-2} + \text{element of } I_p^{k-1}$$

and inductively

$$X^\ell \ldots X^1 g^k = k(k-1) \ldots (k-\ell+1)(X^1g) \ldots (X^\ell g)g^{k-\ell} + \text{element of } I_p^{k-\ell+1}$$

In particular

$$X^k \ldots X^1 g^k = k!(X^1g) \ldots (X^kg) + \text{element of } I_p$$

so

$$d_p^k g^k(X_p^k, \ldots, X_p^1) = k!v(X_p^1) \ldots v(X_p^k) = k!S^k(v)(X_p^k, \ldots, X_p^1) .$$

q.e.d.

If $f \in C^\infty(\xi)$ and $h \in C^\infty(\xi^*)$ then $h \circ f$ will denote the element $x \to h(x)(f(x))$ of $C^\infty(M, \mathbf{C})$. We note that if $f \in Z_p^k(\xi)$ and $h \in Z_p^\ell(\xi^*)$ then $h \circ f \in I_p^{k+\ell+2}$.

LEMMA 3. There is a unique map $d_p^k\colon Z^{k-1}(\xi) \to L_s^k(T(M)_p, \xi_p)$ such that if $f \in Z_p^{k-1}(\xi)$ and $h \in C\ (\xi^*)$ then

$$d_p^k(h \circ f) = h(p) \circ d_p^k f \quad .$$

If $g \in C^\infty(M, \mathbf{C})$ satisfies $g(p) = 0$ and $dg_p = v$ and if $f \in C^\infty(\xi)$ satisfies $f(p) = e$ then $d_p^k(g^k f) = k!(S^k(v) \otimes e)$. Finally the sequence

$$0 \to Z_p^k \to Z_p^{k-1} \xrightarrow{d_p^k} L_s^k(T(M)_p, \xi_p) \to 0$$

is exact.

PROOF. If $h, h' \in C^\infty(\xi^*)$ satisfy $h(p) = h'(p)$ then $h - h' \in Z_p^0(\xi^*)$ so if $f \in Z_p^{k-1}(\xi)$ then $h \circ f - h' \circ f = (h-h') \circ f \in I_p^{k+1}$, hence $d_p^k(h \circ f) - d_p^k(h' \circ f) = d_p^k(h-h') \circ f) = 0$. If $X^1, \ldots, X^k \in T(M)_p$ then it follows that $d_p^k(h \circ f)(X^1, \ldots, X^k)$ depends on h only through its value $h(p)$ at p and is clearly a linear function of $h(p)$, hence by reflexivity there is a unique element $d_p^k f(X^1, \ldots, X^k)$ in ξ_p such that

$$d_p^k(h \circ f)(X^1, \ldots, X^k) = h(p)(d_p^k f(X^1, \ldots, X^k)) \quad .$$

Since $d_p^k(h \circ f)$ is symmetric and multilinear in $X^1, \ldots, X^k$ it follows that $d_p^k f \in L_s^k(T(M)_p, \xi_p)$. The remaining statements of the lemma are now trivial consequences of Lemmas 1 and 2.

q.e.d.

Since $Z_p^k(\xi) \subseteq Z_p^{k-1}(\xi)$, the canonical map $f \mapsto j_k(f)_p$ of $C^\infty(\xi)$ into $J^k(\xi)_p = C^\infty(\xi)/Z_p^k(\xi)$ induces a linear map $j_k(f)_p \mapsto j_{k-1}(f)_p$ of $J^k(\xi)_p$ into $J_p^{k-1}(\xi)$ with kernel $Z_p^{k-1}(\xi)/Z_p^k(\xi)$. By Lemma 3 we have an exact sequence

$$0 \to L_s^k(T(M)_p, \xi_p) \to J^k(\xi)_p \to J^{k-1}(\xi)_p \to 0$$

where the injection $i\colon L_s^k(T(M)_p, \xi_p) \to J^k(\xi)_p$ is characterized by the fact that

$$i(S^k(v) \otimes e) = j_k\left(\frac{1}{k!} g^k f\right)_p \quad ,$$

where g is any element of $C^\infty(M, \mathbf{C})$ satisfying $g(p) = 0$ and $dg_p = v$ and where f is any element of $C^\infty(\xi)$ such that $f(p) = e$. If follows that $J^k(\xi)_p$ is isomorphic to $\bigoplus_{m=0}^k L_s^m(T(M)_p, \xi_p)$. If $e = (e_1, \ldots, e_n)$ is a basis for $T(M)_p$ then $f \to \{f(e^{(\alpha)})\}_{|\alpha|=m}$ is an isomorphism of $L_s^m(T(M)_p, \xi_p)$ with $\bigoplus_{|\alpha|=m} \xi_p$, hence $J^k(\xi)_p$ is isomorphic to $\bigoplus_{|\alpha| \leq k} \xi_p$.

Let $J^k(\xi) = \bigcup_{p \in M} J^k(\xi)_p$ and define $j_k(f)\colon M \to J^k(\xi)$ for $f \in C^\infty(\xi)$ by $j_k(f)(p) = j_k(f)_p$. Since every element of $J^k(\xi)_p$ is of the form $j_k(f)_p$ it follows that there is at most one way to make $J^k(\xi)$ into a C^∞ vector bundle over M such that if $f \in C^\infty(\xi)$ then $j_k(f) \in C^\infty(J^k(\xi))$ and hence such that $j_k\colon f \mapsto j_k(f)$ is a linear map of $C^\infty(\xi)$ into $C^\infty(J^k(\xi))$, called the k-jet extension map.

Let N be either a finite dimensional vector space V or else a half space in V and let W be a finite dimensional complex vector space. Let $\varphi\colon \mathcal{O} \approx N$ be a chart in M and let $\psi\colon \xi|\mathcal{O} \approx \mathcal{O} \times W$ be a trivialization of ξ over $\mathcal{O}$. To prove that the above bundle $J^k(\xi)$ exists we will describe an associated trivialization

$$J^k(\xi)\,|\,\mathcal{O} \approx \mathcal{O} \times \bigoplus_{m=0}^{k} L_s^m(V, W) \approx \mathcal{O} \times \bigoplus_{|\alpha| \leq k} W \quad .$$

It will be obvious that the trivializations so obtained are smoothly related. Namely each $f \in C^\infty(\xi)$ gives rise to a C^∞ map $\tilde{f} = \psi \circ f \circ \varphi^{-1}$ of N into W. By Taylor's Theorem if $p \in N$ then $j_k(f)_p = 0$ if and only if $d^m\tilde{f}_p = 0$ $m = 0, 1, \ldots k$. (See the proof of Lemma 1.) Hence (putting $\bar{p} = \varphi(p)$)

$$j_k(f)_p \to \left(p, \{d^m\tilde{f}_{\bar{p}}\}_{0 \leq m \leq k}\right)$$

defines a trivialization

$$J^k(\xi)\,|\,\mathcal{O} \approx \mathcal{O} \times \bigoplus_{m=0}^{k} L_s^m(V, W) \quad .$$

If $e = (e_1, \ldots, e_n)$ is a basis for V then

$$D^\alpha\tilde{f}(\bar{p}) = d^{|\alpha|}\tilde{f}_{\bar{p}}(e^{(\alpha)})$$

hence $j_k(f) \to (p, \{D^\alpha \tilde{f}(\bar{p})\}_{|\alpha| \leq k})$ defines a trivialization

$$J^k(\xi) \mid \mathcal{O} \approx \mathcal{O} \times \bigoplus_{|\alpha| \leq k} W \quad .$$

The latter gives probably the most intuitive description of a k-jet: the k-jet of f at p is the set of all partial derivatives of f of order less than or equal to k.

We now recapitulate some basic properties of jet bundles.

THEOREM 1. (Jet Bundle Exact Sequence.) There is an exact sequence of bundles

$$0 \to L_s^k(T(M), \xi) \to J^k(\xi) \to J^{k-1}(\xi) \to 0 \ .$$

The map $J^k(\xi) \to J^{k-1}(\xi)$ is given by $j_k(f)_p \mapsto j_{k-1}(f)_p$ and the injection $i\colon L_s^k(T(M), \xi) \to J^k(\xi)$ is characterized by the property that $i(S^k(v) \otimes e) = j_k(\frac{1}{k!} g^k f)$ if $g \in C^\infty(M, \mathbf{C})$ satisfies $g(p) = 0$ and $dg_p = v$ and $f \in C^\infty(\xi)$ satisfies $f(p) = e$.

PROOF. Proved above.

If f vanishes in a neighborhood of p then clearly $j_k(f)_p = 0$ for all k. Hence

THEOREM 2. If $\mathcal{O}$ is open in M then $j_k(f)_p \mapsto j_k(f|\mathcal{O})_p$ induces an isomorphism $J^k(\xi) \mid \mathcal{O} \approx J^k(\xi \mid \mathcal{O})$.

THEOREM 3. Let T be a function on M such that $T(p) \in L(J^k(\xi)_p, \eta_p)$. A necessary and sufficient condition that $T \in C^\infty(L(J^k(\xi), \eta)) = \mathrm{Hom}(J^k(\xi), \eta)$ is that $x \mapsto T(x)j_k(f)_x$ be in $C^\infty(\eta)$ for each $f \in C^\infty(\xi)$.

PROOF. Necessity is clear. Given $p \in M$ choose $\{f_i\}$ in $C^\infty(\xi)$ so that $\{j_k(f_i)_p\}$ is a base for $J^k(\xi)_p$ and hence $\{j_k(f_i)\}$ is a local base for $J^k(\xi)$ near p. Let $h_i \in C^\infty(J^k(\xi)^*)$ so that $h_i(x)(j_k(f_j)_x) = \delta_{ij}$ for x near p. Let $g_1, \ldots, g_s$ be a local basis for η near p and let $T(x)j_k(f_i)_x = \Sigma\, a_{ij}(x)g_j(x)$ near p. Then

$T(x) = \Sigma a_{ij}(x)(h_i(x) \otimes g_j(x))$ near p. If $x \mapsto T(x)j_k(f_i)x$ is in $C^\infty(\eta)$ then a_{ij} is C^∞ and hence T is a smooth section of $J^k(\xi)^* \hat{\otimes} \eta = L(J^k(\xi), \eta)$ near p.

q.e.d.

§3. Differential operators and their symbols

DEFINITION. *A* k-*th order differential operator from* ξ to η is a linear map $D: C^\infty(\xi) \to C^\infty(\eta)$ such that, for each $p \in M$, $j_k(f)_p = 0$ implies $Df(p) = 0$ (i.e., the linear map $f \to Df(p)$ of $C^\infty(\xi)$ into η_p vanishes on $Z_p^k(\xi)$). We denote the set of k-th order differential operators from ξ to η by $\mathrm{Diff}_k(\xi, \eta)$.

We now record some trivial consequences of the definition. First we note that a k-th order differential operator is local, i.e., if $D \in \mathrm{Diff}_k(\xi, \eta)$ and if $f_1, f_2 \in C^\infty(\xi)$ agree on an open set $\mathcal{O}$ then Df_1 and Df_2 agree on $\mathcal{O}$. Secondly $\mathrm{Diff}_{k-1}(\xi, \eta) \subseteq \mathrm{Diff}_k(\xi, \eta)$. Thirdly, $\mathrm{Diff}_k(\xi, \eta)$ is a subspace of $\mathrm{Hom}_{\mathbf{C}}(C^\infty(\xi), C^\infty(\eta))$ and in fact it is a sub $C^\infty(M, \mathbf{C})$ module. Finally we note that if $D \in \mathrm{Diff}_k(\xi, \eta)$ and $T \in \mathrm{Hom}(\eta, \zeta)$ then $T_*D \in \mathrm{Diff}_k(\xi, \zeta)$.

DEFINITION. A k-th order differential operator $U \in \mathrm{Diff}_k(\xi, w)$ will be called a *universal* k-*th order differential operator for* ξ if for each k-th order differential operator $D \in \mathrm{Diff}_k(\xi, \eta)$ there is a unique $T \in \mathrm{Hom}(w, \eta)$ such that $D = T_*U$.

If $U' \in \mathrm{Diff}_k(\xi, w')$ is a second universal k-th order operator of ξ then by the usual uniqueness argument for universal objects there is a unique isomorphism $T: w \simeq w'$ such that $U' = TU$.

THEOREM 1. $j_k: C^\infty(\xi) \to C^\infty(J^k(\xi))$ is a universal k-th order differential operator for ξ.

PROOF. That j_k is a k-th order differential operator is just the tautologous statement that if $j_k(f)_p = 0$ then $j_k(f)_p = 0$. Given

$D \in \mathrm{Diff}_k(\xi, \eta)$ the map $f \to Df(p)$ of $C^\infty(\xi)$ into η_p vanishes on $Z_p^k(\xi)$ hence there is a unique linear map $T(p)$ of $C^\infty(\xi)/Z_p^k(\xi) = J^k(\xi)_p$ into η_p such that $Df(p) = T(p)j_k(f)_p$. By Theorem 3 of Section 2, $T \in \mathrm{Hom}(J^k(\xi), \eta)$ and by definition $D = T_* j_k$.

q.e.d.

COROLLARY 1. The map $T \to T_* j_k$ is an isomorphism of $\mathrm{Hom}(J^k(\xi), \eta)$ with $\mathrm{Diff}_k(\xi, \eta)$ (as $C^\infty(M, \mathbf{C})$ modules).

COROLLARY 2. $T \to T_*$ is an isomorphism of $\mathrm{Hom}(\xi, \eta)$ with $\mathrm{Diff}_0(\xi, \eta)$.

PROOF. Since $Z_p^0(\xi) = \{f \in C^\infty(\xi) \mid f(p) = 0\}$ there is a natural identification of $J^0(\xi)$ with ξ through which j_0 becomes the identity map.

Since differential operators are local it follows that if $D \in \mathrm{Diff}_k(\xi, \eta)$ and $\mathcal{O}$ is open in M there is a unique k-th order differential operator denoted by $D|\mathcal{O}$ from $\xi|\mathcal{O}$ to $\eta|\mathcal{O}$ such that $(D|\mathcal{O})(f|\mathcal{O}) = (Df)|\mathcal{O}$ for each $f \in C^\infty(\xi)$. From Theorem 2 of Section 2 and Corollary 1 above

COROLLARY 3. If $\{\mathcal{O}_\alpha\}$ is an open cover of M and $D_\alpha \in \mathrm{Diff}_k(\xi|O_\alpha, \eta|O_\alpha)$ then a necessary and sufficient condition that there exist $D \in \mathrm{Diff}_k(\xi, \eta)$ such that $D_\alpha = D|\mathcal{O}_\alpha$ is that $D_\alpha|\mathcal{O}_\alpha \cap \mathcal{O}_\beta = D_\beta|\mathcal{O}_\alpha \cap \mathcal{O}_\beta$ for all α, β. Moreover if D exists it is unique.

Let $(v, x) \in T'(M)$ and let $e \in \xi_x$. Then there are infinitely many $g \in C^\infty(M, \mathbf{R})$ such that $dg_x = v$, and infinitely many $f \in C^\infty(\xi)$ such that $f(x) = e$, however given any such g and f the k-jet of $\frac{1}{k!}(g-g(x))^k$ at x is uniquely determined, and in fact by Theorem 1 of Section 2 it is just $i(S^k(v) \otimes e)$, where $i\colon L_s^k(T(M), \xi) \to J^k(\xi)$ is the "inclusion" map of the Jet Bundle Exact Sequence. It follows that if $D \in \mathrm{Diff}_k(\xi, \eta)$ then $D(\frac{1}{k!}(g-g(x))^k f)(x)$ is well-defined.

DEFINITION. If $D \in \mathrm{Diff}_k(\xi, \eta)$ we define a function $\sigma_k(D)$ on $T'(M)$, called the symbol of D, which assigns to each $(v, x) \in T'(M)$ the linear map $\sigma_k(D)(v, x)$ of ξ_x into η_x defined by $\sigma_k(D)(v, x)e = D(\frac{1}{k!}(g-g(x))^k f)(x)$ where $g \in C^\infty(M, R)$ satisfies $dg_x = v$ and $f \in C^\infty(\xi)$ satisfies $f(x) = e$.

THEOREM 2 (Symbol Exact Sequence). The function σ_k is a linear map of $\mathrm{Diff}_k(\xi, \eta)$ into $\mathrm{Smbl}_k^d(\xi, \eta)$. Moreover, if $\mathrm{Diff}_{k-1}(\xi, \eta) \to \mathrm{Diff}_k(\xi, \eta)$ is the inclusion map then the following sequence of complex vector spaces and linear maps is exact

$$0 \to \mathrm{Diff}_{k-1}(\xi, \eta) \to \mathrm{Diff}_k(\xi, \eta) \xrightarrow{\sigma_k} \mathrm{Smbl}_k^d(\xi, \eta) \to 0 \quad .$$

PROOF. Recall that since M is paracompact the additive category $V(M)$ is semi-simple (i.e., every exact sequence of vector bundles over M splits) hence any additive functor from $V(M)$ to any additive category is exact. In particular applying the contravariant functor $L(\ , \eta)\colon V(M) \to V(M)$ to the Jet Bundle Exact Sequence (Theorem 1 of Section 2)

$$0 \to L_s^k(T(M), \xi) \xrightarrow{i} J^k(\xi) \to J^{k-1}(\xi) \to 0$$

we get an exact sequence in $V(M)$; namely

$$0 \to L(J^{k-1}(\xi), \eta) \to L(J^k(\xi), \eta) \xrightarrow{i^*} L(L_s^k(T(M), \xi), \eta) \to 0 \quad .$$

If now we apply the functor C^∞ to this sequence and recall that $C^\infty L = \mathrm{Hom}$, then using Corollary 1 above we get the exact sequence

$$0 \to \mathrm{Diff}_{k-1}(\xi, \eta) \to \mathrm{Diff}_k(\xi, \eta) \xrightarrow{\gamma_k} \mathrm{Hom}(L_s^k(T(M), \xi), \eta) \to 0$$

where $\gamma_k = C^\infty(i^*)$. Let $D \in \mathrm{Diff}_k(\xi, \eta)$ and let T be the unique element of $\mathrm{Hom}(J^k(\xi), \eta)$ such that $D = T_* j_k$. Given $v \in T(M)_x$ and $e \in \xi_x$ choose $g \in C^\infty(M, \mathbf{R})$ with $dg_x = v$ and $f \in C^\infty(\xi)$ with $f(x) = e$. Then by Theorem 1 of Section 2 $i(S^k(v) \otimes e) = j_k(\frac{1}{k!}(g-g(x))^k f)_x$ hence

$$\begin{aligned}\gamma_k(D)(S^k(v) \otimes e) &= (C^\infty(i^*)T)(S^k(v) \otimes e)\\ &= (i^*T(x))(S^k(v) \otimes e)\\ &= T_*(i(S^k(v) \otimes e))\\ &= D(\tfrac{1}{k!}(g-g(x))^k f)(x) = \sigma_k(D)(v, x)e \quad .\end{aligned}$$

If we now compose γ_k with the isomorphism

$$\lambda_k\colon \ \operatorname{Hom}(L_s^k(T(M), \xi), \eta)) \simeq \operatorname{Smbl}_k^d(\xi, \eta)$$

of Section 1 we get the exact sequence

$$0 \to \operatorname{Diff}_{k-1}(\xi, \eta) \to \operatorname{Diff}_k(\xi, \eta) \xrightarrow{\lambda_k \circ \gamma_k} \operatorname{Smbl}_k^d(\xi, \eta) \to 0 \quad .$$

Moreover, by the above calculation

$$\sigma_k(D)(v, x)e = \gamma_k(D)(S^k(v) \otimes e) = \lambda_k\gamma_k(D)(v, x)e$$

i.e., $\sigma_k = \lambda_k \circ \gamma_k$.

q.e.d.

Let us now paraphrase the information contained in the exactness of the Symbol Exact Sequence. First every element of $\operatorname{Smbl}_k^d(\xi, \eta)$ is the symbol of some k-th order differential operator from ξ to η and secondly two such operators have the same symbol if and only if they differ by a differential operator of order $k-1$.

An element σ of $\operatorname{Smbl}_k^d(\xi, \eta)$ is called *elliptic* if $\sigma(v, x)$ is a linear isomorphism of ξ_x with η_x for all $(v, x) \in T'(M)$, and $D \in \operatorname{Diff}_k(\xi, \eta)$ is called an elliptic k-th order operator if and only if its symbol is elliptic. We note that we can now assert the existence of an elliptic operator corresponding to any elliptic symbol.

Caution: If D is an elliptic k-th order operator then D is a $(k+1)^{st}$ order operator but *not* an elliptic $(k+1)^{st}$ order operator, in fact $\sigma_{k+1}(D) = 0$!

We now investigate what differential operators and their symbols look like in coordinates. Let N be either $\mathbf{R}^n$ or a closed half space in $\mathbf{R}^n$ and let V and W be finite dimensional complex vector spaces. A linear map $D\colon \ C^\infty(N, V) \to C^\infty(N, W)$ is called a k-th order partial differential operator with C^∞ coefficients if it is of the form

$$Df = \sum_{|\alpha| \leq k} A_\alpha D^\alpha f$$

where for each n-multi-index α with $|\alpha| \leq k$, A_α is a C^∞ map of N into $L(V, W)$. Since by Section 2 $j_k(f)_p = 0$ is equivalent to $D^\alpha f(p) = 0$ $|\alpha| \leq k$ which implies $Df(p) = 0$ it follows that such a D belongs to $\mathrm{Diff}_k(\xi, \eta)$ where $\xi = N \times W$. Let us compute $\sigma_k(D)(v, y)(e)$ where $y \in N$, $v \in T^*(N)_y = \mathbf{R}^{n*}$ is given by $v = \Sigma_{j=1}^n v_j(dx_j)_y$ (where $x_1, \ldots, x_n$ are the standard coordinates in $\mathbf{R}^n$) and $e \in V$. Let $g = \Sigma_{j=1}^n v_j(x_j - y_j)$, so $g(y) = 0$ and $dg_y = v$, and let $f \in C^\infty(N, V)$ be identically equal to e. Then

$$\sigma_k(D)(v, y)(e) = \frac{1}{k!} D(g^k f)(y)$$

$$= \frac{1}{k!} \sum_{|\alpha| \leq k} A_\alpha(y)(D^\alpha g^k)(y)e \quad .$$

Clearly $D^\alpha g^k(y) = 0$ if $|\alpha| < k$ and $(D^\alpha g^k)(y) = k! v^\alpha$ if $|\alpha| = k$, hence

$$\sigma_k(D)(v, y) = \sum_{|\alpha| = k} v^\alpha A_\alpha(y)$$

the so-called "characteristic polynomial" of D (note the sum is over all n-multi-indices α with $|\alpha| = k$, *not* $|\alpha| \leq k$). In particular D is elliptic if and only if $\Sigma_{|\alpha|=k} v^\alpha A_\alpha(y)$ is a linear isomorphism of V with W for all $y \in N$ and all $v \neq 0$ in $\mathbf{R}^n$.

Now suppose again ξ and η are any complex vector bundles over M and let $T \in \mathrm{Hom}_{\mathbf{C}}(C^\infty(\xi), C^\infty(\eta))$ be any *local* operator. Given a chart $\varphi: \mathcal{O} \simeq N$ in M and trivializations $\psi_1: \xi | \mathcal{O} \simeq \mathcal{O} \times V$, $\psi_2: \eta | \mathcal{O} \simeq \mathcal{O} \times W$ each $f \in C^\infty(\xi)$ defines $\tilde{f} = \psi_1 \circ f \circ \varphi^{-1} \in C^\infty(N, V)$ and each $g \in C^\infty(\eta)$ defines $\tilde{g} = \psi_2 \circ f \circ \varphi^{-1} \in C^\infty(N, W)$ and there is a unique linear map $D: C^\infty(N, V) \to C^\infty(N, W)$ such that

$$\widetilde{Tf} = D\tilde{f} \quad \text{for all} \quad f \in C^\infty(\xi) \quad .$$

If D is a k-th order partial differential operator then clearly $T | \mathcal{O} \in \mathrm{Diff}_k(\xi | \mathcal{O}, \eta | \mathcal{O})$ and it follows from Corollary 3 of Theorem 1 of this section that if this is the case for all choices of φ, ψ_1 and ψ_2 then

$T \in \mathrm{Diff}_k(\xi, \eta)$. Conversely we will now show that if $T \in \mathrm{Diff}_k(\xi, \eta)$ then D is a k-th order partial differential operator. Indeed let $p \in \mathcal{O}$ and let $\varphi(p) = y$. Then we have uniquely determined isomorphisms $\xi_p \simeq V$ and $\eta_p \simeq W$ such that $f(p) \sim \tilde{f}(y)$ for $f \in C^\infty(\xi)$ and $g(p) \sim \tilde{g}(y)$ for $g \in C^\infty(\eta)$. Also as we saw in Section 2 we have a well determined isomorphism $J^k(\xi)_p \simeq \bigoplus_{|\alpha| \leq k} V$ such that $j_k(f)_p \sim \{D^\alpha \tilde{f}(y)\}_{|\alpha| \leq k}$ if $f \in C^\infty(\xi)$. Then if $S(p)$ is any linear map of $J^k(\xi)_p$ into η_p there is a unique collection $A_\alpha(y)$ of linear maps of V into W, one for each n-multi-index α with $|\alpha| \leq k$, such that $S(p) j_k(f)_p \sim \Sigma_{|\alpha| \leq k} A_\alpha(y) D^\alpha \tilde{f}(y)$. Now by Corollary 1 of Theorem 1 above $T = S_* j_k$ for a unique $S \in C^\infty(L(J^k(\xi), \eta))$ hence for each $y \in N$ we get such a collection $\{A_\alpha(y)\}_{|\alpha| \leq k}$ so that

$$\widetilde{Tf}(p) = S(p) j_k(f)_p \sim \sum_{|\alpha| \leq k} A_\alpha(y) D^\alpha \tilde{f}(y) \quad .$$

By the corollary of Theorem 3 of Section 2 it follows that each A_α is a C^∞ map of N into $L(V, W)$ which completes the proof of

THEOREM 3. If $T \in \mathrm{Hom}_{\mathbf{C}}(C^\infty(\xi), C^\infty(\eta))$ then a necessary and sufficient condition that $T \in \mathrm{Diff}_k(\xi, \eta)$ is that for each chart $\varphi\colon \mathcal{O} \simeq N$ in M (where N is $\mathbf{R}^n$ or a closed half space in $\mathbf{R}^n$) and for each choice of trivializations $\psi_1\colon \xi | \mathcal{O} \simeq \mathcal{O} \times V$, $\psi_2\colon \eta | \mathcal{O} \simeq \mathcal{O} \times W$ there should exist a collection $\{A_\alpha\}_{|\alpha| \leq k}$ of C^∞ maps of N into $L(V, W)$ indexed by all n-multi-indices α with $|\alpha| \leq k$ such that

$$\widetilde{Tf} = \sum_{|\alpha| \leq k} A_\alpha D^\alpha \tilde{f}$$

where $\tilde{f} = \psi_1 \circ f \circ \varphi^{-1}$ for $f \in C^\infty(\xi)$ and $\tilde{g} = \psi_2 \circ g \circ \varphi^{-1}$ for $g \in C^\infty(\eta)$. Moreover if this is the case given $p \in \mathcal{O}$ with $\varphi(p) = y$ identify ξ_p with V by $f(p) \sim \tilde{f}(y)$, identify η_p with W by $g(p) \sim \tilde{g}(y)$, and identify $T^*(M)_p$ with $\mathbf{R}^n$ by $(d\varphi_p)^*$.

Then

$$\sigma_k(T)(v, p) \sim \sum_{|\alpha| = k} v^\alpha A_\alpha(y) \quad .$$

We next discuss composition of differential operators. As above N is either $\mathbf{R}^n$ or a half space in $\mathbf{R}^n$, U, V, W are three finite dimensional complex vector spaces and D^1: $C^\infty(N, U) \to C^\infty(N, V)$ and D^2: $C^\infty(N, V) \to C^\infty(N, W)$ are respectively partial differential operators of order k and ℓ given by

$$D^1 f = \sum_{|\alpha| \le k} A_\alpha D^\alpha f$$

$$D^2 g = \sum_{|\beta| \le \ell} B_\beta D^\beta g$$

where the A_α: $N \to L(U, V)$ and B_β: $N \to L(V, W)$ are C^∞ maps. Using the Leibniz Product Formula in the form

$$D^\beta(AF) = \sum_{\lambda \le \beta} \binom{\beta}{\lambda} (D^{\beta-\lambda}A)(D^\lambda F)$$

where A: $N \to L(V, W)$ and F: $N \to V$ are C^∞ maps

$$D^2D^1 f = \sum_{|\beta| \le \ell} B_\beta \sum_{|\alpha| \le k} \sum_{\lambda \le \beta} \binom{\beta}{\lambda} (D^{\beta-\lambda}A_\alpha) D^{\alpha+\lambda} f \quad .$$

Making the substitution $\alpha + \lambda = \gamma$ and interchanging orders of summation we see that

$$D^2D^1 f = \sum_{|\gamma| \le k+\ell} C_\gamma (D^\gamma f)$$

where

$$C_\gamma = \sum_{\substack{|\alpha| \le k \ |\beta| \le \ell \\ \alpha \le \gamma \le \alpha+\beta}} \binom{\beta}{\gamma-\alpha} B_\beta (D^{\alpha+\beta-\gamma} A_\alpha) \quad .$$

Notice that if $|\gamma| = k + \ell$ then

$$C_\gamma = \sum_{\substack{|\alpha|=k \\ \beta=\gamma-\alpha}} B_\beta A_\alpha \quad .$$

If $v \in \mathbf{R}^n$ then $v^{\alpha+\beta} = v^\alpha v^\beta$ hence

$$\sum_{|\gamma|=k+\ell} v^\gamma C_\gamma = \Big(\sum_{|\beta|=\ell} v^\beta B_\beta\Big)\Big(\sum_{|\alpha|=k} v^\alpha A_\alpha\Big)$$

or in other words, the characteristic polynomial of D^2D^1 is the product, in the sense of composition of linear transformations, of the characteristic polynomial of D^2 and the characteristic polynomial of D^1.

Given three vector bundles ξ, η, ζ over M we define a pairing of

$$\mathrm{Hom}(\pi^*\eta, \pi^*\zeta) \times \mathrm{Hom}(\pi^*\xi, \pi^*\eta)$$

into $\mathrm{Hom}(\pi^*\xi, \pi^*\zeta)$ denoted by $(\sigma_2, \sigma_1) \to \sigma_2\sigma_1$ by the formula $\sigma_2\sigma_1(v, x) = \sigma_2(v, x) \circ \sigma_1(v, x)$. Then what we have just calculated together with Theorem 3 above proves

THEOREM 4. If ξ, η, ζ are complex vector bundles over M and $D^1 \in \mathrm{Diff}_k(\xi, \eta)$, $D^2 \in \mathrm{Diff}_\ell(\eta, \zeta)$, then $D^2D^1 \in \mathrm{Diff}_{k+\ell}(\xi, \zeta)$. Moreover, $\sigma_{k+\ell}(D^2D^1) = \sigma_\ell(D^2)\sigma_k(D^1)$.

The following is an often useful criterion for $T\colon C^\infty(\xi) \to C^\infty(\eta)$ to be a first order differential operator.

THEOREM 5. A necessary and sufficient condition that a linear map $T\colon C^\infty(\xi) \to C^\infty(\eta)$ be an element of $\mathrm{Diff}_1(\xi, \eta)$ is that $T(fg)(p) = 0$, whenever $f \in C^\infty(M, \mathbf{R})$ and $g \in C^\infty(\xi)$ satisfy $f(p) = 0$ and $g(p) = 0$.

PROOF. By definition $T \in \mathrm{Diff}_1(\xi, \eta)$ if and only if $T(h)(p) = 0$ whenever $h \in Z^1_p(\xi)$. Now on the one hand $Z^1_p(\xi) = I^2_p \cdot C^\infty(\xi) = I_p \cdot I_p \cdot C^\infty(\xi)$ and it follows that every element of $Z^1_p(\xi)$ is a finite sum of elements fg where $f \in C^\infty(M, \mathbf{R})$ and $g \in C^\infty(\xi)$ each vanish at p. On the other hand if $g \in C^\infty(\xi)$ vanishes at p then by Taylor's Theorem g is a finite sum $g = \Sigma\, k_i h_i$ where $h_i \in C^\infty(\xi)$ and where $k_i \in C^\infty(M, \mathbf{R})$ and $k_i(p) = 0$. Then if $f \in C^\infty(M, \mathbf{R})$ vanishes at p, $fg = \Sigma\,(fk_i)h_i \in I^2_pC^\infty(\xi) = Z^1_p(\xi)$.

q.e.d.

§4. Hermitian bundles and adjoint operators.

A strictly positive, smooth meausre on M is a Radon measure μ on M such that if $\varphi: \mathcal{O} \simeq \mathbf{R}^n$ is a chart in M there is a strictly positive C^∞ function ρ on $\mathbf{R}^n$ such that $\int f d\mu = \int (f \circ \varphi^{-1}(x))\rho(x)dx$ for any continuous, complex valued function f on M having as support a compact subset of $\mathcal{O}$. For example, a Riemannian structure on M gives rise to such a measure, with $\rho(x) = (\det g_{ij}(x))^{\frac{1}{2}}$. We shall assume as given a fixed such measure on M and also one on ∂M and we shall write $\int_M f$ and $\int_{\partial M} f$ for the corresponding integrals. We note that if f is a continuous function on M with compact support then $\int_M |f| = 0 \Longrightarrow f = 0$.

We will denote by Met (ξ) the complex fiber bundle over M whose fiber at x is the space of positive definite, hermitian symmetric, conjugate bilinear forms (i.e., Hilbert space inner products) on ξ_x, with the obvious bundle structure. An hermitian structure for ξ is an element of $C^\infty(\text{Met}(\xi))$ and by an hermitian bundle we mean a complex vector bundle ξ with a specific choice $(\ ,\ )_\xi$ of hermitian structure. If ξ and η are hermitian bundles over M there is a natural map $*$ of $L(\xi, \eta)$ into $L(\eta, \xi)$ (which is a real bundle isomorphism but is conjugate linear) namely if $T \in L(\xi_x, \eta_x)$ then $T^* \in L(\eta_x, \xi_x)$ is defined by $(Te, e')_\eta = (e, T^*e')_\xi$. This gives rise to a conjugate linear map, also denoted by $*$ of $\text{Smbl}_k(\xi, \eta)$ into $\text{Smbl}_k(\eta, \xi)$ defined by $\sigma^*(v, x) = \sigma(v, x)^*$.

If ξ is an hermitian bundle then for $f, g \in C^\infty(\xi)$ we define a C^∞ complex valued function $(f, g)_\xi$ on M by $(f, g)_\xi(x) = (f(x), g(x))_\xi$. Clearly, $(f, g) \to (f, g)_\xi$ is hermitian symmetric and conjugate bilinear, and the support of $(f, g)_\xi$ is included in the intersection of the supports of f and g. In particular if f and g belong to the space $C_c^\infty(\xi)$ of C^∞ cross-section of ξ having compact support, then $(f, g)_\xi$ has compact support and $\langle f, g \rangle_\xi = \int_M (f, g)$ is well defined. Clearly $\langle\ ,\ \rangle_\xi$ is a prehilbert space structure for $C_c^\infty(\xi)$ and the associated norm $\langle f, f \rangle_\xi^{\frac{1}{2}}$ will be denoted by $\|f\|_\xi$.

DEFINITION. If ξ and η are hermitian bundles over M and $D \in \text{Diff}_k(\xi, \eta)$ then $D^* \in \text{Diff}_k(\eta, \xi)$ will be called a formal adjoint for D if $< Df, g >_\eta =$ $< f, D^* g >_\xi$ whenever $f \in C_0^\infty(\xi)$ and $g \in C_0^\infty(\eta)$.

LEMMA 1. If $S \in \mathrm{Diff}_k(\eta, \xi)$ and if $Sg = 0$ for all $g \in C_0^\infty(\eta)$ then $S = 0$.

PROOF. Let $h \in C^\infty(\xi)$. We must show $Sh = 0$, and since Sh is continuous it will suffice to prove that $Sh(p) = 0$ if $p \in \partial M$. Let φ be a C^∞ function with support a compact subset of $M - \partial M$ which is identically one in a neighborhood of p and let $g = \varphi h$. Then $Sg = 0$ and since g agrees with h in a neighborhood of p, $Sh(p) = Sg(p) = 0$.

q.e.d.

LEMMA 2. If $D \in \mathrm{Diff}_k(\xi, \eta)$ has a formal adjoint then it has a unique formal adjoint.

PROOF Suppose T and T' are adjoints for D and let $S = T - T'$. By Lemma 1 it will suffice to show that $Sg = 0$ for all $g \in C_0^\infty(\eta)$. Now if $f \in C_0^\infty(\eta)$

$$< f, Sg >_\xi = < f, Tg >_\xi - < f, T'g >_\xi = < Df, g >_\eta - < Df, g >_\eta = 0 .$$

In particular taking $f = Sg$ gives $\|Sg\|_\xi = 0$ hence $Sg = 0$.

q.e.d.

Next suppose D $\mathrm{Diff}_k(\xi, \eta)$ and that $\{\mathcal{O}_\alpha\}$ is an open cover of M such that for each α $D_\alpha = D|\mathcal{O}_\alpha$ has a formal adjoint $D_\alpha^* \in \mathrm{Diff}_k(\eta|\mathcal{O}_\alpha, \xi|\mathcal{O}_\alpha)$. Then clearly $D_\alpha^*|\mathcal{O}_\alpha \cap \mathcal{O}_\beta$ is a formal adjoint for $D|\mathcal{O}_\alpha \cap \mathcal{O}_\beta$ so by Lemma 2 $D_\alpha^*|\mathcal{O}_\alpha \cap \mathcal{O}_\beta = D_\beta^*|\mathcal{O}_\alpha \cap \mathcal{O}_\beta$. By Corollary 3 of Theorem 1 of Section 3 there is a unique $D^* \in \mathrm{Diff}_k(\eta, \xi)$ such that $D^*|\mathcal{O}_\alpha = D_\alpha^*$ for all α and clearly D^* is a formal adjoint for D (by an obvious partition of unity argument) hence

LEMMA 3. If $D \in \mathrm{Diff}_k(\xi, \eta)$ and if for each chart $\varphi\colon \mathcal{O} \simeq \mathcal{O} \subseteq \mathbf{R}^n$ of an atlas for M, $D|\mathcal{O}$ has a formal adjoint then D has a formal adjoint.

LEMMA 4. Let M be either $\mathbf{R}^n$ or the closed half space $\{x \in \mathbf{R}^n | x_n \le 0\}$. Then $D \in \mathrm{Diff}_k(\xi, \eta)$ has a formal adjoint D^* and $\sigma_k(D^*) = (-1)^k \sigma_k(D)^*$.

PROOF. We shall consider only the case where M is a half space, the proof being essentially the same but a little simpler when $M = \mathbf{R}^n$. Let the measure on M be given by $\int_M f = \int_M f(x)\rho(x)dx$ and let that on $\partial M = \mathbf{R}^{n-1}$ be given by $\int_{\partial M} f = \int_{\mathbf{R}^{n-1}} f(x)\sigma(x)dx$ where ρ and σ are positive C^∞ functions on M and $\mathbf{R}^{n-1}$ respectively and dx are the respective elements of Lebesgue measure. We can assume $\xi = M \times V_1$ and $\eta = M \times V_2$ where V_i are finite dimensional Hilbert spaces with inner products $(\ ,\ )_i$. If $T\colon V_1 \to V_2$ is linear we denote its adjoint by $T'\colon V_2 \to V_1$, so $(Tv, w)_2 = (v, T'w)_1$. The hermitian structure for ξ and η are uniquely given by C^∞ maps A and B of M into the spaces of positive operators on V_1 and V_2 respectively according to the formulas $(e, e')_\xi = (A(x)e, e')_1$ if $e, e' \in \xi_x$ and $(e, e')_\eta = (B(x)e, e')_2$ if $e, e' \in \eta_x$. Then if $T \in L(\xi_x, \eta_x)$ its adjoint $T^*\colon \eta_x \to \xi_x$ is given by $T^* = A(x)^{-1}T'B(x)$. Let $D\colon C^\infty(M, V_1) \to C^\infty(M, V_2)$ be given by

$$Df = \sum_\alpha C_\alpha(D^\alpha f)$$

where the sum is over all n-multi-indices α with $|\alpha| \le k$ and each C_α is a C^∞ map of M into $L(V_1, V_2)$.

If $f, h \in C_c^\infty(\xi) = C_c^\infty(M, V_1)$ then

$$\frac{\partial}{\partial x_m}(f, h)_1 = \left(\frac{\partial}{\partial x_m}, h\right)_1 + \left(f, \frac{\partial h}{\partial x_m}\right)_1$$

so integrating over M with respect to Lebesgue measure gives

$$\int_M \left(\frac{\partial f}{\partial x_m}, h\right)_1 dx - \int_M \left(f, -\frac{\partial h}{\partial x_m}\right)_1 dx = \begin{cases} 0 & m < n \\ \int_{\partial M} \frac{1}{\sigma}(f, h) & m = n \end{cases}$$

and an easy induction gives

$$\int_M (D^\alpha f, h)_1 dx - \int_M (f, (-1)^{|\alpha|}D^\alpha h)_1 dx = \int_{\partial M} G_\alpha(j_{k-1}f, j_{k-1}h)$$

where for each $x \in \mathbf{R}^{n-1} = \partial M$, G_α is a conjugate bilinear map of $J^{k-1}(\xi)_x$ into $\mathbf{C}$. Now $< Df, g >_\eta = \Sigma_\alpha \int (BC_\alpha D^\alpha f, g)_2 \rho dx = \Sigma_\alpha \int (D^\alpha f, \rho C_\alpha' Bg)_1 dx$, hence

$$< Df, g > - \int \Big(f, \sum_{\alpha} (-1)^{|\alpha|} D^{\alpha}(\rho C_{\alpha}' Bg)\Big)_1 dx = \int_{\partial M} G(j_{k-1}f, \bar{j}_{k-1}g)$$

where for each $x \in \partial M$ G is a conjugate bilinear map of $J^{k-1}(\xi) \times J^{k-1}(\eta)_x$ into $\mathbf{C}$ defined by

$$G(j_{k-1}(f), \bar{j}_{k-1}(g)) = \sum_{|\alpha| \leq k} G_{\alpha}\Big(j_{k-1}(f), j_{k-1}(\rho C_{\alpha}' Bg)\Big)$$

Now $\int_M (f, \sum_{\alpha} (-1)^{|\alpha|} D^{\alpha}(\rho C_{\alpha}' Bg))_1 dx = \int (f, D^* g)_{\xi} \rho dx = < f, D^* g >_{\xi}$ where

$$D^* g = \sum_{|\lambda| \leq k} (-1)^{|\lambda|} \frac{1}{\rho} A^{-1} D^{\lambda}(\rho C_{\lambda}' Bg)$$

$$= \sum_{|\alpha| \leq k} \Big(\sum_{\alpha \leq \lambda} (-1)^{|\lambda|} \binom{\lambda}{\alpha} \frac{1}{\rho} A^{-1} D^{\lambda - \alpha}(\rho C_{\lambda}' B)\Big) D^{\alpha} g$$

is a k-th order differential operator from $C^{\infty}(M, V_2) = C^{\infty}(\eta)$ to $C^{\infty}(M, V_1) = C^{\infty}(\xi)$. Thus

$$< Df, g >_{\eta} - < f, D^* g >_{\xi} = \int_{\partial M} G(j_{k-1}f, \bar{j}_{k-1}g)$$

Then if f and g have supports disjoint from ∂M, $G(j_{k-1}f, \bar{j}_{k-1}g) = 0$ so $< Df, g >_{\eta} = < f, D^* g >_{\xi}$ hence D^* is a formal adjoint for D. Moreover the characteristic polynomial for D^* is

$$(-1)^k \sum_{|\alpha|=k} A(x)^{-1} C_{\alpha}'(x) B(x) v^{\alpha} = (-1)^k \sum_{|\alpha|=k} C_{\alpha}^*(x) v^{\alpha}$$

$$= \Big((-1)^k \sum_{|\alpha|=k} C_{\alpha}(x) v^{\alpha}\Big)^* ,$$

which since $\Sigma_{|\alpha|=k} C_{\alpha}(x) v^{\alpha}$ is the characteristic polynomial of D proves that $\sigma_k(D^*) = (-1)^k \sigma_k(D)^*$.

q.e.d.

We note the following

Corollary of Proof. In the case $M = \{x \in \mathbf{R}^n | x_n \leq 0\}$, let $Gr_k(\xi, \eta)$ be the bundle over $\partial M = \mathbf{R}^{n-1}$ whose fiber at x is the space of conjugate bilinear maps of $J^{k-1}(\xi)_x \times J^{k-1}(\eta)_x$ into $\mathbf{C}$. Then for each

$D \in \mathrm{Diff}_k(\xi, \eta)$ there is a cross section $G \in C^\infty(\mathrm{Gr}_k(\xi, \eta))$ such that

$$< Df, g >_\eta - < f, D^* g >_\xi = \int_{\partial M} G(j_{k-1}f, \bar{j}_{k-1}g)$$

whenever $f \in C_c^\infty(\xi)$ and $g \in C_c^\infty(\eta)$.

The main result of this section, which now follows trivially from Lemmas 2, 3 and 4 and Theorem 3 of Section 3 is

THEOREM. If ξ and η are hermitian bundles over M then each $D \in \mathrm{Diff}_k(\xi, \eta)$ has a unique formal adjoint $D^* \in \mathrm{Diff}_k(\eta, \xi)$. Moreover $\sigma_k(D^*) = (-1)^k \sigma_k(D)^*$.

We note that $D^{**} = D$ and if $\bar{D} \in \mathrm{Diff}_\ell(\eta, \zeta)$ then $(\bar{D}D)^* = D^*\bar{D}^*$.

DEFINITION. If ξ is an hermitian bundle over M then $D \in \mathrm{Diff}_{2k}(\xi, \xi)$ is called *strongly elliptic* of order $2k$ if and only if $(-1)^k\sigma_{2k}(D)(v, x)$ is a positive operator on ξ_x (i.e., $((-1)^k\sigma_{2k}(D)(v, x)e, e)_\xi > 0$ for all $e \neq 0$ in ξ_x) for all $(v, x) \in T'(M)$.

COROLLARY. If $D \in \mathrm{Diff}_k(\xi, \eta)$ then D^*D is strongly elliptic of order $2k$ if and only if $\sigma_k(D)(v, x) : \xi_x \to \eta_x$ is injective for all $(v, x) \in T'(M)$. Hence if ξ and η have the same fiber dimension then D is k-th order elliptic if and only if D^*D is $2k$-th order strongly elliptic.

§5. Green's forms

In this section we again assume given strictly positive smooth measures on M and on ∂M and that ξ and η are hermitian bundles over M. If $D \in \mathrm{Diff}_k(\xi, \eta)$ then the formula $< Df, g >_\eta = < f, D^* g >_\xi$ where $f \in C_c^\infty(\xi)$ and $g \in C_c^\infty(\eta)$ have supports disjoint from ∂M suggests that more generally we should be able to express $< Df, g >_\eta - < f, D^* g >_\xi$ as an integral of some expression involving the jets of f and g over ∂M. The theory of boundary value problems requires that this be made precise and we shall now do so.

DEFINITION. We define a bundle $Gr_k(\xi, \eta)$ over ∂M whose fiber at x is the space of conjugate bilinear maps of $J^{k-1}(\xi)_x \times J^{k-1}(\eta)_x$ into $\mathbf{C}$. A C^∞ cross section $G \in C^\infty(Gr_k(\xi, \eta))$ will be called a k-th order Green's form of ξ and η and will be called a Green's form for $D \in \mathrm{Diff}_k(\xi, \eta)$ if

$$< Df, g >_\eta - < f, D^* g >_\xi = \int_{\partial M} G(j_{k-1}(f), \bar{j}_{k-1}(g))$$

for all $f \in C_c^\infty(\xi)$ and $g \in C_c^\infty(\eta)$.

REMARK. Let $M = \{x \in \mathbf{R}^n | x_n \leq 0\}$, $\xi = \eta = M \times \mathbf{C}$. Then if G is a Green's form for $D \in \mathrm{Diff}_2(\xi, \eta)$ so also is G', defined by

$$G'(j_1 f, j_1 g) = G(j_1 f, j_1 g) + \frac{\partial}{\partial x_1}(fg) \quad .$$

This shows that in general Green's forms for operators are not uniquely determined.

REMARK. If $G \in C^\infty(Gr_k(\xi, \eta))$ and φ, ψ are C^∞ complex valued functions on M there is a unique $G' \in C^\infty(Gr_k(\xi, \eta))$ such that $G'(j_{k-1}(f), \bar{j}_{k-1}(g)) = G(j_{k-1}(\varphi f), \bar{j}_{k-1}(\psi g))$. This follows from the obvious fact that $j_{k-1}(\varphi f)_x$ is a bilinear form in $j_{k-1}(\varphi)_x$ and $j_{k-1}(f)_x$, and similarly for $\bar{j}_{k-1}(\psi g)$. Now suppose $\{\mathcal{O}_\alpha\}$ is an open covering in M and let $\{\varphi_\gamma\}$ be a locally finite C^∞ partition of unity for M subordinate to $\{\mathcal{O}_\alpha\}$, say support $(\varphi_\gamma) \subseteq \mathcal{O}_{\alpha(\gamma)}$. Then it follows that if $G_\alpha \in C^\infty(Gr_k(\xi | \mathcal{O}_\alpha, \eta | \mathcal{O}_\alpha))$ then there is a unique $G \in C^\infty(Gr_k(\xi, \eta))$ such that $G(j_{k-1}(f), \bar{j}_{k-1}(g)) = \Sigma_{\lambda,\gamma} G_{\alpha(\lambda)}(j_{k-1}(\varphi_\lambda f), \bar{j}_{k-1}(\varphi_\gamma g))$. Now suppose $D \in \mathrm{Diff}_k(\xi, \eta)$ and that G_α is a Green's form for $D | \mathcal{O}_\alpha$. Given $f \in C_c^\infty(\xi)$ and $g \in C_c^\infty(\eta)$ we have $f = \Sigma_\lambda \varphi_\lambda f$ and $g = \Sigma_\gamma \varphi_\gamma g$ where these sums are finite because f and g have compact support while {support φ_γ} is locally finite. Then

$$\begin{aligned} < Df, g >_\eta - < f, D^* g >_\xi &= \sum_{\lambda,\gamma} (< D\varphi_\lambda f, \varphi_\gamma g >_\eta - < \varphi_\lambda f, D^* \varphi_\lambda g >_\xi) \\ &= \sum_{\lambda,\gamma} G_{\alpha(\lambda)}(j_{k-1}(\varphi_\lambda f), \bar{j}_{k-1}(\varphi_\gamma g)) \\ &= G(j_{k-1}(f), \bar{j}_{k-1}(g)) \quad . \end{aligned}$$

This proves in particular

LEMMA. If $D \in \mathrm{Diff}_k(\xi, \eta)$ and if for each chart $\varphi\colon \mathcal{O} \simeq \mathcal{O}' \subseteq \mathbf{R}^n$ in an atlas for M there exists a Green's form $G \in C^\infty(Gr_k(\xi|\mathcal{O}, \eta|\mathcal{O}))$ for $D|\mathcal{O}$, then D has a Green's form.

THEOREM. Every $D \in \mathrm{Diff}_k(\xi, \eta)$ has a Green's form.

PROOF. Immediate from the Lemma and the Corollary of Proof of Lemma 4 of the preceding section.

§6. Some classical differential operators

a. The Lie derivative

Let ξ be a complex vector bundle over M whose fiber at x consists of all complex valued tensors at x of a fixed variance and symmetry type. Given a vector field X on M define $\partial_X\colon C^\infty(\xi) \to C^\infty(\xi)$ to be the Lie derivative operator. Then by a basic property of ∂_X we have

$$\partial_X(gf) = (Xg)f + g\partial_X f$$

if $g \in C^\infty(M, \mathbf{R})$ and $f \in C^\infty(\xi)$. It follows from Theorem 5 of Section 3 that $\partial_X \in \mathrm{Diff}_1(\xi, \xi)$. Also if $g \in C^\infty(M, \mathbf{R})$ vanishes at x and $dg_x = v$ then

$$\sigma_1(\partial_X)(v, x)f(x) = \partial_X(gf)(x) = v(X)f(x)$$

i.e., $\sigma_1(\partial_X)(v, x)$ is scalar multiplication by $v(X)$. It follows that ∂_X is elliptic if and only if M is one dimensional and X never vanishes.

b. The exterior derivative

Let $\xi = \Lambda(T^*(M)) \otimes \mathbf{C} = \oplus_{i=0}^n \Lambda^i(T^*(M)) \otimes \mathbf{C}$ be the bundle of complex valued differential forms and let $d\colon C^\infty(\xi) \to C^\infty(\xi)$ as usual denote exterior derivation.

If g is a C^∞ real valued function on M and $\omega \in C^\infty(\xi)$ then

$$d(g\omega) = dg \wedge \omega + g \wedge d\omega$$

By Theorem 5 of Section 3 again we see that $d \in \mathrm{Diff}_1(\xi, \xi)$. Also if $g(x) = 0$ and $dg_x = v$ then

$$d(g\omega)_x = v \wedge \omega_x$$

which proves that $\sigma_1(d)(v, x) = v\wedge$, left exterior multiplication by v.

c. The codifferential and Laplacian

Maintaining the notation of (b) assume now in addition that M is an n-dimensional Riemannian manifold. The Riemannian structure for M defines strictly positive smooth measures on M and on ∂M, and also a hermitian structure on ξ. We define two differential operators from ξ to ξ, the codifferential δ, a first order operator and the Laplacian Δ a second order operator, by $\delta = d^*$ and $\Delta = d\delta + \delta d$. Note that $\delta^2 = (d^*)^2 = (d^2)^* = 0$ hence $\Delta = (d+\delta)^2$. Recall that $f \in C^\infty(\xi)$ is called closed if $df = 0$; it is called co-closed if $\delta f = 0$ and harmonic if $\Delta f = 0$. Clearly if f is closed and co-closed it is harmonic. If $f, g \in C_0^\infty(\xi)$

$$< \Delta f, g >_\xi = < d\delta f, g >_\xi + < \delta df, g >_\xi = < \delta f, \delta g >_\xi + < df, dg >_\xi .$$

In particular if $\Delta f = 0$ then taking $g = f$ gives $\delta f = df = 0$, i.e., conversely a harmonic form is closed and co-closed if its support is compact and disjoint from ∂M. In particular on a compact manifold without boundary every harmonic form is closed and co-closed.

To give a more precise description of δ and Δ we assume that M is oriented and we let $\tilde{\omega}$ be the n-form describing the Riemannian measure (i.e., $\tilde{\omega}_x = e_1 \wedge \ldots \wedge e_n$ where $(e_1, \ldots, e_n)$ is any oriented orthonormal base for $T^*(M)_x$). For details of what we sketch below see de Rham's *Variétés Differentiables*. Recall that the inner product in ξ_x is completely described by the properties that the $\Lambda^p(T^*(M)_x) \otimes \mathbf{C}$ are mutually orthogonal and

$$(v_1 \wedge \ldots \wedge v_p, w_1 \wedge \ldots \wedge w_p)_\xi = \sum_\pi \varepsilon(\pi)(v_1, w_{\pi(1)}) \cdots (v_p, w_{\pi(p)})$$

where the sum is over all permutations of $(1, \ldots, p)$. Equivalently, if $(e_1, \ldots, e_n)$ is an orthonormal basis for $T^*(M)_x$ then $\{e_{i_1} \wedge \ldots \wedge e_{i_p}\}$ $(1 \leq p \leq n,\ i_1 < i_2 < \cdots < i_p)$ is an orthonormal basis for ξ_x. It follows that if $[e]_n$ denotes the component in $\Lambda^n(T^*(M)) \otimes \mathbf{C}$ of an element e of ξ then there is a uniquely defined conjugate linear real automorphism $*$ of ξ such that $[\lambda \wedge * \mu]_n = (\lambda, \mu)_\xi \tilde{\omega}_x$ for $\lambda, \mu \in \xi_x$.

Moreover $*$ maps $\Lambda^p(T^*(M)) \otimes C$ into $\Lambda^{n-p}(T^*(M)) \otimes \mathbf{C}$ and $** = \bar{w}$ where $\bar{w}$ is the automorphism of ξ which on $\Lambda^p(T^*(M)) \otimes \mathbf{C}$ is multiplication by $(-1)^{p(n-p)}$. Then $*$ induces a conjugate linear real automorphism, also denoted by $*$, of $C^\infty(\xi)$ and $[f \wedge * g]_n = (f, g)_\xi \tilde{\omega}$ so if $f, g \in C_c^\infty(\xi)$

$$< f, g >_\xi = \int_M [f \wedge * g]_n \quad .$$

Let w be the automorphism of ξ which is multiplication by $(-1)^p$ on $\Lambda^p(T^*(M)) \otimes \mathbf{C}$ so

$$d(f \wedge g) = df \wedge g + w(f) \wedge dg \quad .$$

We note that $[w(f) \wedge d*g]_n = -[f \wedge d*w(g)]_n$ hence if $f, g \in C^\infty(\xi)$ then

$$[d(f \wedge * g)]_n = [df \wedge * g]_n - [f \wedge d*w(g)]_n$$

$$= [df \wedge * g]_n - [f \wedge * \bar{w}*d*w(g)]_n$$

If $f, g \in C_c^\infty(\xi)$ Stokes' formula gives

$$\int_{\partial M} [f \wedge * g]_{n-1} = \int_M [d(f \wedge * g)]_n = < df, g >_\xi - < f, \bar{w}*d*wg >_\xi$$

This proves that $\delta = \bar{w}*d*w$ and moreover that if $\tilde{\nu}$ is the $(n-1)$-form on ∂M defining the Riemannian measure and if we define $G \in C^\infty(Gr_1(\xi, \xi))$ by $[e \wedge * e']_{n-1} = G(e, e')\tilde{\nu}_x$ for $x \in \partial M$ and $e, e' \in J^0(\xi)_x = \xi_x$ then G is a Green's form for d.

We note that δ has degree -1, hence since d has degree $+1$, Δ has degree 0.

Given $v \in T^*(M))_x$ define $i_v\colon \xi_x \to \xi_x$ by $i_v(e_1 \wedge \ldots \wedge e_p) = \Sigma_{j=1}^p (-1)^{j+1}(v, e_j)e_1 \wedge \ldots \wedge \hat{e}_j \wedge \ldots \wedge e_p$. Then we claim that $(v \wedge e, e')_\xi = (e, i_v e')_\xi$. It suffices (since $v \to i_v$ is linear) to prove this for v belonging to an orthonormal basis $(e_1, \ldots, e_n)$ for $T^*(M)_x$ and we can also assume that e and e' belong to the orthonormal basis $\{e_{i_1} \wedge \ldots \wedge e_{i_p}\}$ $(1 \le p \le n;\ i_1 < \ldots < i_p)$ for ξ_x. We leave it to the reader to check the formula in this case. Then since $\sigma_1(d)(v, x) = v \wedge$ it follows from the theorem of Section 4 that $\sigma_1(\delta)(v, x) = -i_v$. Since $\Delta = d\delta + \delta d$ it follows from Theorem 4 of Section 3 that $\sigma_2(\Delta)(v, x) = -(v \wedge i_v + i_v v \wedge)$.

A straightforward application of definitions shows that $v \wedge i_v e + i_v v \wedge e = \|v\|^2 e$, hence $\sigma_2(\Delta)(v, x)$ is scalar multiplication in ξ_x by $-\|v\|^2$, hence Δ is strongly elliptic. Since $\Delta = (d+\delta)^2 = (d+\delta)^*(d+\delta)$, by the corollary at the end of Section 4 $d + \delta$ is elliptic. Note that since d and δ are of degree $+1$ and -1 respectively $d + \delta$ maps a p-form into the sum of a (p-1)-form and a (p+1)-form. Hence if ξ^e and ξ^0 are the sub-bundles of ξ defined by $\xi^e = \bigoplus_p \Lambda^{2p}(T^*(M)) \otimes \mathbf{C}$ and $\xi^0 = \bigoplus_p \Lambda^{2p+1}(T^*(M)) \otimes \mathbf{C}$ then $d + \delta$ maps $C^\infty(\xi^e)$ into $C^\infty(\xi^0)$, and as a differential operator from $C^\infty(\xi^e)$ to $C^\infty(\xi^0)$ is still elliptic. This operator plays a basic role in the Index Theorem. We now compute a Green's form for $d + \delta$. We have seen that if $f, g \in C_c^\infty(\xi)$

$$\int_{\partial M} [f \wedge * g]_{n-1} = \langle df, g \rangle_\xi - \langle f, \delta g \rangle_\xi \quad .$$

Complex conjugating (and noting $\overline{*g} = *\bar{g}$)

$$\int_{\partial M} [\bar{f} \wedge * \bar{g}]_{n-1} = \langle g, df \rangle_\xi - \langle \delta g, f \rangle_\xi \quad .$$

Interchanging f and g in the latter equation and subtracting from the former

$$\langle (d+\delta)f, g \rangle_\xi - \langle f, (d+\delta)g \rangle_\xi = \int_{\partial M} [f \wedge * g - \bar{g} \wedge * \bar{f}]_{n-1}$$

from which a Green's form for $d + \delta$ is clear. To get a Green's form for Δ (the prototype and the namesake of all Green's forms) it is now only necessary to first replace f by $(d+\delta)f$ and next replace g by $(d+\delta)g$ in the above equation and then add the two resulting equations.

d. The operator $\bar{\partial}$

Now let M be a complex analytic manifold of real dimension $n = 2m$. Then $\xi = \bigoplus_{p,q} \xi^{p,q}$ where $(\xi^{p,q})_x$ consists of forms which in holomorphic local coordinate $z_1, \ldots, z_m$ at x have the form

$$\Sigma\, a_{i_1 \ldots i_p j_1 \ldots j_q}\, dz_{i_1} \wedge \ldots \wedge dz_{i_p} \wedge d\bar{z}_{j_1} \wedge \ldots \wedge d\bar{z}_{j_q}$$

$$(i_1 < \ldots < i_p;\ j_1 < \ldots < j_q) \quad .$$

Elements of $\xi^{p,q}$ are called differential forms of type (p, q) and clearly

$\bigoplus_{p+q=r} \xi^{p,q} = \Lambda^r(T^*(M)) \otimes \mathbf{C} = \xi^r$. There are operators ∂ and $\bar{\partial}$ in $\mathrm{Diff}_1(\xi, \xi)$ such that $d = \partial + \bar{\partial}$, $\partial^2 = \bar{\partial}^2 = 0$ and $\partial\bar{\partial} + \bar{\partial}\partial = 0$. Namely, if $z_1, \ldots, z_m$ are local holomorphic coordinates in $\mathcal{O}$ and $f \in C^\infty(\xi)$ can be written in $\mathcal{O}$ as $h\omega$ where $h \in C^\infty(M, \mathbf{C})$ and $\omega = dz_{i_1} \wedge \ldots \wedge dz_{i_q} \wedge d\bar{z}_{j_1} \wedge \ldots \wedge d\bar{z}_{j_q}$ then $\partial f = \Sigma_{i=1}^m \frac{\partial h}{\partial z_i} dz_i \wedge \omega$ and $\bar{\partial} f = \Sigma_{i=1}^m \frac{\partial h}{\partial \bar{z}_i} d\bar{z}_i \wedge \omega$ in $\mathcal{O}$. Clearly ∂ and $\bar{\partial}$ map $C^\infty(\xi^{p,q})$ into $C^\infty(\xi^{p+1,q})$ and $C^\infty(\xi^{p,q+1})$ respectively. We note further that if $h \in C^\infty(M, \mathbf{C})$ is holomorphic in $\mathcal{O}$ and $f \in C^\infty(\xi)$ then (since $\frac{\partial h}{\partial \bar{z}_i} = 0$) $\bar{\partial}(hf) = h\bar{\partial} f$ in $\mathcal{O}$.

If η is a holomorphic vector bundle over M we call $\xi^{p,q} \otimes \eta$ the bundle of differential forms of type (p, q) with coefficients in η and $\xi \otimes \eta$ the bundle of differential forms with coefficients in η. Then we have a unique $\bar{\partial} \in \mathrm{Diff}_1(\xi \otimes \eta, \xi \otimes \eta)$ such that if $\mathcal{O}$ is open in M, $f \in C^\infty(\xi | \mathcal{O})$ and if $g \in C^\infty(\eta | \mathcal{O})$ is holomorphic then $\bar{\partial}(f \otimes g) = (\bar{\partial} f) \otimes g$. In fact if $g_1, \ldots, g_k$ is a basis of holomorphic sections over $\mathcal{O}$ then over $\mathcal{O}$ every $F \in C^\infty(\xi \otimes \eta)$ can be written uniquely as $F = \Sigma_i f_i \otimes g_i$; $f_i \in C^\infty(\xi | \mathcal{O})$. Then if such a $\bar{\partial}$ exists we must have $\bar{\partial} F = \Sigma_i \bar{\partial} f \otimes g_i$ over $\mathcal{O}$. If $h_1, \ldots, h_k$ is another basis of holomorphic sections over $\mathcal{O}$ then $g_i = \Sigma a_{ji} h_j$ where $a_{ij} \in C^\infty(\mathcal{O}, \mathbf{C})$ is holomorphic. Then $F = \Sigma_j(\Sigma_i a_{ji} f_i) \otimes h_j$ and since $\bar{\partial}(a_{ji} f_i) = a_{ji} \bar{\partial} f_i$ we have $\Sigma_i \bar{\partial} f_i \otimes g_i = \Sigma_j \bar{\partial}(\Sigma_i a_{ji} f_i) \otimes h_j$ which proves $\bar{\partial} | \mathcal{O}$ is well defined and unique. Corollary 3 of Theorem 1 of Section 1 completes the proof of the existence of a unique $\bar{\partial}$ with the stated properties. If we give M a Riemannian structure and η an hermitian structure then $\xi \otimes \eta$ has an induced hermitian structure. The computation of the adjoint ϑ of $\bar{\partial}$ and the proof that $\bar{\partial} + \vartheta$ is elliptic is similar to that in (c) above. We refer the reader to F. Hirzebruch's *Neue Topologische Methoden in der Algebraischen Geometrie* (p. 117) for details.

§7. Whitney sums

Given (C^∞-complex) vector bundles ξ_i $(i = 1, \ldots, r)$ over M their Whitney sum is the bundle $\bigoplus_i \xi_i$ over M whose fiber at x is $\bigoplus_i (\xi_i)_x$ and whose bundle structure is characterized by the property that

$(f_1, \ldots, f_r) \to \oplus_i f_i$ is an isomorphism of $\oplus_i C^\infty(\xi_i)$ with $C^\infty(\oplus_i \xi_i)$ (where $(\oplus_i f_i)(x) = \oplus_i f_i(x)$). It follows that $J^k(\oplus_i \xi_i)$ is naturally isomorphic to $\oplus_i J^k(\xi_i)$, the k-jet of $\oplus_i f_i$ at x being $\oplus_i j_k(f_i)_x$.

If $\eta_1, \ldots, \eta_s$ are vector bundles over M we note that there is a canonical isomorphism $\oplus_{ij} \mathrm{Smbl}_k^d(\xi_i, \eta_j) \simeq \mathrm{Smbl}_k^d(\oplus_i \xi_i, \oplus_j \eta_j)$, $\{\sigma_{ij}\} \to \oplus_{i,j} \sigma_{ij}$ defined by

$$(\bigoplus_{i,j} \sigma_{ij})(v, x)(e_1, \ldots, e_r) = (\oplus_i \sigma_{i1}(v, x)e_i, \ldots, \oplus_i \sigma_{is}(v, x)e_i)$$

Similarly there is a linear isomorphism

$$\bigoplus_{i,j} \mathrm{Diff}_k(\xi_i, \eta_j) \simeq \mathrm{Diff}_k(\oplus_i \xi_i, \oplus_j \eta_j), \; \{D_{ij}\} \to \bigoplus_{i,j} D_{ij}$$

where

$$(\bigoplus_{i,j} D_{ij})(\oplus f_i) = (\oplus_i D_{i1} f_i, \ldots, \oplus_i D_{is} f_i) \quad .$$

Given $D \in \mathrm{Diff}_k(\oplus_i \xi_i, \oplus_j \eta_j)$ the corresponding element $\{D_{ij}\}$ of $\oplus_{i,j} \mathrm{Diff}_k(\xi_i, \eta_j)$ will be called the matrix of D and where convenient will be written as a matrix

$$\begin{pmatrix} D_{11} & \cdots & D_{1s} \\ \cdot & & \\ \cdot & & \\ \cdot & & \\ D_{r1} & \cdots & D_{rs} \end{pmatrix}$$

We note that

$$\sigma_k(\bigoplus_{i,j} D_{ij}) = \bigoplus_{i,j} \sigma_k(D_{ij})$$

so $\oplus_{i,j} D_{ij}$ is k^{th} order elliptic if and only if the matrix $((\sigma_k(D_{ij})(v, x)))$ defines an isomorphism of $\oplus_i(\xi_i)_x$ with $\oplus_j(\eta_j)_x$ for all $(v, x) \in T'(M)$.

There is a more general notion of ellipticity due to Douglis and Nirenberg that applies in this situation.

DEFINITION. $\oplus_{i,j} D_{ij}$ is called elliptic in the sense of Douglis and Nirenberg if there exist non-negative integers s_i and t_j such that $D_{ij} \in \mathrm{Diff}_{s_i - t_j}(\xi_i, \eta_j)$ and such that for all $(v, x) \in T'(M)$ the matrix

$$((\sigma_{s_i - t_j}(D_{ij})(v, x)))$$

defines an isomorphism of $\oplus_i(\xi_i)_x$ with $\oplus_j(\eta_j)_x$.

(If $\oplus_{i,j} D_{ij}$ is k^{th} order elliptic we can take $s_i = k$, $t_j = 0$). This becomes a little clearer in the case $r = s$ and $D_{ij} = 0$, $i \neq j$. In this case we say that $\oplus_{i,j} D_{ij}$ is *diagonal* and we put $D_i = D_{ii}$ and $\oplus_i D_i = \oplus_{i,j} D_{ij}$. Then in this case $\oplus_i D_i$ is k^{th} order elliptic if and only if each $D_i \in \mathrm{Diff}_k(\xi_i, \eta_i)$ is k^{th} order elliptic, while $\oplus_i D_i$ is elliptic in the sense of Douglis and Nirenberg if and only if there exist non-negative integers $k_i (= s_i - t_i)$ such that $D_i \in \mathrm{Diff}_{k_i}(\xi_i, \eta_i)$ is k_i^{th} order elliptic $i = 1, \ldots, r$.

§8. Tensor products.

Let M and N be C^∞ manifolds, at least one without boundary, and let ξ_1 and ξ_2 be (C^∞ complex) vector bundles over M and N respectively. Then $\xi_1 \otimes \xi_2$ is the vector bundle over $M \times N$ whose fiber at (x, y) is $(\xi_1)_x \otimes (\xi_2)_y$ and whose bundle structure is characterized by the property that if $f_1 \in C^\infty(\xi_1)$, $f_2 \in C^\infty(\xi_2)$ then $f_1 \otimes f_2 \in C^\infty(\xi_1 \otimes \xi_2)$ (where $f_1 \otimes f_2(x, y) = f_1(x) \otimes f_2(y)$). If we are also given vector bundles η_1 over M and η_2 over N we define a bilinear pairing of $\mathrm{Smbl}_k^d(\xi_1, \eta_1) \times \mathrm{Smbl}_\ell^d(\xi_2, \eta_2)$ into $\mathrm{Smbl}_{k+\ell}^d(\xi_1 \otimes \xi_2, \eta_1 \otimes \eta_2)$, $(\sigma_1, \sigma_2) \to \sigma_1 \otimes \sigma_2$, defined by

$$\sigma_1 \otimes \sigma_2((v_1, v_2), (x, y)) = \sigma_1(v_1, x) \otimes \sigma_2(v_2, y) \quad .$$

LEMMA. If $D_1 \in \mathrm{Diff}_k(\xi_1, \eta_1)$, $D_2 \in \mathrm{Diff}_\ell(\xi_2, \eta_2)$ and $T \in \mathrm{Diff}_{k+\ell}(\xi_1 \otimes \xi_2, \eta_1 \otimes \eta_2)$ satisfies $T(f_1 \otimes f_2) = D_1 f_1 \otimes D_2 f_2$, then $\sigma_{k+\ell}(T) = \sigma_k(D_1) \otimes \sigma_\ell(D_2)$.

PROOF. Let $((v_1, v_2), (x, y)) \in T^*(M \times N)$ and let $e_i \in (\xi_i)_x$. Choose $g_1 \in C^\infty(M, \mathbf{R})$ with $g_1(x) = 0$ and $(dg_1)_x = v_1$ and $g_2 \in C^\infty(N, \mathbf{R})$ with $g_2(y) = 0$ and $(dg_2)_y = v_2$. Define $g \in C^\infty(M \times N, \mathbf{R})$ by $g(x, y) = g_1(x) + g_2(y)$. Then $g(x, y) = 0$ and $dg_{(x,y)} = (v_1, v_2)$ so choosing $f_i \in C^\infty(\xi_i)$ with $f_i(x) = e_i$

$\sigma_{k+\ell}(T)(v_1, v_2)(e_1 \otimes e_2)$

$$= \frac{1}{(k+\ell)!} T(g^{k+\ell} f_1 \otimes f_2)(x, y)$$

$$= \frac{1}{(k+\ell)!} T\Big(\sum_{m \leq k+\ell} \binom{k+\ell}{m} g_1^m f_1 \otimes g_2^{k+\ell-m} f_2\Big)(x, y)$$

$$= \sum_{m \leq k+\ell} \frac{1}{m!} D_1(g_1^m f_1)(x) \otimes \frac{1}{(k+\ell-m)!} D_2(g_2^{k+\ell-m} f_2)(y) .$$

Since $D_1(g_1^m f_1)(x) = 0$ if $m > k$ and since $D_2(g_2^m f_2)(y) = 0$ if $m > \ell$ the only term that contributes is $m = k$, $k+\ell-m = \ell$ and the contribution of this term is exactly $\sigma_k(d_1)(v_1, x)e_1 \otimes \sigma_\ell(D_2)(v_2, y)e_2$.

q.e.d.

THEOREM. Given $D_1 \in \mathrm{Diff}_k(\xi_1, \eta_1)$ and $D_2 \in \mathrm{Diff}_\ell(\xi_2, \eta_2)$ There is a unique $T \in \mathrm{Diff}_{k+\ell}(\xi_1 \otimes \xi_2, \eta_1 \otimes \eta_2)$ such that $T(f_1 \otimes f_2) = D_1 f_1 \otimes D_2 f_2$. Denoting this T by $D_1 \otimes D_2$ we have

$$\sigma_{k+\ell}(D_1 \otimes D_2) = \sigma_k(D_1) \otimes \sigma_\ell(D_2) .$$

PROOF. The second conclusion is just the lemma. To prove the first it suffices by Corollary 3 of Theorem 1, Section 3, to restrict to the case $M = \mathbf{R}^m$ (or a closed half space in $\mathbf{R}^m$) and $N = \mathbf{R}^n$ (or a closed half space in $\mathbf{R}^n$) so $M \times N = \mathbf{R}^{m+n}$ (or a closed half space in $\mathbf{R}^{m+n}$) and we can further assume that $\xi_1 = M \times V_1$, $\xi_2 = N \times V_2$, $\eta_1 = M \times W_1$ and $\eta_2 = N \times W_2$ so $\xi_1 \otimes \xi_2 = (M \times N) \times (V_1 \otimes V_2)$ and $\eta_1 \otimes \eta_2 = (M \times N) \times (W_1 \otimes W_2)$. Given an m-multi-index α_1 and an n-multi-index α_2 let $\alpha_1 \otimes \alpha_2$ denote the m+n multi-index $(\alpha_{11}, \ldots, \alpha_{1m}, \alpha_{21}, \ldots, \alpha_{2n})$ and define $D^{\alpha_1} \otimes D^{\alpha_2} = D^{\alpha_1 \otimes \alpha_2}$. Then if $f_i \in C^\infty(M, V_i)$, $f_1 \otimes f_2 \in C^\infty(M \times N, V_1 \otimes V_2)$ is given by $f_1 \otimes f_2(x_1, \ldots, x_m, y_1, \ldots, y_n) = f_1(x_1, \ldots, x_m) \otimes f_2(y_1, \ldots, y_n)$ so $D^{\alpha_1 \otimes \alpha_2} f_1 \otimes f_2 = D^{\alpha_1} f_1 \otimes D^{\alpha_2} f_2$. The most general $T \in \mathrm{Diff}_{k+\ell}(\xi_1 \otimes \xi_2, \eta_1 \otimes \eta_2)$ is

$$T = \Sigma\, C_{\alpha_1 \otimes \alpha_2} D^{\alpha_1 \otimes \alpha_2}$$

where $|\alpha_1| + |\alpha_2| \leq k+\ell$ and $C_{\alpha_1 \otimes \alpha_2}$ is C^∞ map of $M \times N$ into $L(V_1 \otimes V_2, W_1 \otimes W_2)$. If $D_1 = \Sigma_{|\alpha_1| \leq k} A_{\alpha_1} D^{\alpha_1}$ and $D_2 = \Sigma_{|\alpha_2| \leq \ell} B_{\alpha_2} D^{\alpha_2}$

then T satisfies the required condition if and only if

$$\Sigma\, C_{\alpha_1 \otimes \alpha_2} D^{\alpha_1} f_1 \otimes D^{\alpha_2} f_2 = (\Sigma\, A_{\alpha_1} D^{\alpha_1} f_1) \otimes (\Sigma\, B_{\alpha_2} D^{\alpha_2} f_2)$$

$$= \Sigma (A_{\alpha_1} \otimes B_{\alpha_2})(D^{\alpha_1} f_1 \otimes D^{\alpha_2} f_2) \quad .$$

If we take for f_1 "monomials" of the form $x \to x^{\alpha_1} v_1 (v_1 \in V_1)$ and for f_2 "monomials" of the form $y \to y^{\alpha_2} v_2 (v_2 \in V_2)$ we see that this can happen if and only if $C_{\alpha_1 \otimes \alpha_2} = A_{\alpha_1} \otimes B_{\alpha_2}$.

q.e.d.

There is another kind of "tensor product" operation on operators that depends on hermitian structures and plays an important role in the index theorem. In addition to the assumption above we assume that M and N have strictly positive smooth measures (which of course induce a strictly positive smooth "Fubini product" measure on $M \times N$) and that ξ_1 and η_i have hermitian structures (which induce hermitian structures on $\xi_1 \otimes \eta_1$ etc.). Let $\xi = (\xi_1 \otimes \xi_2) \otimes (\eta_1 \oplus \eta_2)$ and let $\eta = (\eta_1 \otimes \xi_2) \otimes (\xi_1 \oplus \eta_2)$. Let $I_{\xi_1} \in \mathrm{Diff}_0(\xi_1, \xi_1)$ denote the identity operator and similarly for the other bundles. Then given $D_i \in \mathrm{Diff}_k(\xi_i, \eta_i)$ $i = 1, 2$ we define $D_1 \# D_2 \in \mathrm{Diff}_k(\xi, \eta)$ by the matrix

$$D_1 \# D_2 = \begin{pmatrix} D_1 \otimes I_{\xi_2} & I_{\xi_1} \otimes D_2 \\ -I_{\eta_1} \otimes D_2^* & D_1^* \otimes I_{\eta_2} \end{pmatrix}$$

i.e.,

$$D_1 \# D_2 (f_1 \otimes f_2 \oplus g_1 \otimes g_2) = (D_1 f_1 \otimes f_2 - g_1 \otimes D_2^* g_2) \oplus (f_1 \otimes Df_2 + D_1^* g_1 \otimes g_2).$$

The adjoint of $D_1 \# D_2$ (relative to the natural hermitian structures for ξ and η in which the summands are orthogonal) is given by the matrix

$$(D_1 \# D_2)^* = (-1)^k \begin{pmatrix} D_1^* \otimes I_{\xi_2} & -I_{\eta_1} \otimes D_2 \\ I_{\xi_1} \otimes D_2^* & D_1 \otimes I_{\eta_2} \end{pmatrix}$$

hence $(D_1 \# D_2)^* (D_1 \# D_2)$ has the matrix

$$(-1)^k \begin{pmatrix} D_1^*D_1 \otimes I_{\xi_2} + I_{\xi_1} \otimes D_2^*D_2 & 0 \\ 0 & (I_{\eta_1} \otimes D_2D_2^*) + (D_1D_1^* \otimes I_{\eta_2}) \end{pmatrix}$$

from which it follows that $(D_1 \# D_2)^*(D_1 \# D_2)$ is strongly elliptic of order $2k$ hence that $D_1 \# D_2$ is k^{th} order elliptic, provided D_1 and D_2 are k^{th} order elliptic (see Corollary at end of Section 4). Given vector bundles ξ_1 and ξ_2 over M we recall that $\xi_1 \hat{\otimes} \xi_2 = \Delta(\xi_1 \otimes \xi_2)$, or equivalently it is the bundle over M whose fiber at x is $(\xi_1)_x \otimes (\xi_2)_x$ and whose bundle structure is characterized by the property that if $f_i \in C^\infty(\xi_1)$ then $f_1 \hat{\otimes} f_2 \in C^\infty(\xi_1 \hat{\otimes} \xi_2)$ (where $f_1 \hat{\otimes} f_2(x) = f_1(x) \otimes f_2(x)$). If η_1 and η_2 are vector bundles over M then we have a natural bilinear pairing $(\sigma_1, \sigma_2) \to \sigma_1 \hat{\otimes} \sigma_2$ of $\mathrm{Smbl}_k^d(\xi_1, \eta_1) \times \mathrm{Smbl}_k^d(\xi_2, \eta_2)$ into $\mathrm{Smbl}_{k+\ell}^d(\xi_1 \hat{\otimes} \xi_2, \eta_1 \hat{\otimes} \eta_2)$, defined by $(\sigma_1 \hat{\otimes} \sigma_2)(v, x) = \sigma_1(v, x) \otimes \sigma_2(v, x)$. By Theorem 2 of Section 3 given $D_1 \in \mathrm{Diff}_k(\xi_1, \eta_1)$ and $D_2 \in \mathrm{Diff}\ (\xi_2, \eta_2)$ there exists $T \in \mathrm{Diff}_{k+\ell}(\xi_1 \hat{\otimes} \xi_2, \eta_1 \hat{\otimes} \eta_2)$ such that $\sigma_{k+\ell}(T) = \sigma_k(D_1) \hat{\otimes} \sigma_\ell(D_2)$, however unlike the situation above there is no canonical choice for T. (Note it would not do to try to characterize such a T by $T(f_1 \hat{\otimes} f_2) = D_1 f_1 \hat{\otimes} D_2 f_2$. For example let $M = \mathbf{R}$, $\xi = \eta = M \times \mathbf{C}$ so $\xi \hat{\otimes} \eta = M \times \mathbf{C}$ and $f_1 \hat{\otimes} f_2 = f_1 f_2$. Hence if $D_1 = D_2 = d/dx$, T would have to satisfy $T(fg) = f'g'$. But $T(f) = T(f1) = f'1' = 0$ so $T = 0$ a contradiction.) The concept of a connection which we take up next is a partial remedy for this unpleasant situation.

§9. Connections and covariant derivatives

The Jet Bundle Exact Sequency for $k = 1$ is

$$0 \to L(T(M), \xi) \xrightarrow{i} J^1(\xi) \xrightarrow{p} \xi \to 0$$

where $pj_1(f)_x = f(x)$ and $i(dg_x \otimes f(x)) = j_1(gf)_x$ for $f \in C^\infty(\xi)$, $g \in C^\infty(M, \mathbf{R})$ with $g(x) = 0$. By the general splitting principle we can find a C^∞ sub-bundle of $J^1(\xi)$ complementary to the image of i. A choice $C(\xi)$ of such a sub-bundle is called a ***connection*** for ξ. Elements of $C(\xi)$ are called the constant 1-jets of the connection. There is a unique bundle morphism $C\colon\ \xi \to J^1(\xi)$ with image $C(\xi)$ such that pC is the identity. If

$e \in \xi$ then $C(e)$ is called the constant 1-jet through e. Conversely, any bundle morphism $C\colon \xi \to J^1(\xi)$ which is a cross section for p is an injection whose image $C(\xi)$ is a connection for ξ. Dually given a connection $C(\xi)$ there is a unique bundle morphism $T\colon J^1(\xi) \to L(T(M), \xi)$ having $C(\xi)$ as kernel for which Ti is the identity and conversely any morphism $T\colon J^1(\xi) \to L(T(M), \xi)$ such that Ti is the identity has as its kernel a connection $C(\xi)$. The first order differential operator $\nabla = T_* j_1\colon C^\infty(\xi) \to C^\infty(L(T(M), \xi))$ is called the covariant derivative defined by the connection $C(\xi)$. If $g \in C^\infty(M, \mathbf{R})$ and $f \in C^\infty(M, \mathbf{R})$ then since Ti = identity and $i(dg_x \otimes f(x)) = j_1((g-g(x))f)_x$ we have $\nabla((g-g(x))f)(x) = dg_x \otimes f(x)$ or $\nabla(gf) = dg \otimes f + g\nabla f$. Conversely, suppose $\nabla\colon C^\infty(\xi) \to C^\infty(L(T(M), \xi))$ is a linear map satisfying this identity. If $j_1(f)_x = 0$ then by Taylor's Theorem we can find $f_1, \ldots, f_n$ in $C^\infty(\xi)$ with $f_1(x) = 0$ and $g_1, \ldots, g_n \in C^\infty(M, \mathbf{R})$ with $g_i(x) = 0$ such that $f = \Sigma\, g_i f_i$. Then clearly $\nabla f(x) = 0$ hence ∇ is a first order differential operator, and by Corollary 1 of Theorem 1 of Section 3 there is a unique $T \in \mathrm{Hom}(J^1(\xi), L(T(M), \xi))$ such that $\nabla = T_* j_1$. Then working the argument above backward we see that Ti = identity so $\ker(t)$ is a connection and ∇ is the associated covariant derivative. Thus if we make the

DEFINITION. A linear transformation $\nabla\colon C^\infty(\xi) \to C^\infty(L(T(M), \xi))$ is called a covariant derivative if $\nabla(gf) = dg \otimes f + g\nabla f$ for $g \in C^\infty(M, \mathbf{R})$ and $f \in C^\infty(\xi)$,

we have

THEOREM 1. A covariant derivative $\nabla\colon C^\infty(\xi) \to C^\infty(L(T(M), \xi))$ is a first order differential operator and is the covariant derivative associated with a unique connection for ξ.

COROLLARY. $\sigma_1(\nabla)(v, x)e = v \otimes e$.

Remark. The above definition of a covariant derivative is due to Koszul. The present definition of a connection for ξ (one among hundreds) is apparently due to Bott.

DEFINITION. Given a covariant derivative $\nabla\colon C^\infty(\xi) \to C^\infty(L(T(M), \xi))$ and $w \in T(M)_x$ we define a linear map $\nabla_w\colon C^\infty(\xi) \to \xi_x$ by $\nabla_w f = (\nabla f)(w)$. Similarly given $X \in C^\infty(T(M))$ (i.e., a C^∞ vector field on M) we define $\nabla_X\colon C^\infty(\xi) \to C\ (\xi)$ by $(\nabla_X f)(x) = (\nabla f)(X(x))$.

Then clearly

THEOREM 2. If $\nabla\colon C^\infty(\xi) \to C^\infty(L(T(M), \xi))$ is a covariant derivative for ξ then $X \to \nabla_X$ is a $C^\infty(M, \mathbf{R})$ module homomorphism of $C^\infty(T(M))$ into $\mathrm{Diff}_1(\xi, \xi)$. If $g \in C^\infty(M, \mathbf{R})$ and $f \in C^\infty(\xi)$ then

$$\nabla_X(gf) = (Xg)f + g\nabla_X f$$

hence $\sigma_1(\nabla_X)(v, x)$ is scalar multiplication in ξ_x by $v(X)$.

We note also that ∇_w uniquely determine the connection $C(\xi)$ of which ∇ is the associated covariant derivative. Indeed, if $j_1(f)_x \in J^1(\xi)_x$ then $j_1(f)_x \in C(\xi)$ if and only if $\nabla_w f = 0$ for all $w \in T(M)_x$.

LEMMA. Let ξ and ζ be vector bundles over M and ∇ a covariant derivative for ζ. Then given $F \in C^\infty(\xi \hat{\otimes} \zeta)$ and $x \in M$ there exist $f_1, \ldots, f_s \in C^\infty(\xi)$ and $g_1, \ldots, g_s \in C^\infty(\zeta)$ with $(\nabla g_i)(x) = 0$ so that $j_1(F)_x = j_1(\Sigma f_i \hat{\otimes} g_i)_x$.

PROOF. Choose $h_1, \ldots, h_r \in C^\infty(\xi)$ so that the $h_j(x)$ form a basis for ξ_x and $g_1, \ldots, g_s \in C^\infty(\zeta)$ so that the $j_1(g_i)_x$ form a basis for $C(\zeta)$ where C is the connection corresponding to ∇. Then the $g_i(x)$ form a basis for ζ_x hence the $h_j \hat{\otimes} g_i(x)$ form a basis for $(\xi \hat{\otimes} \zeta)_x$, so the $h_j \hat{\otimes} g_i$ form a local basis of sections for $\xi \hat{\otimes} \zeta$ near x, so that we may write F in the form $\Sigma a_{ij} h_j \hat{\otimes} g_i$ near x for $a_{ij} \in C^\infty(M, \mathbf{C})$. Putting $f_i = \Sigma_j a_{ij} h_j$ we have $F = \Sigma f_i \hat{\otimes} g_i$ near x.

q.e.d.

THEOREM 3. Let ξ, η, ζ be vector bundles over M, $D \in \mathrm{Diff}_1(\xi, \eta)$ and ∇ a covariant derivative for ζ. Then there is a unique $T \in \mathrm{Diff}_1(\xi \hat{\otimes} \zeta, \eta \hat{\otimes} \zeta)$ such that $T(f \otimes h)(x) = (Df \otimes h)(x)$ whenever $(\nabla h)(x) = 0$. Denoting this T by $D \hat{\otimes}_\nabla I$ we have moreover that

$$\sigma_1(D \hat{\otimes}_\nabla I) = \sigma_1(D) \hat{\otimes} \sigma_0(I) \quad .$$

Hence $D \hat{\otimes}_\nabla I$ is elliptic if and only if D is.

PROOF. Uniqueness is immediate from the lemma, hence by Corollary 3 of Theorem 1 of Section 3 it will suffice to prove existence locally. Then we can assume that $M = \mathbf{R}^n$ or a closed half space in $\mathbf{R}^n$ and that $\xi = M \times U$, $\eta = M \times V$ and $\zeta = M \times W$, so $\xi \hat{\otimes} \zeta = M \times (U \otimes W)$ and $\eta \otimes \zeta = M \times (V \otimes W)$. Let $D = A_0 + \Sigma_{i=1}^n A_i(\partial/\partial x_i)$ when the A_i are C^∞ maps of M into $L(U, V)$. Let $h_1, \ldots, h_s$ be a basis of sections for ζ. Then if $F \in C^\infty(\xi \hat{\otimes} \zeta)$ F can be written uniquely as $F = \Sigma_{j=1}^s f_j \hat{\otimes} h_j$; $f_j \in C^\infty(\xi)$, and we define

$$TF = \sum_j (Df_j) \hat{\otimes} h_j + \sum_{i,j} A_i f_j \hat{\otimes} \nabla_i h_j \quad ,$$

where $\nabla_i = \nabla_{\partial/\partial x_i}$. If $f \in C^\infty(\xi)$ and $h \in C^\infty(\zeta)$ then $h = \Sigma g_j h_j$ for unique $g_j \in C^\infty(M, \mathbf{C})$, so $f \hat{\otimes} h = \Sigma_j (g_j f) \hat{\otimes} h_j$. By Theorem 2, $\nabla_i h = \Sigma_j (\partial g_j/\partial x_i) h_j + g_j \nabla_i h_j$, hence

$$T(f \otimes h) = Df \hat{\otimes} h + \sum_i A_i f \otimes \nabla_i h$$

by a straightforward calculation which we leave to the reader. It is evident from the latter that T has the desired property.

q.e.d.

In following if $\xi_1, \ldots, \xi_m$ are bundles over M then π_j will denote the canonical isomorphism of $\xi_1 \hat{\otimes} \ldots \hat{\otimes} \xi_j \hat{\otimes} \ldots \hat{\otimes} \xi_m$ with $\xi_j \hat{\otimes} \xi_1 \hat{\otimes} \ldots \hat{\otimes} \xi_{j-1} \hat{\otimes} \xi_{j+1} \hat{\otimes} \ldots \hat{\otimes} \xi_m$.

THEOREM 4. If ξ and η are vector bundles over M with covariant derivatives ∇_ξ and ∇_η respectively, then there is a uniquely determined covariant derivative

$\nabla_{\xi \hat{\otimes} \eta}$ for $\xi \hat{\otimes} \eta$ such that

$$\nabla_{\xi \hat{\otimes} \eta} (f \hat{\otimes} g) = \nabla_\xi f \hat{\otimes} g + \pi_2 f \hat{\otimes} \nabla_\eta g$$

for $f \in C^\infty(\xi)$ and $g \in C^\infty(\eta)$.

PROOF. Granted the existence of $\nabla_{\xi \hat{\otimes} \eta}$ uniqueness is clear, and it is also clear that an operator $\nabla_{\xi \hat{\otimes} \eta}$ satisfying the above identity is a covariant derivative for $\xi \hat{\otimes} \eta$. Using Theorem 3 we define

$$\nabla_{\xi \otimes \eta} = \nabla_\xi \hat{\otimes}_{\nabla_\eta} I + \pi_2 \circ (I_{\nabla_\xi} \hat{\otimes} \nabla_\eta)$$

and it will suffice to verify the identity. Given $p \in M$ let $f_1, \ldots, f_r$ be a local base of sections for ξ near p with $(\nabla_\xi f_i)_p = 0$ and let $g_1, \ldots, g_s$ be a local base of sections for η at p with $(\nabla_\eta g_j)_p = 0$. Let $f = \Sigma a_i f_i$ and $g = \Sigma b_j g_j$ near p. Then $f \hat{\otimes} g = \Sigma a_i b_j f_i \hat{\otimes} g_j$ near p hence

$$\nabla_{\xi \hat{\otimes} \eta} (f \otimes g)(p) = \sum \left[\nabla_\xi (a_i b_j f_i) \hat{\otimes} g_j + \pi_2 f_i \hat{\otimes} \nabla_\eta (a_i b_j g_j) \right](p)$$

$$= \sum \Big[d(a_i b_j) \hat{\otimes} f_i \otimes g_j + a_i b_j \nabla_\zeta f_i \otimes g_j$$

$$+ \pi_2 f_i \hat{\otimes} d(a_i b_j) \hat{\otimes} g_j + \pi_2 f_i \hat{\otimes} a_i b_j \nabla_\eta g_j \Big](p)$$

while

$$(\nabla_\xi f \hat{\otimes} g + \pi_2 f \hat{\otimes} \nabla_\eta g)(p) = \sum \Big[(da_i \otimes f + a_i \nabla_\xi f_i) \otimes b_j g_j$$

$$+ \pi_2 a_i f_i \hat{\otimes} (db_j \hat{\otimes} g_j + b_j \nabla_\eta g_j) \Big](p) \quad .$$

The equality of the right hand sides of the above expressions is immediate from the identity $d(a_i b_j) = (da_i) b_j + a_i (db_j)$ while the equality of the left hand sides is the identity we sought.

q.e.d.

COROLLARY. If ∇_ξ is a connection for ξ and ∇_{T^*} is a connection for $T^*(M)$, then there is a unique connection $\nabla_\xi^{(k)}$ for $\otimes^k T^*(M) \hat{\otimes} \xi$ such that if $f_1, \ldots, f_k \in C^\infty(T^*(M))$ and $g \in C^\infty(\xi)$ then

$$\nabla_\xi^{(k)}(f_1\hat{\otimes}\ \dots\ \hat{\otimes}\ f_k\otimes g) = \sum_{i=1}^{k} \pi_i(f_1\hat{\otimes}\ \dots\ \hat{\otimes}\ \nabla_{T^*}f_i\hat{\otimes}\ \dots\ \hat{\otimes}\ f_k)\ \hat{\otimes}\ g$$

$$+ \pi_{k+1}(f_1\hat{\otimes}\ \dots\ \hat{\otimes}\ f_k\ \ \hat{\otimes}\ \nabla_\xi g) \quad .$$

DEFINITION. Let $D_k \in \mathrm{Diff}_k(\xi, L_s^k(T(M), \xi))$, say $D_k = D_{(k)}j_k$ where $D_{(k)} \in \mathrm{Hom}(J^k(\xi), L_s^k(T(M), \xi))$. We shall call D_k a kth total differential for ξ if $D_{(k)}$ splits the jet bundle exact sequence

$$0 \to L_s^k(T(M), \xi) \to J^k(\xi) \to J^{k-1}(\xi) \to 0 \quad .$$

THEOREM 5. $D_k \in \mathrm{Diff}_k(\xi, L_s^k(T(M), \xi)$ is a kth total differential for ξ if and only if $\sigma_k(D_k)(v, x)\ e = S^k(v) \otimes e$.

PROOF. Let $D_k = D_{(k)}j_k$. Then D_k is a kth total differential if and only if $D_{(k)}i$ is the identity morphism of $L_s^k(T(M), \xi)$, where i is the inclusion map of the jet bundle sequence. Hence by [§2, Theorem 1] D_k is a kth total differential if and only if $v \in T^*(M)_x$ and $e \in \xi_x$ we have

$$\begin{aligned} S^k(v) \otimes e &= D_{(k)}i(S^k(v) \otimes e) \\ &= D_{(k)}j_k(\tfrac{1}{k!}\ g^k f)(p) \\ &= \tfrac{1}{k!}\ D_k(g^k f)(p) \end{aligned}$$

provided $f \in C^\infty(\xi)$ satisfies $f(p) = e$ and $g \in C^\infty(M)$ satisfies $g(p) = 0$ and $dg_p = v$. But by definition [§3]

$$\sigma_k(D_k)(v, x)e = \tfrac{1}{k!}\ D_k(g^k f)(p)$$

q.e.d.

Recall [§1] that $\mathrm{Smbl}_k^d(\xi, \eta)$ is the image of $\mathrm{Hom}(L_s^k(T(M),\xi),\eta)$ order an isomorphism λ_k, where $\lambda_k(F)(v, x)e = F(S^k(v) \otimes e)$ and that the inverse isomorphism is denoted by $\sigma \to \tilde{\sigma}$, so that if $\sigma \in \mathrm{Smbl}_k^d(\xi, \eta)$ $\tilde{\sigma} \in \mathrm{Hom}(L_s^k(T(M), \xi), \eta)$ is characterized by $\tilde{\sigma}(S^k(v) \otimes e) = \sigma(v, x)e$.

THEOREM 6. Given a kth total differential D_k for ξ define a linear map, denoted by $\tilde{D}_k$, of

$Smbl_k^d(\xi, \eta)$ into $Diff_k(\xi, \eta)$ by

$$\widetilde{D}_k(\sigma) = \widetilde{\sigma}_* \cdot D_k \quad .$$

Then $\widetilde{D}_k$ is a cross-section for the map σ_k: $Diff_k(\xi, \eta) \to Smbl_k^d(\xi, \eta)$ and hence a splitting of the symbol exact sequence [§3; Theorem 2].

PROOF. $\sigma_k(\widetilde{D}_k(\sigma))(v, x)e = \sigma_k(\widetilde{\sigma}_* \cdot D_k)(v, x)e = \sigma_0(\widetilde{\sigma}_*)\sigma_k(D_k)(v, x)e = \widetilde{\sigma}(S^k(v) \otimes e)$ by Theorem 5. Since by the definition of $\widetilde{\sigma}$, just above, we have $\widetilde{\sigma}(S^k(v) \otimes e) = \sigma(v, x)e$ we get $\sigma_k(\widetilde{D}_k(\sigma)) = \sigma$.

q.e.d.

If ξ and η are vector bundles then recall [§1] there is a natural projection $S^{(k)}$ of the bundle $\hat{\otimes}^k \xi \otimes \eta$ onto the sub-bundle $S^k(\xi) \otimes \eta$, namely symmetrization, defined by

$$S^{(k)}(e_1 \otimes \ldots \otimes e_k \otimes f) = \frac{1}{k!} \Sigma\, e_{\pi(1)} \otimes \ldots \otimes e_{\pi(k)} \otimes f$$

where the sum is over all $k!$ permutations of $\{1, 2, \ldots, k\}$.

THEOREM 7. Let ∇_ξ be a covariant derivative for a bundle ξ over M and let ∇_{T^*} be a covariant derivative for $T^*(M)$ then $D_k = S_*^{(k)} \nabla_\xi^{(k-1)} \ldots \nabla_\xi^{(1)} \nabla_\xi$ is a kth total differential for ξ.

PROOF.

$$\sigma_k(D_k)(v, x)e = \sigma_0(S_*^{(k)})(v, x)\sigma_1(\ _\xi^{(k-1)})(v, x) \ \ldots \ \sigma_1(\ _\xi)(v, x)e$$

$$= S^{(k)}(v \otimes (\ldots \otimes (v \otimes e)\ldots))$$

$$= S^{(k)}((v \otimes \ldots \otimes v) \otimes e) = (v \otimes \ldots \otimes v) \otimes e$$

and in the canonical identification of $S^k(T^*(M)) \hat{\otimes} \xi$ with $L_s^k(T(M), \xi)$ $(v \otimes \ldots \otimes v) \otimes e$ corresponds to $S^k(v) \otimes e$.

q.e.d.

COROLLARY. Given ∇_ξ and ∇_{T^*} there is a canonical isomorphism $J^k(\xi) \approx \bigoplus_{m=0}^{k} L_s^m(T(M), \xi)$ such that $j_k(f) \approx \{D_m(f)\}_{0 \leq m \leq k}$.

PROOF. Immediate from the theorem and the definition of a kth total differential.

§10. Spin structures and Dirac operators

We begin by recalling some basic facts about Clifford algebras and spinor groups. Details can be found in J. Milnor's mimeographed (1963) notes "The Representation Rings of Some Classical Groups."

The Clifford algebra A_n is characterized to within unique isomorphism by the following:

1) A_n is a real algebra with unit;

2) $\mathbf{R}^n \subseteq A_n$ and generates A_n;

3) $e_i^2 = -1$ and $e_i e_j = -e_j e_i$ where $e_1, \ldots, e_n$ is the standard basis for $\mathbf{R}^n$.

It follows that $\{e_1^{i_1} e_2^{i_2} \ldots e_n^{i_n}\}$ $(i_k = 0 \text{ or } 1)$ is a basis for A_n so in particular $\dim A_n = 2^n$. Also $A_n = A_n^+ \oplus A_n^-$, where A_n^+ and A_n^- are the subspaces spanned by those elements of the above basis having an even and odd number of i_k equal one respectively. Then A_n^+ is a subalgebra, $A_n^- A_n^- \subseteq A_n^+$ and $A_n^+ A_n^- = A_n^- A_n^+ \subseteq A_n^-$, and the correspondence $a_0 + a_1 \to a_0 + a_1 e_n$ where $a_0 \in A_{n-1}^+$, $a_1 \in A_{n-1}^-$ is an isomorphism of A_{n-1} with A_n^+.

Those units u of A_n such that $\rho(u)v = uvu^{-1}$ is in $\mathbf{R}^n$ for all $v \in \mathbf{R}^n$ form a subgroup pin(n) of A_n and ρ is a homomorphism of pin(n) onto O(n). The inverse image of SO(n) under ρ is denoted by Spin(n), the n-dimensional spinor group. Then Spin(n) is a connected (for $n > 1$) subgroup of A_n^+ and ρ restricted to Spin(n) has kernel ± 1. Since $\pi_1(SO(n)) = \mathbf{Z}_2$ for $n > 2$ it follows that Spin(n) is the universal covering group of SO(n) for $n > 2$.

If $n = 2k$ is even then the complexified algebra $A_n \otimes \mathbf{C}$ is simple and hence has to within isomorphism a unique irreducible left module S_n which we can choose to be some minimal left ideal in $A_n \otimes \mathbf{C}$. Elements of S_n are called n-dimensional spinors. Considered as an $A_n^+ \otimes \mathbf{C}$ module S_n splits uniquely as a direct sum $S_n = S_n^+ \oplus S_n^-$ of two inequivalent irreducible modules, elements of which are called positive and negative spinors respectively. Moreover $A_n^- S_n^\pm \subseteq S_n^\pm$ so in particular since $\mathbf{R}^n \subseteq A_n^-$ we have $vS_n^+ \subseteq S_n^-$ and $vS_n^- \subseteq S_n^+$ for $v \in \mathbf{R}^n$. Since $\mathrm{Spin}(n) \subseteq A_n^+$ we can regard S_n and S_n^- as Spin(n) modules, and as such they are still irreducible. If $u \in \mathrm{Spin}(n)$ and $v \in \mathbf{R}^n$ then we note that for $s \in S_n$ $u(vs) = (uvu^{-1})(us) = (\rho(u)v)(us)$.

Now let M be an oriented Riemannian manifold. By a spin structure for M is meant a reduction of the structural group of $T(M)$ from $SO(n)$ to Spin(n). Expressed in the language of coordinate bundles this means the following. We are given an indexed set $\{(\mathcal{O}_\lambda; X_1^\lambda, \ldots, X_n^\lambda)\}$ where $\{\mathcal{O}_\lambda\}$ is an open covering of M and $X_1^\lambda, \ldots, X_n^\lambda$ are C^∞ vector fields defined on $\mathcal{O}_\lambda$ forming an oriented orthonormal basis at each point. And we are also given maps $g_{\lambda\mu}: \mathcal{O}_\lambda \cap \mathcal{O}_\lambda \to \mathrm{Spin}(n)$ satisfying $g_{\lambda\lambda}(x) = 1$ for $x \in \mathcal{O}_\lambda$ and $g_{\lambda\mu}(x)g_{\mu\nu}(x) = g_{\mu\nu}(x)$ for $x \in \mathcal{O}_\lambda \cap \mathcal{O}_\mu \cap \mathcal{O}_\nu$, and finally $\rho(g_{\lambda\mu}(x))_{ij} = (X_j^\lambda(x), X_i^\mu(x))$ or equivalently $X_j^\lambda = \Sigma_i\, \rho(g_{\lambda\mu})_{ij} X_i^\mu$. Given such a spin structure we let $S_n(M)$ be the associated bundle with fiber S_n. Thus the total space of $S_n(M)$ is the disjoint union of the sets $\mathcal{O}_\lambda \times S_n \times \{\lambda\}$ with the identifications $(x, g_{\lambda\mu}(x)s, \lambda) \sim (x, s, \mu)$, $x \in \mathcal{O}_\lambda \cap \mathcal{O}_\mu$. Since S_n^+ and S_n^- are Spin(n) invariant submodules of S_n it follows that $S_n(M)$ splits canonically as the Whitney sum of sub-bundles $S_n^+(M)$ and $S_n^-(M)$. There is a bilinear pairing $T(M) \times S_n(M) \to S_n(M)$ given as follows: if $w \in T(M)_x$, $x \in O_\mu$ and $w = \Sigma_i\, v_i X_i^\mu(x)$ then

$$w(x, s, \mu) = (x, vs, \mu) .$$

The identity $u(vs) = (\rho(u)v)(us)$, noted above, with $u = g_{\lambda\mu}(x)$ shows this definition is consistent with the identifications. Since $\mathbf{R}^n S_n^+ \subseteq S_n^-$ it follows that we have induced bilinear maps $T(M) \times S_n^+(M) \to S_n^-(M)$ and $T(M) \times S_n^-(M) \to S_n^+(M)$. We now define $\sigma \in \mathrm{Smbl}_1^d(S_n(M), S_n(M))$ by $\sigma(v, x)s = vs$ (where we have identified $T^*(M)$ with $T(M)$ via the Riemannian structure). By the above we can consider σ by restriction to be in $\mathrm{Smbl}_1^d(S_n^+(M), S_n^-(M))$ or $\mathrm{Smbl}_1^d(S_n^-(M), S_n^+(M))$. If $v \neq 0$ then $\sigma(v, x)$ maps $S_n(M)_x$ isomorphically onto itself, in fact $\sigma(v, x)^2 s = -\|v\|^2$ by the defining relations of the Clifford algebras. Thus σ is an elliptic symbol and of course remains such when we consider it as an element of $\mathrm{Smbl}_1^d(S_n^+(M), S_n^-(M))$ or $\mathrm{Smbl}_1^d(S_n^-(M), S_n^+(M))$.

We now define $D \in \mathrm{Diff}_1(S_n(M), S_n(M))$ having this symbol and called the Dirac operator. Let ∇ be a covariant derivative for $S_n(M)$ obtained by taking the direct sum of covariant derivatives for $S_n^+(M)$ and $S_n^-(M)$ (there is a canonical choice for ∇ associated with the Riemannian connection for $T(M)$ but there seems to be no particular advantage involved in taking it). Let $v_1, \ldots, v_n$ and $w_1, \ldots, w_n$ be two orthonormal bases for $T(M)_x$ so that $w_j = \Sigma\, u_{ij} v_i$ where u_{ij} is an orthogonal matrix. Then if $f \in C^\infty(S_n(M))$ $\Sigma_j\, w_j \nabla_{w_j} f = \Sigma_j\, w_j\, \Sigma_i\, u_{ij} \nabla_{v_i} f = \Sigma_k\, v_i \nabla_{v_i} f$ we can define $Df(x) = \Sigma\, v_i \nabla_{v_i} f$ for any orthonormal bases $v_1, \ldots, v_n$ for $T(M)_x$. That $D \in \mathrm{Diff}_1(S_n(M), S_n(M))$ follows from the fact that in $\mathcal{O}_\lambda$ we have $D|\,\mathcal{O}_\lambda = \Sigma_i\, X_i^\lambda \nabla_{X_i^\lambda}$. Since ∇ restricts to covariant derivatives for $S_n^+(M)$ and $S_n^-(M)$ it follows that D maps $C^\infty(S_n^+)$ into $C^\infty(S_n^-)$ and vice versa.

Now let $v \in T(M)_x$ and let $g \in C^\infty(M, \mathbf{R})$ with $g(x) = 0$ and $dg_x = v$, i.e., $dg_x(w) = (w, v)$. Then if $s \in S_n(M)_x$ and $f \in C^\infty(S_n(M))$ with $f(x) = s$ then $\nabla_{w_i}(gf)(x) = dg(w_i)s = (w_i, v)s$ hence

$$\sigma_1(d)(v, x)s = D(gf)(x) = \sum_i (w_i, v) w_i s = vs = \sigma(v, x)s$$

which proves that D has the required symbol and hence is elliptic.

CHAPTER V

ANALYTICAL INDICES OF SOME CONCRETE OPERATORS

Robert M. Solovay

In §1, we review Hodge theory. This will be used in §§2, 3 to check the index theorem in a number of concrete cases. This check will play a role in the proof of the index theorem in general. In §4, we show that the topological index of a differential operator on an odd dimensional manifold is zero.

§1. Review of Hodge theory

1.0. Let X be a closed oriented Riemannian manifold of dimension n. We shall recall the principal properties of the operators d, δ, and $*$ introduced in Chapter IV, §6.

1.1. Let $\xi^k = \Lambda^k(T^*(X)) \otimes \mathbf{C}$ be the bundle of complex valued differential k-forms over X. The Riemannian structure on X gives rise to a Hermitian structure on ξ^k, and to a strictly positive smooth measure on X. In this way, we get a Hermitian inner product on $C^\infty(\xi^k)$ which we denote by (α, β): $(\alpha, \beta \in C^\infty(\xi^k))$.

1.2. There is a bundle isomorphism

$$*: \Lambda^k(T^*(X)) \otimes \mathbf{C} \cong \Lambda^{n-k}(T^*(X)) \otimes \mathbf{C} \quad . \tag{1}$$

If V is the fibre of $T^*(X)$ at the point x of X, then, on the fibre of ξ^k over x, (1) is the complexification of the isomorphism

$$*: \Lambda^k(V) \cong \Lambda^{n-k}(V)$$

discussed in III, §6. The induced isomorphism of $C^\infty(\xi^p)$ with $C^\infty(\xi^{n-p})$ will also be denoted by $*$ Recall the following properties of the map $*$:

(2) $$(\alpha, \beta) = \int \alpha \wedge * \bar{\beta}\ , \quad (\alpha, \beta \in C^\infty(\xi^k));$$

(3) $$*^2 = (-1)^{k(n-k)} \quad \text{on} \quad C^\infty(\xi^k)\ .$$

If n is even, (3) simplifies to

(4) $$*^2 = (-1)^k \quad \text{on} \quad C^\infty(\xi^k), \qquad (\dim X \ \text{even}).$$

(5) $$*\bar{\beta} = \overline{*\beta}, \quad \text{i.e.,} \quad * \ \text{is real.}$$

1.3. Let $d\colon C^\infty(\xi^k) \to C^\infty(\xi^{k+1})$ be the exterior derivative. Then $d^2 = 0$. DeRham's theorem asserts that the cohomology groups of X with complex coefficients, $H^*(X; \mathbf{C})$, are canonically isomorphic to the cohomology groups of the complex

$$C^\infty(\xi^0) \xrightarrow{d} C^\infty(\xi^1) \xrightarrow{d} \dots C^\infty(\xi^k) \xrightarrow{d} C^\infty(\xi^{k+1}) \longrightarrow \dots \quad .$$

Let $\delta\colon C^\infty(\xi^{k+1}) \to C^\infty(\xi^k)$ be the adjoint of d. When X is even-dimensional, we have

(6) $$\delta = -*d* \qquad (\dim X \ \text{even}).$$

Let $\xi = \Lambda(T^*(X)) \otimes \mathbf{C} = \Sigma_{i=0}^n \xi^i$. Then $d + \delta\colon C^\infty(\xi) \to C^\infty(\xi)$ is formally self-adjoint, (i.e., equal to its formal adjoint). We put $\Delta = (d+\delta)^2 = d\delta + \delta d$. Then Δ is homogeneous of degree zero: $\Delta\colon C^\infty(\xi^k) \to C^\infty(\xi^k)$. We have, for $\varphi \in C^\infty(\xi)$,

(7) $$\Delta\varphi = 0 \longleftrightarrow (d+\delta)\varphi = 0 \longleftrightarrow d\varphi = \delta\varphi = 0$$

If $\Delta\varphi = 0$, we say that φ is harmonic. In that case, by (7), we hav4 $d\varphi = 0$; by DeRhams's theorem, φ represents a cohomology class $\alpha \in H^*(X, C)$. One says that φ is the harmonic representative of α.

1.4. The fundamental result of Hodge theory is a converse of this: *every* $\alpha \in H^*(X, \mathbf{C})$ *has a harmonic representative,* φ, *and this representative is unique*. Thus there is a canonical isomorphism: $H^*(X, \mathbf{C}) \cong \ker \Delta$.

§2. The Euler Characteristic

2.0. Let X be a closed oriented C^∞-manifold; let ζ, η be Hermitian vector bundles over X and let

$$D: \quad C^{\infty}(\zeta) \to C^{\infty}(\eta)$$

be an elliptic differential operator. Let D^*: $C^{\infty}(\eta) \to C^{\infty}(\zeta)$ be the formal adjoint of D. It will be shown in XI that ker D and ker D^* are finite dimensional vector spaces and (cf. XI Theorem 8) that

$$i_a(D) = \dim \ker D - \dim \ker D^* \tag{8}$$

We shall use (8) as our working definition of the analytical index of D.

2.1. Let X, ξ^k be as in §1. Let $b_i = \dim H^i(X, \mathbf{C})$; b_i is the ith Betti number of X. The alternating sum,

$$\sum_{i=0}^{n} (-1)^i b_i,$$

is called the Euler characteristic of X.

Let $\xi^e = \oplus_p \xi^{2p}$, $\xi^o = \oplus_p \xi^{2p+1}$. Since d is of degree +1, and δ is of degree -1, $d + \delta$ maps $C^{\infty}(\xi^e)$ into $C^{\infty}(\xi^o)$. In IV, §6 e), it is shown that $d + \delta$ is elliptic.

PROPOSITION 1. The analytical index of the operator

$$d + \delta: \quad C^{\infty}(\xi^e) \to C^{\infty}(\xi^o) \tag{9}$$

is the Euler characteristic of X.

PROOF. Let D denote the operator of (9). We shall show that

$$\dim \ker D = \sum_{i=0}^{[n/2]} b_{2i} \; ; \quad \dim \ker D^* = \sum_{i=0}^{[n/2]} b_{2i+1} \; . \tag{10}$$

In view of (8), this will prove the proposition. Now by (7), the kernel of $d + \delta$: $C^{\infty}(\xi^e) \to C^{\infty}(\xi^o)$ is exactly the even-dimensional harmonic forms. By Hodge theory, (cf. §1.4), such forms are in 1-1 correspondence with even-dimensional elements of $H^*(X, \mathbf{C})$. This establishes the first half of (10).

To get the second half of (10), note that since $d + \delta$: $C^{\infty}(\xi) \to C^{\infty}(\xi)$ is formally self-adjoint, the formal adjoint of (9), D^*, is just

$$d + \delta: \quad C^{\infty}(\xi^o) \to C^{\infty}(\xi^e)$$

The second half of (10) now follows from the argument of the preceding paragraph.

COROLLARY 2. Let X be an *even-dimensional* closed oriented manifold. Then the index theorem is valid for the operator $d + \delta: C^\infty(\xi^e) \to C^\infty(\xi^o)$.

PROOF. The symbol of $d+\delta$ is, according to IV, §6 b) and c), given by the formula

$$\sigma_1(d+\delta)(v, x) = v \wedge - i_v \quad .$$

Thus it "arises from a universal construction" in the sense of III, §4. Since X is even-dimensional, Proposition 5.1 of III applies: the topological index of (9) is

(11) $$\chi(X)[X] \quad ;$$

where $\chi(X)$ is the Euler class of the tangent bundle of X.

q.e.d.

We shall apply this corollary only when $X = S^{2k}$. In that case, it is easy to check directly that the Euler class of S^{2k} is twice the generator of $H^{2k}(S^{2k}, \mathbf{Z})$, (by using the definition of $\chi(X)$ as an obstruction class).

§3. The Hirzebruch signature theorem

In this paragraph we shall interpret the signature of a manifold X as the analytical index of an elliptic operator D_X. Using the results of III, we shall compute the topological index of D_X: it turns out to be the L-genus of X. This allows us to verify that $i_t(D_X) = i_a(D_X)$ when X is a complex projective space, $CP(2m)$. More generally, this shows that the previous equality is equivalent to Hirzebruch's signature theorem for X.

3.1. We recall the definition of the signature of a manifold. First, let V be a finite dimensional real vector space. Let $\langle\ ,\ \rangle$ be a non-degenerate symmetric bilinear form on V. Then a standard result of linear algebra states that there is a basis, $\{e_1, \ldots, e_m, f_1, \ldots, f_n\}$, of V such that

(12) $$\langle e_i, e_j \rangle = \delta_{ij}, \quad \langle f_i, f_j \rangle = -\delta_{ij}, \quad \langle e_i, f_j \rangle = 0.$$

(Here $\delta_{ij} = 1$ if $i = j$, and 0 otherwise.) The integer $m-n$ is called the signature of the bilinear $< , >$; it does not depend on the choice of basis satisfying (12).

Now let X be a closed oriented manifold of dimension $4k$. Then there is a natural symmetric bilinear form on $H^{2k}(X, \mathbf{R})$:

$$< \alpha, \beta > = \alpha \cup \beta[X] \qquad (\alpha, \beta \in H^{2k}(X, \mathbf{R})) \quad . \tag{13}$$

The Poincaré duality theorem states, in part, that (13) is non-degenerate. The signature of X is the signature of the bilinear form (13). If X is a closed oriented manifold whose dimensions is not divisible by 4, then the signature of X is defined to be zero.

3.2. Now let X be a closed oriented Riemannian manifold of dimension 2ℓ. As in §1, we put

$$\xi^k = \Lambda^k(T^*(X) \otimes \mathbf{C}) \ , \quad \xi = \oplus_k \xi^k \quad .$$

We define a bundle map $\alpha\colon \xi \to \xi$ as follows: on ξ^k,

$$\alpha = i^{k(k-1)+\ell} * \quad . \tag{14}$$

It follows from (4) that $\alpha^2 = 1$.

LEMMA 3. There are subbundles ξ^+ and ξ^- of ξ, such that

$$\xi = \xi^+ \oplus \xi^- \quad ; \tag{15}$$

moreover, if v lies in the total space of ξ^+ (resp. ξ^-) then $\alpha(v) = v$ (resp. $\alpha(v) = -v$).

PROOF. Let P be the principal $SO(2\ell)$-bundle of X. Let $V = \mathbf{R}^{2\ell}$. Then ξ is (canonically isomorphic to) $P \times_{SO(2\ell)} \Lambda(V^*) \otimes \mathbf{C}$. As discussed in III, §6.1, there is a map,

$$\alpha\colon \Lambda^*(V^*) \otimes \mathbf{C} \to \Lambda^*(V^*) \otimes \mathbf{C} \quad , \tag{16}$$

which is equivariant under $SO(2\ell)$ and satisfies $\alpha^2 = 1$. This map gives rise to the map $\alpha\colon \xi \to \xi$ in an obvious way. Let $\Lambda_{\pm}$ be the eigenspace of (16) corresponding to the eigenvalue ± 1. Then

$$\Lambda^*(V) \otimes \mathbf{C} = \Lambda_+ \oplus \Lambda_-$$

(since $\alpha^2 = 1$). If we now put

$$\xi^{\pm} = P \times_{SO(2\ell)} \Lambda_{\pm}$$

the assertions of the lemma are clearly satisfied.

3.3. We shall also denote by α the map of $C^\infty(\xi)$ into itself induced by $\alpha\colon\ \xi \to \xi$. Then $C^\infty(\xi^{\pm}) = \{\varphi \in C^\infty(\xi)\colon\ \alpha\varphi = \pm\varphi\}$.

From (4), (6) and (14), we get the important formula

$$\alpha(d+\delta) = -(d+\delta)\alpha \tag{17}$$

by a straightforward computation. The formula (17) implies that $d+\delta$ defines maps

$$\begin{aligned} d+\delta\colon\ & C^\infty(\xi^+) \to C^\infty(\xi^-) \\ d+\delta\colon\ & C^\infty(\xi^-) \to C^\infty(\xi^+) \end{aligned} \tag{18}$$

(For example, if $\varphi \in C^\infty(\xi^+)$, $\alpha((d+\delta)\varphi)) = -(d+\delta)\alpha\varphi = -(d+\delta)\varphi$; i.e., $(d+\delta)\varphi \in C^\infty(\xi^-)$).

Since $d+\delta\colon\ C^\infty(\xi) \to C^\infty(\xi)$ is formally self-adjoint, the two maps of (18) are formally adjoint to one another. We shall denote the first map of (18) by D_X.

LEMMA 4. The operator D_X is elliptic.

PROOF. According to IV, §6 c), the operator $d+\delta\colon\ \xi \to \xi$ is elliptic. I.e., the map $\sigma_1(d+\delta)\colon\ \pi^*\xi \to \pi^*\xi$ is an isomorphism. By the functorial properties of the symbol map, (cf. IV, §3, Theorem 4), there is a commutative diagram:

$$\begin{array}{ccc} \pi^*\xi^+ & \xrightarrow{\ \sigma_1(D_X)\ } & \pi^*\xi^- \\ \cap & & \cap \\ \pi^*\xi & \xrightarrow{\ \sigma_1(d+\delta)\ } & \pi^*\xi \end{array}$$

Since $\sigma_1(d+\delta)$ is an isomorphism, $\sigma_1(D_X)$ must be 1-1. Similarly, $\sigma_1(D_X^*)$ is 1-1.

It remains to show that $\sigma_1(D_X)$ is onto, or equivalently that the map $\sigma_1(D_X)^*$ is 1-1. But by the theorem of IV, §4, $\sigma_1(D_X)^*$ is just $-\sigma_1(D_X^*)$, which we know to be 1-1. The proof is complete.

3.4. THEOREM 5. The analytical index of D_X is the signature of X.

PROOF. 1. By (17), $\alpha(d+\delta) = -(d+\delta)\alpha$. Since $\Delta = (d+\delta)^2$, it follows that $\alpha\Delta = \Delta\alpha$. Thus α maps $\ker \Delta$ into itself. Identifying $\ker \Delta$ (= harmonic forms) with $H^*(X, \mathbf{C})$, we get a map $\alpha: H^*(X, \mathbf{C}) \to H^*(X, \mathbf{C})$ such that $\alpha^2 = 1$. Thus we get a direct sum decomposition,

$$H^*(X, \mathbf{C}) = H_+^*(X, \mathbf{C}) \oplus H_-^*(X, \mathbf{C}) \quad ,$$

where $H_\pm^*(X, \mathbf{C}) = \{x \in H^*(X, \mathbf{C}) \mid \alpha x = \pm x\}$.

2. Using Hodge theory as in the proof of Proposition 1, one sees that

$$\text{(19)} \qquad i_a(D_X) = \dim H_+^*(X, \mathbf{C}) - \dim H_-^*(X, \mathbf{C})$$

3. Let $0 \le k < \ell$. Since $\alpha: H^p(X, \mathbf{C}) \to H^{2\ell-p}(X, \mathbf{C})$, α leaves the sub-spaces

$$H^k(X, \mathbf{C}) \oplus H^{2\ell-k}(X, \mathbf{C}) \quad \text{and} \quad H^\ell(X, \mathbf{C}) \quad \text{invariant.}$$

Let $H_\pm^k = \{x \in H^k \oplus H^{2\ell-k} \mid \alpha x = \pm x\}$, for $0 \le k < \ell$. $H_\pm^\ell$ is defined similarly. Then

$$\text{(20)} \qquad H_\pm^* = \bigoplus_{0 \le p \le \ell} H_\pm^p \quad .$$

4. We wish to show that

$$\text{(21)} \qquad i_a(D_X) = \dim H_+^\ell - \dim H_-^\ell \quad .$$

In view of (19) and (20), it suffices to show that

$$\dim H_+^k = \dim H_-^k = \dim H^k(X, \mathbf{C}) \qquad (0 \le k < \ell) \quad .$$

But this is clear since

$$H_\pm^k = \{x \pm \alpha x \mid x \in H^k(X, \mathbf{C})\} \quad .$$

5. We must now consider 2 cases.

Case 1: $\ell = 2k + 1$. In this case, the signature of X is zero by definition. Moreover, (14) implies that $\alpha: H^\ell \to H^\ell$ is $i*$. Since $*$ is real,

$$\alpha(\bar{\varphi}) = -\overline{\alpha(\varphi)} \qquad (\varphi \in H^\ell(X, \mathbf{C})) \quad .$$

It follows that the map $\varphi \to \bar{\varphi}$ sets up an isomorphism of $H_+^\ell(X, \mathbf{C})$ with

$H^\ell_-(X, \mathbf{C})$. Thus $\dim H^\ell_+ - \dim H^\ell_- = 0$.

Case 2: $\ell = 2k$. Thus $\dim X = 4k$. In this case, the signature of X is the signature of the bilinear form $< , >$ on $H^\ell(X, \mathbf{R})$:

$$< \alpha, \beta > = \int \alpha \wedge \beta \quad .$$

(We are identifying a cohomology class α with its harmonic representative.) Moreover, (14) implies that $\alpha = *$ on $H^\ell(X, \mathbf{C})$. Since $*$ is real,

$$H^\ell_\pm(X, \mathbf{C}) = H^\ell_\pm(X, \mathbf{R}) \otimes \mathbf{C}$$

where $H^\ell_\pm(X, \mathbf{R}) = H^\ell_\pm(X, \mathbf{C}) \cap H^\ell(X, \mathbf{R})$. Thus, (21) becomes

(22) $$i_a(D_X) = \dim H^\ell_+(X, \mathbf{R}) - \dim H^\ell_-(X, \mathbf{R}) \quad .$$

6. We shall now compute the signature of X (cf. §3. 1). The form $(\ , \ )$

$$(\beta, \gamma) = \int \beta \wedge * \bar{\gamma} \qquad (\beta, \gamma \in H^\ell(X, \mathbf{R}))$$

is clearly real-valued and positive definite on $H^\ell(X, \mathbf{R})$. Moreover, we have

(23) $$< \beta, \gamma > = (\beta, * \gamma) \qquad (\beta, \gamma \in H^\ell(X, \mathbf{R}))$$

(Apply (2) to the right hand side and observe that $*^2 = 1$ on $H^{2k}(X, \mathbf{R})$ by (4).)

Thus if we select orthonormal bases $\{e_1, \ldots, e_m\}$ for H^ℓ_+ and $\{f_1, \ldots, f_n\}$ for H^ℓ_-, then

(24) $$< e_i, e_j > = \delta_{ij}, \qquad < f_i, f_j > = -\delta_{ij} \quad .$$

In fact, by definition, $*\varphi = \pm \varphi$ if $\varphi \in H^\ell_\pm(X, R)$; $(* = \alpha!)$; so $< e_i, e_j > = (e_i, *e_j) = (e_i, e_j)$ and $<f_i, f_j > = (f_i, *f_j) = -(f_i, f_j)$. moreover $< e_i, f_j > = 0$ since $< e_i, f_j > = (e_i, *f_j) = -(e_i, f_j) = -(f_j, e_i) = -(f_j, *e_i) = - < f_j, e_i > = - < e_i, f_j >$. It is now clear that the signature of X is equal to $m-n = \dim H^\ell_+(X, \mathbf{R}) - \dim H^\ell_-(X, \mathbf{R})$. In view of (22), the proof is complete.

The following proposition follows immediately from Proposition 6.2 of III.

PROPOSITION 6. The topological index of D_X is

$$\prod_i y_i/\tanh y_i[X]$$

where the Pontrjagin classes of X are viewed as the elementary symmetric functions in the y_i^2.

The equality

(25) $$\prod_i y_i/\tanh y_i[X] = \text{signature } (X)$$

is the Hirzebruch signature theorem. Hirzebruch's proof involves a direct check that both sides of (25) equal 1 if $X = CP(2m)$ (complex projective space of 2m complex dimensions) (cf. [1, p. 14, 73]). Granting this check, Theorem 5 and Proposition 6 imply the following propositions:

PROPOSITION 7. The index theorem is valid for the operator $D_{CP(2m)}$.

In fact, we see more generally that the equality $i_a(D_X) = i_t(D_X)$ is equivalent to (25); consequently, the former is a consequence of Hirzebruch's signature theorem [1]. However, the general index theorem will be proved without making use of this equality, except in the special case of Prop. 7, and therefore the signature theorem will appear as a corollary.

§4. Odd-dimensional manifolds

PROPOSITION 8. Let X be an odd-dimensional manifold (closed, oriented and C^∞ as always). Let ζ and η be complex vector bundles over X, and

$$D: \ C^\infty(\zeta) \to C^\infty(\eta)$$

be an elliptic differential operator of order k. Then the topological index of D, $i_t(D)$, is zero.

Remark. In XI a broader class of elliptic operators than the elliptic differential operators is described. Proposition 8 is not valid, in general, for D in this larger class.

PROOF. We give X a Riemannian structure. Let $B(X)$ (resp. $S(X)$) denote the unit ball subbundle (resp. the unit sphere subbundle of X).

Since D is elliptic, the symbol of D gives rise to an isomorphism

$$\sigma_k(D): \quad \pi^*\zeta \cong \pi^*\eta \qquad (\pi: \ S(X) \to X) \quad .$$

Thus if $v \in S(X)$, and $x = \pi(v)$, $\sigma_k(D)(v): \ \zeta_x \cong \eta_x$. Because D is a differential operator, $\sigma_k(D)$ is, for fixed $x \in X$, the restriction of a homogeneous polynomial map of degree k, $\{T^*(X)_x \to L(\zeta_x, \eta_x)\}$. If follows that

(26) $$\sigma_k(D)(-v) = (-1)^k \sigma_k(D)(v)$$

The difference construction of II yields an element

$$\gamma(D) = d(\pi^*\zeta, \ \pi^*\eta, \ \sigma_k(D))$$

of $K(B(X), S(X))$. Let $T: \ (B(X), S(X)) \to (B(X), S(X))$ be defined by $T(v) = -v \ \ (v \in B(X))$.

4.1. LEMMA. $T^!(\gamma(D)) = \gamma(D)$.

PROOF. BY II, §3.2, Lemma 1(i),

$$T^!(\gamma(D)) = d(T^*\pi^*\zeta, \ T^*\pi^*\eta, \ T^*\sigma_k(D)) \quad .$$

Since $\pi \circ T = \pi$, $T^*\pi^* = \pi^*$; (26) then shows that $T^*\sigma_k(D) = (-1)^k \sigma_k(D)$. Thus

$$T^!\gamma(D) = d(\pi^*\zeta, \ \pi^*\eta, \ (-1)^k \sigma_k(D)) \quad .$$

The homotopy $\{t \to e^{i\pi kt} \sigma_k(D) \mid 0 \leq t \leq 1\}$ between $\sigma_k(D)$ and $(-1)^k \sigma_k(D)$ shows (cf. II, §3.2, Lemma 1(ii)),

$$T^!\gamma(D) = d(\pi^*\zeta, \ \pi^*\eta, \ \sigma_k(D)) = \gamma(D) \quad .$$

q.e.d.

Applying ch to Lemma 4.1, we get

(27) $$T^*\mathrm{ch}(\gamma(D)) = \mathrm{ch}(\gamma(D)) \quad .$$

4.2. LEMMA. Let $\alpha \in H^*(B(X), S(X); Q)$. Then

(28) $$T^*\alpha = -\alpha \quad .$$

PROOF. Let $n = \dim X$. Let $U \in H^n(B(X), S(X); \mathbf{Q})$ be the Thom class (cf. III, §1.0). On each fibre, T induces a map of degree $(-1)^n = -1$ (n is odd). Thus $T^*U = -U$. As recalled in III, §1.0, we have

$$\alpha = U \cup \pi^* \beta, \quad \text{for some} \quad \beta \in H^*(X, \mathbf{Q}).$$

Here π is the projection map of B(X) onto X. Since $T^*\pi^* = \pi^*$, $T^*\alpha = T^*U \cup T^*\pi^*\beta = -(U \cup \pi^*\beta)$. I.e., $T^*\alpha = -\alpha$.

Comparing (27) with (28), we see that $ch(\gamma(D)) = 0$. It follows immediately that $i_t(D)$ is zero. In fact,

$$i_t(D) = ch(D)\, \mathscr{T}(X)[X]; \; ch(D) = \pm\, \varphi_*^{-1}\, ch(\gamma(D)) \quad ,$$

where $\varphi_*: H^*(X) \cong H^*(B(X), S(X); \mathbf{Q})$ is the Thom isomorphism and $\mathscr{T}(X)$ is the Todd class of X.

Remark. Proposition 8 generalizes the well-known result that the Euler characteristic of an odd-dimensional manifold is zero.

REFERENCES

[1] F. Hirzebruch, Neue Topologische Methoden in der Algebraischen Geometrie, Springer-Verlag, 1956.

[2] John Milnor, "Lectures on Characteristic Classes," mimeographed notes, Princeton,. 1957.

CHAPTER VI

REVIEW OF FUNCTIONAL ANALYSIS

Richard S. Palais

In this section we collect the theorems of functional analysis we shall need in later sections.

If X is a Banach space we shall denote by X^* the ***anti***-dual of X, i.e., the space of continuous ***conjugate*** linear functionals on X with the norm $\|\ell\| = \text{Sup}\{|\ell(x)| \mid \|x\| = 1\}$. The map $\ell \to \bar{\ell}$ (where the bar denotes complex conjugation) is an anti-linear isometry of X^* with the more customary dual space of X, so that the standard facts about the dual of X imply corresponding facts about X^*.

If S is a subspace of X then $\{\ell \in X^* \big| \ell|S = 0\}$ is a closed subspace of X^* which we denote by $S^\perp$. If S is a closed subspace of X then we recall that X/S is a Banach space in the norm $\|x + S\| = \text{Inf}\{\|x + s\| \mid s \in S\}$ and the natural projection $\pi_S\colon X \to X/S$ is both continuous and open. From the openness of π_S it follows that if $T\colon X \to Y$ is a continuous linear map which is zero on S then the induced map $\tilde{T}\colon X/S \to Y$ such that $\tilde{T} \circ \pi_S = T$ is continuous.

If X and Y are Banach spaces we denote by $L(X, Y)$ the Banach space of continuous linear maps of X into Y with the norm $\|T\|_\infty = \text{Sup}\{\|Tx\| \mid \|x\| = 1\}$. If $S \in L(Y, Z)$ then $\|ST\|_\infty \leq \|S\|_\infty\|T\|_\infty$. If $T \in L(X', Y)$ then $T^* \in L(Y^*, X^*)$ is defined by $(T^*\ell)(x) = \ell(Tx)$, and we recall that as an easy consequence of the Hahn-Banach Theorem (Theorem 2 below) $\|T^*\| = \|T\|$.

THEOREM 1. (Open Mapping Theorem) If X and Y are Banach spaces and $T \in L(X, Y)$ is surjective then T is an open map (hence if T is bijective it is an isomorphism of X with Y as topological vector spaces).

PROOF. Loomis, *Abstract Harmonic Analysis*,

COROLLARY. If $0 \to X \to Y \to Z \to 0$ is an exact sequence of Banach spaces and continuous linear maps then the natural bijection of $Y/\mathrm{im}(X)$ onto Z is an isomorphism of topological vector spaces.

THEOREM 2. (Hahn-Banach) If S is a closed subspace of a Banach space X and $\ell \in S^*$ then there exists $f \in X^*$ with $\|f\| = \|\ell\|$ and $f|S = \ell$. In particular if $X^* \to S^*$ is the restriction map then $0 \to S^\perp \to X^* \to S^* \to 0$ is exact, so that S^* and $X^*/S^\perp$ are canonically isomorphic as topological vector spaces.

PROOF. Loomis, *loc.cit.*, p. 19.

THEOREM 3. An n-dimensional real (complex) normed vector space V is isomorphic (as a topological vector space) to $\mathbf{R}^n(\mathbf{C}^n)$, hence in particular is a Banach space.

PROOF. We give the proof in the real case, the complex case being essentially identical. Let $v_1, \ldots, v_n$ be a basis for V and define $T\colon \mathbf{R}^n \to V$ by $Tx = \Sigma_{i=1}^n x_i v_i$ so that T is a linear isomorphism. The continuity of T is obvious so it will suffice to prove that T^{-1} is continuous. Norm $\mathbf{R}^n$ by $\|x\| = \max|x_i|$. Then $S = \{x \in \mathbf{R}^n | \|x\| = 1\}$ is compact and does not contain zero, hence

$$A = \mathrm{Inf}\{\|Tx\| \,|x \in S\} > 0$$

and clearly $\|T^{-1}\| = A^{-1} < \infty$.

q.e.d.

COROLLARY. A finite dimensional subspace of a real or complex normed space V is a closed in V.

THEOREM 4. A locally compact real (or complex) topological vector space X is finite dimensional.

PROOF. (A. Gleason) Let U be a compact neighborhood of zero and choose $a_1, \ldots, a_m \in U$ so that $U \subseteq \bigcup_{i=1}^m (a_i + \frac{1}{2}U)$ and hence

$\frac{1}{2^n} U \subseteq \cup_{i=1}^{m} \left(\frac{1}{2^n} a_i + \frac{1}{2^{n+1}} U \right)$. Given $u \in U$ choose inductively a sequence $\{j(n)\}$ in $\{1, 2, \ldots, m\}$ so that $u - a_{j(0)} - \frac{1}{2} a_{j(1)} - \cdots - \frac{1}{2^n} a_{j(n)}$ is in $\frac{1}{2^{n+1}} U$. Since U is compact $\frac{1}{2^n} U$ is eventually inside any neighborhood of zero, hence $u = \sum_{n=0}^{\infty} \frac{1}{2^n} a_{j(n)}$. Defining $C_i = \sum_{j(n)=i} \frac{1}{2^n}$, $u = C_1 a_1 + \cdots + C_m a_m$. Since U generates X, $a_1, \ldots, a_m$ spans X.

q.e.d.

THEOREM 5. If S and T are complementary closed subspaces of a Banach space X then $(s, t) \to s + t$ is an isomorphism of $S \oplus T$ with X (as topological vector spaces).

PROOF. Recall $\|(s, t)\| = \|s\| + \|t\|$, so $(s, t) \to s + t$ is clearly continuous. Since it is bijective, Theorem 1 completes the proof.

THEOREM 6. If S is a closed subspace of a Banach space X and if either $\dim S$ or $\operatorname{codim} S = \dim X/S$ is finite then S admits a closed complementary subspace T and hence $X \cong S \oplus T$.

PROOF. If $\dim S < \infty$ let $x_1, \ldots, x_n$ be a basis for S and (Theorem 2) choose $\ell_1, \ldots, \ell_n$ in X^* such that $\ell_1|S, \ldots, \ell_n|S$ is the dual basis for S^*. Then $P(x) = \sum_{i=1}^{n} \ell_i(x)x_i$ is a continuous linear projection of X onto S hence $\ker P = P^{-1}(0)$ is a closed linear complement of S. If $\operatorname{codim} S < \infty$ then an algebraic linear complement for S is finite dimensional hence by the corollary of Theorem 3 is automatically closed in X.

q.e.d.

THEOREM 7. Let X be a Banach space and let $S \subseteq T$ be subspaces of X. If S is closed in X and has finite codimensions in X then the same is true of T.

PROOF. Since X/S is finite dimensional so is the subspace T/S, hence T/S is closed in X/S (Corollary of Theorem 3), so $T = \pi_S^{-1}(T/S)$ is closed in X.

q.e.d.

THEOREM 9. If X and Y are Banach spaces and if $T \in L(X, Y)$ has a continuous inverse $S \in L(Y, X)$ then so does any $T' \in L(X, Y)$ such that $\|T-T'\|_\infty < \|S\|_\infty^{-1}$.

PROOF. Let $A = T - T'$ so $\|SA\|_\infty < \|S\|_\infty \|T - T'\|_\infty < 1$. Since $\|(SA)^n\|_\infty < \|SA\|_\infty^n$ the series $I_X + SA + (SA)^2 + \ldots + (SA)^n + \ldots$ converges absolutely in $L(X, X)$ to an element B and clearly $B(I_X - SA) = (I_X - SA)B = I_X$, so $I_X - SA$ is a topological linear automorphism of X. Then $T(I_X - SA) = T - A = T'$ is a topological linear isomorphism of X onto Y and in fact $(T')^{-1} = (I_X - SA)^{-1}T^{-1} = BS \in L(Y, X)$.

q.e.d.

THEOREM 10. If X and Y are Banach spaces and $T \in L(X, Y)$ then $\ker(T^*) = T(X)^\perp$. If in addition $T(X)$ is closed in Y then $T^*(Y^*) = (\ker T)^\perp$, so in particular $T^*(Y^*)$ is closed in X^*.

PROOF. $T^*(\ell) = 0 \iff T^*(\ell)(x) = 0$ all $x \in X \iff \ell(Tx) = 0$ all $x \in X \iff \ell \in T(X)^\perp$. If $T(X)$ is closed in Y then by the corollary of Theorem 1, $\tilde{T}: X/\ker T \to T(X)$ is an isomorphism and we let $S: T(X) \to X/\ker T$ be its inverse. If $\ell \in (\ker T)^\perp$ then ℓ induces an element $\tilde{\ell} \in (X/\ker T)^*$ satisfying $\tilde{\ell} \circ \pi = \ell$ where $\pi: X \to X/\ker T$ is canonical. By Theorem 2, $S^*\tilde{\ell} \in T(X)^*$ can be extended to $\ell' \in Y^*$. Now $\tilde{T} \circ \pi = T$ so $\pi = S\tilde{T}\pi = ST$, hence $T^*\ell'(x) = \ell'(Tx) = S^*\tilde{\ell}(Tx) = \tilde{\ell}(STx) = \tilde{\ell}(\pi x) = \ell(x)$, i.e., $T^*\ell' = \ell$ which proves $(\ker T)^\perp \subseteq T^*(Y^*)$. On the other hand if $\ell \in T^*Y^*$, say $\ell = T^*\ell'$, then if $x \in \ker T$, $\ell(x) = \ell'(Tx) = 0$, so $\ell \in (\ker T)^\perp$ and $T^*(Y^*) \subseteq (\ker T)^\perp$.

q.e.d.

COROLLARY 1. If S is a closed subspace of a Banach space X then π_S^* is an isomorphism of $(X/S)^*$ with $S^\perp$ (as topological vector spaces).

PROOF. Since π_S is surjective, π_S^* is injective and its image is $(\ker \pi_S)^\perp = S^\perp$. Since $S^\perp$ is closed in X^*, hence a Banach space, Theorem 1 completes the proof.

COROLLARY 2. If $T \in L(X, Y)$ has closed range

1) $\ker(T^*) \cong (Y/T(X))^* = (\operatorname{coker} T)^*$;

2) $(\ker T)^* \cong X^*/T^*(Y^*) = \operatorname{coker}(T^*)$.

PROOF. By the theorem $\ker(T^*) = T(X)^{\perp}$ which by Corollary 1 is isomorphic to $(Y/T(X))^*$. By Theorem 2, $(\ker T)^*$ is isomorphic to $X^*/(\ker T)^{\perp}$, and by the theorem $(\ker T)^{\perp} = T^*(Y^*)$.

q.e.d.

DEFINITION. If X and Y are Banach spaces we denote by $K(X, Y)$ the set of completely continuous (or compact) linear maps of X into Y, i.e., linear maps $T\colon X \to Y$ such that T maps the unit ball B_X of X (and hence any bounded subset of X) into a relatively compact subset of Y.

If $T \in L(X, Y)$ is in the closure of $K(X, Y)$ and $\varepsilon > 0$, choose $S \in K(X, Y)$ such that $\|T - S\|_\infty < \varepsilon/3$ and choose $x_1, \ldots, x_n \in B_X$ such that $Sx_1, \ldots, Sx_n$ are $\varepsilon/3$ dense in SB_X. Then by the triangle inequality $Tx_1, \ldots, Tx_n$ is ε-dense in TB_X, hence TB_X has compact closure in Y so $T \in K(X, Y)$, i.e., $K(X, Y)$ is closed in $L(X, Y)$. Since a scalar multiple of a relatively compact subset of Y or the sum of two relatively compact subsets of Y is again relatively compact, $K(X, Y)$ is a subspace of $L(X, Y)$. If $T \in K(X, Y)$ and $S \in L(Y, Z)$ then since TB_X is relatively compact and S continuous STB_X is relatively compact in Z. If $R \in L(Z, X)$ then RB_Z is bounded in X so TRB_Z is relatively compact in Y. Recapitulating

THEOREM 11. If X and Y are Banach spaces then $K(X, Y)$ is a closed subspace of $L(X, Y)$. If Z is a third Banach space then $L(Y, Z)K(X, Y) \subseteq K(X, Z)$ and $K(X, Y)L(Z, X) \subseteq K(Z, Y)$.

COROLLARY. $K(X, X)$ is a closed ideal in $L(X, X)$.

LEMMA. If K is a compact subset of a Banach space X then any sequence in the unit ball of X^* has a subsequence which converges uniformly on K.

PROOF. By Ascoli's theorem it will suffice to prove that the elements of B_{X^*} are uniformly bounded and equicontinuous on K. But clearly $\ell \in B_{X^*}$ implies $|\ell(x)| \leq \mathrm{Sup}\{\|k\| \mid k \in K\}$, and since $|\ell(x) - \ell(y)| \leq \|x - y\|$ the elements of B_{X^*} are even equicontinuous on X.

q.e.d.

THEOREM 12. If X and Y are Banach spaces and $T \in K(X, Y)$ then $T^* \in K(Y^*, X^*)$.

PROOF. By the lemma if $\{\ell_n\}$ is a sequence in B_{Y^*} then $\{\ell_n\}$ has a subsequence which converges uniformly on $\overline{TB_X}$ hence on TB_X, or equivalently (since $T^*\ell_n(x) = \ell_n(Tx))T^*\ell_n$ has a subsequence which converges uniformly on B_X, i.e., which converges in X^*. But this means precisely that $T^*B_{Y^*}$ is relatively compact in X^*.

q.e.d.

THEOREM 13. (F. Riesz) Let X be a Banach space, $k \in K(X, X)$ and $T = I - k$. Then

1) $\ker T = T^{-1}(0)$ is finite dimensional;
2) $T(X)$ is closed in X and $\mathrm{coker}\, T = X/T(X)$ is finite dimensional.

PROOF. Let $V = \ker T$. Then if B_V is the unit ball of V $k(b) = b - T(b) = b$ for $b \in B_V$, i.e., $k(B_V) = B_V$. But, $k(B_V)$ is relatively compact, hence V is locally compact and by Theorem 4 $\dim V < \infty$, proving 1).

By Theorem 6, $X = V \oplus W$ where W is a closed subspace of X, and clearly T maps W one-to-one onto T(X). It will suffice to prove that $(T|W)^{-1}$ is bounded, i.e., that for some $\varepsilon > 0$ $\|Tw\| > \varepsilon \|w\|$ for $w \in W$, for then T(X) being isomorphic to X will be a Banach space, hence closed in X. If not there is a sequence $\{w_n\}$ in W such that $\|w_n\| = 1$ and $Tw_n \to 0$, and we can assume $k(w_n) \to x \in X$. Then, since $w_n - k(w_n) = Tw_n \to 0$, $w_n \to x$ so $x \in W$. But $Tx = \lim Tw_n = 0$ so $x \in \ker T = V$ hence $x \in V \cap W$ so $x = 0$. But $\|x\| = \lim \|w_n\| = 1$, a contradiction. Finally by Corollary 2 of Theorem 10, $(X/T(X))^* = \ker T^* = \ker (I-k^*)$. By Theorem 12, $k^* \in K(X^*, X^*)$ so by 1) $\dim (X/T(X))^* < \infty$, hence $\dim (X/T(X)) < \infty$.

q.e.d.

THEOREM 14. If X and Y are Banach spaces, $T \in L(X, Y)$ and $\dim T(X) < \infty$ then $T \in K(X, Y)$.

PROOF. $T(B_X)$ is a bounded subset of $T(X)$ and hence by Theorem 3 it is relatively compact.

THEOREM 15. If H is a Hilbert space then the group G of invertible elements of $L(H, H)$ is a connected subset of $L(H, H)$.

PROOF. If $T \in G$ then T^*T is a strictly positive operator on H and hence has a strictly positive square root A. Let $U = TA^{-1}$ so $U^*U = A^{-1}T^*TA^{-1} = A^{-1}A^2A^{-1} = I$ and U is unitary. Since the set of strictly positive operators is clearly a convex subset of G there is an arc in G from A to I, hence an arc from $T = UA$ to U. Let $1/i \log$ be the inverse of the function $t \to e^{it}$ of $[0, 2\pi)$ onto $\{z \in \mathbf{C} | \; |z| = 1\}$. Then $1/i \log$ is a bounded Borel function on the spectrum of U so by the functional calculus for normal operators $B = 1/i \log U$ is a bounded self adjoint operator (equivalently if $U = \int_0^{2\pi} e^{it} dP_t$ is the spectral decomposition of U then $B = \int_0^{2\pi} t\,dP_t$). Then $U = e^{iB}$ and $t \to e^{itB}$ $0 \leq t \leq 1$ is an arc in G from I to U.

q.e.d.

LEMMA. If H is a Hilbert space and $T \in K(H, H)$ is self adjoint then either $\|T\|_\infty$ or $-\|T\|_\infty$ is an eigenvalue of T.

PROOF. Choose a sequence $\{x_n\}$ on the unit sphere of H with $\|Tx_n\| \to \|T\|_\infty$. Since T is completely continuous we can assume $Tx_n \to y$ and then $\|y\| = \|T\|_\infty$. By Schwartz's inequality

$$\|Ty\| = \lim \|T^2x_n\| \geq \lim (T^2x_n, x_n) = \lim \|Tx_n\|^2 = \|T\|_\infty^2$$

and

$$\|T^2y\| \cdot \|y\| \geq (T^2y, y) = \|Ty\|^2 \geq \|T\|_\infty^4 = \|T\|_\infty^2 \|y\|^2 \geq \|T^2y\| \cdot \|y\|$$

so $(T^2y, y) = \|T^2y\| \cdot \|y\|$ and therefore T^2y is a scalar multiple of y, the scalar being $(T^2y, y)/(y, y) = \|T\|_\infty^4/\|T\|_\infty^2 = \|T\|_\infty^2$. We can assume $T \neq 0$ and we define $x = y + \|T\|_\infty^{-1}Ty$. If $x = 0$ then y is an eigenvector of T

belonging to the eigenvalue $-\|T\|_\infty$ while if $x \neq 0$ then x is an eigenvector of T belonging to the eigenvalue $\|T\|_\infty$.

q.e.d.

THEOREM 16. Let H be a Hilbert space and let $T \in K(H, H)$ be self adjoint. Given $\lambda \in \mathbf{R}$ let $E_\lambda(T) = \{x \in H | Tx = \lambda x\}$. Then the $E_\lambda(T)$ are mutually orthogonal subspaces of H, and H is their Hilbert space direct sum. Moreover, the $E_\lambda(T)$, with the possible exception of $E_0(T)$, are finite dimensional. In fact, if $\varepsilon > 0$ then $\oplus_{|\lambda| \geq \varepsilon} E_\lambda(T)$ is finite dimensional, hence the set $\{\lambda \in \mathbf{R} | E_\lambda(T) \neq 0\}$ of eigenvalues of T has no limit point except possibly zero.

PROOF. If $x \in E_\lambda(T)$ and $y \in E_\mu(T)$ then $\lambda(x, y) = (Tx, y) = (x, Ty) = \mu(x, y)$ and so $(x, y) = 0$ if $\lambda \neq \mu$. If $V = \oplus_{|\lambda| \geq \varepsilon} E_\lambda(T)$ then $TV \subseteq V$ and $S = T|V \in K(V, V)$. Since $\|Sv\| \geq \varepsilon\|v\|$ S has a continuous inverse so the unit ball of V has compact closure and, by Theorem 4, V is finite dimensional. Let $Y = \oplus_{\lambda \neq 0} E_\lambda(T)$, $y \in Y$ and $x \in Y^\perp$. Then $(Tx, y) = (x, Ty) = 0$, since $TY \subseteq Y$; hence $TY^\perp \subseteq Y^\perp$, so $T|Y^\perp \in K(Y^\perp, Y^\perp)$ and is self adjoint. Since clearly $T|Y^\perp$ has no non zero eigenvalue, by the lemma $\|T|Y^\perp\|_\infty = 0$, hence $T|Y^\perp = 0$ so $Y^\perp = E_0(T)$.

q.e.d.

COROLLARY. There is a sequence $\{f_n\}$ of eigenvectors of T which form an orthonormal basis for H. Moreover, if $\{\lambda_n\}$ is the sequence of corresponding eigenvalues (i.e., $Tf_n = \lambda_n f_n$) then $\lambda_n \to 0$.

If X is a compact space we denote by $C(X)$ the algebra of continuous complex valued functions on X with the norm $\|f\|_\infty = \operatorname{Sup}\{|f(x)| \,|\, x \in X\}$.

If H is a Hilbert space and $A \in L(H, H)$, then the spectrum of $A = sp(A) = \{\lambda \in \mathbf{C} \mid A - \lambda$ is not a unit of the algebra $L(H, H)\}$.

THEOREM 17. If H is a Hilbert space and $A \in L(H, H)$ is self adjoint, then $sp(A)$ is a non empty compact subset of $\mathbf{R}$ and there is a norm preserving algebra isomorphism $f \to f(A)$ of $C(sp(A))$ onto the subalgebra of $L(H, H)$ generated by A and I, which is uniquely characterized by the properties that the identity map of $sp(A)$ corresponds to A and that $\bar{f}(A) = f(A)^*$.

PROOF. A short, elegant, and completely elementary proof, due to John von Neumann, can be found in Appendix I of S. Lang's "Introduction to Differentiable Manifolds" (Interscience, 1962). Lang in fact only constructs the isomorphism $f \to f(A)$ for real valued f and the resulting $f(A)$ are self adjoint. If $f = g + ih$ where g, h are real valued then the definition $f(A) = g(A) + ih(A)$ is clearly the unique extension satisfying $\bar{f}(A) = f(A)^*$.

If $A \in K(H, H)$ then by the corollary of Theorem 16, H has a complete orthonormal basis $\{f_n\}$ of eigenvectors of A, $Af_n = \lambda_n f_n$, and $\lambda_n \to 0$. Clearly, $sp(A) = \{0\} \cup \{\lambda_n\}$ and the map $f \to f(A)$ is given by $f(A)(f_n) = f(\lambda_n)f_n$ and it follows that

COROLLARY. If A is completely continuous then $f(A)$ is completely continuous if and only if $f(0) = 0$.

Recall that if $\mathcal{O} \subseteq \mathbf{C}$ is open and $f\colon \mathcal{O} \to X$ is a map of $\mathcal{O}$ into a complex Banach space X, then f is called holomorphic in $\mathcal{O}$ if for each $z_0 \in \mathcal{O}$ $\lim_{z \to z_0} (z-z_0)^{-1}(f(z) - f(z_0))$ exists in X.

LEMMA. Given $z \in \mathbf{C}$ with $\operatorname{Re} z > 0$ define $p_z\colon [0, \infty) \to \mathbf{C}$ by $p_z(t) = e^{z \log t}$ if $t > 0$ and $p_z(0) = 0$. Then p_z is continuous and satisfies $p_{z+z'} = p_z p_{z'}$ and $p_{\bar{z}} = \bar{p}_z$. Moreover, if $L > 0$ then $z \to p_z|[0, L]$ is a holomorphic map of $\operatorname{Re} z > 0$ into $C([0, L])$.

PROOF. If $z = x + iy$, $x > 0$ then $|p_z(t)| = |e^{x \log t}|$ and since $x \log t \to -\infty$ as $t \to 0$ it follows that p_z is continuous. The equalities $p_{z+z'} = p_z p_{z'}$ and $p_{\bar{z}} = \bar{p}_z$ are obvious. If for $\operatorname{Re} z > 0$ we define $q_z(t) = (\log t)p_z(t)$ for $t > 0$ and $q_z(0) = 0$ then (recalling that by L'Hospital's rule $\lim_{t\to 0+} (\log t)^n e^{x \log t} = 0$ for $x > 0$ and n a positive integer) just as above it follows that q_z is continuous. moreover, an elementary calculation gives $h^{-1}(p_{z+h}(t) - p_z(t)) - q_z(t) = (e^{z \log t}) h^{-1}(e^{h \log t} - 1 - h \log t)$ which by Taylor's theorem equals $h(\frac{1}{2}(\log t)^2 e^{(z+\rho h) \log t})$ $0 < \rho < 1$, so putting $x = \text{Re } z > 0$, $|h^{-1}(p_{z+h}(t) - p_z(t)) - q_z(t)| \leq |h|(\frac{1}{2}(\log t)^2 e^{(x-|h|)\log t})$ and since $(\log t)^2 e^{(x+|h|) \log t}$ is bounded on $[0, L]$ it follows that as $h \to 0$, $h^{-1}(p_{z+h}(t) - p_z(t))$ tends uniformly on $[0, L]$ to $q_z(t)$.

q.e.d.

THEOREM 18. Let H be a Hilbert space and let $A \in L(H, H)$ be a positive operator. Then $sp(A) \subseteq [0, \infty)$ and hence if $z \in \mathbf{C}$ with $\text{Re } z > 0$ and p_z is as in the lemma then $A^z = p_z(A)$ is a well-defined element of $L(H, H)$. Moreover,

1) $z \to A^z$ is a holomorphic map of $\text{Re } z > 0$ into $L(H, H)$ and is a semi-group homomorphism (i.e., $A^{z+z'} = A^z A^{z'}$);
2) $A^{\bar{z}} = (A^z)^*$;
3) If A is completely continuous and $\text{Re } z > 0$ then A^z is completely continuous;
4) If A is strictly positive then so is A^x for $x \geq 0$. Moreover $z \to A^z$ extends to a (not necessarily continuous) function of $\text{Re } z \geq 0$ into $L(H, H)$ whose value at a point iy of the imaginary axis is a unitary operator A^{iy}, in such a way that $z \to A^z v$ is a continuous map of $\text{Re } z \geq 0$ into H for each $v \in H$. Moreover, $A^{x+iy} = A^{iy}A^x$ if $x > 0$.

PROOF. If $f \in C(sp(A))$ then $f(A)$ is positive if and only if f is non-negative on $sp(A)$ (cf. S. Lang, *loc. cit.* page 118) hence in particular if we take f = identity map of $sp(A)$ we get A is positive if and only if $sp(A) \subseteq [0, \infty)$. The existence of A^z as well as properties 1), 2), and 3) now follow from the lemma together with Theorem 17 and its corollary. If $t > 0$ then $A^t = (A^{t/2})^*(A^{t/2})$ is clearly positive. If $0 < t < 1$ then $A = A^t A^{1-t}$ hence if A is strictly positive so is A^t. More generally if $t > 0$ then $A^t = (A^{t/n})^n$ where $n = [t] + 1$ and so again A^t is strictly positive if A is.

Now if A is strictly positive, and hence injective, then $V = \text{im}(A)$ is dense in H (since $\bar{V} = (\ker A^*)^{\perp} = (\ker A)^{\perp}$). Define $A^{iy}: V \to H$ by $A^{iy}v = A^{1+iy}\omega$ if $v = A\omega$. Then $\text{im}(A^{iy}) = \text{im}(A^{1+iy})$, hence the closure of $\text{im}(A^{iy})$ is the orthogonal complement of $\ker(A^{1+iy})^*$ $= \ker(A^{1-iy})$. But A, and hence A^2, is injective and $A^2 = (A^{1+iy})(A^{1-iy})$ so $\ker(A^{1-iy}) = 0$ and $\text{im}(A^{iy})$ is dense in H. Now if $v = A\omega \in V$

$$\begin{aligned}\|A^{iy}v\|^2 &= (A^{1+iy}\omega, A^{1+iy}\omega)\\ &= (A^{1-iy} A^{1+iy}\omega, \omega) = (A^2\omega, \omega)\\ &= (A\omega, A\omega) = \|v\|^2 \qquad ,\end{aligned}$$

hence A^{iy} extends uniquely to a unitary map of H onto itself. Note that

$$\lim_{z \to iy} A^z v = \lim_{z \to iy} A^{1+z}\omega = A^{1+iy}\omega = A^{iy}v$$

if $v = A\omega \in V$. In general given $u \in H$ and $\varepsilon > 0$ we can find $v \in V$ with $\|u-v\| < \varepsilon$. Then

$$\begin{aligned}\|A^z u - A^{iy}u\| &\leq \|A^z(u-v)\| + \|A^z v - A^{iy}v\| + A^{iy}(v-u)\|\\ &\leq (1 + \|A^z\|_\infty)\varepsilon + \|A^z v - A^{iy}v\| \qquad .\end{aligned}$$

Since $\|A^z\|_\infty \leq \text{Sup}\{|e^{z \log t}| \mid 0 \leq t \leq \|A\|_\infty\}$, which clearly converges to unity as $z \to iy$, $\overline{\lim}_{z \to iy}\|A^z u - A^{iy}u\| \leq 2\varepsilon$ and since ε is arbitrary $A^z u \to A^{iy}u$ as $z \to iy$. Thus $z \to A^z u$ is a continuous map of $\text{Re}\, z \geq 0$ into H. Since $A^{z+z'}u = A^z A^{z'}u$ holds for $\text{Re}\, z$, $\text{Re}\, z' > 0$ it continues to hold, by continuity, for $\text{Re}\, z$, $\text{Re}\, z' \geq 0$, and in particular $A^{x+iy} = A^{iy}A^x$.

q.e.d.

CHAPTER VII

FREDHOLM OPERATORS

Richard S. Palais

DEFINITION. If X and Y are Banach spaces, an element T of $L(X, Y)$ is called a Fredholm operator from X to Y (or simply an F-operator) if

1) $\ker T = T^{-1}(0)$ is finite dimensional;
2) $\operatorname{coker} T = Y/T(X)$ is finite dimensional.

We denote the set of F-operators from X to Y by $F(X, Y)$ and define the index function $\operatorname{ind}\colon F(X, Y) \to \mathbf{Z}$ by $\operatorname{ind}(T) = \dim \ker T - \dim \operatorname{coker} T$.

THEOREM 1. If X and Y are Banach spaces and $T \in F(X, Y)$ then $T(X)$ is closed in Y, $T^* \in F(Y^*, X^*)$ and $\operatorname{ind}(T^*) = -\operatorname{ind}(T)$.

PROOF. The first conclusion holds even for $T \in L(X, Y)$ such that $\dim \operatorname{coker} T < \infty$. Indeed since T factors as Sh where $h\colon X \to X/\ker T$ is canonical and S is injective, and since $T(X) = S(X/\ker T)$, we can suppose T is injective. Let W be a linear complement to $T(X)$ in Y. Then $\dim W < \infty$ so [VI, Theorem 3] W is a Banach space. Define $\bar{T}\colon X \oplus W \to Y$ by $\bar{T}(x, w) = Tx + w$. Then $\bar{T}$ is clearly continuous, linear, and bijective hence [VI, Theorem 1] an isomorphism of X and Y as topological vector spaces. Since X is closed in $X \oplus W$, $T(X) = \bar{T}(X)$ is closed in Y.

Then by [VI, Corollary 2 of Theorem 10] $\dim \ker(T^*) = \dim \operatorname{coker} T$ and $\dim \ker T = \dim \operatorname{coker}(T^*)$ and the other conclusions follow.

q.e.d.

THEOREM 2. Let X and Y be Banach spaces, $T \in L(X, Y)$ and suppose there exists $S, S' \in L(Y, X)$ such that $ST - I_X \in K(X, X)$ and $TS' - I_Y \in K(Y, Y)$. Then $T \in F(X, Y)$. Conversely, if $T \in F(X, Y)$ there is in fact an $S \in L(Y, X)$ such that $ST - I_X$ and $TS - I_Y$ have finite rank (hence by [VI, Theorem 14] belong to $K(X, X)$ and $K(Y, Y)$ respectively).

PROOF. $T^{-1}(0) \subseteq (ST)^{-1}(0)$ which is finite dimensional by [VI, Theorem 13]. By the same theorem $(TS')(Y)$ is a closed subspace of Y of finite codimension and since $T(X) \supseteq (TS')(Y)$ it follows from [VI, Theorem 7] that $T(X)$ is closed and of finite codimension in Y. Hence, $T \in F(X, Y)$.

Conversely given $T \in F(X, Y)$ it follows from [VI, Theorem 6] that $X = T^{-1}(0) \oplus V$ and $Y = T(X) \oplus W$ where V and W are closed subspaces of X and Y respectively. Then T maps V bijectively onto $T(X)$ and by [VI, Theorem 1] $(T|V)^{-1}$ is continuous. Extend $(T|V)^{-1}$ to a continuous map $S\colon Y \to X$ by letting S be zero on W. Then $ST - I_X$ = -projection of X onto $T^{-1}(0)$ along V, $TS - I_Y$ = -projection of Y onto W along $T(X)$.

q.e.d.

COROLLARY 1. If $T \in F(X, Y)$ and $k \in K(X, Y)$ then $T + k \in F(X, Y)$.

PROOF. Choose $S \in L(Y, X)$ so that $ST - I_X$ and $TS - I_Y$ are compact operators. Then $S(T + k) - I_X = (ST - I_X) + Sk$ and $(T + k)S - I_Y = (TS - I_Y) + kS'$ are also compact operators by [VI, Theorem 11].

q.e.d.

COROLLARY 2. $F(X, Y)$ is open in $L(X, Y)$.

PROOF. Given $T \in F(X, Y)$ choose $S \in L(Y, X)$ such that $ST - I_X = k \in K(X, X)$ and $TS - I_Y = k' \in K(Y, Y)$. We will show that if $T' \in L(X, Y)$ and $\|T-T'\|_\infty < \|S\|_\infty^{-1}$ then $T' \in F(X, Y)$. Let $A = T - T'$, so $\|SA\|_\infty < 1$ and by [VI, Theorem 9] $I_X - SA$ is an invertible element of the algebra $L(X, X)$. Let B be its inverse and let $S' = BS$. Then

$ST' = ST - SA = k + (I_X - SA)$ so $S'T' = BST' = Bk + I_X$ or $S'T' - I_X = Bk$. Similarly $I_Y - AS$ has an inverse C in $L(Y, Y)$ and if $S'' = SC$ then $T'S = TS - AS = k' + (I_Y - AS)$ so $T'S'' = T'SC = k'C + I_Y$ or $T'S'' - I_Y = k'C$. Now $Bk \in K(X, X)$ and $k'C \in K(Y, Y)$ by [VI, Theorem 11] and the corollary follows.

q.e.d.

COROLLARY 3. If X, Y and Z are Banach spaces, $T_1 \in F(X, Y)$ and $T_2 \in F(Y, Z)$ then $T = T_2T_1 \in F(X, Z)$.

PROOF. Choose $S_1 \in L(Y, X)$ and $S_2 \in L(Z, Y)$ so that $k_1 = S_1T_1 - I_X$, $k_2 = T_1S_1 - I_Y$, $k_3 = S_2T_2 - I_Y$ and $k_4 = T_2S_2 - I_Z$ are compact operators and let $S = S_1S_2$. Then $ST = S_1(S_2T_2)T_1 = S_1(k_3 + I_Y)T_1 = S_1k_3T_1 + S_1T_1 = S_1k_3T_1 + k_1 + I_X$ or $ST - I_X = S_1k_3T_1 + k_1$. But $S_1k_3T_1 + k_1$ is a compact operator by [VI, Theorem 11]. Similarly $TS - I_X = T_2k_2S_2 + k_4$ which again is a compact operator.

q.e.d.

THEOREM 3. Let X, Y and Z be Banach spaces $T \in F(X, Y)$ and $S \in F(Y, Z)$. Then

$$\text{ind}(ST) = \text{ind}(S) + \text{ind}(T) \quad .$$

PROOF. We have just seen that $ST \in F(X, Z)$ so that $\text{ind}(ST)$ is well defined. From the exact sequence

$$0 \rightarrow T^{-1}(0) \rightarrow T^{-1}S^{-1}(0) \xrightarrow{T} S^{-1}(0) \cap T(X) \rightarrow 0$$

we get

$$\dim T^{-1}S^{-1}(0) = \dim T^{-1}(0) + \dim(S^{-1}(0) \cap T(X))$$

or

1) $\dim \ker (ST) = \dim \ker T + \dim \ker S - \dim(S^{-1}(0)/S^{-1}(0) \cap T(X))$.

From the exact sequence

$$0 \rightarrow SY/STX \rightarrow Z/STX \rightarrow Z/SY \rightarrow 0$$

we get

2) $\dim \text{coker}(ST) = \dim \text{coker } S + \dim(SY/STX)$. From the exact sequence

$$0 \rightarrow T(X) + S^{-1}(0) \rightarrow Y \xrightarrow{\tilde{S}} SY/STX \rightarrow 0$$

$$SY/STX \cong Y/T(X) + S^{-1}(0) \cong (Y/T(X))/(T(X) + S^{-1}(0)/T(X))$$

so

2') $\dim \operatorname{coker}(ST) = \dim \operatorname{coker} S + \dim \operatorname{coker} T - \dim(T(X) + S^{-1}(0)/TX)$

Hence by 1) and 2')

3) $\operatorname{ind}(ST) = \operatorname{ind}(S) + \operatorname{ind}(T) + \dim(TX + S^{-1}(0)/TX) - \dim(S^{-1}(0)/S^{-1}(0) \cap TX)$

But

$$0 \to S^{-1}(0) \cap TX \to S^{-1}(0) \to TX + S^{-1}(0)/TX \to 0$$

is exact so that

$$\dim(S^{-1}(0)/S^{-1}(0) \cap TX) = \dim(TX + S^{-1}(0)/TX)$$

which with 3) completes the proof.

q.e.d.

THEOREM 4. If X and Y are Banach spaces then $\operatorname{ind}: F(X, Y) \to \mathbf{Z}$ is constant on each component of $F(X, Y)$.

PROOF. Let $T \in F(X, Y)$. It will suffice to prove that $\operatorname{ind}(S) = \operatorname{ind}(T)$ if S is sufficiently close to T. By [VI, Theorem 6] we can choose closed subspaces V and W of X and Y respectively such that $X = \ker T \oplus V$ and $Y = T(X) \oplus W$. Given $S \in L(X, Y)$ consider the map $(v, w) \mapsto Sv + w$ of $V \oplus W$ into Y. If $S = T$ this map is a bijection, hence by [VI, Theorem 1] an isomorphism of $V \oplus W$ with Y. It follows by [VI, Theorem 9] that the same is true for S near T; hence for S near T, S maps V isomorphically onto a closed subspace $S(V)$ of Y, and $\operatorname{codim} S(V) = \dim W = \dim \operatorname{coker} T$. Since S is one-to-one on V we can write $X = \ker S \oplus Z \oplus V$ and then S is one-to-one on $Z \oplus V$, so SZ is disjoint from SV, and $\dim SZ = \dim Z$. Then $Y = W' \oplus SX = W' \oplus SZ \oplus SV$ so $\dim \operatorname{coker} S = \dim W' = \operatorname{codim} SV - \dim SZ = \dim \operatorname{coker} T - \dim Z$. On the other hand, $\dim \ker S + \dim Z = \operatorname{codim} V = \dim \ker T$ so

$$\operatorname{ind} S = \dim \ker S - \dim \operatorname{coker} S = \dim \ker T - \dim \operatorname{coker} T = \operatorname{ind} T.$$

q.e.d.

COROLLARY. If $T \in F(X, Y)$ and $k \in K(X, Y)$ then $\operatorname{ind}(T + k) = \operatorname{ind}(T)$.

PROOF. By Corollary 1 of Theorem 2, $T + K(X, Y) \subseteq F(X, Y)$ and since $K(X, Y)$ is connected (in fact a subspace of $L(X, Y)$) the corollary follows.

LEMMA. Let X and Y be Hilbert spaces, $T \in F(X, Y)$ with $\operatorname{ind}(T) \geq 0$ and let V be a subspace of X with $\dim V = \operatorname{ind}(T)$. Then there exists T_1 in the same component of $F(X, Y)$ as T such that $T_1 : X \to Y$ is surjective and $\ker(T_1) = V$.

PROOF. Since $\dim \ker(T) - \dim T(X)^{\perp} = \operatorname{ind}(T) \geq 0$ we can find a subspace W of $\ker T$ and an isomorphism P of W onto $T(X)^{\perp}$ and extend P to an element of $L(X, Y)$ by letting P be zero on $W^{\perp}$. Then tP has finite rank and hence is in $K(X, Y)$ for $0 \leq t \leq 1$, hence $S = T + P$ is in the same component of $L(X, Y)$ as T by Corollary 1 of Theorem 2. Clearly, S is surjective so $\operatorname{ind}(S) = \dim \ker(S)$ and since $\operatorname{ind}(S) = \operatorname{ind}(T) = \dim V$ by Theorem 4, there is a unitary map U of X onto itself such that $U(V) = \ker S$. Let $T_1 = SU$. Then $\ker T_1 = U^{-1}S^{-1}(0) = V$ so it will suffice to prove that T_1 is in the same component of $F(X, Y)$ as S. But by [VI, Theorem 15] there is a path $U(t)$ in the group G of automorphisms of X from U to I_X. Since $G \subseteq F(X, X)$ it follows from Corollary 3 of Theorem 2 that $SU(t)$ is a path in $F(X, Y)$ from T_1 to S.

q.e.d.

THEOREM 5. If X and Y are Hilbert spaces and if two elements S and T of $F(X, Y)$ have the same index, then they are in the same component of $F(X, Y)$.

PROOF. Since $T \to T^*$ maps $F(X, Y)$ topologically onto $F(Y^*, X^*)$ and $\operatorname{ind}(T^*) = -\operatorname{ind}(T)$ it suffices to consider the case where S and T have non negative index. By the lemma choose T_1 and S_1 in the same components of $F(X, Y)$ as T and S respectively, such that T_1 and S_1 are surjective and $\ker T_1 = \ker S_1 = V$. Then by [VI, Theorem 1] S_1 and T_1 map $V^{\perp}$ isomorphically onto Y, hence $A = T^{-1}S_1$ is in the group G of automorphism of $V^{\perp}$. By [VI, Theorem 15] there is a path A_t from A to the identity map of $V^{\perp}$ lying in $G \subseteq F(V^{\perp}, V^{\perp})$. The orthogonal projection P of X onto $V^{\perp}$ is clearly in $F(X, V^{\perp})$, so by Corollary 3 of Theorem 2, $T_1 A_t P$ is a path in $F(X, Y)$ from $T_1 AP$ to $T_1 P$. But clearly $T_1 AP = S_1$ and $T_1 P = T_1$, hence S_1 and T_1 are in the same component of $F(X, Y)$, hence so also are S and T.

q.e.d.

Let X be a Hilbert space of infinite dimension. By [VI, Corollary of Theorem 11] $K(X, X)$ is a closed ideal in $L(X, X)$, hence $A = L(X, X)/K(X, X)$ is a Banach algebra and we let $\pi\colon L(X, X) \to A$ be the canonical homomorphism. Let U be the group of units of A and U_0 the identity component of U. By Theorem 2, $F(X, X) = \pi^{-1}(U)$. By the corollary of Theorem 4 there is a well-defined map $\widetilde{\text{ind}}\colon U \to \mathbf{Z}$ such that $\widetilde{\text{ind}} \circ \pi = \text{ind}$, and by Theorem 3 $\widetilde{\text{ind}}$ is a group homomorphism. From Theorem 5 it follows that $\ker(\widetilde{\text{ind}}) = U_0$. Let V be a one-dimensional subspace of X and let T be an isomorphism of X onto $V^{\perp}$. Then $\text{ind}(T) = -1$ so $\widetilde{\text{ind}}(\pi(T)) = -1$ and since -1 generates $\mathbf{Z}$ the sequence

$$0 \to U_0 \to U \xrightarrow{\widetilde{\text{ind}}} \mathbf{Z} \to 0$$

is exact.

CHAPTER VIII

CHAINS OF HILBERTIAN SPACES

Richard S. Palais

§1. Chains

If X is a Banach space and we change the norm in X to an equivalent norm, then the norm on X^* is also changed only to within equivalence. In other words, if X is the underlying topological vector space of a Banach space then X^* is a well defined topological vector space. We shall call a topological vector space X *hilbertian* if it is the underlying topological vector space of a hilbert space, H. If $< , >$ is the inner product in H then $x \to < x, \ >$ is an isomorphism of H with X^* (this is precisely the reason we chose to define X^* as the anti-dual rather than the dual of X). If H is a hilbert space we shall always regard this canonical isomorphism as an identification, so that $H^* = H$. It follows that if X is an hilbertian space then there will be no confusion if we write $< \ell, x >$ for $\ell(x)$ when $x \in X$ and $\ell \in X^*$. Moreover, by the reflexivity of hilbertian spaces we can identify X^{**} with X and then $< x, \ell > = \overline{< \ell, x >}$ if $x \in X$ and $\ell \in X^*$.

DEFINITION. Let $\mathscr{I}$ denote either the integers or real numbers and $\mathscr{I}^+ = \{k \in \mathscr{I} \mid k \geq 0\}$. A chain of hilbertian spaces is a set $\{H^k\}$ of hilbertian spaces indexed by $\mathscr{I}^+$ such that:

1) If $k > \ell \geq 0$ then the underlying vector space of H^k is a linear subspace of the underlying vector space of H^ℓ and the inclusion map $H^k \to H^\ell$ is continuous;

2) $H^\infty = \cap_k H^k$ is dense in each H^k;

3) H^0 is a hilbert space (so $(H^0)^* = H^0$).

If whenever $k > \ell \geq 0$ the inclusion $H^k \to H^\ell$ is not only continuous but even completely continuous then we shall say that the chain $\{H^k\}$ satisfies the Rellich Condition or is a *Rellich Chain.*

If $\mathcal{I} = \mathbf{Z}$ we call $\{H^k\}$ a *discrete* chain of hilbertian spaces, while if $\mathcal{I} = \mathbf{R}$ we call $\{H^k\}$ a *continuous* chain of hilbertian spaces.

If $\{H^k\}$ is a chain of hilbertian spaces then we define $H^{-k} = (H^k)^*$ if $k > 0$. If $k < 0$ we then have $H^{-k} = (H^k)^*$ by reflexivity, while if $k = 0$ we still have $H^{-k} = (H^k)^*$ by 3) of the definition.

If $k > \ell \geq 0$ then by 2) H^k is dense in H^ℓ, hence if we define $j_{(\ell,k)}: H^k \to H^\ell$ to be the inclusion map then $j_{(-k,-\ell)} = j^*_{(\ell,k)}: H^{-\ell} \to H^{-k}$ is injective, and since $j_{(\ell,k)}$ is injective it follows that the image of $j_{(-k,-\ell)}$ is dense in H^{-k}. Moreover, if $m > k$ then $j_{(\ell,m)} = j_{(\ell,\ m)} = j_{(\ell,k)}j_{(k,m)}$ so $j_{(-m,-\ell)} = j_{(-m,-k)}j_{(-k,-\ell)}$ and it follows that we may consistently regard $H^{-\ell}$ as a dense linear subspace of H^{-k}, the inclusion map being $j_{(-k,-\ell)}$. If $k \geq 0 \geq -\ell$ then $j_{(-\ell,k)} = j_{(-\ell,\ 0)}j_{(0,k)}$ defines the inclusion of H^k onto a dense linear subspace of $H^{-\ell}$. Thus if we define $H^{-\infty} = \cup_k H^k$ we can regard each H^k as a vector subspace of $H^{-\infty}(\infty > k > -\infty)$ and if $\infty > k > \ell > -\infty$ we have a continuous inclusion $j_{(\ell,k)}: H^k \to H^\ell$ and $j_{(-k,-\ell)} = j^*_{(\ell,k)}$. Denote, temporarily the pairing of H^k and H^{-k} by $< , >_k$. If $f \in H^k$ and $g \in H^{-k}$ and $k > \ell$ then $f \in H^\ell$. If it should so happen that also $g \in H^{-\ell}$ then

$$< g, f >_\ell = < g, j_{(\ell,k)}f >_\ell = < j_{(-k,\ -\ell)}g, f >_k = < g, f >_k \quad .$$

It follows in particular that for each $k < , >_k$ extends the pairing $< , >_0$ of H^0 with itself and henceforth we will write $< g, f >_k = < g, f >_0$ for $f \in H^k$ and $g \in H^{-k}$. We note that $< g, f >_0$ is then well defined if $g \in H^{-\infty}$ and $f \in H^\infty$. We topologize H^∞ as the inverse limit $\varprojlim H^k$, i.e., with the least fine topology such that each inclusion $H^\infty \to H^k$ is continuous and we topologize $H^{-\infty}$ as the inductive limit $\varinjlim H^{-k}$, i.e., with the finest topology such that each inclusion $H^k \to H^{-\infty}$ is continuous. Then it follows that $< , >_0$ is a continuous conjugate bilinear pairing of $H^{-\infty}$ with H^∞ (in fact it is easily seen that H^∞ and $H^{-\infty}$ are locally convex topological vector spaces and that $H^{-\infty}$ is the antidual of H^{∞}, i.e., all continuous conjugate linear functionals on H^{∞}).

DEFINITION. If $\{H_1^k\}$ and $\{H_2^k\}$ are chains of hilbertian spaces a morphism $\{H_1^k \to \{H_2^k\}$ is a collection $\{T_k\}$ such that $T_k\colon H_1^k \to H_2^k$ is for each $k \in \mathscr{I}$ a continuous linear map, and $T_k = T_\ell | H_1^k$ if $k > \ell$. We denote the set of such morphisms by $\mathrm{Hom}(\{H_1^k\}, \{H_2^k\})$.

We note that the operation $\alpha\{T_k\} + \beta\{T_k'\} = \{\alpha T_k + \beta T_k'\}$ makes $\mathrm{Hom}(\{H_1^k\}, \{H_2^k\})$ a vector space. Also $\{S_k\} \in \mathrm{Hom}(\{H_2^k\}, \{H_3^k\})$ then $\{S_k T_k\} \in \mathrm{Hom}(\{H_1^k\}, \{H_3^k\})$, and clearly with this composition law the class of discrete (continuous) chains of hilbertian spaces forms an additive category (not abelian; there are kernels but not cokernels).

If $\{T_k\} \in \mathrm{Hom}(\{H_1^k\}, \{H_2^k\})$ and $f \in H_1^{\infty}$ then since $T_k = T_\ell | H_1^k$ if $k > \ell$ it follows that $T_k f = T_\ell f = T_\infty f$ is well defined. Also since $T_\infty f = T_k f \in H_2^k$ for all k, $T_\infty f \in H_2^{\infty}$, i.e., T_∞ is a linear map of H_1^{∞} into H_2^{∞}. Since H_1^{∞} is dense in each H_1^k, T_∞ determines each T_k, namely T_k is the unique continuous extension of T_∞ to a map of H_1^k into H_2^k.

DEFINITION. If $\{H_1^k\}$ and $\{H_2^k\}$ are two discrete (continuous) chains of hilbertian spaces and $r \in \mathbf{Z}(\mathbf{R})$ we define $OP_r(\{H_1^k\}, \{H_2^k\})$ to be the vector space of all linear maps $T\colon H_1^{\infty} \to H_2^{\infty}$ such that for each $k \in \mathbf{Z}(\mathbf{R})$ T extends to a continuous linear map $T_k\colon H_1^k \to H_2^{k-r}$.

Remark. We note that since H_1^{∞} is dense in H_1^k it follows that T_k is uniquely determined by T, and since $H_1^k \to H_1^\ell$ is continuous and $H_2^{k-r} \to H_2^{\ell-r}$ is continuous if $k > \ell$, it follows that $T_k = T_\ell | H_1^k$. In particular, if $r = 0$ it follows that $\{T_k\} \in \mathrm{Hom}(\{H_1^k\}, \{H_2^k\})$. Since the corresponding T_∞ is clearly T we have:

THEOREM 1. If $\{H_1^k\}$ and $\{H_2^k\}$ are two discrete (continuous) chains of hilbertian spaces then the map $\{T_k\} \to T_\infty$ defined above is a linear isomorphism of $\mathrm{Hom}(\{H_1^k\}, \{H_2^k\})$ with $OP_0(\{H_1^k\}, \{H_2^k\})$.

DEFINITION. If $\{H_1^k\}$ and $\{H_2^k\}$ are two discrete (continuous) chains of hilbertian spaces and $r \in \mathbf{Z}(\mathbf{R}) L(H_1^k, H_2^{k-r})$ is a Banach space (in the topology of uniform convergence on bounded sets) and we take the weakest topology on OP_r such that each of the maps $T \to T_k$ of $OP_r \to L(H_1^k, H_2^{k-r})$ is continuous (i.e. a net $\{T^\alpha\}$ in $OP_r(\{H_1^k\}, \{H_2^k\})$ converges to T if and only if for each k and each bounded set $B \subseteq H_1^k$ the net $\{T_k^\alpha\}$ in $L(H_1^k, H_2^{k-r})$ converges uniformly to T_k on B).

Remark. Note in particular that by Theorem 1 this topologizes $\mathrm{Hom}(\{H_1^k\}, \{H_2^k\})$.

THEOREM 2. Let $\{H_1^k\}$ and $\{H_2^k\}$ be chains of hilbertian spaces and let $r, s \in \mathscr{I}$ with $r > s$. Then $OP_s(\{H_1^k\}, \{H_2^k\})$ is a subspace of $OP_r(\{H_1^k\}, \{H_2^k\})$ and the inclusion map is continuous. Moreover, if either $\{H_1^k\}$ or $\{H_2^k\}$ satisfies the Rellich condition and $T \in OP_s(\{H_1^k\}, \{H_2^k\})$ then for each $k \in \mathscr{I}$ the unique continuous extension of T to a linear map of H_1^k into H_2^{k-r} is in fact completely continuous.

PROOF. Let $t = r - s$ and given $k \in \mathscr{I}$ let $j\colon H_1^k \to H_1^{k-t}$ and $j'\colon H_2^{k-s} \to H_2^{k-s-t} = H_2^{k-r}$ be the inclusion map, so j and j' are continuous and j is completely continuous if $\{H_1^k\}$ satisfies the Rellich condition while j' is completely continuous if $\{H_2^k\}$ satisfies the Rellich condition. If $T \in OP_s(\{H_1^k\}, \{H_2^k\})$ let $T_{k-t}\colon H_1^{k-t} \to H_2^{k-t-s} = H_2^{k-r}$ and $T_k\colon H_1^k \to H_2^{k-s}$ be continuous extensions of T. Then either $T_{k-t}j$ or $j'T_k$ give continuous extensions of T to linear maps $H_1^k \to H_2^{k-r}$ which proves $T \in OP_r$. Since the composition of a continuous and a completely continuous map is completely continuous [VI, Theorem 11] the final conclusion is immediate. Finally, suppose $T^{(\alpha)} \to T$ in OP_s and let $k \in \mathscr{I}$ and let B be a bounded set in H_1^k. Then $T_k^{(\alpha)} \to T_k$ uniformly on B, hence, $j'T_k^{(\alpha)} \to j'T_k$ uniformly on B which proves continuity.

q.e.d.

THEOREM 3. Let $\{H_1^k\}$, $\{H_2^k\}$, and $\{H_3^k\}$ be discrete (continuous) chains of hilbertian spaces and let $r, s \in \mathscr{I}$. Then the map $(S, T) \to ST$ is a continuous map of $OP_s(\{H_2^k\}, \{H_3^k\}) \times OP_r(\{H_1^k\}, \{H_2^k\})$ into $OP_{r+s}(\{H_1^k\}, \{H_3^k\})$.

PROOF. Obvious.

DEFINITION. Let $\{H_1^k\}$ and $\{H_2^k\}$ be chains of hilbertian spaces and $T\colon H_1^\infty \to H_2^\infty$ a linear map. A linear map $S\colon H_2^\infty \to H_1^\infty$ is called a transpose of T if $< Tf, g >_0 = < f, Sg >_0$ for all $f \in H_1^\infty$, $g \in H_2^\infty$.

Remark. If S' is a second transpose for T then $< f, (S-S')g >_0 = 0$ for all $f \in H_1^\infty$ and $g \in H_2^\infty$; hence since H_1^∞ is dense in H^0 it follows that $S = S'$, i.e., if a transpose for T exists it is unique and will be denoted by T^t. We note that $T^{tt} = T$.

THEOREM 4. Let $\{H_1^k\}$ and $\{H_2^k\}$ be two chains of hilbertian spaces and suppose $T\colon H_1^\infty \to H_2^\infty$ belongs to $OP_r(\{H_1^k\}, \{H_2^k\})$ for some $r \in \mathscr{I}$. Then T has a transpose and moreover $T^t \in OP_r(\{H_2^k\}, \{H_1^k\})$ and $(T^t)_k\colon H_2^k \to H_1^{k-r}$ is the adjoint map of $T_{-k+r}\colon H_1^{-k+r} \to H_2^{-k}$ for each $k \in \mathscr{I}$.

PROOF. By assumption for each $k \in \mathscr{I}$, T extends to a continuous linear map $T_{-k+r}\colon H_1^{-k+r} \to H_2^{-k}$. Define $(T^t)_k = (T_{-k+r})^*\colon H_2^k \to H_1^{k-r}$. If $k > \ell$ then $T_{-\ell+r} = T_{-k+r}|H_1^{-\ell+r}$ and it follows that $(T^t)_k = (T^t)_\ell|H_2^k$ so $(T^t)_k|H_2^\infty$ is a well-defined function T^t on H_2^∞ independent of k. If $f \in H_2^\infty$ then $T^tf = (T^t)_{k+r}f \in H_1^k$ for all k, hence $T^tf \in H_1^\infty$, hence T^t is a linear map of H_2^∞ into H_1^∞. If $f \in H_1^\infty$ and $g \in H_2^\infty$ then $< Tf, g >_0 = < T_0f, g >_0 = < f, (T_0)^*g >_0 = < f, (T^t)_{-r}g >_0 = < f, T^tg >_0$ so T^t is in fact the transpose of T. Since for each k T^t is by definition the restriction of the continuous linear map $(T_{-k+r})^*\colon H_2^k \to H_1^{k-r}$ the final conclusion is immediate.

THEOREM 5. Let $\{H_1^k\}$ and $\{H_2^k\}$ be discrete (continuous) chains of hilbertian spaces and suppose $T\colon H_1^\infty \to H_2^\infty$ is a linear map with a transpose T^t. Let $r, s \in \mathcal{I}$ and suppose that for each $k \in \mathcal{I}$ with $k \geq s$, T admits a continuous linear extension $T_k\colon H_1^k \to H_2^{k-r}$ and that for each $k \in \mathcal{I}$ with $k > r - s$, T^t admits a continuous linear extension $(T^t)_k\colon H_2^k \to H_1^{k-r}$. Then $T \in OP_r(\{H_1^k\}, \{H_2^k\})$ and if $k < s$, T_k is the adjoint of $(T^t)_{-k+r}$.

PROOF. If $k < s$ then $-k + r > r - s$ so T^t admits a continuous linear extension $(T^t)_{-k+r}\colon H_2^{-k+r} \to H_1^{-k}$, hence $T_k = (T^t)^*_{-k+r}$ is a continuous linear map of H_1^k into H_2^{k-r}. If $f \in H_1^\infty$ then for all $g \in H_2^\infty$ we have $< T_kf, g >_0 = < f, (T^t)_{-k+r}g >_0 = < f, T^tg >_0 = < Tf, g >_0$ and, since H_2^∞ is dense in H_2^0, $T_kf = Tf$ so T_k extends T.

q.e.d.

COROLLARY 1. If T extends to a continuous linear map $T_k\colon H_1^k \to H_2^k$ for all $k \geq 0$ and T^t extends to a continuous linear map $(T^t)_k\colon H_2^k \to H_1^k$ for all $k > 0$ then $T \in OP_0(\{H_1^k\}, \{H_2^k\})$, hence (Theorem 1) T defines a morphism of $\{H_1^k\}$ into $\{H_2^k\}$.

PROOF. Take $r = s = 0$.

COROLLARY 2. If $\{H_1^k\}$ and $\{H_2^k\}$ are discrete chains of hilbertian spaces and if T extends to a continuous linear map $T_k\colon H_1^k \to H_2^{k-1}$ for each integer $k \geq 1$ and if T^t extends to a continuous linear map $(T^t)_k\colon H_2^k \to H_1^{k-1}$ for each integer $k \geq 1$ then $T \in OP_1(\{H_1^k\}, \{H_2^k\})$.

PROOF. Take $r = s = 1$ and note that $k > r - s = 0$ is equivalent to $k \geq 1$ since $\mathcal{I} = \mathbf{Z}$.

q.e.d.

§2. Quadratic interpolation of pairs of hilbert spaces.

Given a continuous chain of hilbertian spaces, by restricting the indexing set to the integers we get a discrete chain, and this correspondence is clearly functorial from the category $C_{\mathbf{R}}$ of continuous chains to the category $C_{\mathbf{Z}}$ of discrete chains. In this and the next section we will construct a sectioning (i.e. right inverse) functor $C_{\mathbf{Z}} \rightsquigarrow C_{\mathbf{R}}$ called quadratic interpolation.

Let $H_{\{0,1\}}$ denote the category whose objects are pairs (H_0, H_1) of hilbert spaces such that $H_0 \subseteq H_1$ and the inclusion map $H_0 \to H_1$ is a continuous linear map of H_0 onto a dense subspace of H_1, and whose morphisms $T: (H_0, H_1) \to (H_0', H_1')$ are all continuous linear maps $T_0: H_0 \to H_0'$ which extend to continuous linear maps $T_1: H_1 \to H_1'$. We denote by $\widetilde{H}_{\{0,1\}}$ the analogous category formed with hilbertian rather than hilbert spaces and note that there is an obvious "weakening of structure" or "forgetful" functor $F: H_{\{0,1\}} \rightsquigarrow \widetilde{H}_{\{0,1\}}$. Similarly, we define $H_{[0,1]}$ to be the category whose objects are indexed sets $\{H_t\}$ of hilbert spaces, indexed by $[0, 1]$, such that if $0 \leq s < t \leq 1$ then $H_s \subseteq H_t$ and the inclusion $H_s \to H_t$ is a continuous linear map of H_s onto a dense subspace of H_t, and whose morphisms $T: \{H_t\} \to \{H_t'\}$ are all continuous linear maps $T_0: H_0 \to H_0'$ which for all $t \in [0, 1]$ extend to a continuous linear map $T_t: H_t \to H_t'$. Again we define $\widetilde{H}_{[0,1]}$ to be the analogous category formed with hilbertian rather than hilbert spaces and again we have an obvious forgetful functor $F: H_{[0,1]} \rightsquigarrow \widetilde{H}_{[0,1]}$.

If $\{H_t\}$ is an object of $\widetilde{H}_{[0,1]}$ then since the inclusion $i_t: H_0 \to H_t$, $t \in [0,1]$ has dense range, its adjoint, the restriction map $i_t^*: H_t^* \to H_0^*$ is injective, and i_t^* has dense range because i_t is injective. If we identify H_t^* with its image under i_t^* then $\{H_{1-t}^*\}$ is another object of $\widetilde{H}_{[0,1]}$ which we also denote by $\{H_t\}^*$ or $D\{H_t\}$ and call the anti-dual of $\{H_t\}$. If $T_0 = T: \{H_t\} \to \{H_t'\}$ is a morphism and T_t: $H_t \to H_t'$ is the continuous extension of T_0, then $T_1^*: H_1'^* \to H_1^*$ extends to $T_t^*: H_t'^* \to H_t^*$. Thus if we define $D(T) = T_1^*$ then $D: \widetilde{H}_{[0,1]} \rightsquigarrow \widetilde{H}_{[0,1]}$ is a contravariant functor. Similarly, if for (H_0, H_1) an object of $H_{\{0,1\}}$ we define $D(H_0, H_1) = (H_1^*, H_0^*)$ (where we identify H_1^* with its image under the adjoint of the inclusion $i: H_0 \to H_1$) and for a morphism $T: (H_0, H_1) \to (H_0', H_1')$ we define $D(T) = T_1^*$ then $D: \tilde{H}_{\{0,1\}} \rightsquigarrow \tilde{H}_{\{0,1\}}$ is a contravariant functor, the anti-dual functor.

Given an object (H_0, H_1) of $H_{\{0,1\}}$ let $(\ ,\ )_i$ denote the inner product of H_i. Since the inclusion $H_0 \to H_1$ is continuous (say with norm C) if $x \in H_0$ then $y \mapsto (x, y)_1$ is an element of H_0^*, hence there is a unique element Ax of H_0 such that $(x, y)_1 = (Ax, y)_0$ for all $y \in H_0$. Clearly, $A: H_0 \to H_0$ is linear and since $|(Ax, y)_0| = |(x, y)_1| \leq \|x\|_1 \|y\|_1 \leq C^2 \|x\|_0 \|y\|_0$ it follows that $\|A\|_\infty \leq C^2$ and A is continuous. Since $(Ax, x)_0 = (x, x)_1 > 0$ if $x \neq 0$, A is a strictly positive operator.

DEFINITION. If (H_0, H_1) is an object of $H_{\{0,1\}}$ the *defining operator* of (H_0, H_1) is the unique bounded, strictly positive operator $A: H_0 \to H_0$ such that $(x, y)_1 = (Ax, y)_0$ for all $x, y \in H_0$. If $0 \leq t \leq 1$ then A^t [VI, Theorem 18, 4)] is strictly positive continuous operator on H_0 hence $(x, y)_t = (A^t x, y)_0$ is a positive definite inner product on H_0 and we denote the completion of H_0 relative to the corresponding norm $\|x\|_t = (A^t x, x)_0^{1/2} = \|A^{t/2}x\|_0$ by $Q_t(H_0, H_1)$ and write $Q(H_0, H_1)$ for the indexed set $\{Q_t(H_0, H_1)\}$. If $T: (H_0, H_1) \to (H_0', H_1')$ is a morphism of $H_{\{0,1\}}$ we define $Q(T) = T$.

Remark. The fact that Q is, as the notation suggests, a functor $H_{\{0,1\}} \rightsquigarrow H_{[0,1]}$ will be proved in Theorem 1. The proof of functoriality was discovered independently by several persons, including E. Stein whose previously unpublished proof is used here. Q is called quadratic interpolation.

It is clear that $Q_0(H_0, H_1) = H_0$ and that (with an obvious identification) $Q_1(H_0, H_1) = H_1$. For simplicity we shall often put $Q_t(H_0, H_1) = H_t$. If $0 \leq s \leq t \leq 1$ then $\|x\|_t = \|A^{t/2}x\|_0 = \|A^{(t-s)/2}A^{s/2}x\|_0 \leq \|A^{(t-s)/2}\|_\infty \|x\|_s$ so that the identity map of H_0 extends to a continuous linear map $H_s \to H_t$. Since the composition $H_0 \to H_s \to H_t \to H_1$ is just the inclusion of H_0 in H_1 it follows that $H_s \to H_t$ is injective and that *we may regard each* H_t *as included in* H_1 (the image of $H_t \to H_1$) so that $H_s \to H_t$ become inclusion maps. Since H_0 is by definition dense in H_t, it follows that *a fortiori* H_s is dense in H_t if $0 \leq s < t \leq 1$, so that with the above convention $Q(H_0, H_1) = \{H_t\}$ is an object of $H_{[0,1]}$. Now suppose $H_0 \to H_1$ is completely continuous and let $\{x_n\}$ be a bounded sequence in H_0. Then passing to a subsequence we can suppose $\{x_n\}$ is Cauchy in H_1, i.e. that $\|x_m - x_n\|_1 = \|A^{1/2}(x_n - x_m)\|_0 \to 0$, hence $A^{1/2}$: $H_0 \to H_0$ is completely continuous and by [VI, Theorem 18, 3)] so is $A^{r/2}$ if $0 < r \leq 1$. Then if $0 \leq s < t \leq 1$ and $\{x_n\}$ is a sequence in H_0 such that $\|x_n\|_s = \|A^{s/2}x_n\|_0$ is bounded, by passing to a subsequence we can suppose that $A^{(t-s)/2} A^{s/2}x_n$ is Cauchy in H_0, i.e., that

$$\|A^{(t-s)/2} A^{s/2}(x_n - x_m)\|_0 = \|x_n - x_m\|_t$$

converges to zero, i.e. that $\{x_n\}$ is Cauchy in H_t. Since H_0 is dense in H_s it follows that the inclusion $H_s \to H_t$ is completely continuous.

THEOREM 1. Q: $H_{\{0,1\}} \rightsquigarrow H_{[0,1]}$ is a functor which is the "identity" on morphisms. Moreover, $Q_0(H_0, H_1) = H_0$, $Q_1(H_0, H_1) = H_1$, and if the inclusion $H_0 \to H_1$ is completely continuous then so is the inclusion $Q_s(H_0, H_1) \to Q_t(H_0, H_1)$ for $0 \leq s < t \leq 1$.

PROOF. Except for functoriality everything is immediate from the definition of Q or has been proved above. What we must show then is that if T: $(H_0, H_1) \to (H_0', H_1')$ is a morphism of $H_{\{0,1\}}$, i.e., $T = T_0$: $H_0 \to H_0'$ is a bounded linear map which extends to a bounded linear map T_1: $H_1 \to H_1'$; then for each $t \in [0, 1]$, T_0 extends to a bounded linear map T_t: $H_t \to H_t'$. Let B denote the defining operator for (H_0', H_1') and $(\ ,\ )_t'$ the inner product in H_t' so

$$(x, y)_t' = (B^t x, y)_0'$$

if $x, y \in H_0'$. What we shall in fact show is that if $M = \text{Max}\{\|T_0\|_\infty, \|T_1\|_\infty\}$ then for $0 \leq t \leq 1/2$ we have

$$|(Tu, v)_{2t}'| \leq M$$

for all $u \in H_0$, $v \in H_0'$ with $\|u\|_{2t} = \|v\|_{2t}' = 1$. This implies not only that T_{2t} exists but even that $\|T_{2t}\|_\infty \leq M$. Since A^{1-t} is self adjoint and injective its range is dense in H_0 hence also in H_{2t}, so it will suffice to prove the above with $u = A^{1-t}x_0$ and similarly we can suppose that $v = B^{1-t}y_0$. Note that $\|Ax_0\|_0 = \|A^t A^{1-t}x_0\|_0 = \|u\|_{2t} = 1$ and similarly $\|By_0\|_0' = 1$ so what we must show is that

$$|(TA^{1-t}x_0, B^{1-t}y_0)_{2t}'| = |(B^{2t}TA^{1-t}x_0, B^{1-t}y_0)_0'|$$

$$= |(B^tTA^{1-t}x_0, By_0)_0'|$$

is less than M for $0 \leq t \leq 1/2$ if $\|Ax_0\|_0 = \|By_0\|_0' = 1$.

Let $S = \{z \in \mathbf{C} | 0 \leq \operatorname{Re} z \leq 1/2\}$, $\partial S = \{z \in \mathbf{C} | \operatorname{Re} z = 0$ or $\operatorname{Re} z = 1/2\}$, and $\mathring{S} = S - \partial S$. Define $\Phi\colon S \to \mathbf{C}$ by

$$\Phi(z) = (B^z TA^{1-z}x_0, By_0)_0' \quad .$$

Then we shall prove the stronger result that $|\Phi(z)| \leq M$ if $z \in S$.

LEMMA 1. $\Phi\colon S \to \mathbf{C}$ is continuous and the restriction of Φ to $\mathring{S}$ is holomorphic. Moreover

1) $|\Phi|$ is bounded on S and

2) $|\Phi| \leq M$ on ∂S.

PROOF. That Φ is continuous on S and holomorphic on $\mathring{S}$ is clear from [VI, Theorem 18, 1) and 4)]. Now

$$|\Phi(t+is)| = |(TA^{-is}\,A^{1-t}x_0, B^{-is}\,B^{1+t}y_0)_0'|$$

$$\leq \|T_0\|_\infty \, \|A^{-is}\,A^{1-t}x_0\|_0 \, \|B^{-is}\,B^{1+t}y_0\|_0' \quad .$$

Since A^{-is} is a unitary map of H_0 and B^{-is} is a unitary map of H_0' [VI, Theorem 18, 4)] it follows that $|\Phi(t+is)| \leq \|T_0\|_\infty \|A^{1-t}x_0\|_0 \|B^{1+t}y_0\|_0'$. Now by [VI, Theorem 18, 4)] $t \to \|A^{1-t}x_0\|_0 \|B^{1+t}y_0\|_0'$ is continuous hence bounded on $[0, 1/2]$, so $|\Phi(t+is)|$ is bounded for $0 \leq t \leq 1/2$, i.e. for $t + is \in S$. Since $\|Ax_0\|_0 = \|By_0\|_0' = 1$, by assumption, $|\Phi(is)| \leq \|T_0\|_\infty \leq M$. Finally

$$|\Phi(1/2 + is)| = |(BTA^{-is}A^{1/2}x_0, B^{-is}B^{1/2}y_0)_0'|$$

$$= |(TA^{-is}A^{1/2}x_0, B^{-is}B^{1/2}y_0)_1'|$$

$$\leq \|T_1\|_\infty \, \|A^{-is}A^{1/2}x_0\|_1 \cdot \|B^{-is}B^{1/2}y_0\|_1'$$

$$= \|T_1\|_\infty \, \|A^{-is}Ax_0\|_0 \|B^{-is}By_0\|_0' \quad .$$

Since A^{-is} is a unitary map of H_0 and B^{-is} a unitary, map of H_0' and since $\|Ax_0\|_0 = \|By_0\|_0' = 1$ we get $|\Phi(1/2 + is)| \leq \|T_1\|_\infty \leq M$.

q.e.d.

The desired result, namely that $|\Phi(z)| \leq M$ if $z \in S$ now follows from Lemma 1 and the following well-known maximum principle of Phragmén-Lindelöff.

LEMMA 2. Let $f\colon S \to \mathbf{C}$ be holomorphic in $\mathring{S}$ and continuous and bounded on S. If $|f| \leq M$ on ∂S then $|f| \leq M$ on S.

PROOF. If we assume $f(t + is)$ tends to zero, uniformly in T, as $|s| \to \infty$, the conclusion follows by applying the maximum modulus principle to f in a rectangle $\{t + is \mid 0 \leq t \leq 1/2,\ |s| \leq \sigma\}$ where $|f(t + is)| \leq M$ if $|s| \geq \sigma$. If n is a positive integer then $\exp(z^2/n)$ is such a function. Indeed, $|\exp((t + is)^2/n| = \exp((t^2 - s^2)/n) \leq \exp((1/4 - s^2)/n)$ which on the one hand is bounded by $\exp(1/4n)$ and on the other hand tends to zero as $|s| \to \infty$. Since $|f|$ is bounded $f_n(z) = f(z)\exp(z^2/n)$ also satisfies the special case, and since $|f_n| \leq M \exp(1/4n)$ on ∂S, if $z \in S$ then $|f(z)\exp(z^2/n)| = |f_n(z)| \leq M \exp(1/4n)$. Fixing z and letting $n \to \infty$ gives $|f(z)| \leq M$.

q.e.d.

This completes the proof of Theorem 1.

THEOREM 2. There is a unique functor $\tilde{Q}\colon \tilde{H}_{\{0,1\}} \rightsquigarrow \tilde{H}_{[0,1]}$ making the following diagram commutative.

$$\begin{array}{ccc}
H_{\{0,1\}} & \overset{Q}{\rightsquigarrow} & H_{[0,1]} \\
F \downarrow \wr & & \wr \downarrow F \\
\tilde{H}_{\{0,1\}} & \underset{\tilde{Q}}{\rightsquigarrow} & \tilde{H}_{[0,1]}
\end{array}$$

PROOF. Since the forgetful functor $F\colon \mathcal{H}_{\{0,1\}} \rightsquigarrow \widetilde{\mathcal{H}}_{\{0,1\}}$ is clearly surjective (by definition every hilbertian space is the underlying topological vector space of a hilbert space) what we must show is that if $F(H_0, H_1) = F(H_0', H_1')$ then $FQ(H_0, H_1) = FQ(H_0', H_1')$. Now $F(H_0, H_1) = F(H_0', H_1')$ means precisely that H_i and H_i' have the same underlying hilbertian space, or in other words that the identity map I of H_0 is an isomorphism $I\colon (H_0, H_1) \to (H_0', H_1')$ of the category $\mathcal{H}_{\{0,1\}}$. Then by Theorem 1 (i.e., the functoriality of Q) $Q(I) = I$ is an isomorphism of $Q(H_0, H_1)$ with $Q(H_0', H_1')$, i.e., the identity map of H_0 extends to a continuous linear map (clearly an identity map) of $Q_t(H_0, H_1)$ onto $Q_t(H_0', H_1')$ if $0 \leq t \leq 1$. But this says precisely that $FQ(H_0, H_1) = FQ(H_0', H_1')$.

q.e.d.

DEFINITION. The functor $\widetilde{Q}\colon \widetilde{\mathcal{H}}_{\{0,1\}} \to \widetilde{\mathcal{H}}_{[0,1]}$ of Theorem 2 will again be called *quadratic interpolation.*

Since Q and both of the forgetful functors F are the "identity" on morphisms, the same is clearly true of $\widetilde{Q}$.

We note the following diagram is commutative:

$$\begin{array}{ccc}
\widetilde{\mathcal{H}}_{\{0,1\}} & \overset{D}{\rightsquigarrow} & \widetilde{\mathcal{H}}_{\{0,1\}} \\
\widetilde{Q}\Big\downarrow\wr & & \Big\downarrow\wr \\
\widetilde{\mathcal{H}}_{[0,1]} & \underset{D}{\rightsquigarrow} & \widetilde{\mathcal{H}}_{[0,1]}
\end{array}$$

where D represents the contravariant anti-dual functors defined at the beginning of this section. Stated explicitly, what this amounts to is that if (H_0, H_1) is an object of $\mathcal{H}_{\{0,1\}}$ then

$$Q_t(H_0, H_1)^* = Q_{1-t}(H_1^*, H_0^*) \quad .$$

To see this let A be the defining operator of (H_0, H_1). Since $A^{1-t/2}$ is strictly positive, hence injective, we can make its image K_t a hilbert space with inner product $\langle\ ,\ \rangle_t$ by declaring that $A^{1-t/2}\colon H_0 \approx K_t$ is an isometry, i.e., $\langle A^{1-t/2}x, A^{1-t/2}y \rangle_t = (x, y)_0$. In particular, $A^{1/2}\colon H_0 \approx K_1$ is an isometry. Let $T\colon H_0^* \approx H_0$ be the natural isomorphism i.e., $\ell(x) = (T\ell, x)_0$ for all $\ell \in H_0^*$, $x \in H_0$. Then $S = A^{1/2}T: H_0^* \approx K_1$ is an isometry. We next will show that S maps H_{1-t}^* isometrically onto K_t and so is an isomorphism $\{H_{1-t}^*\} \approx \{K_t\}$. Suppose $S\ell = A^{1-t/2}v \in K_t$. Then $T\ell = A^{(1-t)/2}v$ and $\|S\ell\|_{K_t} = \|v\|_0 = \operatorname{Sup}\{|v, x)_0| \,\big|\, \|x\|_0 = 1\}$. Since $A^{(1-t)/2}$ has range dense in H_0 and $\|A^{(1-t)/2}x\|_0 = \|x\|_{1-t}$, we get

$$\begin{aligned}\|S\ell\|_{K_t} &= \operatorname{Sup}\{|(v, A^{(1-t)/2}x)_0| x \in H_0, \|x\|_{1-t} = 1\} \\ &= \operatorname{Sup}\{|T\ell, x)| \,\big|\, x \in H_0, \|x\|_{1-t} = 1\} \\ &= \operatorname{Sup}\{|\ell(x)| \,\big|\, x \in H_0, \|x\|_{1-t} = 1\} = \|\ell\|_{1-t} \quad .\end{aligned}$$

Hence it will suffice to prove that $Q_t(K_0, K_1) = K_t$. But if $u, v \in K_0$, say $u = Ax$, $v = Ay$, then $< u, v >_t = < Ax, Ay >_t = (A^{t/2}x, A^{t/2}y)_0 = < A^tAx, Ay >_0 = < A^tu, v >_0$ and the desired result follows.

Another property of $\tilde{Q}$ we shall need later is its "transitivity" or "convexity" which is expressed by the formula

$$\tilde{Q}_r(\tilde{Q}_s(H_0, H_1), \tilde{Q}_t(H_0, H_1)) = \tilde{Q}_{s+r(t-s)}(H_0, H_1)$$

if $0 \le s \le t \le 1$ and $0 \le r \le 1$. Because of Theorem 2 it will suffice to show that Q has the analogous property. If A is the defining operator for (H_0, H_1) then for $x, y \in H_0$ we have

$$(x, y)_t = (A^tx, y)_0 = (A^sA^{t-s}x, y)_0 = (A^{t-s}x, y)_s$$

from which it follows that $Q_r(Q_s(H_0, H_1), Q_t(H_0, H_1))$ is the completion of H_0 relative to the inner product $(A^{r(t-s)}x, y)_s = (A^sA^{r(t-s)}x, y)_0 = (A^{s+r(t-s)}x, y)_0$ which is just the definition of $Q_{s+r(t-s)}(H_0, H_1)$.

For future reference we recapitulate the properties of $\tilde{Q}$.

THEOREM 3. The quadratic interpolation functor $\tilde{Q}$: $\tilde{H}_{\{0,1\}} \rightsquigarrow \tilde{H}_{[0,1]}$ has the following properties:

1) $\tilde{Q}_0(H_0, H_1) = H_0$ and $Q_1(H_0, H_1) = H_1$;

2) $\tilde{Q}$ is the "identity" on morphisms;

3) If $H_0 \to H_1$ is completely continuous then so is $\tilde{Q}_s(H_0, H_1) \to \tilde{Q}_t(H_0, H_1)$ for $0 \le s < t \le 1$;

4) $Q_t(H_0, H_1)^* = Q_{1-t}(H_1^*, H_0^*)$;

5) $Q_r(Q_s(H_0, H_1), Q_t(H_0, H_1)) = Q_{s+r(t-s)}(H_0, H_1)$
if $0 \leq s \leq t \leq 1$ and $0 \leq r \leq 1$.

Given objects (H_0, H_1) and (H_0', H_1') of $\widetilde{H}_{\{0,1\}}$ with $H_1 = H_0'$, (H_0, H_1') is another object of $\widetilde{H}_{\{0,1\}}$ which we denote by $(H_0, H_1) : (H_0', H_1')$. In particular if H_1 has the structure of a hilbert space then we have a canonical identification $H_1 \approx H_1^*$ and we can form $(H_0, H_1) : (H_1^*, H_0^*)$.

Similarly, given two objects $\{H_t\}$ and $\{H_t'\}$ of $\widetilde{H}_{[0,1]}$ with $H_1 = H_0'$ we can define a third object $\{H_t\} : \{H_t'\} = \{H_t''\}$ by $H_t'' = H_{2t}$, $0 \leq t \leq 1/2$ and $H_t'' = H_{2t-1}'$, $1/2 \leq t \leq 1$. We note that by the "convexity" of quadratic interpolation if (H_0, H_1) is an object of $\widetilde{H}_{\{0,1\}}$ and $H_{1/2} = \widetilde{Q}_{1/2}(H_0, H_1)$ then $\widetilde{Q}(H_0, H_1) = \widetilde{Q}(H_0, H_{1/2}) : \widetilde{Q}(H_{1/2}, H_1)$. We now show that if (H_0, H_1) is an object of $\widetilde{H}_{\{0,1\}}$ and H_1 has the structure of a hilbert space then

$$\widetilde{Q}((H_0, H_1) : (H_1^*, H_0^*)) = \widetilde{Q}(H_0, H_1) : \widetilde{Q}(H_1^*, H_0^*) \quad .$$

We can assume H_0 is a hilbert space and we let A be the defining operator of (H_0, H_1). Let K_t be the completion of H_0 in the norm derived from the inner product $((x, y))_t = (A^{2t}x, y)_0$, $0 \leq t \leq 1$. Then clearly K_t is an object of $H_{[0,1]}$ with $K_0 = H_0$. In fact (K_0, K_1) has defining operator $B = A^2$ and it follows that $K_t = Q_t(K_0, K_1)$. Clearly $K_{1/2} = H_1$ so

$$\widetilde{Q}(K_0, K_1) = \widetilde{Q}((K_0, K_{1/2}) : (K_{1/2}, K_1)) = \widetilde{Q}((H_0, H_1) : (K_{1/2}, K_1))$$
$$= \widetilde{Q}(H_0, H_1) : \widetilde{Q}(K_{1/2}, K_1)$$

so it will suffice to identify $(K_{1/2}, K_1)$ with (H_1^*, H_0^*). Now $K_{1/2}$ is the completion of H_0 relative to the norm derived from the inner product $((x, y))_{1/2} = (Ax, y)_0 = (x, y)_1$, so, by definition, $K_{1/2} = H_1 = H_1^*$. Moreover if $y \in K_{1/2}$ then

$$((y, y))_1^{1/2} = \operatorname{Sup}\{ |((x, y))_1| \;\big|\; ((x, x))_1 = 1\}$$
$$= \operatorname{Sup}\{ |(A^2x, y)_0| \;\big|\; \|Ax\|_0^{\,2} = 1\}$$

or, since A has dense range in H_0,

$$((y, y))_1^{1/2} = \operatorname{Sup}\{|(Ax, y)_0| \mid \|x\|_0 = 1\}$$
$$= \operatorname{Sup}\{|(x, y)_1| \mid \|x\|_0 = 1\}$$

which is just the norm of y as an element of H_0^*. Thus H_0^* is the completion of $K_{1/2} = H_1^*$ with respect to the norm derived from the inner product $((\ ,\ ))_1$, i.e., $(K_{1/2}, K_1) = (H_1^*, H_0^*)$. With some obvious changes in notation we can restate this result as:

THEOREM 4. Let (H_k, H_0) be an object of $\tilde{H}_{\{0,1\}}$ with H_0 a hilbert space and $k > 0$. For $k \geq t \geq 0$ define $H_t = \tilde{Q}_{t/k}(H_k, H_0)$ and let $H_{-t} = H_t^*$ $(= \tilde{Q}_{1-t/k}(H_0^*, H_k^*)$ by [Theorem 3, 4)]). Then for $k \geq r \geq s \geq -k$

$$\tilde{Q}_t(H_r, H_s) = H_{r+t(s-r)} \quad .$$

§3. Quadratic interpolation of chains

We now define a functor from the category $C_{\mathbf{Z}}$ of discrete chains of hilbertian spaces to the category $C_{\mathbf{R}}$ of continuous chains of hilbertian spaces, which we again denote by Q and call quadratic interpolation. If $H = \{H^k\}$ is an object of $C_{\mathbf{Z}}$ then we define $Q(H) = \{Q(H)^s\}$, an object of $C_{\mathbf{R}}$, by

$$Q(H)^{k+1-s} = \tilde{Q}_s(H^{k+1}, H^k)$$

for k a non-negative integer and $0 \leq s \leq 1$, so that by [§2, Theorem 3, 1)] we have $Q(H)^k = H^k$ if k is a non-negative integer. It is immediate that $Q(H)$ is a continuous chain of hilbertian spaces and that $Q(H)^\infty = H^\infty$. Also by [§2, Theorem 3, 3)] if H is a Rellich chain so is $Q(H)$.

If k is a negative integer then for $0 \leq s \leq 1$

$$\begin{aligned} Q(H)^{k+1-s} &= (Q(H)^{-k-(1-s)})^* \\ &= \tilde{Q}_{1-s}(H^{-k}, H^{-k-1})^* \\ &= \tilde{Q}_{1-s}((H^k)^*, (H^{k+1})^*)^* \end{aligned}$$

so by [§2, Theorem 3, 4)]

$$Q(H)^{k+1-s} = \tilde{Q}_s(H^{k+1}, H^k)^{**}$$

and finally by reflexivity

$$Q(H)^{k+1-s} = \tilde{Q}_s(H^{k+1}, H^k)$$

so the formula which defines $Q(H)^t$ when $t \geq 0$ remains true for $t < 0$. We note also that $Q(H)^{-\infty} = H^{-\infty}$.

Given two discrete chains H_1 and H_2 we recall that for $r \in \mathbf{Z}$ $OP_r(H_1, H_2)$ consists of all linear maps $T\colon H_1^\infty \to H_2^\infty$ which for each $k \in \mathbf{Z}$ extend to a continuous linear map $T_k\colon H_1^k \to H_2^{k-r}$. It follows that $T_{k+1}\colon (H_1^{k+1}, H_1^k) \to (H_2^{k+1-r}, H_2^{k-r})$ is a morphism of the category $\tilde{H}_{\{0,1\}}$ and so by [§2, Theorem 3, 2)] it is also a morphism $T_{k+1}\colon \tilde{Q}(H_1^{k+1}, H_1^k) \to \tilde{Q}(H_2^{k+1-r}, H_2^{k-r})$ of the category $\tilde{H}_{[0,1]}$ i.e., T_{k+1} (hence T) extends to a continuous linear map T_{k+1-s} of $\tilde{Q}_s(H_1^{k+1}, H_1^k) = Q(H_1)^{k+1-s}$ into $\tilde{Q}_s(H_2^{k+1-r}, H_2^{k-r}) = Q(H_2)^{k+1-s-r}$, $0 \leq s \leq 1$. Since $H_i^\infty = Q(H_i)^\infty$ this says that $T \in OP_r(Q(H_1), Q(H_2))$, so we have proved $OP_r(H_1, H_2) \subseteq OP_r(Q(H_1), Q(H_2))$ if $r \in \mathbf{Z}$. The reverse inequality being a trivial consequence of $Q(H_i)^k = H_i^k$ we in fact have $OP_r(H_1, H_2) = OP_r(Q(H_1), Q(H_2))$ if $r \in \mathbf{Z}$.

Recalling the canonical identification of $\mathrm{Hom}(H_1, H_2)$ with $OP_0(H_1, H_2)$ where H_1 and H_2 are two discrete or continuous chains of hilbertain spaces [§1, Theorem 1] we get as a corollary that $\mathrm{Hom}(Q(H_1), Q(H_2)) = \mathrm{Hom}(H_1, H_2)$ and hence $Q\colon C_{\mathbf{Z}} \rightsquigarrow C_{\mathbf{R}}$ is indeed a functor which is the "identity" on morphisms.

To recapitulate.

THEOREM. The quadratic interpolation functor Q from the category $C_{\mathbf{Z}}$ of discrete chains of hilbertian spaces to the category $C_{\mathbf{R}}$ of continuous chains of hilbertain spaces has the following properties:

1) $Q(H)^{k+1-s} = \tilde{Q}_s(H^{k+1}, H^k)$ for $k \in \mathbf{Z}$ and $0 \leq s \leq 1$, so in particular $Q(H)^k = H^k$ if $k \in \mathbf{Z}$. Also $Q(H)^\infty = H^\infty$, $Q(H)^{-\infty} = H^{-\infty}$ and $OP_r(Q(H), Q(H')) = OP_r(H, H')$ if $r \in \mathbf{Z}$.

2) $Q(T) = T$ if T is a morphism of $C_{\mathbf{Z}}$;

3) If H is a discrete Rellich chain then $Q(H)$ is a continuous Rellich chain.

The above theorem seems adequate justification for the following abuse of notation: if $H = \{H^k\}$ is a discrete chain of hilbertian spaces then we will denote $Q(H)$ by $\{H^k\}$ also and refer to it as the continuous chain that arises from the discrete chain $\{H^k\}$ by quadratic interpolation. To distinguish between H and $Q(H)$ where necessary we shall write $\{H^k\}_{k \in \mathbf{Z}}$ for the former and $\{H^k\}_{k \in \mathbf{R}}$ for the latter and only revert to the "Q"-notation where necessary for clarity.

§4. Scales and the chains $\{\ell_k^2(\mathbf{Z}^n, V)\}$.

Following the Russian terminology we make the following definition.

DEFINITION. A continuous chain of hilbertian spaces $\{H^k\}$ is called a *scale* if given $k, \ell \in \mathbf{R}$ with $k \geq \ell$ and $t \in [0, 1]$ we have

$$\tilde{Q}_t(H^k, H^\ell) = H^{k+t(\ell-k)} .$$

THEOREM 1. If a continuous chain $\{H^k\}_{k \in \mathbf{R}}$ is a scale then it arises from the discrete chain $\{H^k\}_{k \in \mathbf{Z}}$ by quadratic interpolation. If a continuous chain $\{H^k\}_{k \in \mathbf{R}}$ arises from a discrete chain by quadratic interpolation then it is a scale if and only if given integers $k \geq \ell \geq 0$

$$H^\ell = \tilde{Q}_{(k-\ell)/k}(H^k, H^0) .$$

PROOF. The first statement is trivial and the second follows easily from [§2, Theorem 3, 4) and 5) and Theorem 4].

DEFINITION. Let X be a measure space, α a measurable positive real-valued function on X which is bounded away from zero and let V be an hermitian vector space. For each real number k let $L_k^2(X, V, \alpha)$ denote the hilbert space of measurable maps $f\colon X \to V$ such that $\|f\|_k^2 = \int \|f(x)\|^2 \alpha(x)^k < \infty$.

THEOREM 2. Given X, V, and α as in the above definition, $\{L_k^2(X, V, \alpha)\}$ is a continuous chain of hilbertian spaces and in fact a scale.

PROOF. Let $m = \operatorname{Inf}\{\alpha(x) \mid x \in X\}$. Then if $k > \ell$ we have $\|f\|_\ell^2 \leq m^{(\ell-k)}\|f\|_k^2$ which proves that $L_k^2(X, V, \alpha) \subseteq L_\ell^2(X, V, \alpha)$ and the inclusion is continuous. Given $k \geq 0$, $f \in L_k^2(X, V, \alpha)$, and a positive integer n define $f_n\colon X \to V$ by $f_n(x) = f(x)$ if $\alpha(x) \leq n$ and $f_n(x) = 0$ if $\alpha(x) > n$. Clearly $f_n \in \cap_k L_k^2(X, V, \alpha)$ and also $f_n \to f$ in $L_k^2(X, V, \alpha)$ so $\{L_k^2(X, V, \alpha)\}_{k>0}$ is a continuous chain. Note that the map $f \to \alpha^{k/2}f$ is an isometry of $L_k^2(X, V, \alpha)$ onto $L_0^2(X, V, \alpha)$. It follows that $L_k^2(X, V, \alpha)^* \cong L_{-k}^2(X, V, \alpha)$, the pairing being given by $< f, g > = < \alpha^{-k}f, \alpha^k g >_0 = \int < f(x), g(x) >$ so that $\{L_k^2(X, V, \alpha)\}_{k\in\mathbf{R}}$ is a continuous chain. If $k > \ell$ then $(L_k^2(X, V, \alpha), L_\ell^2(X, V, \alpha))$ is an object of $H_{\{0,1\}}$ and the defining operator $A\colon L_k^2(X, V, \alpha) \to L_k^2(X, V, \alpha)$ is clearly given by $Af = \alpha^{(\ell-k)}f$. If $t \in [0, 1]$ then $A^t f = \alpha^{t(\ell-k)}f$ so $Q_t(L_k^2(X, V, \alpha), L_\ell^2(X, V, \alpha))$ is the completion of $L_k^2(X, V, \alpha)$ with respect to the norm $f \to \|\alpha^{t(\ell-k)/2}f\|_k = \|f\|_{k+t(\ell-k)}$, i.e.,

$$Q_t(L_k^2(X, V, \alpha), L_\ell^2(X, V, \alpha)) = L_{k+t(\ell-k)}^2(X, V, \alpha)$$

which proves that $\{L_k^2(X, V, \alpha)\}$ is a scale.

q.e.d.

The following class of scales will be of particular interest in the sequel.

DEFINITION. If V is an hermitian vector space then for each $k \in \mathbf{R}$ we define $\ell_k^2(\mathbf{Z}^n, V)$ to be the hilbert space of functions $f\colon \mathbf{Z}^n \to V$ such that

$$\|f\|_k^2 = \sum_{\nu\in\mathbf{Z}^n} \|f(\nu)\|^2(1 + \|\nu\|^2)^k < \infty$$

THEOREM 3. If V is an hermitian vector space then $\{\ell_k^2(\mathbf{Z}^n, V)\}_{k\in\mathbf{R}}$ is, for each non-negative integer n, a continuous Rellich chain and a scale.

PROOF. If we make $\mathbf{Z}^n$ into a measure space by declaring each set measurable and each point to have mass one, and define $\alpha(\nu) = (1+\|\nu\|^2)$ then clearly $\ell_k^2(\mathbf{Z}^n, V) = L_k^2(\mathbf{Z}^n, V, \alpha)$, so by Theorem 2 above all that remains is to verify the Rellich condition. Let $k > \ell$. Given $\varepsilon > 0$ let F be the finite set of $\nu \in \mathbf{Z}^n$ such that $(1+\|\nu\|^2)^{\ell-k} > \varepsilon^2/2$. Then the subspace $\ell^2_\ell(F, V)$ of $\ell^2_\ell(\mathbf{Z}^n, V)$ consisting of f such that $f(\nu) = 0$ if $\nu \notin F$ is finite dimensional, so the unit ball of $\ell^2_\ell(F, V)$ is compact and we can choose $f_1, \ldots, f_m$, $\varepsilon/\sqrt{2}$ -dense in it. If f belongs to the unit ball of $\ell^2_k(\mathbf{Z}^n, V)$ then

$$\sum_{\nu\in F} \|f(\nu)\|^2(1+\|\nu\|^2)^\ell \leq \sum_{\nu\in \mathbf{Z}^n} \|f(\nu)\|^2(1+\|\nu\|^2)^k$$
$$\leq \|f\|_k^2 \leq 1$$

hence we can choose f_i so that

$$\sum_{\nu\in F} \|f(\nu) - f_i(\nu)\|^2(1+\|\nu\|^2)^\ell < \frac{\varepsilon^2}{2} .$$

On the other hand since $(1+\|\nu\|^2)^{\ell-k} \leq \varepsilon^2/2$ if $\nu \notin F$ and $f_i(\nu) = 0$ if $\nu \notin F$

$$\sum_{\nu\notin F} \|f(\nu) - f_i(\nu)\|^2(1+\|\nu\|^2)^\ell = \sum_{\nu\notin F} \|f(\nu)\|^2(1+\|\nu\|^2)^\ell$$
$$\leq \sum_{\nu\notin F} \|f(\nu)\|^2(1+\|\nu\|^2)^k \ \frac{\varepsilon^2}{2}$$
$$\leq \|f\|_k^2 \frac{\varepsilon^2}{2} \leq \frac{\varepsilon^2}{2}$$

so $\|f-f_i\|_\ell^2 = \Sigma_{\nu\in \mathbf{Z}^n} \|f(\nu)-f_i(\nu)\|^2(1+\|\nu\|^2)^\ell \leq \varepsilon^2$. This proves that $f_1, \ldots, f_m$ is ε-dense in the unit ball of $\ell^2_k(\mathbf{Z}^n, V)$ relative to the metric of $\ell^2_\ell(\mathbf{Z}^n, V)$. Since $\varepsilon > 0$ was arbitrary, the unit ball of $\ell^2_k(\mathbf{Z}^n, V)$ is a totally bounded (precompact) subset of $\ell^2_\ell(\mathbf{Z}^n, V)$ i.e., the inclusion $\ell^2_k(\mathbf{Z}^n, V) \to \ell^2_\ell(\mathbf{Z}^n, V)$ is completely continuous.

q.e.d.

LEMMA 1. Given $k > 1/2$ let $B_k = 2\int_0^\infty (1+y^2)^{-k}dy$ and let $b_k = \int_1^\infty (1+y^2)^{-k}dy$. Then if $c \geq 1$

$$b_k \leq \sum_{\mu\in \mathbf{Z}} c^{-1}(1 + \frac{\mu^2}{c^2})^{-k} \leq B_k$$

PROOF. By the Maclaurin method of estimating sums

$$\int_1^\infty c^{-1}(1 + \frac{x^2}{c^2})^{-k}\,dx \leq \sum_{n=1}^\infty c^{-1}(1 + \frac{n^2}{c^2})^{-k} \leq \int_0^\infty c^{-1}(1 + \frac{x^2}{c^2})^{-k}\,dx$$

The substitution $y = x/c$ transforms the integral on the right to $\int_0^\infty (1+y^2)^{-k}\,dy$ and the integral on the left to

$$\int_{1/c}^{\infty} (1+y^2)^{-k}\,dy = \int_{1/c}^{1} (1+y^2)^{-k} + \int_{1}^{\infty} (1+y^2)^{-k}\,dy \geq b_k$$

and the lemma follows easily.

q.e.d.

LEMMA 2. If $k > 1/2$, $c \geq 1$ and a_μ is a non-negative real number for each $\mu \in \mathbf{Z}$ then

$$\Big(\sum_{\mu\in\mathbf{Z}} a_\mu\Big)^2 c^{k-1/2} \leq B_k \sum_{\mu\in\mathbf{Z}} a_\mu^2 (c + \mu^2)^k .$$

PROOF. Replacing c by c^2 the inequality becomes $(\Sigma_\mu a_\mu)^2 \leq B_k \Sigma_\mu a_\mu^2\, c(1+\mu^2/c^2)^k$ which follows from Lemma 1 and the Schwarz inequality $(\Sigma_\mu x_\mu y_\mu)^2 \leq (\Sigma_\mu x_\mu^2)(\Sigma_\mu y_\mu^2)$ with $x_\mu^2 = c^{-1}(1+\mu^2/c^2)^{-k}$ and $y_\mu^2 = a_\mu^2\, c(1+\mu^2/c^2)^k$.

q.e.d.

THEOREM 4. Let n be a positive integer, $k \geq 1/2$ and let $f \in \ell_k^2(\mathbf{Z}^n, V)$. Then for each $\lambda \in \mathbf{Z}^{n-1}$ the series $\Sigma_{\mu\in\mathbf{Z}} f(\lambda, \mu)$ converges absolutely and the function $\rho(f)\colon \mathbf{Z}^{n-1} \to V$ defined by $\rho(f)(\lambda) = \Sigma_{\mu\in\mathbf{Z}} f(\lambda, \mu)$ belongs to $\ell^2_{k-1/2}(\mathbf{Z}^{n-1}, V)$. Moreover, $\rho\colon \ell_k^2(\mathbf{Z}^n, V) \to \ell^2_{k-1/2}(\mathbf{Z}^{n-1}, V)$ is a continuous linear map and has a continuous linear section (i.e. right inverse) $\chi\colon \ell^2_{k-1/2}(\mathbf{Z}^{n-1}, V) \to \ell_k^2(\mathbf{Z}^n, V)$.

PROOF. Taking $a_\mu = \|f(\lambda, \mu)\|$ and $c = (1+\|\lambda\|^2)$ in Lemma 2 gives

$$\Big(\sum_{\mu\in\mathbf{Z}} \|f(\lambda, \mu)\|\Big)^2 (1+\|\lambda\|^2)^{k-1/2} \leq B_k \sum_{\mu\in\mathbf{Z}} \|f(\lambda, \mu)\|^2 (1+\|\lambda\|^2 + \mu^2)^k .$$

Since the sum on the right is clearly no greater than $\|f\|_k^2$ this proves the absolute convergence of $\Sigma_\mu f(\lambda, \mu)$ to an element $\rho(f)(\lambda) \in V$ and gives

$$\|\rho(f)(\lambda)\|^2 (1+\|\lambda\|^2)^{k-1/2} \le B_k \sum_{\mu\in\mathbf{Z}} \|f(\lambda,\mu)\|^2(1+\|\lambda\|^2+\mu^2)^k$$

Summing over all $\lambda \in \mathbf{Z}^{n-1}$ gives

$$\|\rho(f)\|^2_{k-1/2} \le B_k \|f\|^2_k$$

which proves that ρ is a continuous (obviously linear) map of $\ell^2_k(\mathbf{Z}^n, V)$ into $\ell^2_{k-1/2}(\mathbf{Z}^{n-1}, V)$. Given $g \in \ell^2_{k-1/2}(\mathbf{Z}^{n-1}, V)$ define $\chi(g)\colon \mathbf{Z}^n \to V$ by

$$\chi(g)(\lambda,\mu) = g(\lambda)(1+\|\lambda\|^2)^{-1/2}\,\gamma(\lambda)\left(1+\frac{\mu^2}{1+\|\lambda\|^2}\right)^{-k}$$

$$= g(\lambda)(1+\|\lambda\|^2)^{-1/2}\,\gamma(\lambda)\left[\frac{1+\|\lambda\|^2}{1+\|\lambda\|^2+\mu^2}\right]^k$$

for $\lambda \in \mathbf{Z}^{n-1}$, $\mu \in \mathbf{Z}$, where

$$\gamma(\lambda) = \left[\sum_{\mu\in\mathbf{Z}} (1+\|\lambda\|^2)^{-1/2}\left(1+\frac{\mu^2}{1+\|\lambda\|^2}\right)^{-k}\right]^{-1}$$

Clearly $\sum_{\mu\in\mathbf{Z}} \chi(g)(\lambda,\mu) = g(\lambda)$ for all $\lambda \in \mathbf{Z}^{n-1}$. Taking $c = (1+\|\lambda\|^2)^{1/2}$ in Lemma 1 gives $\gamma(\lambda) \le 1/b_k$ so

$$\|\chi(g)(\lambda,\mu)\|^2(1+\|\lambda\|^2+\mu^2)^k = \|g(\lambda)\|^2(1+\|\lambda\|^2)^{k-1}\,\gamma(\lambda)^2\left[\frac{1+\|\lambda\|^2}{1+\|\lambda\|^2+\mu^2}\right]^k$$

$$\le \|g(\lambda)\|^2 (1+\|\lambda\|^2)^{k-1/2}(1/b_k)^2 (1+\|\lambda\|^2)^{-1/2}\left(1+\frac{\mu^2}{1+\|\lambda\|^2}\right)^{-k}.$$

Summing over all $\mu \in \mathbf{Z}$, Lemma 1 gives

$$\sum_{\mu\in\mathbf{Z}} \|\chi(g)(\lambda,\mu)\|^2 (1+\|\lambda\|^2+\mu^2)^k \le \|g(\lambda)\|^2 (1+\|\lambda\|^2)^{k-1/2}(B_k/b_k^2)$$

hence summing over all $\lambda \in \mathbf{Z}^{n-1}$ gives

$$\|\chi(g)\|^2_k \le (B_k/b_k^2)\,\|g\|_{k-1/2}$$

which proves that $\chi(g) \in \ell^2_k(\mathbf{Z}^n, V)$ and that $\chi\colon \ell^2_{k-1/2}(\mathbf{Z}^{n-1}, V) \to \ell^2_k(\mathbf{Z}^n, V)$ is a (clearly linear) continuous map. Since $\rho\chi(g)(\lambda) = \sum_{\mu\in\mathbf{Z}} \chi(g)(\lambda,\mu) = g(\lambda)$, χ is a section for ρ.

q.e.d.

THEOREM 5. Let n and ℓ be integers, $n > \ell \geq 0$, and let $s = (n-\ell)/2$. If $k > s$ and $f \in \ell^2_k(\mathbf{Z}^n, V)$ then for each $\lambda \in \mathbf{Z}^\ell$ the series

$$\sum_{\mu \in \mathbf{Z}^{n-\ell}} f(\lambda, \mu)$$

converges absolutely, and the function $\rho(f): \mathbf{Z}^\ell \to V$ defined by $\rho(f)(\lambda) = \Sigma_{\mu \in \mathbf{Z}^{n-\ell}} f(\lambda, \mu)$ belongs to $\ell^2_{k-s}(\mathbf{Z}^\ell, V)$. Moreover, $\rho: \ell^2_k(\mathbf{Z}^n, V) \to \ell^2_{k-s}(\mathbf{Z}^\ell, V)$ is a continuous linear map and has a continuous linear section

$$\chi : \ell^2_{k-s}(\mathbf{Z}^\ell, V) \to \ell^2_k(\mathbf{Z}^n, V) \quad .$$

PROOF. Immediate from Theorem 4 by induction on $(n-\ell)$.

COROLLARY. If n is a positive integer and $k > n/2$ there is a constant B such that $f \in \ell^2_k(\mathbf{Z}^n, V)$ then $\Sigma_{\nu \in \mathbf{Z}^n} f(\nu)$ converges absolutely and

$$\left\| \sum_{\nu \in \mathbf{Z}^n} f(\nu) \right\| \leq B\|f\|_k \quad .$$

PROOF. This is just the case $\ell = 0$ of the theorem.

CHAPTER IX

THE DISCRETE SOBOLEV CHAIN OF A VECTOR BUNDLE

Richard S. Palais

In this section M will denote a compact C^∞ manifold, possibly with boundary, and ξ, η, ζ will denote hermitian vector bundles over M. We shall also assume that M is equipped with a fixed strictly positive smooth measure.

§1. The spaces $C^k(\xi)$

We let $C^k(\xi)$, k a non-negative integer, denote the complex vector space of C^k cross sections of ξ. We give $C^0(\xi)$ the compact-open topology and note that $|||f|||_0 = \mathrm{Sup}\{\|f(x)\| \,|\, x \in M\}$ is a norm for $C^0(\xi)$ in which it is complete. Thus $C^0(\xi)$ is the underlying topological vector space of a Banach space. We recall from Chapter IV that if $\varphi\colon \mathcal{O} \cong \mathbf{R}^n$ is a chart in M and if $\psi\colon \xi|\mathcal{O} \cong \mathcal{O} \times V$ is a trivialization of ξ over $\mathcal{O}$, and if for $f \in C^\infty(\xi)$ we represent $f|\mathcal{O}$ by the map $\tilde{f} = \psi \circ f \circ \varphi^{-1}\colon \mathbf{R}^n \to V$, then $J^k(\xi)|\mathcal{O} \cong \mathcal{O} \times \oplus_{|\alpha| \leq k} V$ and $j_k(f)|\mathcal{O}$ is then represented by the map $j_k(\tilde{f})\colon \mathbf{R}^n \to \oplus_{|\alpha| \leq k} V$ defined by $j_k(\tilde{f})(y) = \{D^\alpha \tilde{f}(y)\}_{|\alpha| \leq k}$. It follows that the k-jet extension map $j_k\colon C^\infty(\xi) \to C^\infty(J^k(\xi))$ extends naturally to a map $C^k(\xi) \to C^0(J^k(\xi))$ so that the same coordinate representation still holds for this extended map, which we continue to denote by j_k. Then $j_k\colon C^k(\xi) \to C^0(J^k(\xi))$ is clearly injective and we topologize $C^k(\xi)$ by the requirement that j_k shall be a homeomorphism into. Then $f_n \to f$ in $C^k(\xi)$ means that, in terms of the above "coordinates," if $|\alpha| \leq k$ and K is a compact subset of $\mathbf{R}^n$ then $D^\alpha \tilde{f}_n$ converges uniformly to $D^\alpha \tilde{f}$ on K, from which we see that j_k maps $C^k(\xi)$ isomorphically onto a closed subspace of $C^0(J^k(\xi))$ (so $C^k(\xi)$ is the underlying topological vector space of a Banach space) and that the topology of $C^k(\xi)$ is just the usual "C^k topology."

§2. The hilbert space $H^0(\xi)$

We recall that by Section 4 of Chapter IV $< f, g >_\xi = \int_M (f(x), g(x))_\xi$ defines a prehilbert space inner product on $C^\infty(\xi)$. We define $H^0(\xi)$ to be the completion of this prehilbert space. Clearly we can (and will) regard $H^0(\xi)$ as the set of measurable cross-sections f of ξ such that $\|f\|_\xi^2 = \int_M (f(x), f(x))_\xi < \infty$, where we identify two such cross sections which are equal almost everywhere.

THEOREM 1. The underlying hilbertian space of $H^0(\xi)$ is independent of the measure on M.

PROOF. If ρ is the Radon Nikodym derivative of a second strictly positive smooth measure on M relative to the given measure then both ρ and $\sqrt{\rho}$ are strictly positive C^∞ functions on M, hence multiplication by $\sqrt{\rho}$ and $1/\sqrt{\rho}$ are inverse bounded linear transformations of $H^0(\xi)$ onto itself. But $\|\sqrt{\rho} f\|_\xi$ is just the norm of f in the H^0 formed relative to the second measure.

q.e.d.

THEOREM 2. If $T \in \mathrm{Hom}(\xi, \eta)$ then $T_*: C^\infty(\xi) \to C^\infty(\eta)$ extends to a bounded linear transformation of $H^0(\xi)$ into $H^0(\eta)$.

PROOF. Let $N(T)(p)$ be the norm of the linear map $T(p)$: $\xi_p \to \eta_p$. Then $N(T): M \to \mathbf{R}$ is continuous, hence $A = \mathrm{Sup}\{N(T)(p) \mid p \in M\} < \infty$. Since clearly $\|T_* f\|_\eta \le A\|f\|_\xi$ for $f \in C^\infty(\xi)$ the theorem follows.

q.e.d.

COROLLARY. The underlying hilbertian space of $H^0(\xi)$ is independent of the hermitian structure of ξ.

PROOF. If η is ξ with a second hermitian structure, then by the theorem the identity element of $\mathrm{Hom}(\xi, \eta)$ extends to an isomorphism (of topological vector spaces) of $H^0(\xi)$ with $H^0(\eta)$. But this extension is clearly just the identity map of $H^0(\xi)$.

q.e.d.

THEOREM 3. $C^0(\xi)$ is dense in $H^0(\xi)$ and the inclusion of $C^0(\xi)$ into $H^0(\xi)$ is continuous.

PROOF. If $f \in C^0(\xi)$ then $\|f\|_\xi^2 = \int_M \|f(x)\|_\xi^2 \le \int_M |||f|||_0^2 = |||f|||_0^2 \int_M 1$ from which it follows both that $C^0(\xi) \subseteq H^0(\xi)$ and that the inclusion map is continuous. Since $C^\infty(\xi) \subseteq C^0(\xi)$ and $C^\infty(\xi)$ is dense in $H^0(\xi)$, so is $C^0(\xi)$.

q.e.d.

§3. The spaces $H^k(\xi)$

While there is no canonical hermitian structure on the complex vector bundle $J^k(\xi)$ it follows from the corollary of Theorem 2 of the preceding section that $H^0(J^k(\xi))$ is a well-defined hilbertian space. We define the hilbertian space $H^k(\xi)$ to be the completion of $C^\infty(\xi)$ with respect to the topology which makes the linear injection

$$j_k\colon\ C^\infty(\xi) \to C^\infty(J^k(\xi)) \subseteq H^0(J^k(\xi))$$

a homeomorphism of $C^\infty(\xi)$ into $H^0(J^k(\xi))$. Note that by definition it follows that j_k extends to a continuous linear isomorphism $\bar{j}_k$ of $H^k(\xi)$ onto the closure of the image of j_k in $H^0(J^k(\xi))$.

THEOREM 1. If k and ℓ are non-negative integers, $k > \ell$, then the identity map of $C^\infty(\xi)$ extends to a continuous linear map $j_{\ell k}\colon\ H^k(\xi) \to H^\ell(\xi)$.

PROOF. Let $C^\infty_{[k]}(\xi)$ denote $C^\infty(\xi)$ as a topological subspace of $H^k(\xi)$, so by definition $j_k\colon\ C^\infty_{[k]}(\xi) \to H^0(J^k(\xi))$ is a homeomorphism. Let $T_{\ell k} \in \mathrm{Hom}(J^k(\xi), J^\ell(\xi))$ be the canonical projection defined by $T_{\ell k}(j_k(f)_p) = j_\ell(f)_p$, so that if $(T_{\ell k})_*\colon\ C^\infty(J^k(\xi)) \to C^\infty(J^\ell(\xi))$ is the induced map then $(T_{\ell k})_* j_k = j_\ell$, or $j_\ell^{-1}(T_{\ell k})_* j_k$ is the identity map of $C^\infty(\xi)$. Now by Theorem 2 of the preceding section $(T_{\ell k})_*$ extends to a continuous map of $H^0(J^k(\xi))$ into $H^0(J^\ell(\xi))$, hence $j_\ell^{-1}(T_{\ell k})_* j_k$ is a continuous map of $C^\infty_{[k]}(\xi)$ into $C^\infty_{[\ell]}(\xi)$ and therefore extends to a continuous map $j_{\ell k}\colon\ H^k(\xi) \to H^\ell(\xi)$.

q.e.d.

Remark. Note that if $m > k$ then $j_{\ell k} j_{km} = j_{\ell m}$, since both sides are continuous maps of $H^m(\xi)$ into $H^\ell(\xi)$ which are the identity on the dense subspace $H^\infty(\xi)$ of $H^m(\xi)$.

LEMMA. $C_0^\infty(\xi)$ is dense in $H^0(\xi)$.

PROOF. Let T_1 be a tubular neighborhood of ∂M (relative to some Riemannian metric) say of width 1 and let T_n be the concentric tubular neighborhood of width $1/n$. Since ∂M has measure zero and is the intersection of the T_n it follows that m_n = the measure of T_n tends to zero. Let $g_n\colon M \to [0, 1]$ be C^∞ with $g_n = 1$ on $M - T_n$ and (support $g_n) \cap \partial M = \emptyset$. If $f \in C^\infty(\xi)$ then $\|f-g_nf\|_\xi^2 \leq m_n \operatorname{Sup}\{\|f(x)\|^2 \,|\, x \in M\} \to 0$ so $g_nf \to f$ in $H^0(\xi)$. Since $g_nf \in C_0^\infty(\xi)$ and $C^\infty(\xi)$ is dense in $H^0(\xi)$ the lemma follows.

q.e.d.

THEOREM 2. Given non-negative integers k and ℓ with $k > \ell$ the continuous linear map $j_{\ell k}\colon H^k(\xi) \to H^\ell(\xi)$ which extends the identity map of $C^\infty(\xi)$ is injective.

PROOF. Choose any hermitian structure for $J^k(\xi)$ and let $< \, , \, >_{J^k(\xi)}$ denote the resulting inner product of $H^0(J^k(\xi))$. Then $< f, g >_k = < \bar{j}_k f, \bar{j}_k g >_{J^k(\xi)}$ is an admissible inner product for $H^k(\xi)$, since $\bar{j}_k$ maps $H^k(\xi)$ isomorphically into $H^0(J^k(\xi))$. Since $j_k\colon C^\infty(\xi) \to C^\infty(J^k(\xi))$ is an element of $\operatorname{Diff}_k(\xi, J^k(\xi))$ [IV, §3, Theorem 1] if follows from the Theorem of [IV, §4] that there is a unique formal adjoint $j_k^* \in \operatorname{Diff}_k(J^k(\xi), \xi)$ which satisfies $< j_k f, g >_{J^k(\xi)} = < f, j_k^* g >_\xi$ if $f \in C^\infty(\xi)$ and $g \in C_0^\infty(J^k(\xi))$. Now suppose $f \in H^k(\xi)$ and that $j_{\ell k}(f) = 0$. We must show that $f = 0$ and, since $\bar{j}_k\colon H^k(\xi) \to H^0(J^k(\xi))$ is an isomorphism into, it will suffice to show that $\bar{j}_k(f) = 0$. Let $\{f_n\}$ be a sequence in $C^\infty(\xi)$ converging in $H^k(\xi)$ to f. Then $j_k(f_n)$ converges in $H^0(J^k(\xi))$ to $\bar{j}_k(f)$ hence if $g \in C_0^\infty(J^k(\xi))$ then

$$
\begin{aligned}
< \bar{j}_k(f), g >_{J^k(\xi)} &= \lim_{n \to \infty} < j_k(f_n), g >_{J^k(\xi)} \\
&= \lim_{n \to \infty} < f_n, j_k^* g >_\xi \quad .
\end{aligned}
$$

Now in $H^0(\xi)$ we have $f_n = J_{ok}(f_n)$ so

$$
\lim_{n \to \infty} f_n = \lim_{n \to \infty} j_{ok}(f_n) = j_{ok}(f) = j_{o\ell} j_{\ell k}(f) = 0
$$

since by assumption $j_{\ell k}(f) = 0$. It follows that $\lim_{n\to\infty} < f_n, h >_\xi = 0$ for all $h \in H^0(\xi)$ so in particular taking $h = j_k^* g$ where $g \in C_0^\infty(\xi)$ we get $< \bar{j}_k(f), g >_{J^k(\xi)} = 0$, i.e., $\bar{j}_k(f)$ is orthogonal in $H^0(J^k(\xi))$ to $C_0^\infty(J^k(\xi))$. But by the lemma this implies $\bar{j}_k(f) = 0$.

q.e.d.

Remark. We will regard injections j_{ok}: $H^k(\xi) \to H^0(\xi)$ as identifications, i.e., henceforth we will consider the underlying vector space of $H^k(\xi)$ to be a subspace of $H^0(\xi)$ and j_{ok} to be the inclusion map. Since $j_{\ell k} = j_{o\ell}^{-1} j_{ok}$, it follows that $j_{\ell k}$: $H^k(\xi) \to H^\ell(\xi)$ are then also inclusion maps.

THEOREM 3. Let k be a non-negative integer. Then $C^k(\xi) \subseteq H^k(\xi)$ and the inclusion map $C^k(\xi) \to H^k(\xi)$ is continuous.

PROOF. Let $C^\infty_{(k)}(\xi)$ denote $C^\infty(\xi)$ with the topology induced from $C^k(\xi)$ and let $j_{(k)}$ denote j_k considered as a map of $C^\infty_{(k)}(\xi)$ into $C^0(J^k(\xi))$, so by definition of the topology of $C^k(\xi)$ [§1] $j_{(k)}$ is continuous and in fact a homeomorphism into. On the other hand by Theorem 3 of §2, i: $C^0(J^k(\xi)) \to H^0(J^k(\xi))$ is continuous. Now if we write $C^\infty_{[k]}(\xi)$ for $C^\infty(\xi)$ with the topology induced from $H^k(\xi)$ and $j_{[k]}$ for j_k considered as a map of $C^\infty_{[k]}(\xi)$ into $H^0(J^k(\xi))$ then, by definition of $H^k(\xi)$, $j_{[k]}$ is a homeomorphism into, hence $j_{[k]}^{-1}\, i j_{(k)}$: $C^\infty_{(k)}(\xi) \to C^\infty_{[k]}(\xi)$ is continuous. But of course $j_{[k]}^{-1}\, i j_{(k)}$ is just the identity map of $C^\infty(\xi)$. It follows that the identity map of $C^\infty(\xi)$ extends to a continuous map of $C^k(\xi)$ into $H^k(\xi)$. Because of our identification of $H^k(\xi)$ as a subset of $H^0(\xi)$ it follows that this map is an inclusion.

q.e.d.

THEOREM 4. If ξ is an hermitian vector bundle over M then $\{H^k(\xi)\}$ is a discrete chain of hilbertian spaces.

PROOF. Since $C^\infty(\xi)$ is dense in $H^k(\xi)$, $H^\infty(\xi) = \cap_k H^k(\xi) \supseteq C^\infty(\xi)$, and so $H^\infty(\xi)$ is dense in each $H^k(\xi)$. By the remark following Theorem 2, we have a continuous linear inclusion $H^k(\xi) \to H^\ell(\xi)$ if $k > \ell$, and by §2, $H^0(\xi)$ is a hilbert space. q.e.d.

Remark. In [X, §4, Corollary of Theorem 4] we shall see that not only is $C^\infty(\xi)$ included in $H^\infty(\xi)$ but in fact the two spaces are equal.

We shall carry over the concepts and notations of Chapter VIII. If k is a negative integer $H^k(\xi)$ denotes the anti-dual of $H^{-k}(\xi)$, and $H^{-\infty}(\xi) = \underrightarrow{\lim}\, H^{-k}(\xi)$.

THEOREM 5. Assume ∂M is empty and let $D \in \mathrm{Diff}_k(\xi, \eta)$. Then D has a transpose D^t, and in fact D^t is the formal adjoint of D, $D^* \in \mathrm{Diff}_k(\eta, \xi)$.

PROOF. Since ∂M is empty we have $< Df, g >_\eta = < f, D^*g >_\xi$ for all $f \in C^\infty(\xi)$ and $g \in C^\infty(\eta)$, by definition of D^*. But this says precisely that $D^* = D^t$.

q.e.d.

THEOREM 6. If $D \in \mathrm{Diff}_r(\xi, \eta)$ then, for each positive integer $k \geq r$, D extends to a continuous linear map $D_k\colon H^k(\xi) \to H^{k-r}(\eta)$.

PROOF. Let $s = k-r$ and let $\tilde{j}_s\colon C^\infty(\eta) \to C^\infty(J^s(\eta))$ be the s-jet extension map. Then $\tilde{j}_s \in \mathrm{Diff}_s(\eta, J^s(\eta))$ [IV, §3, Theorem 4] hence there is a unique $T \in \mathrm{Hom}(J^k(\xi), J^s(\eta))$ such that $\tilde{j}_s D = T_* j_k$ [IV, §3, Corollary 1 of Theorem 1]. If we write $C^\infty_{[k]}(\xi)$ for $C^\infty(\xi)$ with the topology induced from $H^k(\xi)$ and similarly $C^\infty_{[s]}(\eta)$ for $C^\infty(\eta)$ with the topology induced from $H^s(\eta)$, then by definition of $H^k(\xi)$ and $H^s(\eta)$ the maps $j_k\colon C^\infty_{[k]}(\xi) \to H^0(J^k(\xi))$ and $\tilde{j}_s\colon C^\infty_{[s]}(\eta) \to H^0(J^s(\eta))$ are homeomorphisms into. Also by Theorem 2 above, T_* extends to a continuous linear map of $H^0(J^k(\xi))$ into $H^0(J^s(\xi))$. It follows that $D = \tilde{j}_s^{-1} T_* j_k$ is a continuous linear map of $C^\infty_{[k]}(\xi)$ into $C^\infty_{[s]}(\eta)$ and hence extends to a continuous linear map D_k of $H^k(\xi)$ into $H^s(\eta)$.

q.e.d.

THEOREM 7. If $T \in \mathrm{Hom}(\xi, \eta)$ then the induced map $T_*\colon C^\infty(\xi) \to C^\infty(\eta)$ is an element of $OP_0(\xi, \eta)$.

PROOF. Recall that $T_* \in \mathrm{Diff}_0(\xi, \eta)$ [IV, §3, Corollary 2 of Theorem 1] hence by Theorem 6 for each non-negative integer k, T_* extends to a continuous linear map $(T_*)_k\colon H^k(\xi) \to H^k(\eta)$. T_* has a transpose

$(T^*)_* \in \mathrm{Diff}_0(\eta, \xi)$ and, by Theorem 6 again, for each positive integer k, $(T^*)_*$ extends to a continuous linear map of $H^k(\eta)$ into $H^k(\xi)$. Then [VIII, Corollary 1 of Theorem 5] completes the proof.

q.e.d.

THEOREM 8. $\xi \rightsquigarrow \{H^k(\xi)\}$ is a covariant functor from the category of hermitian vector bundles over M to the category of discrete chains of hilbertian spaces. If $T \in \mathrm{Hom}(\xi, \eta)$ then the induced morphism $\{T_k\} \in \mathrm{Hom}(\{H^k(\xi)\}, \{H^k(\eta)\})$ is defined by the requirement that T_k: $H^k(\xi) \to H^k(\eta)$ is the continuous extension of T_*: $C^\infty(\xi) \to C^\infty(\eta)$.

PROOF. This is essentially a restatement of Theorem 7 (see [VIII, Theorem 1]).

THEOREM 9. If ∂M is empty then $\mathrm{Diff}_1(\xi, \eta) \subseteq OP_1(\xi, \eta)$.

PROOF. If $D \in \mathrm{Diff}_1(\xi, \eta)$ then by Theorem 6 for each integer $k \geq 1$, D: $C^\infty(\xi) \to C^\infty(\eta)$ extends to a continuous linear map D_k: $H^k(\xi) \to H^{k-1}(\eta)$. By Theorem 5, D has a transpose D^t and in fact $D^t = D^* \in \mathrm{Diff}_1(\eta, \xi)$, so again by Theorem 6 for each integer $k \geq 1$, D^t extends to a continuous linear map $(D^t)_k$: $H^k(\eta) \to H^{k-1}(\xi)$. Then [VIII, Corollary 2 of Theorem 5] completes the proof.

q.e.d.

LEMMA. If k and ℓ are non-negative integers then $\mathrm{Diff}_{k+\ell}(\xi, \eta) = \mathrm{Diff}_\ell(J^k(\xi), \eta) \circ \mathrm{Diff}_k(\xi, J^k(\xi))$.

PROOF. Let j_k: $C^\infty(\xi) \to C^\infty(J^k(\xi))$, $j_{k+\ell}$: $C^\infty(\xi) \to C^\infty(J^{k+\ell}(\xi))$ and $\tilde{j}_\ell$: $C^\infty(J^k(\xi)) \to C^\infty(J^\ell(J^k(\xi)))$ be jet-extension maps. We note that $j_{k+\ell}(f)_p = 0$ if and only if $\tilde{j}_\ell(j_k(f))_p = 0$ (indeed in local coordinates the the first means $D^\alpha\tilde{f}(p) = 0$ if $|\alpha| \leq k+\ell$ while the second means $D^\alpha D^\beta\tilde{f}(p) = 0$ if $|\alpha| \leq \ell$ and $|\beta| \leq k$). It follows that there is a bundle monomorphism S of $J^{k+\ell}(\xi)$ onto a sub-bundle of $J^\ell(J^k(\xi))$ such that $S(j_{k+\ell}(f)_p) = \tilde{j}_\ell(j_k(f))_p$. Since exact sequences of vector bundles split we can find $T \in \mathrm{Hom}(J^\ell(J^k(\xi)), J^{k+\ell}(\xi))$ such that ST = identity, i.e., such that $T_* \tilde{j}_\ell j_k = j_{k+\ell}$. Then if $D \in \mathrm{Diff}_{k+\ell}(\xi, \eta)$ there is a unique $R \in \mathrm{Hom}(J^{k+\ell}(\xi), \eta)$ such that $D = R_* j_{k+\ell} = ((RT)_* \tilde{j}_\ell) \circ j_k$. But $j_k \in \mathrm{Diff}_k(\xi, J^k(\xi))$ while $(RT)_* \tilde{j}_\ell \in \mathrm{Diff}_\ell(J^k(\xi), \eta)$.

q.e.d.

THEOREM 10. If ∂M is empty then for each non-negative integer k, $\mathrm{Diff}_k(\xi, \eta) \subseteq \mathrm{OP}_k(\xi, \eta)$.

PROOF. The cases $k = 0$ and $k = 1$ are just Theorems 7 and 9 respectively. Hence we can assume that $k > 1$ and, inductively, that the theorem is true when k is replaced by $k-1$. By the lemma we can write $D \in \mathrm{Diff}_k(\xi, \eta)$ as $D_1 D_2$ where $D_2 \in \mathrm{Diff}_{k-1}(\xi, J^{k-1}(\xi))$ and $D_1 \in \mathrm{Diff}_1(J^{k-1}(\xi), \eta)$. By the inductive hypothesis $D_2 \in \mathrm{OP}_{k-1}(\xi, J^{k-1}(\xi))$ and by Theorem 9 $D_1 \in \mathrm{OP}_1(J^{k-1}(\xi), \eta)$; hence by [VIII, Theorem 3] $D = D_1 D_2$ is in $\mathrm{OP}_k(\xi, \eta)$.

q.e.d.

If $M = [0, 1]$, ξ is the trivial line bundle over M and $D \in \mathrm{Diff}_1(\xi, \xi)$ is the usual derivative, $Df = f'$, then if D had a transpose D^t we would have for all $f \in C^\infty(\xi)$ that

$$f(1) - f(0) = \int_0^1 f'(s)ds = \langle Df, 1 \rangle_\xi = \langle f, D^t 1 \rangle_\xi$$
$$= \int_0^1 f(s)(D^t 1)(s)ds \quad .$$

or in other words the measure with mass one at 1 and mass minus one at 0 is absolutely continuous with respect to Lebesgue measure, a contradiction. Thus D does not have a transpose so $D \notin \mathrm{OP}_1(\xi, \xi)$ and in fact $D \notin \mathrm{OP}_k(\xi, \xi)$ for any k by [VIII, Theorem 4]. This shows that the hypothesis $\partial M = \emptyset$ is in fact essential in Theorems 5, 9, and 10.

CHAPTER X

THE CONTINUOUS SOBOLEV CHAIN OF A VECTOR BUNDLE

Richard S. Palais

§1. Continuous Sobolev chains

We recall that in VII, §3 we defined a functor (quadratic interpolation) $C_{\mathbf{Z}} \rightsquigarrow C_{\mathbf{R}}$ which to each discrete chain of hilbertian spaces $\{H^k\}_{k\in \mathbf{Z}}$ associated a continuous chain $\{H^k\}_{k\in\mathbf{R}}$ and which was the identity on morphisms. If M is a compact manifold with a strictly positive smooth measure and ξ is an hermitian vector bundle over M then applying this functor to the discrete Sobolev chain $\{H^k(\xi)\}_{k\in\mathbf{Z}}$ we get a continuous chain $\{H^k(\xi)\}_{k\in\mathbf{R}}$ called the *continuous Sobolev chain of* ξ. By [VIII, §3, Theorem 1)] if $r \in \mathbf{Z}$ then $OP_r(\{H^k(\xi)\}_{k\in\mathbf{R}}, \{H^k(\eta)\}_{k\in\mathbf{R}}) = OP_r(\{H^k(\xi)\}_{k\in\mathbf{Z}}, \{H^k(\eta)\}_{k\in\mathbf{Z}}$ (where η is a second hermitian bundle over M) so we define

$$OP_r(\xi, \eta) = OP_r(\{H^k(\xi)\}_{k\in\mathbf{R}}, \{H^k(\eta)\}_{k\in\mathbf{R}}\}$$

for $r \in \mathbf{R}$.

In the following theorem we are identifying $\mathrm{Hom}(\{H^k(\xi)\}_{k\in\mathbf{R}}, \{H^k(\eta)\}_{k\in\mathbf{R}})$ with $OP_0(\xi, \eta)$ [VIII, §1, Theorem 1]. Thus if $f\colon \xi \to \eta$ is a bundle map then the induced map $f_*\colon H^\infty(\xi) \to H^\infty(\eta)$ is in $\mathrm{Hom}(\{H^k(\xi)\}_{k\in\mathbf{R}}, \{H^k(\eta)\}_{k\in\mathbf{R}})$ [IX, §3, Theorem 7].

THEOREM. Let M be a compact manifold with strictly positive smooth measure. Then $\xi \rightsquigarrow \{H^k(\xi)\}_{k\in\mathbf{R}}$ is a functor from the category V(M) of hermitian vector bundles over M to the category $C_{\mathbf{R}}$ of continuous chains of hilbertian spaces. If $f\colon \xi \to \eta$ is a morphism of V(M) then $f_*\colon H^\infty(\xi) \to H^\infty(\eta)$ is the associated morphism of $C_{\mathbf{R}}$.

PROOF. [IX, §3, Theorem 8] and [VII, §3, Theorem].

§2. The chains $\{H^k(T^n, V)\}$

If k is a non-negative integer and α is a n-multi-index with $|\alpha| \leq k$ then we define $C_\alpha^k = k!/(\alpha!(k-|\alpha|)!$ so that by the multinomial theorem if $y \in \mathbf{R}^n$ then $(1+\|y\|^2)^k = \Sigma_{|\alpha| \leq k} C_\alpha^k y^{2\alpha}$. If V is an hermitian vector space we denote by $\oplus_{|\alpha| \leq k} V$ the direct sum of copies of V, one for each n-multi-index α with $|\alpha| \leq k$, made into an hermitian vector space by the inner product

$$(\{u_\alpha\}, \{v\}_\alpha) = \sum_{|\alpha| \leq k} C_\alpha^k(u_\alpha, v_\alpha) \quad .$$

T^n will denote the n-dimensional torus $\mathbf{R}^n/2\pi\, \mathbf{Z}^n$, so a function (of class C^k) on T^n may be regarded as a function (of class C^k) on $\mathbf{R}^n$ having each element of $2\pi\, \mathbf{Z}^n$ as a period. An integral of a vector valued function defined on T^n is to be understood to be the integral of the corresponding function on $\mathbf{R}^n$ over the "fundamental cube" $\{x \in \mathbf{R}^n | -\pi \leq x_i < \pi\}$ with respect to Lebesgue measure.

If k is a positive integer or ∞ we will write $C^k(T^n, V)$ for the space of C^k maps of T^n into V, which we identify with $C^k(\xi)$, ξ being the trivial bundle over T^n with fiber V. By [IV, §2] we have a canonical identification of $J^k(\xi)$ with the trivial bundle over T^n with fiber $\oplus_{|\alpha| \leq k} V$; the k-jet extension map

$$j_k\colon\ C^k(T^n, V) \to C^0(T^n, \bigoplus_{|\alpha| \leq k} V)$$

being given by $j_k(f)(x) = \{D^\alpha f(x)\}_{|\alpha| \leq k}$. Now the norm for $C^0(T^n, V)$ is

$$|||f|||_0^2 = \mathrm{Sup}\{\|f(x)\|^2 | x \in T^n\}$$

and it follows from [IX, §1] that the norm in $C^k(T^n, V)$ is given by

$$|||f|||_k^2 = \sup\{\sum_{|\alpha| \leq k} C_\alpha^k \|D^\alpha f(x)\|^2 \Big| x \in T^n\} \quad .$$

Similarly, if we write $H^k(T^n, V)$ for $H^k(\xi)$ (k a non-negative integer) then by [IX, §2] $H^0(T^n, V)$ is the completion of $C^0(T^n, V)$ in the norm

$$\|f\|_0^2 = \int_{T^n} \|f(x)\|^2 \, dx$$

and hence $H^k(T^n, V)$ is the completion of $C^k(T^n, V)$ in the norm

$$\|f\|_k^2 = \sum_{|\alpha| \leq k} c_\alpha^k \|D^\alpha f\|_0^2 \quad .$$

Now $\{H^k(T^n, V)\}$ is a discrete chain of hilbertian (in fact hilbert) spaces, the discrete Sobolev chain of ξ, and following our notational conventions we will write $\{H^k(T^n, V)\}_{k\in\mathbf{R}}$ for the continuous chain it gives rise to by quadratic interpolation (which, by definition, is the continuous Sobolev chain of ξ).

DEFINITION. For each $\nu \in \mathbf{Z}^n$, e_ν will denote the element of $C^\infty(T^n, \mathbf{C})$ defined by $e_\nu(x) = (2\pi)^{-n/2} e^{i\nu\cdot x}$. For $f \in C^\infty(T^n, V)$ we define $\hat{f}\colon \mathbf{Z}^n \to V$ by

$$\hat{f}(\nu) = (2\pi)^{-n/2} \int_{T^n} e^{-i\nu\cdot x} f(x)dx$$

so that $f \in C^\infty(T^n, \mathbf{C})$ then $\hat{f}(\nu) = \langle f, e_\nu \rangle_0$.

LEMMA 1. $\{e_\nu\}_{\nu\in \mathbf{Z}^n}$ is an orthonormal basis for $H^0(T^n, \mathbf{C})$.

PROOF. That $\langle e_\mu, e_\nu \rangle_0 = \delta_{\mu\nu}$ is clear, so it will suffice to prove that the space E of finite linear combinations of the e_ν is dense in $H^0(T^n, \mathbf{C})$. Now E is clearly an algebra, separates points, and is stable under complex conjugation so by the Stone-Weierstrass theorem, E is dense in $C^0(T^n, \mathbf{C})$. By [IX, §2, Theorem 3] E is dense in $H^0(T^n, \mathbf{C})$.

q.e.d.

LEMMA 2. If $k \in \mathbf{R}$ then $\{(1+\|\nu\|^2)^{-k/2} e_\nu\}_{\nu\in \mathbf{Z}^n}$ is an orthonormal basis for $H^k(T^n, \mathbf{C})$ and $\{(1+\|\nu\|^2)^{k/2} e_\nu\}_{\nu\in \mathbf{Z}^n}$ is the dual basis of $H^{-k}(T^n, \mathbf{C})$.

PROOF. Because $\{H^k(T^n, \mathbf{C})\}_{k\in\mathbf{R}}$ arises by quadratic interpolation from $\{H^k(T^n, \mathbf{C})\}_{k\in\mathbf{Z}}$ it will suffice to prove this for k a positive integer. Now $D^\alpha e_\nu = (i)^{|\alpha|} \nu^\alpha e_\nu$ and the formal adjoint of D^α is

$(-1)^{|\alpha|}D^{\alpha}$, hence if $f \in C^{\infty}(T^n, C)$, $< D^{\alpha}f, D^{\alpha}e_{\nu} >_0 = (-1)^{|\alpha|}< f, D^{2\alpha}e_{\nu} >_0$ $= \nu^{2\alpha}< f, e_{\nu} >_0$ and recalling the identity $\Sigma_{|\alpha| \leq k} C^k_{\alpha}\nu^{2\alpha} = (1+\|\nu\|^2)^k$ mentioned at the beginning of this section $< f, e_{\nu} >_k = \Sigma_{|\alpha| \leq k} C^k_{\alpha} < D^{\alpha}f,$ $D^{\alpha}e_{\nu} >_0$. Since $C^{\infty}(T^n, \mathbf{C})$ is dense in $H^k(T^n, \mathbf{C})$ the same equality holds for all $f \in H^k(T^n, \mathbf{C})$. It follows from Lemma 1 that $\{(1+\|\nu\|^2)^{-k/2}e_{\nu}\}_{\nu \in \mathbf{Z}^n}$ is orthonormal in $H^k(T^n, \mathbf{C})$. If $< f, e_{\nu} >_k = 0$ for all $\nu \in \mathbf{Z}^n$ then $< f, e_{\nu} >_0 = 0$ for all $\nu \in \mathbf{Z}^n$ and by Lemma 1, $f = 0$ so $\{(1+\|\nu\|^2)^{-k/2}e_{\nu}\}_{\nu \in \mathbf{Z}^n}$ is an orthonormal basis. Since $< (1+\|\nu\|^2)^{-k/2}e_{\nu},$ $(1+\|\nu\|^2)^{k/2}e_{\nu} >_0 = < e_{\nu}, e_{\nu} >_0 = \delta_{\mu\nu}$ it follows that $\{(1+\|\nu\|^2)^{k/2}e_{\nu}\}_{\nu \in \mathbf{Z}^n}$ is the dual basis for $H^{-k}(T^n, C)$.

q.e.d.

We recall that in [VIII, §4] we defined $\ell^2_k(\mathbf{Z}^n, V)$ to be the hilbert space of maps $g: \mathbf{Z}^n \to V$ such that

$$\|g\|^2_k = \sum_{\nu \in \mathbf{Z}^n} \|g(\nu)\|^2(1+\|\nu\|^2)^k < \infty .$$

THEOREM 1. For each $k \in \mathbf{R}$ the map $f \to \hat{f}$ extends (from $C^{\infty}(T^n, V)$) to an isometry of $H^k(T^n, V)$ onto $\ell^2_k(\mathbf{Z}^n, V)$, which we continue to denote by $f \to \hat{f}$. Moreover if $f \in H^k(T^n, V)$ then the series $\Sigma_{\nu \in \mathbf{Z}^n} \hat{f}(\nu)e_{\nu}$ converges absolutely to f in $H^k(T^n, V)$.

PROOF. We note that $H^k(T^n, V_1 \oplus V_2) = H^k(T^n, V_1) \oplus H^k(T^n, V_2)$ and that $\ell^2_k(\mathbf{Z}^n, V_1 \oplus V_2) = \ell^2_k(\mathbf{Z}^n, V_1) \oplus \ell^2_k(\mathbf{Z}^n, V_2)$ and that if $f_1 \oplus f_2 \in$ $C^{\infty}(T^n, V_1 \oplus V_2)$ then $(f_1 \oplus f_2)^{\wedge} = \hat{f}_1 \oplus \hat{f}_2$, from which the validity of the theorem for V_1 and for V_2 implies it for $V_1 \oplus V_2$. Since V is isometric to a direct sum of copies of $\mathbf{C}$ we can restrict attention to the case $V = \mathbf{C}$.

In this case for $f \in H^{-\infty}(T^n, \mathbf{C})$, $< f, e_{\nu} >_0$ is a well defined element of $\mathbf{C}$, since $e_{\nu} \in C^{\infty}(T^n, \mathbf{C}) \subseteq H^{\infty}(T^n, \mathbf{C})$. If $f \in C^{\infty}(T^n, \mathbf{C})$ then $< f, e_{\nu} >_0 = \hat{f}(\nu)$, so we define $\hat{f}(\nu) = < f, e_{\nu} >_0$ for all $f \in H^{-\infty}(T^n, \mathbf{C})$. Then by Lemma 2, if $f \in H^k(T^n, \mathbf{C})$ we have

$$\|f\|_k^2 = \sum_{\nu\in Z^n} |< f, (1+\|\nu\|^2)^{k/2} e_\nu >_0|^2$$

$$= \sum_{\nu\in Z^n} |\hat{f}(\nu)|^2 (1+\|\nu\|^2)^k = \|\hat{f}\|_k^2$$

and the series $\Sigma_{\nu\in \mathbf{Z}^n} < f, (1+\|\nu\|^2)^{k/2} e_\nu >_0 (1+\|\nu\|^2)^{-k/2} e_\nu = \Sigma_{\nu\in \mathbf{Z}^n} \hat{f}(\nu) e_\nu$ converges absolutely to f in $H^k(T^n, \mathbf{C})$.

q.e.d.

COROLLARY. The chains $\{H^k(T^n, V)\}$ and $\{\ell_k^2(\mathbf{Z}^n, V)\}$ are isomorphic. In particular, [VIII, §4, Theorem 3] $\{H^k(T^n, V)\}$ is a Rellich chain and a scale.

In the following lemma, $E(T^n, V)$ will denote the space of maps $f: T^n \to V$ of the form $f(x) = \Sigma_{\nu\in \mathbf{Z}^n} e_\nu(x) g(\nu)$ where $g: \mathbf{Z}^n \to V$ is zero except for finitely many values of ν.

Also given $f: T^n \to V$ and $a \in T^n$ we define $f_a: T^n \to V$ by $f_a(x) = f(a+x)$.

LEMMA. If V is any hermitian vector space then

1) $E(T^n, V)$ is dense in $H^k(T^n, V)$ for all $k \in \mathbf{R}$.

2) If $f \in E(T^n, V)$, $a \in T^n$ then $f_a \in E(T^n, V)$ and $\|f_a\|_k = \|f\|_k$ for all $k \in \mathbf{R}$.

3) if $f \in E(T^n, V)$, α is an n-multi-index with $|\alpha| \leq r$ then $D^\alpha f \in E(T^n, V)$ and $\|D^\alpha f\|_{k-r} \leq \|f\|_k$ for all $k \in \mathbf{R}$.

PROOF. As in the proof of Theorem 1, it suffices to prove the lemma with $V = \mathbf{C}$. Now $E(T^n, \mathbf{C})$ is just the linear span of $\{e_\nu\}_{\nu\in \mathbf{Z}^n}$. Since by Lemma 2 of Theorem 1 $\{(1+\|\nu\|^2)^{-k/2} e_\nu\}_{\nu\in \mathbf{Z}^n}$ is an orthonormal basis for $H^k(T^n, \mathbf{C})$ and since $(e_\nu)_a = e^{i\nu\cdot a} e_\nu$ while $D^\alpha e_\nu = (i)^{|\alpha|} \nu^\alpha e_\nu$ the lemma is immediate.

q.e.d.

THEOREM 2. (Sobolev) If V is an hermitian vector space, r a non-negative integer and k a real number with $k > \frac{n}{2} + r$ then $H^k(T^n, V) \subseteq C^r(T^n, V)$ and the inclusion map is completely continuous.

PROOF. It will suffice to prove that the inclusion map is continuous, for we can factor it as

$$H^k(T^n, V) \to H^\ell(T^n, V) \to C^r(T^n, V)$$

where $k > \ell > \frac{n}{2} + r$, and by the corollary of Theorem 1 $H^k(T^n, V) \to H^\ell(T^n, V)$ is completely continuous.

Let $f \in E(T^n, V)$, so (e.g. by Theorem 1) $f = \sum_{\nu \in \mathbf{Z}^n} e_\nu \hat{f}(\nu)$, where $\hat{f}(\nu) = 0$ except for finitely many $\nu \in \mathbf{Z}^n$. In particular $f(0) = \sum_{\nu \in \mathbf{Z}^n} \hat{f}(\nu)$, hence

$$\|f(0)\| = \|\sum_{\nu \in \mathbf{Z}^n} \hat{f}(\nu)\| \leq B\|\hat{f}\|_{k-r}$$

by [VIII, §4, corollary of Theorem 5] since $k - r > \frac{n}{2}$. By Theorem 1 above

$$\|f(0)\| \leq B\|f\|_{k-r} \quad .$$

If $a \in T^n$ then replacing f by f_a and using 2) of the lemma gives

$$\|f(a)\| \leq B\|f\|_{k-r}$$

since $f_a(0) = f(a)$. Since this holds for each $a \in T^n$ and $|||f|||_0 = \operatorname{Sup}\{\|f(a)\| \,|\, a \in T^n\}$,

$$|||f|||_0 \leq B\|f\|_{k-r} \quad .$$

If α is an n-multi-index with $|\alpha| \leq r$ then 3) of the lemma gives

$$|||D^\alpha f|||_0 \leq B\|f\|_k$$

and recalling that

$$|||f|||_r^2 = \operatorname{Sup}\left\{\sum_{|\alpha| \leq r} c_\alpha^k \|D^\alpha f(x)\|^2 \,|\, x \in T^n\right\}$$

$$\leq \sum_{|\alpha| \leq r} c_\alpha^k \, |||D^\alpha f|||_0^2$$

we get finally

$$|||f|||_r^2 \leq \left(B \sum_{|\alpha| \leq k} c_\alpha^k\right) \|f\|_k^2$$

i.e., the identity map of $E(T^n, V)$ is continuous from the topology induced on it by $H^k(T^n, V)$ to that induced by $C^r(T^n, V)$. Then 1) of the lemma completes the proof.

q.e.d.

COROLLARY. If r is a positive integer $k > \frac{n}{2} + r$, then $\sum_{\nu \in \mathbf{Z}^n} e_\nu \hat{f}(\nu)$ converges absolutely to f in $C^r(T^n, V)$ for each $f \in H^k(T^n, V)$. In particular if $f \in C^\infty(T^n, V)$ then $\sum_{\nu \in \mathbf{Z}^n} e_\nu \hat{f}(\nu)$ converges to f in the C^∞-topology.

PROOF. Immediate from Theorem 1 and Theorem 2.

THEOREM 3. Let n and ℓ be integers with $n > \ell \geq 0$, and let $s = (n-\ell)/2$. Then if k is any real number larger than s the restriction map $C^\infty(T^n, V) \to C^\infty(T^\ell, V)$ extends uniquely to a continuous linear map $\rho: H^k(T^n, V) \to H^{k-s}(T^\ell, V)$. Moreover ρ has a continuous linear section $\chi: H^{k-s}(T^\ell, V) \to H^k(T^n, V)$.

PROOF. Let $f \in C\ (T^n, V)$. By the above corollary, if $x = (y, z) \in T^\ell \times T^{n-\ell}$ then

$$f(y, z) = \sum_{(\lambda,\mu)} e_{(\lambda,\mu)}(y, z)\hat{f}(\lambda, \mu)$$

$$= \sum_{(\lambda,\mu)} e_\lambda(y)e_\mu(z)\hat{f}(\lambda, \mu)$$

where the summation is over all (λ, μ) in $\mathbf{Z}^\ell \times \mathbf{Z}^{n-\ell} = \mathbf{Z}^n$ and the convergence is uniform on T^n. Then since $e_\mu(0) = (2\pi)^{-s}$ we have

$$f(y, 0) = \sum_{\lambda \in \mathbf{Z}^\ell} e_\lambda(y)\Big(\sum_{\mu \in \mathbf{Z}^{n-\ell}} \hat{f}(\lambda, \mu)\Big)$$

where the convergence is uniform on T^ℓ. It follows that

$$(f|T^\ell)\hat{}(\lambda) = (2\pi)^{-s} \sum_{\mu \in \mathbf{Z}^{n-\ell}} \hat{f}(\lambda, \mu) \quad .$$

The theorem is now an immediate consequence of Theorem 1 above and [VIII, §4, Theorem 5].

q.e.d.

§3. An extension theorem

Let $B^n = \{x \in \mathbf{R}^n \mid \|x\| < 1\}$ and let $B^n_+ = \{x \in B^n \mid x_n \geq 0\}$. If V is an hermetian vector space then, letting X denote either B^n or B^n_+, we define $C^\infty_0(X, V)$ to be the space of C^∞ maps of X into V having compact support, and for k a non-negative integer we define $C^k_0(X, V)$ to be Banach space that results from completing $C^\infty_0(X, V)$ with respect to the norm

$$|||f|||^2_k = \operatorname{Sup}\left\{ \sum_{|\alpha| \leq k} c^k_\alpha \, \|D^\alpha f(x)\|^2 \,|\, x \in X\right\}$$

and similarly we define $H^k_0(X, V)$ to be the hilbert space that results by completing $C^\infty_0(X, V)$ with respect to the norm

$$\|f\|^2_k = \sum_{|\alpha| \leq k} c^k_\alpha \int_X \|D^\alpha f(x)\|^2 \, dx \quad .$$

It is clear that $\{H^k_0(X, V)\}$ is a discrete chain of hilbert spaces and as usual we write $\{H^k_0(X, V)\}_{k \in \mathbf{R}}$ for the continuous chain that arises from it by quadratic interpolation. If $f \in C^\infty_0(B^n, V)$ then $f|B^n_+ \in C^\infty_0(B^n_+, V)$ and $|||f|B^n_+|||_k \leq |||f|||_k$ and $\|f|B^n_+\|_k \leq \|f\|_k$ hence

THEOREM 1. The restriction map $f \to f|B^n_+$ of $C^\infty_0(B^n, V)$ into $C^\infty_0(B^n_+, V)$ extends, for k a non-negative integer, to a continuous linear map, $C^k_0(B^n, V) \to C^k_0(B^n_+, V)$. For k a non-negative real number it extends to a continuous linear map $H^k_0(B^n, V) \to H^k_0(B^n_+, V)$.

THEOREM 2. If k is a non-negative integer then the restriction map

$$C^k_0(B^n, V) \to C^k_0(B^n_+, V)$$

has a continuous linear section

$$E\colon \; C^k_0(B^n_+, V) \to C^k_0(B^n, V).$$

Moreover, E can be so chosen that if ℓ is an integer

with $0 \le \ell \le k$ then E extends to a continuous linear section $E_{(\ell)}: C_0^\ell(B_+^n, V) \to C_0^\ell(B^n, V)$ of the restriction map $C_0^\ell(B^n, V) \to C_0^\ell(B_+^n, V)$ and if ℓ is a real number with $0 \le \ell \le k$ then E extends to a continuous linear section $E_{[\ell]}: H_0^\ell(B_+^n, V) \to H_0^\ell(B^n, V)$ of the restriction map $H_0^\ell(B^n, V) \to H_0^\ell(B_+^n, V)$.

PROOF. Given $f \in C_0^k(B_+^n, V)$ define $E(f): B^n \to V$ by

$$E(f)(x) = \begin{cases} f(x) & x_n \ge 0 \\ \sum_{m=0}^{k} C_m f(x_1, \ldots, x_{n-1}, (-\frac{m}{k+1})x_n) & x_n < 0 \end{cases}$$

where we will choose the real numbers C_m independently of f so that $E(f)$ is C^k across B^{n-1}. Namely we must choose the C_m so that, whatever f,

$$\frac{\partial^r f}{\partial x_n^r}(x_1, \ldots, x_{n-1}, 0) = \sum_{m=0}^{k} \left(-\frac{m}{k+1}\right)^r C_m \frac{\partial^r f}{\partial x_n^r}(x_1, \ldots, x_{n-1}, 0)$$

for $r = 0, 1, \ldots, k$. This will certainly be the case if

$$\sum_{m=0}^{k} a_{rm} C_m = 1 \qquad r, m = 0, 1, \ldots, k$$

where $a_{rm} = (-\frac{m}{k+1})^r$. But a_{rm} is just the Vandermonde matrix of $0, \frac{-1}{k+1}, \frac{-2}{k+1}, \ldots, \frac{-k}{k+1}$ and hence its determinant is, by the well-known formula,

$$\prod_{0 \le i < j \le k} \left(\frac{j-i}{k+1}\right) \ne 0$$

so (*) has a unique solution $(C_0, C_1, \ldots, C_k)$. Then E, defined by this choice of the C_i, is clearly a linear map of $C_0^k(B_+^n, V)$ into $C_0^k(B^n, V)$ and by definition, $E(f)|B_+^n = f$ i.e., E is a section for the restriction map. Given an n-multi-index α with $|\alpha| \le k$ it is clear from the definition of E that

$$D^\alpha E(f)(x) = \sum_{m=0}^{k} \left(-\frac{m}{k+1}\right)^{\alpha_n} C_m D^\alpha f(x_1, \ldots, x_{n-1}, (\tfrac{-m}{k+1})\, x_n)$$

if $x_n < 0$ from which it follows easily that if ℓ is an integer with $0 \le \ell \le k$ then $|||E(f)|||_\ell \le$ constant $\|f\|_\ell$ and similarly $\|E(f)\|_\ell \le$

constant $\|f\|_\ell$ from which the existence of $E_{(\ell)}$ and $E_{[\ell]}$ follows. The existence of $E_{[\ell]}$ when ℓ is any real number with $0 \leq \ell \leq k$ now follows from the basic interpolation property of quadratic interpolation.

q.e.d.

Since B^n is included in the fundamental cube $\{x \in \mathbf{R}^n \mid -\pi \leq x_i < \pi\}$ we may regard B^n as a subset of T^n. Moreover if $f \in C_0^\infty(B^n, V)$ we may regard f as being an element of $C^\infty(T^n, V)$ by extending it to be zero in the complement of B^n. We call this the *canonical identification map* of $C_0^\infty(B^n, V)$ into $C^\infty(T^n, V)$. It is an immediate consequence of the definitions of the various norms involved that this map is isometric from $C_0^\infty(B^n, V)$ as a subspace of $C_0^k(B^n, V)$ (respectively $H_0^k(B^n, V)$) into $C^k(T^n, V)$ (respectively $H^k(T^n, V)$). Hence

THEOREM 3. The canonical identification map $C_0^\infty(B^n, V) \to C^\infty(T^n, V)$ extends to isometries of $C_0^k(B^n, V)$ into $C^k(T^n, V)$ and of $H_0^k(B^n, V)$ into $H^k(T^n, V)$ for each non-negative integer k.

§4. The Rellich, Sobolev, and restriction theorems

In this section M will denote n-dimensional compact manifold (possibly with boundary) with a strictly positive smooth measure, and ξ will denote an hermitian vector bundle over M.

Let $\varphi_i : \mathcal{O}_i \approx \mathbf{R}^n_+$ $(i = 1, \ldots, t)$ be charts for M such that

$$\partial M = \bigcup_{i=1}^{t} \varphi_i^{-1}(B^{n-1}_{1/2})$$

where $B^{n-1}_{1/2} = \{x \in \mathbf{R}^{n-1} \mid \|x\| < \frac{1}{2}\}$. Choose additional charts

$$\varphi_i : \mathcal{O}_i \approx \mathbf{R}^n \qquad (i = t+1, \ldots, r)$$

for M such that

$$M = \bigcup_{i=1}^{r} \varphi_i^{-1}(B^n_{1/2}) \quad .$$

Let $\lambda_1, \ldots, \lambda_r$ be a C^∞ partition of unity for M with (support λ_i) $\subseteq \varphi_i^{-1}(B^n)$ and let $\mu_1, \ldots, \mu_r$ be C^∞ real valued functions on M such that (support μ_i) $\subseteq \varphi_i^{-1}(B^n)$ and μ_i is identically one on (support λ_i). Finally let $\psi_i: \xi|\mathcal{O}_i \cong \mathcal{O}_i \times V$ $(i = 1, \ldots, r)$ be C^∞ trivializations of the bundle $\xi|\mathcal{O}_i$, where V is a fixed hermitian vector space.

DEFINITION. We define linear maps

$$P^i: C^\infty(T^n, V) \to C^\infty(\xi) \qquad (i = 1, \ldots, r)$$
$$P: \bigoplus_{i=1}^{r} C^\infty(T^n, V) \to C^\infty(\xi)$$

depending only on $(\varphi_i, \psi_i, \mu_i)$ by

$$P^i(g)(x) = \begin{cases} 0 & \text{if } x \notin \varphi_i^{-1}(B_n) \\ \mu_i(x)\psi_i^{-1}(g(\varphi_i(x))) & \text{if } x \in \mathcal{O}_i \end{cases}$$

$$P(g_1, \ldots, g_r) = P^1g_1 + P^2g_2 + \ldots + P^rg_r \quad .$$

THEOREM 1. For each non-negative integer k the linear map $P: \oplus_{i=1}^r (T^n, V) \to C^\infty(\xi)$ extends to a continuous linear map

$$P_{(k)}: \bigoplus_{i=1}^{r} C^k(T^n, V) \to C^k(\xi)$$

and also to a continuous map

$$P_{[k]}: \bigoplus_{i=1}^{r} H^k(T^n, V) \to H^k(\xi) \quad .$$

PROOF. Recall that we have trivializations $\psi_i^k: J^k(\xi)|\mathcal{O}_i \cong \mathcal{O}_i \times \oplus_{|\alpha| \leq k} V$ defined by $j_k(f)_p \to \{D^\alpha\tilde{f}(\varphi_i(p))\}_{|\alpha| < k}$ where $\tilde{f} = \psi_i \circ f \circ \varphi_i^{-1}$ [IX, §2]. It follows from the definitions of $C^k(\xi)$ and $H^k(\xi)$ [IX, §§1 and 2] that the case $k = 0$ applied to the bundle $J^k(\xi)$ and hermitian space $\oplus_{|\alpha| \leq k} V$ will give the desired result for the bundle ξ and hermitian space V, hence we may suppose $k = 0$.

Clearly it will suffice to prove that each of the maps $P^i: C^\infty(T^n, V) \to C^\infty(\xi)$ extends to a continuous linear map

$$P^i_{(0)}: C^0(T^n, V) \to C^0(\xi)$$

and to a continuous linear map $P^i_{[0]}: H^0(T^n, V) \to H^0(\xi)$. Now if $i = 1, \ldots, r$ is fixed for the moment then we can clearly construct an hermitian structure on ξ such that $(e, e')_\xi = (\psi_i(e), \psi_i(e'))$ if $e, e' \in \xi_x$ where $x \in \varphi_i^{-1}(B^n)$. Also we can construct a strictly positive smooth measure on M such that $\int_M g = \int_{\mathbf{R}^n} g(\varphi_i^{-1}(x))dx$ if (support g) $\leq \varphi_i^{-1}(B^n)$. But then as we saw in [IX, §§1 and 2] $|||f|||_0 = \operatorname{Sup}\|f(x)\|$ and $\|f\|_0^2 = \int_M \|f(x)\|^2$ are admissible norms for $C^0(\xi)$ and $H^0(\xi)$ respectively. Using these norms we have

$$|||P^i g|||_0 = \operatorname{Sup}|\mu_i(x)|\,\|g(\varphi_i(x))\| \leq C\,|||g|||_0$$

$$|||P^i g|||_0^2 = \int_{B^n} |\mu_i(\varphi_i^{-1}(x))|^2 \|g(x)\|^2 dx \leq C^2 \|g\|_0^2$$

where $C = \operatorname{Sup}|\mu_i(x)|$. This proves the existence of $P^i_{(0)}$ and of $P^i_{[0]}$.

q.e.d.

THEOREM 2. For each non-negative integer k there exists a continuous linear section

$$\gamma_{(k)}: C^k(\xi) \to \bigoplus_{i=1}^r C^k(T^n, V)$$

for the map $P_{(k)}: \oplus_{i=1}^r C^k(T^n, V) \to C^k(\xi)$. Moreover, we can choose $\gamma_{(k)}$ that for each integer ℓ with $0 \leq \ell \leq k$, $\gamma_{(k)}$ extends to a continuous linear section $\gamma_{(\ell)}: C^\ell(\xi) \to \oplus_{i=1}^r C^\ell(T^n, V)$ for $P_{(\ell)}$ and also to a continuous linear section $\gamma_{[\ell]}: H^\ell(\xi) \to \oplus_{i=1}^r H^\ell(T^n, V)$ for $P_{[\ell]}$.

PROOF. Let $E = E_{(k)}: C_0^k(B_+^n, V) \to C_0^k(B^n, V)$ be as in Theorem 2 of §3. Given $f \in C^k(\xi)$ let $f_i = \lambda_i f$ where $\lambda_1, \ldots, \lambda_r$ is the partition of unity for M chosen above. Clearly, $\psi_i \circ f_i \circ \varphi_i^{-1} \in C_0^k(B_+^n, V)$ $i = 1, \ldots, t$ so $E(\psi_i \circ f_i \circ \varphi_i^{-1}) \in C_0^k(B^n, V)$ $i = 1, \ldots, t$. Also $\psi_i \circ f_i \circ \varphi_i^{-1} \in C_0^k(B^n, V)$. Using the canonical identification of $C_0^k(B^n, V)$ with a subspace of $C^k(T^n, V)$ [§3, Theorem 3] we define a map $\gamma_{(k)}$, $f \to (\gamma^1_{(k)}(f), \ldots, \gamma^r_{(k)}(f))$ of $C^k(\xi) \to \oplus_{i=1}^r C^k(T^n, V)$ by $\gamma^i_{(k)}(f) = E(\psi_i \circ f_i \circ \varphi_i^{-1})$ if $i \leq t$ and $\gamma^i_{(k)}(f) = \psi_i \circ f_i \circ \varphi_i^{-1}$ if $i > t$. The continuity of $f \to f_i = \lambda_i f$ as a map of $C^k(\xi) \to C^k(\xi)$ is obvious, and as a map $H^k(\xi) \to H^k(\xi)$ it follows from [IX, Theorem 9]. Since φ_i is a diffeomorphism and ψ_i a bundle equivalence the continuity of $f_i \to \psi_i \circ f_i \circ \varphi_i^{-1}$ as a map of $C^k(\xi) \to C^k(B_+^n, V)$ or $H^k(\xi) \to H^k(B_+^n, V)$ is clear, and the continuity of $\gamma_{(k)}$ and the fact that it extends continuously to maps $\gamma_{(\ell)}$ and $\gamma_{[\ell]}$ now follow directly from Theorem 2 of §3. Finally, if $f \in C^k(\xi)$

then (support $\gamma^i_{(k)}(f)) \subseteq$ (support λ_i) hence, since $\mu_i = 1$ on support λ_i, $\mu_i \gamma^i_{(k)}(f) = \gamma^i_{(k)}(f)$. Thus

$$P^i_{(k)}\gamma^i_{(k)}(f) = \psi_i^{-1}(\gamma^i_{(k)}(f) \circ \varphi_i) = f_i$$

hence $P_{(k)}\gamma_{(k)}(f) = f_1 + \ldots + f_r = (\lambda_1 + \ldots + \lambda_r)f = f$ and $\gamma_{(k)}$ is a section for $P_{(k)}$. if ℓ is an integer, $0 \leq \ell \leq k$ then $P_{(\ell)}\gamma_{(\ell)}: C^\ell(\xi) \to C^\ell(\xi)$ is continuous and the identity on the dense subspace $C^k(\xi)$ and hence on all of $C^\ell(\xi)$ i.e., $\gamma_{(\ell)}$ is a section for $P_{(\ell)}$. Similarly, $\gamma_{[\ell]}$ is a section for $P_{[\ell]}$.

q.e.d.

COROLLARY 1. If ℓ is any real number with $0 \leq \ell \leq k$ then $P_{[k]}$ extends to a continuous linear map $P_{[\ell]}: \oplus_{i=1}^r H^\ell(T^n, V) \to H^\ell(\xi)$ and $\gamma_{[k]}$ extends to a continuous linear section $\gamma_{[\ell]}: H^\ell(\xi) \to \oplus_{i=1}^r H\,(T^n, V)$ for $P_{[\ell]}$.

PROOF. Since $H^\ell(\xi)$ (resp. $H^\ell(T^n, V)$) for ℓ non integral is obtained by quadratic interpolation from $H^{[\ell]}(\xi)$ and $H^{[\ell]+1}(\xi)$ (resp. $H^{[\ell]}(T^n, V)$ and $H^{[\ell]+1}(T^n, V)$) it suffices to prove the theorem for ℓ integral. But that case is just the preceding two theorems.

q.e.d.

COROLLARY 2. If ℓ is an integer, $0 \leq \ell \leq k$ then $\gamma_{(\ell)}$ maps $C^\ell(\xi)$ isomorphically onto a closed subspace of $\oplus_{i=1}^r C^\ell(T^n, V)$. If ℓ is a real number, $0 \leq \ell \leq k$, then $\gamma_{[\ell]}$ maps $H^\ell(\xi)$ isomorphically onto a closed subspace of $\oplus_{i=1}^r H^\ell(T^n, V)$.

PROOF. If $\gamma_{(\ell)}(x_m) \to 0$ then $x_m = P_{(\ell)}\gamma_{(\ell)}(x_m) \to 0$. Hence $\gamma_{(\ell)}$ is an isomorphism into. Its image is therefore complete, hence closed in $\oplus_{i=1}^r C^\ell(T^n, V)$. A similar proof works for $\gamma_{[\ell]}$.

q.e.d.

Remark. Since $\oplus_{i=1}^r C^\ell(T^n, V)$ and $\oplus_{i=1}^r H^\ell(T^n, V)$ are explicitly normed (cf. §2) we may regard Corollary 2 as giving a norm for $C^\ell(\xi)$ and $H^\ell(\xi)$.

THEOREM 3. $\{H^k(\xi)\}_{k\in\mathbf{R}}$ is a Rellich chain and a scale.

PROOF. Let ℓ, m be real numbers with $0 \le \ell < m$. Choose k to be an integer greater than m. Let j denote the inclusion $H^m(\xi) \to H^\ell(\xi)$, i the inclusion $H^m(T^n, V) \to H^\ell(T^n, V)$ and $i^{(r)}$ the induced inclusion $\oplus_{i=1}^r H^m(T^n, V) \to \oplus_{i=1}^r H^\ell(T^n, V)$. Then we have the following diagram, the maps $\gamma_{[m]}$ and $P_{[\ell]}$ being as in Corollary 1 above:

$$\begin{array}{ccc} H^m(\xi) & \xrightarrow{\gamma_{[m]}} & \bigoplus_{i=1}^r H^m(T^n, V) \\ {\scriptstyle j}\downarrow & & \downarrow{\scriptstyle i^{(r)}} \\ H^\ell(\xi) & \xleftarrow[P_{[\ell]}]{} & \bigoplus_{i=1}^r H^\ell(T^n, V) \end{array}$$

Moreover, this diagram is clearly commutative, for if f is in the dense subspace $C^k(\xi)$ of $H^m(\xi)$ then $P_{[\ell]} i^{(r)} \gamma_{[m]} f = P_{[\ell]} i^{(r)} \gamma_{(k)} f = P_{[\ell]} \gamma_{(k)} f$ $= P_{(k)} \gamma_{(k)} f = f = jf$. Since $\gamma_{[m]}$ and $P_{[\ell]}$ are continuous while [§2, the corollary of Theorem 1] i and hence $i^{(r)}$ is completely continuous, it follows that j is completely continuous, i.e, that $\{H^k(\xi)\}_{k\in\mathbf{R}}$ is a Rellich chain.

Next let $k > \ell$ be non-negative integers, $0 \le s \le 1$, and $m = k + s(\ell - k)$. Now $\oplus_{i=1}^r H^k(T^n, V)$ is naturally isometric with $H^k(T^n, \oplus_{i=1}^r V)$ so it follows from [§2, corollary of Theorem 1] that $\{\oplus_{i=1}^r H^k(T^n, V)\}_{k\in\mathbf{R}}$ is a scale, so in particular

$$Q_s\Big(\bigoplus_{i=1}^r H^k(T^n, V), \bigoplus_{i=1}^r H^\ell(T^n, V)\Big) = \bigoplus_{i=1}^r H^m(T^n, V) \quad .$$

Since $\gamma_{[k]}$ and $P_{[k]}$ extend to $\gamma_{[\ell]}$ and $P_{[\ell]}$ it follows by the fundamental interpolative property of quadratic interpolation that they also extend to maps $\gamma_{\{m\}}$ and $P_{\{m\}}$

$$Q_s(H^k(\xi), H^\ell(\xi)) \underset{P_{\{m\}}}{\overset{\gamma_{\{m\}}}{\rightleftarrows}} \bigoplus_{i=1}^r H^m(T^n, V) \quad .$$

On the other hand we have the extensions $\gamma_{[m]}$ and $P_{[m]}$ of $\gamma_{[k]}$

$$H^m(\xi) \underset{P_{[m]}}{\overset{\gamma_{[m]}}{\rightleftarrows}} \bigoplus_{i=1}^{r} H^m(T^n, V) \quad .$$

If f is in the space $H^k(\xi)$, which is dense in both $H^m(\xi)$ and $Q_s(H^k(\xi),\ H^{\ell}(\xi))$, then $P_{[m]}\gamma_{\{m\}}f = P_{(k)}\gamma_{(k)}f = f$ and it follows that $Q_s(H^k(\xi),\ H^{\ell}(\xi)) = H^m(\xi)$, so by [VIII, §4, Theorem 1] $\{H^k(\xi)\}_{k\in\mathbf{R}}$ is a scale.

q.e.d.

COROLLARY 1. If $T \in OP_{r-1}(\xi, \eta)$ then for each $k \in \mathbf{Z}$, T extends to a completely continuous map of $H^k(\xi)$ into $H^{k-r}(\eta)$.

PROOF. [VIII, Theorem 2].

COROLLARY 2. If $T \in OP_{-1}(\xi, \eta)$ then for each $k \in \mathbf{Z}$, T extends to a completely continuous map of $H^k(\xi)$ into $H^k(\eta)$.

THEOREM 4 (Sobolev). If s is a non-negative integer and ℓ is a real number, $\ell > \frac{1}{2}(\dim M) + s$, then $H^{\ell}(\xi) \subseteq C^s(\xi)$ and the inclusion map $H^{\ell}(\xi) \to C^s(\xi)$ is completely continuous.

PROOF. Recall that $\dim M = n$ so $\ell > \frac{n}{2} + s$. Choose k any positive integer larger than ℓ and let

$$i^{(r)}: \bigoplus_{i=1}^{r} H^{\ell}(T^n, V) \to \bigoplus_{i=1}^{r} C^s(T^n, V)$$

be the completely continuous inclusion map [Theorem 2 of §2]. Then we have the diagram

$$\begin{array}{ccc} H^{\ell}(\xi) & \xrightarrow{\ \gamma_{[\ell]}\ } & \bigoplus_{i=1}^{r} H^{\ell}(T^n, V) \\ \Big\downarrow j & & \Big\downarrow i^{(r)} \\ C^s(\xi) & \xleftarrow[\ P_{(s)}\ ]{} & \bigoplus_{i=1}^{r} C^s(T^n, V) \end{array}$$

where j is defined to make the diagram commutative and hence is completely continuous. The argument of Theorem 3 shows that j restricts to the identity map on $C^k(\xi)$ and since $C^k(\xi)$ is dense in $H^{\ell}(\xi)$ the theorem follows.

q.e.d.

COROLLARY. $C^\infty(\xi) = H^\infty(\xi)$. Moreover the topology that $H^\infty(\xi)$ gets as the inverse limit $\varprojlim H^k(\xi)$ is the same that is gets as $\varprojlim C^k(\xi)$, i.e., it is the C^∞ topology.

PROOF. Immediate from the theorem and [IX, §3, Theorem 3].

Remark. It follows that we can regard $H^{-\infty}(\xi)$ as $\varinjlim C^{-k}(\xi)$, where $C^{-k}(\xi)$ denotes the antidual of $C^k(\xi)$. In other words, $H^{-\infty}(\xi)$ is just the space of "distributional sections" of ξ.

Henceforth we shall not distinguish between $C^\infty(\xi)$ *and* $H^\infty(\xi)$ *and use the two symbols interchangeably.*

THEOREM 5. Let M be an n-dimensional compact C^∞ manifold with boundary. There exists an n-dimensional compact C^∞ manifold M^* without boundary, having M as a C^∞ submanifold, such that every C^∞ vector bundle over M is the restriction of a C^∞ vector bundle over M^*.

PROOF. Let M^* be the double of M. The differential structure of M^* is determined by giving an explicit diffeomorphism of $\partial M \times [0, 1]$ with a neighborhood U of ∂M in M. If ξ is a vector bundle over M then by the covering homotopy theorem $\xi|U$ is equivalent to $(\xi|\partial M) \times [0, 1]$ and a choice of C^∞ bundle equivalence defines a C^∞ bundle structure for the double of ξ, making the latter a C^∞ bundle over M^* whose restriction to M is ξ.

q.e.d.

THEOREM 6. Let N be a compact C^∞ submanifold of M having the same dimension as M. The restriction map $f \to f|N$ of $C^\infty(\xi)$ into $C^\infty(\xi|N)$ extends to a continuous linear map $\rho_{(k)}: C^k(\xi) \to C^k(\xi|N)$ for each non-negative integer k, and to a continuous linear map $\rho_{[k]}: H^k(\xi) \to H^k(\xi|N)$ for each non-negative real number k. Moreover, if k is a non-negative integer then there exists a continuous linear section $\chi_{(k)}: C^k(\xi|N) \to C^k(\xi)$ for $\rho_{(k)}$ which for each real number ℓ with $0 \le \ell \le k$ extends to a continuous linear section $\chi_{[\ell]}$ for $\rho_{[\ell]}$ and, if ℓ is an integer, to a continuous linear section $\chi_{(\ell)}$ for $\rho_{(\ell)}$.

PROOF. Because of Theorem 5 we can assume $\partial M = \emptyset$. We can assume the charts φ_i so chosen that $\varphi_i|(\mathcal{O}_i \cap N)$ $i = 1, \ldots, r'$ is an atlas for N and $\mathcal{O}_i \cap N = \emptyset$ if $i > r'$. Let $\bar{P}_{(k)}: C^k(\xi|N) \to \oplus_{i=1}^{r'} C^k(T^n, V)$ and $\bar{\gamma}_{(k)}: \oplus_{i=1}^{r'} C^k(T^n, V) \to C^k(\xi|N)$ be the maps constructed analogously to $P_{(k)}$ and $\gamma_{(k)}$. then letting π and i be the canonical projection and injection respectively we define $\rho_{(k)}$ and $\chi_{(k)}$ to make the inside and outside of the following diagram commutative

$$\begin{array}{ccc}
C^k(\xi) & \underset{\gamma_{(k)}}{\overset{P_{(k)}}{\rightleftarrows}} & \bigoplus_{i=1}^{r} C^k(T^n, V) \\
\chi_{(k)} \uparrow \downarrow \rho_{(k)} & & \pi \downarrow \uparrow i \\
C^k(\xi|N) & \underset{\bar{\gamma}_{(k)}}{\overset{\bar{P}_{(k)}}{\rightleftarrows}} & \bigoplus_{i=1}^{r'} C^k(T^n, V)
\end{array}$$

The fact that $\rho_{(k)}$ is the restriction map follows easily from the fact that $\mathcal{O}_i \cap N = \emptyset$ if $i > r'$. From the fact that $\gamma_{(k)}$, i, and $\bar{\gamma}_{(k)}$ are respectively sections for $P_{(k)}$, π, and $\bar{P}_{(k)}$ it is a formal consequence that $\chi_{(k)}$ is a section for $\rho_{(k)}$. The remaining facts follow easily from Theorem 2 above together with its first corollary.

q.e.d.

THEOREM 7 (Restriction Theorem). Let N be a compact C^∞ submanifold of M, and let $s = \frac{1}{2}(\dim M - \dim N)$. Then for any real number m larger than s the restriction map $f \to f|N$ of $C^\infty(\xi) \to C^\infty(\xi|N)$ extends to a continuous linear map ρ: $H^m(\xi) \to H^{m-s}(\xi|N)$. Moreover, ρ has a continuous linear section χ: $H^{m-s}(\xi|N) \to H^m(\xi)$ (equivalently, ρ is surjective).

PROOF. Because of Theorems 5 and 6 above we can suppose that $\partial M = \emptyset$ and that $\ell = \dim N < \dim M = n$. We can assume the charts $\varphi_i \colon \mathcal{O}_i \approx \mathbf{R}^n$ $(i = 1, \ldots, r)$ are so chosen that $\varphi_i | (\mathcal{O}_i \cap N) \colon (\mathcal{O}_i \cap N) \approx \mathbf{R}^\ell_+$ $(i = 1, \ldots, t)$ $\varphi_i | (\mathcal{O}_i \cap N) \colon \mathcal{O}_i \cap N \approx \mathbf{R}^\ell$ $(i = t+1, \ldots, r')$ $N \subseteq \bigcup_{i=1}^{r'} \varphi_i^{-1}(B^\ell_{1/2})$ while $\mathcal{O}_i \cap N = \emptyset$ if $i > r'$.

Define $\bar{P} \colon \oplus_{i=1}^{r'} C^\infty(T^\ell, V) \to C^\infty(\xi | N)$ analogously to the definition of P at the beginning of this section, but with $(\varphi_i(\mathcal{O}_i \cap N),$ $\psi_i | (\bar{\mathcal{O}}_i \cap N), \mu_i | N)_{i=1, \ldots, r'}$ replacing $(\varphi_i, \psi_i, \mu_i)_{i=1, \ldots, r}$, and let $\bar{P}_{(\ell)}$ and $\bar{P}_{[\ell]}$ be the extensions given by Theorem 1 above. Similarly, let k be an integer greater than m and let $\bar{\gamma}_{(k)} \colon C^k(\xi | N) \to \oplus_{i=1}^{r'} C^k(T^\ell, V)$ be the section for $\bar{P}_{(k)}$ constructed analogously to $\gamma_{(k)}$ in Theorem 2 above, but again restricting everything to N and letting $i = 1, \ldots, r'$. Finally let $\rho \colon H^m(T^n, V) \to H^{m-s}(T\ , V)$ and $\chi \colon H^{m-s}(T^k, V) \to H^m(T^n, V)$ be as in [§2, Theorem 3]. Then we define $\rho \colon H^m(\xi) \to H^{m-s}(\xi | N)$ and $\chi \colon H^{m-s}(\xi | N) \to H^m(\xi)$ to make both the inside and outside of the following diagram commute

$$\begin{array}{ccc} H^m(\xi) & \begin{matrix} \xleftarrow{\;P_{[m]}\;} \\ \xrightarrow[\;\gamma_{[m]}\;]{} \end{matrix} & \bigoplus_{i=1}^{r} H^m(T^n, V) \\ \chi \uparrow \; \downarrow \rho & & \pi\rho^{(r)} \downarrow \; \uparrow i\chi^{(r')} \\ H^{m-s}(\xi | N) & \begin{matrix} \xleftarrow{\;\bar{P}_{[m-s]}\;} \\ \xrightarrow[\;\bar{\gamma}_{[m-s]}\;]{} \end{matrix} & \bigoplus_{i=1}^{r'} H^{m-s}(T^\ell, V) \end{array} .$$

The fact that $\rho | C^\infty(\xi)$ is the restriction map $C^\infty(\xi) \to C\ (\xi | N)$ follows from the fact that $\mathcal{O}_i \cap N = \emptyset$ if $i > r'$ by a straightforward unwinding of definitions of the maps involved which we leave to the reader. On the other hand the fact that γ is a section for ρ is a formal consequence of the fact that $\gamma_{[m]}$, $\bar{\gamma}_{[m-s]}$ and $i\chi^{(r')}$ are sections for $P_{[m]}$, $\bar{P}_{[m-s]}$ and $\pi\rho^{(r)}$ respectively.

q.e.d.

In the sequel we will need only the following special case:

COROLLARY. The restriction map $f \to f|\partial M$ of $C^\infty(\xi)$ into $C^\infty(\xi|\partial M)$ extends to a continuous linear surjection

$$H^1(\xi) \to H^{1/2}(\xi|\partial M) \quad .$$

CHAPTER XI

THE SEELEY ALGEBRA

Richard S. Palais

In this chapter M will denote a compact C^{∞} manifold without boundary and with a fixed choice of strictly positive smooth measure, and ξ, η, ζ will denote hermitian vector bundles over M.

In his paper, "Integro-differential operators on vector bundles," to appear in Trans. Amer. Math. Soc., Seeley constructs for each integer k a subspace $\mathrm{Int}_k(\xi, \eta)$ of $\mathrm{OP}_k(\xi, \eta)$ and a linear symbol map $\sigma_k\colon \mathrm{Int}_k(\xi, \eta) \to \mathrm{Smbl}_k(\xi, \eta)$ with the following properties:

(S1) $\mathrm{OP}_{k-1}(\xi, \eta) \subseteq \mathrm{Int}_k(\xi, \eta)$ and is precisely the kernel of σ_k;

(S2) $\mathrm{Diff}_k(\xi, \eta) \subseteq \mathrm{Int}_k(\xi, \eta)$ if $k \geq 0$ and the symbol map σ_k on $\mathrm{Int}_k(\xi, \eta)$ extends the symbol map on $\mathrm{Diff}_k(\xi, \eta)$ defined in Chapter IV;

(S3) If $T \in \mathrm{Int}_k(\xi, \eta)$ and $S \in \mathrm{Int}_\ell(\eta, \zeta)$ then $ST \in \mathrm{Int}_{k+\ell}(\xi, \eta)$ and $\sigma_{k+\ell}(ST) = \sigma_\ell(S)\sigma_k(T)$;

(S4) If T is in $\mathrm{Int}_k(\xi, \eta)$ then the transpose T^t of T (which exists and is in $\mathrm{OP}_k(\eta, \xi)$ by [VIII, Theorem 4]) is in $\mathrm{Int}_k(\eta, \xi)$ and $\sigma_k(T^t) = (-1)^k \sigma_k(T)^*$;

(S5) There is a map $\chi_k\colon \mathrm{Smbl}_k(\xi, \eta) \to \mathrm{Int}_k(\xi, \eta)$ (*not canonical*) which is a right inverse for σ_k. Moreover χ_k is continuous from $\mathrm{Smbl}_k(\xi, \eta)$ (with the C^{∞}-topology) to $\mathrm{Int}_k(\xi, \eta)$ (with the induced topology from $\mathrm{OP}_k(\xi, \eta)$ [VIII, Definition following Theorem 1]).

It should be remarked that σ_k is *not* continuous and indeed it is easily shown that its kernel, $\mathrm{OP}_{k-1}(\xi, \eta)$, is not closed in $\mathrm{OP}_k(\xi, \eta)$.

In addition, there is a sixth property (S6) which will be introduced in [XIV, §4]. The actual construction of $\mathrm{Int}_k(\xi, \eta)$, σ_k, and χ_k, and the verification of (S1)-(S6) will be taken up in Chapter XVI. However, there will be no reference to material in the intervening chapters in Chapter XVI so the reader interested in doing so can read that chapter at this point. In the present chapter, and those immediately subsequent, we shall derive the basic consequences of (S1)-(S6).

DEFINITION. $\mathrm{Int}(\xi, \eta) = \bigcup_{k \in \mathbf{Z}} \mathrm{Int}_k(\xi, \eta)$.

THEOREM 1. $\mathrm{Int}(\xi, \eta) = \bigcup_{k \in \mathbf{Z}} \mathrm{OP}_k(\xi, \eta)$.

PROOF. $\mathrm{Int}_k \subseteq \mathrm{OP}_k \subseteq \mathrm{Int}_{k+1}$.

THEOREM 2. If $T \in \mathrm{Int}(\xi, \eta)$ then there is a unique continuous extension $\bar{T}: H^{-\infty}(\xi) \to H^{-\infty}(\eta)$ of T. This $\bar{T}$ is linear as is the map $T \to \bar{T}$. If $S \in \mathrm{Int}(\eta, \zeta)$ then $ST \in \mathrm{Int}(\xi, \zeta)$ and $\overline{ST} = \bar{S}\bar{T}$. If $I_\xi \in \mathrm{Diff}_0(\xi, \xi) \subseteq \mathrm{Int}_0(\xi, \xi) \subseteq \mathrm{Int}(\xi, \xi)$ is the identity map of $H^\infty(\xi)$ then $\bar{I}_\xi$ is the identity map of $H^{-\infty}(\xi)$. Finally, if $T \in \mathrm{OP}_k(\xi, \eta)$ then $\bar{T}|H^r(\xi) = T_r$ for all $r \in \mathbf{Z}$ and in particular $\bar{T}(H^r(\xi)) \subseteq H^{r-k}(\xi)$.

PROOF. By Theorem 1, $T \in \mathrm{OP}_k(\xi, \eta)$ for some $k \in \mathbf{Z}$. Then T extends uniquely to a continuous linear map $T_r: H^r(\xi) \to H^{r-k}(\eta)$ for each $r \in \mathbf{Z}$ and $T_{r+1} = T_r|H^{r+1}(\xi)$. That $\bar{T} = \bigcup_r T_r$ is a continuous map of $H^{-\infty}(\xi)$ into $H^{-\infty}(\eta)$ is now an immediate consequence of the fact that $H^{-\infty}(\xi) = \varinjlim H^{-r}(\xi)$. The uniqueness of $\bar{T}$ follows from the density of $H^\infty(\xi)$ in each $H^r(\xi)$, hence in $H^{-\infty}(\xi)$, and the other conclusions follow trivially from uniqueness.

q.e.d.

THEOREM 3 (Symbol Exact Sequence).

$$0 \to \mathrm{OP}_{k-1}(\xi, \eta) \to \mathrm{Int}_k(\xi, \eta) \xrightarrow{\sigma_k} \mathrm{Smbl}_k(\xi, \eta) \to 0$$

is exact.

PROOF. Immediate from (S1) and (S5).

Remark. This should be compared with [IV, §3, Theorem 2].

DEFINITION. An element σ of $\mathrm{Smbl}_k(\xi, \eta)$ is called elliptic if $\sigma(v, x)$ maps ξ_x isomorphically onto η_x for all $(v, x) \in T'(M)$, i.e., if $\sigma \in \mathrm{Iso}(\pi^*\xi, \pi^*\eta)$, and $T \in \mathrm{Int}_k(\xi, \eta)$ is called k^{th} order elliptic if $\sigma_k(T)$ is elliptic; we denote the set of such T by $E_k(\xi, \eta)$ and note that by (S2) $E_k(\xi, \eta) \cap \mathrm{Diff}_k(\xi, \eta)$ is just the set of kth order elliptic differential operators from ξ to η [IV, §3].

LEMMA. If $\sigma \in \mathrm{Smbl}_k(\xi, \eta)$ is elliptic, then σ^{-1}, defined by $\sigma^{-1}(v, x) = \sigma(v, x)^{-1}$, is in $\mathrm{Smbl}_{-k}(\eta, \xi)$ and is elliptic.

PROOF. If $I(\pi^*\xi, \pi^*\eta)$ denotes the open subset of $L(\pi^*\xi, \pi^*\eta)$ whose fiber over (v, x) is all linear isomorphisms of ξ_x onto η_x, then $e \to e^{-1}$ is clearly a C^∞ diffeomorphism of $I(\pi^*\xi, \pi^*\eta)$ onto $I(\pi^*\eta, \pi^*\xi)$. Since $\sigma \in \mathrm{Iso}(\pi^*\xi, \pi^*\eta) = C^\infty(I(\pi^*\eta, \pi^*\eta))$ it follows that $\sigma^{-1} \in C^\infty(I(\pi^*\eta, \pi^*\xi)) = \mathrm{Iso}(\pi^*\eta, \pi^*\xi)$. And since $\sigma(\rho v, x) = \rho^k\sigma(v, x)$ if $\rho > 0$ it follows that $\sigma^{-1}(\rho v, x) = (\rho^k\sigma(v, x))^{-1} = \rho^{-k}\sigma^{-1}(v, x)$, hence σ^{-1} is an elliptic element of $\mathrm{Smbl}_{-k}(\eta, \xi)$.

q.e.d.

THEOREM 4. If $T \in E_k(\xi, \eta)$ then there exists $T' \in E_{-k}(\eta, \xi)$ such that $\sigma_{-k}(T\ ) = \sigma_k(T)^{-1}$ and any such T' satisfies $T'T - I_\xi \in OP_{-1}(\xi, \xi)$ and $TT' - I_\eta \in OP_{-1}(\eta, \eta)$.

PROOF. By the lemma and Theorem 3 we can find $T' \in E_{-k}(\eta, \xi)$ such that $\sigma_{-k}(T')(v, x) = \sigma_k(T)(v, x)^{-1}$. Then by (S3), $T'T \in OP_0(\xi, \xi)$, $TT' \in OP_0(\eta, \eta)$ and $\sigma_0(T'T) = \sigma_0(I_\xi)$ and $\sigma_0(TT') = \sigma_0(I_\eta)$. Then by Theorem 3, $T'T - I_\xi \in OP_{-1}(\xi, \xi)$ and $TT' - I_\eta \in OP_{-1}(\eta, \eta)$.

q.e.d.

THEOREM 5 (Regularity Theorem). Let $T \in E_k(\xi, \eta)$. If $f \in H^{-\infty}(\xi)$ and $\bar{T}f \in H^r(\eta)$ then $f \in H^{r+k}(\xi)$.

PROOF. By definition, $H^{-\infty}(\xi) = \bigcup_m H^m(\xi)$ so $f \in H^m(\xi)$ for some $m \in \mathbf{Z}$. By induction, it will suffice to prove $m < r + k \Longrightarrow f \in H^{m+1}(\xi)$. We note that since $m + 1 \leq r + k$, $H^{r+k}(\xi) \subseteq H^{m+1}(\xi)$. By Theorem 4 choose $T \in E_{-k}(\eta, \xi)$ so that $T'T - I_\xi \in OP_{-1}(\xi, \xi)$. Then by Theorem 2 since $f \in H^m(\xi)$, $(\overline{T'}\,\bar{T}f - f) = (\overline{T'T - I_\xi})f \in H^{m+1}(\xi)$. On the other hand, since $T' \in OP_{-k}(\eta, \xi)$, and $\bar{T}f \in H^r(\eta)$ by hypothesis, Theorem 2 gives $\bar{T}'\bar{T} \in H^{r+k}(\xi) \subseteq H^{m+1}(\xi)$. Hence $f = \bar{T}'\bar{T}f - (\bar{T}'\bar{T}f - f) \in H^{m+1}(\xi)$.

q.e.d.

COROLLARY 1. If $\bar{T}f \in H^\infty(\eta)$ then $f \in H^\infty(\xi)$. In other words, if $T_r\colon H^r(\xi) \to H^{r-k}(\eta)$ is the continuous extension of T then $T_r(H^r(\xi)) \cap H^\infty(\eta) = T(H^\infty(\xi))$.

COROLLARY 2. If $\bar{T}f = 0$ then $f \in H^\infty(\xi)$. In other words, if $T_r\colon H^r(\xi) \to H^{r-k}(\eta)$ is the continuous extension of T then $\ker T_r = \ker T$.

THEOREM 6. If $T \in E_k(\xi, \eta)$ then for each integer r its continuous linear extension $T_r\colon H^r(\xi) \to H^{r-k}(\eta)$ is an F-operator.

PROOF. By Theorem 4 choose $T' \in E_{-k}(\eta, \xi)$ so that $T'T - I_\xi \in OP_{-1}(\xi, \xi)$ and $TT' - I_\eta \in OP_{-1}(\eta, \eta)$. Then by [X, §4, Corollary 2 of Theorem 3], $T'_{r-k}T_r - I_\xi$ is a completely continuous map of $H^r(\xi)$ into itself and similarly $T_rT'_{r-k} - I_\eta$ is a completely continuous map of $H^{r-k}(\eta)$ into itself so that T_r is an F-operator by [VII, Theorem 2].

q.e.d.

COROLLARY. $T(H^\infty(\xi))$ is a closed subspace of $H^\infty(\eta)$ and $\ker T$ is a finite dimensional closed subspace of $H^\infty(\xi)$.

PROOF. Immediate from Corollaries 1 and 2 of Theorem 5 and the fact that the topology of $H^\infty(\xi) = \varprojlim H^k(\xi)$ is stronger than that induced from any $H^r(\xi)$.

THEOREM 7. If $T \in E_k(\xi, \eta)$ then $T^t \in E_k(\eta, \xi)$. Moreover, $\ker T^t$ is a finite dimensional closed subspace of $H^\infty(\eta)$ complementary to $T(H^\infty(\xi))$;

and in fact $T(H^\infty(\xi))$ and $\ker T^t$ are orthogonal complements of each other in $H^\infty(\eta)$ relative to the inner product of $H^0(\eta)$.

PROOF. If $(v, x) \in T(M)$ then since $\sigma_k(T)(v, x)$ is an isomorphism of ξ_x with η_x, by (S4) $\sigma_k(T^t)(v, x) = (-1)^k\sigma_k(T)(v, x)^*$ is an isomorphism of η_x with ξ_x, so $T^t \in E_k(\eta, \xi)$. If $g = Tf \in T(H^\infty(\xi))$ and $h \in \ker T^t$ then $< g, h >_\eta = < Tf, h >_\eta = < f, T^t h >_\xi = 0$ so $T(H^\infty(\xi))$ and $\ker T^t$ are orthogonal with respect to $< , >_\eta$. If $(T^t)_0 \colon H^0(\eta) \to H^{-k}(\xi)$ is the continuous extension of T^t, then by Corollary 2 of Theorem 5, $\ker T^t = \ker(T^t)_0$ is a closed subspace of $H^0(\eta)$ hence there is an orthogonal projection $P\colon H^0(\eta) \to \ker T^t$. If $g \in H^\infty(\eta)$ then $Pg \in \ker T^t \subseteq H^\infty(\eta)$ so $h = g - Pg \in H^\infty(\eta)$. It remains only to show that $h \in T(H^\infty(\xi))$. Now, by Theorem 6, $(T^t)_0(H^0(\eta))$ is closed in $H^{-k}(\xi)$ so by [VI, Theorem 10] $(T^t)_0^*(H^k(\xi))$ is the orthogonal complement of $\ker(T^t)_0$ or, by Corollary 2 of Theorem 5, the orthogonal complement of $\ker T^t$, in $H^0(\eta)$. But by [VIII, Theorem 4] $(T^t)_0^* = T_k$, the continuous extension of T to a map $H^k(\xi) \to H^0(\eta)$. Thus we have finally, $T_k(H^k(\xi)) = (\ker T^t)^\perp$. Now since $h = g - Pg \in (\ker T^t)^\perp$ and $h \in H^\infty(\eta)$, we have $h \in T_k(H^k(\xi)) \cap H^\infty(\eta)$ or $h \in T(H^\infty(\xi))$ by Corollary 1 of Theorem 5.

q.e.d.

THEOREM 8. If $T \in E_k(\xi, \eta)$ then all the following integers are equal

1) $\mathrm{ind}(T_r)$ where $T_r\colon H^r(\xi) \to H^{r-k}(\eta)$ is the unique continuous extension of T (an F-operator by Theorem 6);
2) $\dim \ker T - \dim \ker T^t$;
3) $\dim \ker T - \dim \operatorname{coker} T$.

PROOF. $\mathrm{ind}(T_r) = \dim \ker T_r - \dim \ker (T_r)^*$. Now $\ker T_r = \ker T$ by Corollary 2 of Theorem 5 and since $(T_r)^* = (T^t)_{r-k}$ by [VIII, Theorem 4] $\ker(T_r)^* = \ker T^t$ by Corollary 2 of Theorem 5 again. Finally, by Theorem 7, $\ker T^t$ is a complementary subspace of $T(H^\infty(\xi))$ in $H^\infty(\eta)$ so $\dim \operatorname{coker} T = \dim \ker T^t$.

q.e.d.

DEFINITION. If $T \in E_k(\xi, \eta)$ then the integer defined by any of the equivalent expressions of Theorem 8 is called the index of T and denoted by $\operatorname{ind}(T)$.

THEOREM 9. If $T \in E_k(\xi, \eta)$ then $\operatorname{ind}(T^t) = -\operatorname{ind}(T)$.

PROOF. Trivial.

COROLLARY. If $T \in E_k(\xi, \xi)$ and $T^t = \lambda T$ for some $\lambda \in \mathbf{C}$ then $|\lambda| = 1$ and $\operatorname{ind}(T) = 0$.

PROOF. $T = (T^t)^t = \bar{\lambda} T^t = |\lambda|^2 T$. Since T, being elliptic, is not zero, $|\lambda| = 1$. Also, $\ker \lambda T = \ker T$ and $\operatorname{coker} \lambda T = \operatorname{coker} T$ so $\operatorname{ind}(T) = \operatorname{ind}(\lambda T) = \operatorname{ind}(T^t) = -\operatorname{ind}(T)$.

q.e.d.

THEOREM 10. If $T, T' \in E_k(\xi, \eta)$ and if $\sigma_k(T) = \sigma_k(T')$ then $\operatorname{ind}(T) = \operatorname{ind}(T')$.

PROOF. By Theorem 3, $T - T' \in OP_{k-1}(\xi, \eta)$ hence by [X, §4, Corollary 1 of Theorem 3] $T_r - T_r' : H^r(\xi) \to H^{r-k}(\eta)$ is completely continuous. Then by [VII, Corollary of Theorem 4] $\operatorname{ind} T_r = \operatorname{ind} T_r'$, so $\operatorname{ind}(T) = \operatorname{ind}(T')$.

q.e.d.

THEOREM 11. If $T \in E_k(\xi, \eta)$ and $S \in E_\ell(\eta, \zeta)$ then $ST \in E_{k+\ell}(\xi, \zeta)$ and $\operatorname{ind}(ST) = \operatorname{ind} S + \operatorname{ind} T$.

PROOF. $ST \in E_{k+\ell}(\xi, \zeta)$ is obvious from (S3). For any $r \in \mathbf{Z}$ if $T_r : H^r(\xi) \to H^{r-k}(\eta)$, $S_{r-k} : H^{r-k}(\eta) \to H^{r-k-\ell}(\zeta)$, and $(ST)_r : H^r(\zeta) \to H^{r-k-\ell}(\zeta)$ are the continuous extensions of T, S and ST then $(ST)_r = S_{r-k} T_r$ so by [VIII, Theorem 3] $\operatorname{ind}(ST)_r = \operatorname{ind}(S_{r-k}) + \operatorname{ind}(T_r)$, hence $\operatorname{ind}(ST) = \operatorname{ind} S + \operatorname{ind} T$.

q.e.d.

THEOREM 12. Let $T \in E_k(\xi, \eta)$ and suppose $\operatorname{ind}(T) = 0$ and $\ker T = 0$. Then $T: H^\infty(\xi) \to H^\infty(\eta)$ is bijective. Moreover, $T^{-1} \in E_{-k}(\eta, \xi)$ and $\sigma_{-k}(T^{-1}) = \sigma_k(T)^{-1}$. Also $T_r : H^r(\xi) \to H^{r-k}(\eta)$ is an isomorphism of topological spaces for all $r \in \mathbf{Z}$.

PROOF. Since $\text{ind}(T) = 0$ and $\ker T = 0$ it follows that $\ker T^t = 0$ so the surjectivity of T follows from Theorem 7. Since $\ker T_r = \ker T = 0$ (Corollary 2 of Theorem 5) and $\text{ind}\, T_r = \text{ind}\, T = 0$ it follows that T_r is also bijective and hence [VI, Theorem 1] and isomorphsim of topological vector spaces. Thus T_r^{-1} is a continuous extension of T^{-1} to a map of $H^{r-k}(\eta)$ into $H^r(\xi)$ and it follows that $T^{-1} \in OP_{-k}(\eta, \xi)$. As in Theorem 4, choose $T' \in E_{-k}(\eta, \xi)$ with $\sigma_{-k}(T') = \sigma_k(T)^{-1}$ so that $T'T - I_\xi \in OP_{-1}(\xi, \xi)$. To prove $T^{-1} \in E_{-k}(\eta, \xi)$ and $\sigma_{-k}(T^{-1}) = \sigma_k(T)^{-1}$ it will suffice by Theorem 3 to prove that $S = T' - T^{-1} \in OP_{-k-1}(\eta, \xi)$. Now $S = (ST)T^{-1}$ and since $ST = T'T - I_\xi \in OP_{-1}(\xi, \xi)$ while $T^{-1} \in OP_{-k}(\eta, \xi)$, [VIII, Theorem 3] completes the proof.

q.e.d.

THEOREM 13. Assume $\sigma \in \text{Smbl}_1(\xi, \xi)$ is elliptic and satisfies $\sigma^* = \sigma$. Then there exists $\Lambda \in E_1(\xi, \xi)$ such that

1) $\sigma_1(\Lambda) = \sigma$;
2) $\Lambda^t = -\Lambda$;
3) Λ is bijective; $\Lambda^k \in E_k(\xi, \xi)$, $\text{ind}(\Lambda^k) = 0$ and $\sigma_k(\Lambda^k) = \sigma^k$ all $k \in \mathbf{Z}$;
4) $(\Lambda^k)_r : H^r(\xi) \to H^{r-k}(\xi)$ is an isomorphism of topological vector spaces, all $k, r \in \mathbf{Z}$.
5) $T \to T\Lambda^k$ is a (linear) bijection of $\text{Int}_0(\xi, \eta)$ with $\text{Int}_k(\xi, \eta)$ and of $E_0(\xi, \eta)$ with $E_k(\xi, \eta)$ for all $k \in \mathbf{Z}$. Moreover, if $T \in E_0(\xi, \eta)$, $\text{ind}(T\Lambda^k) = \text{ind}(T)$.

PROOF. By Theorem 3 there exists $S \in E_1(\xi, \xi)$ with $\sigma_1(S) = \sigma$. Let $\Lambda_0 = \frac{1}{2}(S - S^t)$. Then clearly $\Lambda_0 = -\Lambda_0^t$ and $\sigma_1(\Lambda_0) = \frac{1}{2}(\sigma_1(S) - \sigma_1(S^t)) = \frac{1}{2}(\sigma - (-\sigma)) = \sigma$. Since $H^0(\xi)$ is separable Λ_0 has at most countably many eigen values, hence we can choose λ pure imaginary so that $\Lambda_0 - \lambda I_\xi = \Lambda$ has zero kernel. By Theorem 3 (since $\lambda I_\xi \in OP_0(\xi, \xi)$), $\Lambda \in E_1(\xi, \xi)$ and in fact $\sigma_1(\Lambda) = \sigma_1(\Lambda_0) = \sigma$. Since λ is pure imaginary $(\lambda I_\xi)^t = -(\lambda I_\xi)$ so $\Lambda^t = -\Lambda$. Then $\text{ind}(\Lambda) = 0$ by the corollary of Theorem 9 and, since $\ker \Lambda = 0$, Λ is bijective, $\Lambda^{-1} \in E_{-1}(\xi, \xi)$, and $\sigma_{-1}(\Lambda^{-1}) = \sigma^{-1}$ by

Theorem 12. By Theorem 11, $\Lambda^k \in E_k(\xi, \xi)$ and $\operatorname{ind}(\Lambda^k) = 0$ for all $k \in \mathbf{Z}$, and by (S3) $\sigma_k(\Lambda^k) = \sigma^k$. Since $\ker \Lambda = 0$, $\ker \Lambda^k = 0$ and by Theorem 12, $(\Lambda^k)_r\colon H^r(\xi) \to H^{r-k}(\xi)$ is an isomorphism of topological vector spaces for all $k, r \in \mathbf{Z}$. Finally by (S3), $T \to T\Lambda^k$ is a (clearly linear) map of $\operatorname{Int}_0(\xi, \eta)$ into $\operatorname{Int}_k(\xi, \eta)$ and $S \to S\Lambda^{-k}$ a two sided inverse. By Theorem 11, $T \in E_0(\xi, \eta)$ if and only if $T\Lambda^k \in E_k(\xi, \eta)$ and also $\operatorname{ind}(T\Lambda^k) = \operatorname{ind}(T) + \operatorname{ind}(\Lambda^k) = \operatorname{ind}(T)$.

q.e.d.

THEOREM 14. Let $S \in E_k(\xi, \xi)$, $k \neq 0$ and suppose $S = S^t$. Then there is an orthonormal basis $\{f_n\}$ of $H^0(\xi)$ consisting of eigenvectors of S (in particular, $f_n \in H^\infty(\xi)$) and the corresponding eigenvalues $\{\lambda_n\}$ are real and satisfy $\lambda_n \to 0$ if $k < 0$ and $\lambda_n^{-1} \to 0$ if $k > 0$. If $f \in H^{-\infty}(\xi)$ then $f \in H^{kr}(\xi)$ if and only if

$$\sum_n |\lambda_n|^{2r} \cdot |< f, f_n >_\xi|^2 < \infty \quad .$$

In fact if $\ker S = 0$ then

$$(f, g)_{kr} = \sum_n |\lambda_n|^{2r} < f, f_n >_\xi \overline{< g, f_n >_\xi}$$

is an admissible inner product for $H^{kr}(\xi)$.

PROOF. We assume first that $\ker S = 0$. If $k < 0$ then by [X, §4, Corollary 2 of Theorem 3] S extends to a completely continuous map $\tilde{S}\colon H^0(\xi) \to H^0(\xi)$. Since $H^\infty(\xi)$ is dense in $H^0(\xi)$ and

$$< \tilde{S}f, g >_\xi = < Sf, g >_\xi = < f, S^t g >_\xi = < f, Sg >_\xi = < f, \tilde{S}g >_\xi$$

for $f, g \in H^\infty(\xi)$ it follows that $\tilde{S}$ is self adjoint. By [VI, Corollary of Theorem 16] there is a sequence $\{\lambda_n\}$ of real numbers and an orthonormal basis $\{f_n\}$ of $H^0(\xi)$ such that $\tilde{S}f_n = \lambda_n f_n$ and $\lambda_n \to 0$. Since $\ker S = 0$ $\ker \tilde{S} = 0$ [Corollary 2 of Theorem 5] hence $\lambda_n \neq 0$ and $f_n = (\lambda_n)^{-1}\tilde{S}f_n$. Then inductively $f_n \in H^{-mk}(\xi)$ for $m > 0$ and since $k < 0$, $f_n \in H^\infty(\xi)$ so $Sf_n = \tilde{S}f_n = \lambda_n f_n$. Now $S^r \in E_{kr}(\xi, \xi)$ and $(S^r)_{kr}\colon H^{kr}(\xi) \to H^0(\xi)$ is an isomorphism of topological vector spaces by Theorem 12 (and the Corollary of Theorem 9). Thus $(f, g)_{kr} = <(S^r)_{kr}f, (S^r)_{kr}g>_\xi$ is an admissible inner product for $H^{kr}(\xi)$. But since $\{f_n\}$ is an orthonormal base for $H^0(\xi)$

$$(f, g)_{kr} = \sum_n <(S^r)_{kr}f, f_n>_\xi \overline{<(S^r)_{kr}g, f_n>_\xi} .$$

Now $<(S^r)_{kr}f, f_n>_\xi = <f, (S^r)^*_{kr}f_n>_\xi = <f, ((S^r)^t)_0 f_n>_\xi$ by [VIII, Theorem 4]. Also $(S^r)^t = (S^t)^r = S^r$ and since $f_n \in H^\infty(\xi)$ $(S^r)_0 f_n = S^r f_n = \lambda_n^r f_n$ so $<(S^r)_{kr}f, f_n>_\xi = \lambda_n^r <f, f_n>_\xi$, so $(f, g)_{kr} = \Sigma_n |\lambda_n|^{2r} <f, f_n>_\xi \overline{<g, f_n>_\xi}$. If $k > 0$ then by Theorem 12, $S^{-1} \in E_{-k}(\xi, \xi)$ and $-k < 0$. Since an eigenvector of S^{-1} belonging to λ is an eigenvector of S belonging to λ^{-1} the case $k > 0$ follows trivially from the case $k < 0$. Finally, assume that $\ker S$ is not necessarily 0. In any case $\ker S$ is a finite dimensional subspace of $H^\infty(\xi)$. Let P denote the orthogonal projection of $H^0(\xi)$ onto $\ker S$, restricted to $H^\infty(\xi)$. If $\{e_1, \ldots, e_n\}$ is an orthonormal basis for $\ker S$ then $Pf = \Sigma_{m=1}^n <f, e_m>_\xi e_m$. Given $\ell, q \in \mathbf{Z}$ we have $e_m \in H^{-\ell}(\xi)$ and $e_m \in H^{\ell-q}(\xi)$ so $f \to \Sigma_{m=1}^n <f, e_m>_\xi e_m$ is a continuous extension of P to a map $H^\ell(\xi) \to H^{\ell-q}(\xi)$ and hence $P \in OP_q(\xi, \xi)$ for all $q \in \mathbf{Z}$ and in particular for $q = k - 1$. By Theorem 3, $S_1 = S + P \in E_k(\xi, \xi)$ and since $S = S^t$ it follows from Theorem 7 that $\ker S_1 = 0$, so we have the theorem for S_1. On the other hand, we get S from S_1 by making a certain finite number of eigenvectors belonging to 1 into eigenvectors belonging to zero, so the theorem follows for S also.

q.e.d.

COROLLARY. Let $S \in E_k(\xi, \eta)$, $k > 0$. Then $H^0(\xi)$ has an orthonormal basis $\{f_n\}$ of eigenvectors of S^tS. The corresponding eigenvalues $\{\lambda_n\}$ are non-negative and $\lambda_n \to \infty$. Moreover, for each $r \in \mathbf{Z}$ $\{(1+\lambda_n)^{-r/2}f_n\}$ is a complete orthonormal basis with respect to an admissible inner product for $H^{kr}(\xi)$.

PROOF. $S^tS \in E_{2k}(\xi, \xi)$ by Theorems 7 and 11 and $(S^tS)^t = S^tS^{tt} = S^tS$, so the existence of $\{f_n\}$ is immediate from the theorem. Also $<Sf_n, Sf_n>_\eta = <S^tSf_n, f_n>_\xi = \lambda_n <f_n, f_n>_\xi$ from which $\lambda_n \geq 0$.

Since $k > 0$, $I = I_\xi \in OP_0(\xi, \xi) \subseteq OP_{k-1}(\xi, \xi)$, so by Theorem 3, $T = (S^tS + I) \in E_{2k}(\xi, \xi)$. Moreover if $Tf = 0$ then $0 = < Tf, f >_\xi = < Sf, < Sf, Sf >_\eta + < f, f >_\xi$, hence $< f, f >_\xi = 0$ so $f = 0$, i.e., $\ker T = 0$ and since $T = T^t$, ind $T = 0$. Then by Theorem 12, $T^r \in E_{2kr}(\xi, \xi)$ and $(T^r)_{kr}$ maps $H^{kr}(\xi)$ isomorphically onto $H^{-kr}(\xi) = H^{kr}(\xi)^*$ for all $r \in \mathbf{Z}$. It follows that $(f, g)_{kr} = < (T^r)_{kr}f, g >_\xi$ defines a non-degenerate bilinear pairing of $H^{kr}(\xi)$ with itself. It follows from the theorem that linear combinations of the f_n are dense in $H^\ell(\xi)$ for arbitrarily large ℓ, hence in $H^{kr}(\xi)$. Moreover, since $(T^r)_{kr}f_n = T^rf_n = (1+\lambda_n)^rf_n$ it follows that $(f_n, f_n)_{kr} = (1+\lambda_n)^r$ so $\{(1+\lambda_n)^{-r/2}f_n\}$ is orthonormal with respect to $(\ , \ )_{kr}$. It follows from this that $(\ , \ )_{kr}$ is positive definite and hence an admissible inner product for $H^{kr}(\xi)$ and that $\{(1+\lambda_n)^{-r/2}f_n\}$ is an orthonormal basis.

q.e.d.

CHAPTER XII

HOMOTOPY INVARIANCE OF THE INDEX

Richard S. Palais

In this section we assume M is a compact Riemannian manifold without boundary and we use the Riemannian structure of M to identity $T(M)$ with $T^*(M)$ in the canonical fashion. We denote the unit sphere bundle of $T(M)$ by $S(M)$. As usual ξ, η, ζ are hermitian vector bundles over M and we denote by $\tilde{\xi}$ the restriction of the bundle $\pi^*\xi$ over $T'(M)$ to $S(M)$, and similarly for $\tilde{\eta}$ and $\tilde{\zeta}$.

The element σ of $\mathrm{Smbl}_1(\xi, \xi)$ defined by $\sigma(v, x)e = \|v\|e$ is clearly elliptic and satisfies $\sigma^* = \sigma$. It follows from [XI, Theorem 13] that

THEOREM 1. There exists $\Lambda \in E_1(\xi, \xi)$ such that

1) Λ is bijective and $\Lambda^k \in E_k(\xi, \xi)$ for all $k \in \mathbf{Z}$;

2) $\sigma_k(\Lambda^k)(v, x)e = \|v\|^k e \quad k \in \mathbf{Z}$;

3) If $T \in E_k(\xi, \eta)$ then $T\Lambda^{-k} \in E_0(\xi, \eta)$ and $\mathrm{ind}(T\Lambda^{-k}) = \mathrm{ind}(T)$.

THEOREM 2. The map $\sigma \to \tilde{\sigma}$ defined by $\tilde{\sigma} = \sigma|S(M)$ is a bijection of $\mathrm{Smbl}_k(\xi, \eta)$ with $\mathrm{Hom}(\tilde{\xi}, \tilde{\eta})$ for each $k \in \mathbf{Z}$, the inverse map being given by $\sigma(v, x) = \|v\|^k \tilde{\sigma}(v/\|v\|, x)$. Moreover $\sigma \in \mathrm{Smbl}_k(\xi, \eta)$ is elliptic if and only if $\tilde{\sigma} \in \mathrm{Iso}(\tilde{\xi}, \tilde{\eta})$.

PROOF. Immediate from the definitions.

DEFINITION. We define the map $\tilde{\sigma}_k\colon \mathrm{Int}_k(\xi, \eta) \to \mathrm{Hom}(\tilde{\xi}, \tilde{\eta})$ by $\tilde{\sigma}_k(T) = \sigma_k(T)|S(M)$. We note that $\tilde{\sigma}_k$ is clearly linear, that if $T \in \mathrm{Int}_k(\xi, \eta)$ and $S \in \mathrm{Int}_\ell(\eta, \zeta)$ then $\tilde{\sigma}_{k+\ell}(ST) = \tilde{\sigma}_\ell(S)\tilde{\sigma}_k(T)$ [XI, (S3)], and that by [XI, Theorem 3] and Theorem 1 above

$$0 \to OP_{k-1}(\xi, \eta) \to \mathrm{Int}_k(\xi, \eta) \xrightarrow{\tilde{\sigma}_k} \mathrm{Hom}(\tilde{\xi}, \tilde{\eta}) \to 0$$

is exact. Finally it also follows from Theorem 1 that $T \in E_k(\xi, \eta)$ if and only if $\tilde{\sigma}_k(T) \in \mathrm{Iso}\ (\tilde{\xi}, \tilde{\eta})$.

LEMMA. If $k \neq \ell$ then $E_k(\xi, \eta) \cap E_\ell(\xi, \eta) = \emptyset$.

PROOF. Suppose $k > \ell$. If $T \in E_\ell(\xi, \eta)$ then since $E_\ell(\xi, \eta) \subseteq \mathrm{Int}_{k-1}(\xi, \eta)$ $\sigma_k(T) = 0$ by [XI, Theorem 3] so $T \notin E_k(\xi, \eta)$.

q.e.d.

DEFINITION. We define the set $E(\xi, \eta)$ of elliptic operators from ξ to η by $E(\xi, \eta) = \bigcup_{k \in \mathbf{Z}} E_k(\xi, \eta)$. If $T \in E(\xi, \eta)$ we define the *order* k of T to be the integer (unique by the lemma) such that $T \in E_k(\xi, \eta)$ and we define the restricted symbol map $\Sigma\colon E(\xi, \eta) \to \mathrm{Iso}(\tilde{\xi}, \tilde{\eta})$ by $\Sigma(T) = \tilde{\sigma}_k(T)$ where k is the order of T.

Remark. We note that if $T \in E(\xi, \eta)$ and $S \in E(\eta, \zeta)$ have orders k and ℓ respectively, then by [XI, Theorem 11] $ST \in E(\xi, \zeta)$ and has order $k + \ell$ so $\Sigma(ST) = \tilde{\sigma}_{k+\ell}(ST) = \tilde{\sigma}_\ell(S)\sigma_k(T) = \Sigma(S)\Sigma(T)$.

LEMMA 1. If $\Lambda \in E_1(\xi, \xi)$ satisfies the conditions of Theorem 1 then $\Sigma(\Lambda^k)$ is the identity automorphism of $\tilde{\xi}$ for all $k \in \mathbf{Z}$, hence if $T \in E(\xi, \eta)$ then $\Sigma(T\Lambda^k) = \Sigma(T)\Sigma(\Lambda^k) = \Sigma(T)$.

PROOF. If $(v, x) \in S(M)$ then $\|v\| = 1$ so that

$$\Sigma(\Lambda^k)(v, x)e = \tilde{\sigma}_k(\Lambda^k)(v, x)e = \sigma_k(\Lambda^k)(v, x)e = \|v\|^k e = e.$$

q.e.d.

Now let $L(\tilde{\xi}, \tilde{\eta})$ denote as usual the complex vector bundle over $S(M)$ whose fiber at (v, x) is the space of all linear maps of ξ_x into η_x and let $I(\tilde{\xi}, \tilde{\eta})$ denote the open subset of $L(\tilde{\xi}, \tilde{\eta})$ whose fiber over (v, x) is all linear isomorphisms of ξ_x with η_x ($I(\tilde{\xi}, \tilde{\eta})$ is a C^∞ fiber bundle over $S(M)$, but *not* a vector bundle, and is empty unless ξ and η have the same fiber dimension). We recall that $\mathrm{Hom}(\tilde{\xi}, \tilde{\eta})$ is naturally isomorphic to $C^\infty(L(\tilde{\xi}, \tilde{\eta}))$ and similarly $\mathrm{Iso}(\tilde{\xi}, \tilde{\eta})$ is naturally isomorphic to the set $C^\infty(I(\tilde{\xi}, \tilde{\eta}))$ of C^∞-sections of $I(\tilde{\xi}, \tilde{\eta})$.

DEFINITION. Let $h_t \in \mathrm{Iso}(\tilde{\xi}, \tilde{\eta})$ $0 \leq t \leq 1$. If the map $h\colon S(M)\times[0, 1] \to I(\tilde{\xi}, \tilde{\eta})$ defined by $h((v,x),t) = h_t(v,x)$ is C^∞ we call $\{h_t\}$ a C^∞ regular homotopy of h_0 with h_1 and say that h_0 and h_1 are C^∞ regularly homotopic.

LEMMA 2. Let $S, T \in E_0(\xi, \eta)$ and suppose $\Sigma(S)$ and $\Sigma(T)$ are C^∞ regularly homotopic. Then $\mathrm{ind}(S) = \mathrm{ind}(T)$.

PROOF. Let $\{h_t\}$ be a regular homotopy of $\Sigma(S)$ with $\Sigma(T)$ and define (Theorem 2) for each $t \in [0, 1]$, $H_t \in \mathrm{Smbl}_0(\xi, \eta)$ by $H_t(v, x) = h_t(v/\|v\|, x)$ so that $H_0 = \sigma_0(S)$ and $H_1 = \sigma_0(T)$. Then $((v, x), t) \to H_t(v, x)$ is a C^∞ map of $T'(M) \times [0, 1]$ into $L(\pi^*\xi, \pi^*\eta)$ from which it follows that $t \to H_t$ is a continuous arc in $\mathrm{Smbl}_0(\xi, \eta)$ when the latter is given the C^∞ topology. Then if $\chi_0\colon \mathrm{Smbl}_0(\xi, \eta) \to \mathrm{Int}_0(\xi, \eta)$ is the map of (S5) at the beginning of Chapter XI, then $t \to \chi_0(H_t)$ is a continuous arc in $OP_0(\xi, \eta)$ hence $t \to \chi_0(H_t)_0$ is a continuous arc in the space $L(H^0(\xi), H^0(\eta))$ by definition of the topology of $OP_0(\xi, \eta)$. Since each $h_t \in \mathrm{Iso}(\tilde{\xi}, \tilde{\eta})$, by Theorem 2, each H_t is an elliptic element of $\mathrm{Smbl}_0(\xi, \eta)$ so each $\chi_0(H_t)$ is in $E_0(\xi, \eta)$ hence [XI, Theorem 6] each $\chi_0(H_t)_0$ is an F-operator, so by [VII, Theorem 4] $\mathrm{ind}(\chi_0(H_0)_0) = \mathrm{ind}(\chi_0(H_1)_0)$ hence $\mathrm{ind}(\chi_0(H_0)) = \mathrm{ind}(\chi_0(H_1))$. But $\sigma_0(\chi_0(H_0)) = H_0 = \sigma_0(S)$ and $\sigma_0(\chi_0(H_1)) = H_1 = \sigma_0(T)$, hence by [XI, Theorem 10]

$$\mathrm{ind}(S) = \mathrm{ind}(\chi_0(H_0)) = \mathrm{ind}(\chi_0(H_1)) = \mathrm{ind}(T) \quad .$$

q.e.d.

THEOREM 3. Let $S, T \in E(\xi, \eta)$ and suppose $\Sigma(S)$ and $\Sigma(T)$ are C^∞ regular homotopic. Then $\mathrm{ind}(S) = \mathrm{ind}(T)$.

PROOF. Choose $\Lambda \in E_1(\xi, \xi)$ satisfying the conditions of Theorem 1 and let S and T have orders ℓ and k respectively. Then $S\Lambda^{-\ell}$ and $T\Lambda^{-k}$ are in $E_0(\xi, \eta)$ and $\Sigma(S\Lambda^{-\ell}) = \Sigma(S)$ and $\Sigma(T\Lambda^{-k}) = \Sigma(T)$ by Lemma 1, hence by Lemma 2 $\mathrm{ind}(S\Lambda^{-\ell}) = \mathrm{ind}(T\Lambda^{-k})$. But by 3) of Theorem 1, $\mathrm{ind}(S\Lambda^{-\ell}) = \mathrm{ind}\, S$ and $\mathrm{ind}(T\Lambda^{-k}) = \mathrm{ind}(T)$.

q.e.d.

As in [IX, §1] we make the space $C^0(L(\tilde{\xi}, \tilde{\eta}))$ of continuous cross sections of $L(\tilde{\xi}, \tilde{\eta})$ into a Banach space with the compact open topology. Of course $C^0(L(\tilde{\xi}, \tilde{\eta}))$ can be naturally identified with the space of continuous bundle morphisms of $\tilde{\xi}$ into $\tilde{\eta}$ and $\mathrm{Hom}(\tilde{\xi}, \tilde{\eta}) = C^\infty(L(\tilde{\xi}, \tilde{\eta}))$ is a dense linear subspace of $C^0(L(\tilde{\xi}, \tilde{\eta}))$. Similarly, the space $C^0(I(\tilde{\xi}, \tilde{\eta}))$ of continuous cross sections of $I(\tilde{\xi}, \tilde{\eta})$ is naturally isomorphic to the continuous vector bundle isomorphisms of $\tilde{\xi}$ with $\tilde{\eta}$, and since $I(\tilde{\xi}, \tilde{\eta})$ is open in $L(\tilde{\xi}, \tilde{\eta})$, $C^0(I(\tilde{\xi}, \tilde{\eta}))$ is an open subspace of $C^0(L(\tilde{\xi}, \tilde{\eta}))$, hence $\mathrm{Iso}(\tilde{\xi}, \tilde{\eta}) = \mathrm{Hom}(\tilde{\xi}, \tilde{\eta}) \cap C^0(I(\tilde{\xi}, \tilde{\eta}))$ is dense in $C^0(I(\tilde{\xi}, \tilde{\eta}))$.

DEFINITION. We define $\Delta(\xi, \eta)$ to be the set of arc components of $C^0(I(\tilde{\xi}, \tilde{\eta}))$ and if $\sigma \in C^0(I(\tilde{\xi}, \tilde{\eta}))$ we denote by $[\sigma]$ the arc component to which σ belongs. If $[\sigma] = [\sigma']$ we say that σ and σ' are homotopic. We define a map $\delta\colon E(\xi, \eta) \to \Delta(\xi, \eta)$ by $\delta(T) = [\Sigma(T)]$.

LEMMA. The map $\sigma \to [\sigma]$ of $\mathrm{Iso}(\tilde{\xi}, \tilde{\eta})$ into $\Delta(\xi, \eta)$ is surjective. Moreover, if $\sigma_0, \sigma_1 \in \mathrm{Iso}(\tilde{\xi}, \tilde{\eta})$ are homotopic (i.e., if $[\sigma_0] = [\sigma_1]$) then they are C^∞ regularly homotopic.

PROOF. Since $C^0(L(\tilde{\xi}, \tilde{\eta}))$ is a Banach space it is locally arcwise connected, hence, since $C^0(I(\tilde{\xi}, \tilde{\eta}))$ is open in $C^0(L(\tilde{\xi}, \tilde{\eta}))$, if δ is an arc component of $C^0(I(\tilde{\xi}, \tilde{\eta}))$ then δ is open in $C^0(L(\tilde{\xi}, \tilde{\eta}))$ and since, as noted above, $\mathrm{Iso}(\tilde{\xi}, \tilde{\eta})$ is dense in $C^0(I(\tilde{\xi}, \tilde{\eta}))$, we can find $\sigma \in \mathrm{Iso}(\tilde{\xi}, \tilde{\eta}) \cap \delta$, so $[\sigma] = \delta$, proving surjectivity. If we form the bundles $\tilde{\xi} \times [0, 1]$ and $\tilde{\eta} \times [0, 1]$ over $S(M) \times [0, 1]$ then $C^\infty(I(\tilde{\xi} \times [0, 1], \tilde{\eta} \times [0, 1]))$ is dense in $C^0(I(\tilde{\xi} \times [0, 1], \tilde{\eta} \times [0, 1]))$ for the same reasons that $C^\infty(I(\tilde{\xi}, \tilde{\eta}))$ is dense in $C^0(I(\tilde{\xi}, \tilde{\eta}))$. The second statement of the lemma is an obvious consequence.

q.e.d.

Remark. This lemma is of course just a special case of the classical theorem that if γ is a C^∞ fiber bundle then we can approximate any continuous cross section of γ uniformly (and hence to within homotopy) by a C^∞ section and we can replace any continuous homotopy between C^∞ sections by a "C^∞ homotopy" of these sections.

THEOREM 4. The map $\delta\colon E(\xi, \eta) \to \Delta(\xi, \eta)$ is surjective, and in fact if $\delta_0 \in \Delta(\xi, \eta)$ then for any $k \in \mathbf{Z}$ we can find $T \in E_k(\xi, \eta)$ with $\delta(T) = \delta_0$. Moreover if $T \in E(\xi, \eta)$ and $\delta(S) = \delta(T)$ then $\text{ind}(S) = \text{ind}(T)$.

PROOF. By the lemma we can find $\sigma_0 \in \text{Iso}(\tilde{\xi}, \tilde{\eta})$ with $[\sigma_0] = \delta_0$. By Theorem 2 we can find σ elliptic in $\text{Smbl}_k(\xi, \eta)$ with $\tilde{\sigma} = \sigma_0$. By [XI, Theorem 3] we can find $T \in E_k(\xi, \eta)$ with $\sigma_k(T) = \sigma$. Then $\delta(T) = [\Sigma(T)] = [\tilde{\sigma}_k(T)] = [\tilde{\sigma}] = [\sigma_0] = \delta_0$, proving the first statement. If $\delta(S) = \delta(T)$, i.e., if $[\Sigma(S)] = [\Sigma(T)]$ then by the lemma $\Sigma(S)$ and $\Sigma(T)$ are C^∞ regularly homotopic so by Theorem 3, $\text{ind}(S) = \text{ind}(T)$.

DEFINITION. We define a function $\text{ind}\colon \Delta(\xi, \eta) \to \mathbf{Z}$ by the requirement that $\text{ind}\,\delta(T) = \text{ind}(T)$ if $T \in E(\xi, \eta)$ (that this function is well defined is essentially just a restatement of Theorem 4).

The natural pairing of $C^0(I(\tilde{\eta}, \tilde{\zeta})) \times C^0(I(\tilde{\xi}, \tilde{\eta}))$ into $C^0(I(\tilde{\xi}, \tilde{\zeta}))$ induces a pairing of $\Delta(\eta, \zeta) \times \Delta(\xi, \eta)$ into $\Delta(\xi, \zeta)$. Similarly the inverse map $\sigma \to \sigma^{-1}$ of $C^0(I(\tilde{\xi}, \tilde{\eta}))$ into $C^0(I(\tilde{\eta}, \tilde{\xi}))$ induces an inverse map $[\sigma] \to [\sigma]^{-1} = [\sigma^{-1}]$ of $\Delta(\xi, \eta)$ into $\Delta(\eta, \xi)$. In particular, $\Delta(\xi, \xi)$ is a group; the group of components of the topological group $C^0(I(\tilde{\xi}, \tilde{\xi}))$.

THEOREM 5. If $\delta \in \Delta(\xi, \eta)$ and $\delta' \in \Delta(\eta, \zeta)$ then $\text{ind}(\delta'\delta) = \text{ind}(\delta') + \text{ind}(\delta)$ and $\text{ind}(\delta^{-1}) = -\text{ind}(\delta)$. In particular, $\text{ind}\colon \Delta(\xi, \xi) \to \mathbf{Z}$ is a homomorphism.

PROOF. Choose (by Theorem 4) $T \in E(\xi, \eta)$ and $S \in E(\eta, \zeta)$ with $\delta(T) = \delta$ and $\delta(S) = \delta'$. Then $\delta(ST) = [\Sigma(ST)] = [\Sigma(S)\Sigma(T)] = [\Sigma(S)][\Sigma(T)] = \delta'\delta$ so $\text{ind}\,\delta'\delta = \text{ind}(ST) = \text{ind}(S) + \text{ind}(T) = \text{ind}\,\delta' + \text{ind}\,\delta$. Also, $\delta^{-1}\delta = [\Sigma(T)]^{-1}[\Sigma(T)] = [\Sigma(T)^{-1}\Sigma(T)] = [\Sigma(I_\xi)]$ so $0 = \text{ind}\, I_\xi = \text{ind}(\delta^{-1}\delta) = \text{ind}\,\delta^{-1} + \text{ind}\,\delta$.

q.e.d.

Remark. There is also a map $\delta \to \delta^*$ of $\Delta(\xi, \eta)$ into $\Delta(\eta, \xi)$ induced by the map $\sigma \to \sigma^*$ of $C^0(I(\tilde{\xi}, \tilde{\eta}))$ into $C^0(I(\tilde{\eta}, \tilde{\xi}))$. But $\delta^* = \delta^{-1}$, i.e., if $\sigma_1 \in C^0(I(\tilde{\xi}, \tilde{\eta}))$ then there exists $\sigma_0 \in C^0(I(\tilde{\xi}, \tilde{\eta}))$ with $[\sigma_0] = [\sigma_1]$ and $\sigma_0^* = \sigma_0^{-1}$. Indeed, by polar decomposition we can write

$\sigma_1 = \sigma_0\sigma$ where $\sigma_0 \in C^0(I(\widetilde{\xi}, \widetilde{\eta}))$ and $\sigma_0(v, x): \xi_x \to \eta_x$ is unitary and $\sigma \in C^0(I(\widetilde{\xi}, \widetilde{\xi}))$ and $\sigma(v, x): \xi_x \to \xi_x$ is strictly positive. Then $\sigma_t = \sigma_0(t\sigma + (1-t)\widetilde{\sigma}_0(I_\xi))$ is an arc in $C^0(I(\widetilde{\xi}, \widetilde{\eta}))$ from σ_0 to σ_1.

CHAPTER XIII

WHITNEY SUMS

Richard S. Palais

§1. Direct sums of chains of hilbertian spaces.

Let $\{H_1^k\}$ and $\{H_2^k\}$ be two chains of hilbertian spaces and let $H^k = H_1^k \oplus H_2^k$. Then it is immediate that $\{H^k\}$ is again a chain of hilbertian spaces with $H^\infty = H_1^\infty \oplus H_2^\infty$; we denote it by $\{H_1^k\} \oplus \{H_2^k\}$. Since the natural identification of a hilbert space with its anti-dual respects direct sums, and since the anti-dual of a direct sum of hilbertian spaces is naturally isomorphic to the direct sum of their anti-duals, we have $H^k = H_1^k \oplus H_2^k$ for $k < 0$ and hence $H^{-\infty} = H_1^{-\infty} \oplus H_2^{-\infty}$. Let $i_k^1\colon H_1^k \to H^k$, $i_k^2\colon H_2^k \to H^k$ and $i^1\colon H_1^\infty \to H^\infty$, $i^2\colon H_2^\infty \to H^\infty$ be the natural injections and let $P_k^1\colon H^k \to H_1^k$, $P_k^2\colon H^k \to H_2^k$ and $P^1\colon H^\infty \to H_1^\infty$, $P^2\colon H^\infty \to H_2^\infty$ be the natural projections. Then clearly:

$$\{i_k^1\} \in \mathrm{Hom}(\{H_1^k\}, \{H^k\}), \quad i^1 \in OP_0(\{H_1^k\}, \{H^k\})$$
$$\{i_k^2\} \in \mathrm{Hom}(\{H_2^k\}, \{H^k\}), \quad i^2 \in OP_0(\{H_2^k\}, \{H^k\})$$
$$\{P_k^1\} \in \mathrm{Hom}(\{H^k\}, \{H_1^k\}), \quad P^1 \in OP_0(\{H^k\}, \{H_1^k\})$$
$$\{P_k^2\} \in \mathrm{Hom}(\{H^k\}, \{H_2^k\}), \quad P^2 \in OP_0(\{H^k\}, \{H_2^k\})$$

Moreover $\{P_k^1\}\{i_k^1\}$ is the identity morphism of $\{H_1^k\}$, $\{P_k^2\}\{i_k^2\}$ is the identity morphism of $\{H_2^k\}$, and $\{i_k^1\}\{P_k^1\} + \{i_k^2\}\{P_k^2\}$ is the identity morphism of $\{H^k\}$, i.e. $\{H^k\}$ is a "biproduct" of $\{H_1^k\}$ and $\{H_2^k\}$ in the sense of additive categories. This proves the fact already stated in Chapter VIII that the category of chains of hilbertian spaces is in fact additive.

Now suppose $\{H_3^k\}$ is another chain of hilbertian spaces and $T_j\colon H_j^\infty \to H_3^\infty$ is in $OP_r(\{H_j^k\}, \{H_3^k\})$ $(j = 1, 2)$. Then by [VIII, Theorem 3] $T_1 \oplus T_2\colon H^\infty \to H_3^\infty$ defined by $T_1 \oplus T_2 = T_1P^1 \oplus T_2P^2$ is in $OP_r(\{H^k\}, \{H_3^k\})$. Conversely, given T in $OP_r(\{H^k\}, \{H_3^k\})$ then $T_j = Ti^j \in OP_r(\{H_j^k\}, \{H_3^k\})$

and $T = T_1 \oplus T_2$. Similarly, if $T_j\colon H_3^\infty \to H_j^\infty$ is in $OP_r(\{H_3^k\}, \{H_j^k\})$ ($j = 1, 2$) then $T_1 \oplus T_2\colon H_3^\infty \to H^\infty$ defined by $T_1 \oplus T_2 = i^1T_1 + i^2T_2$ is in $OP_r(\{H_3^k\}, \{H^k\})$ while if $T\colon H_3^\infty \to H^\infty$ is in $OP_r(\{H_3^k\}, \{H^k\})$ and we define $T_j\colon H_3^\infty \to H_j^\infty$ by $T_j = P^jT$ then $T_j \in OP_r(\{H_3^k\}, \{H_j^k\})$ and $T = T_1 \oplus T_2$. Thus

THEOREM. Let $\{H_j^k\}$ ($j=1, 2, 3$) be three chains of hilbertian spaces and let $i^j\colon H_j^\infty \to H_1^\infty \oplus H_2^\infty$ ($j=1, 2$) and $P^j\colon H_1^\infty \oplus H_2^\infty \to H_j^\infty$ ($j = 1, 2$) be the natural injections and projections. Then $T \to (Ti^1, Ti^2)$ is an isomorphism of $OP_r(\{H_1^k\} \oplus \{H_2^k\}, \{H_3^k\})$ with $OP_r(\{H_1^k\}, \{H_3^k\}) \oplus OP_r(\{H_2^k\}, \{H_3^k\})$ and $T \to (P^1T, P^2T)$ is an isomorphism of $OP_r(\{H_3^k\}, \{H_1^k\} \oplus \{H_2^k\})$ with $OP_r(\{H_3^k\}, \{H_1^k\}) \oplus OP_r(\{H_3^k\}, \{H_2^k\})$.

§2. The Sobolev chain of a Whitney sum

Let M be a compact C^∞ manifold without boundary and with a strictly positive smooth measure. Then as we have seen [IX, Theorem 10] $\xi \to \{H^k(\xi)\}$ is a covariant functor, the Sobolev functor, from the category of hermitian vector bundles over M to the category of discrete chains of hilbertian spaces. If $T \in \mathrm{Hom}(\xi, \eta)$ then the induced map $T_*\colon H^\infty(\xi) \to H^\infty(\eta)$ is in $OP_0(\xi, \eta)$ [IX, Theorem 9] and corresponds via [VIII, Theorem 1] to $H^k(T)$. Since if $S \in \mathrm{Hom}(\xi, \eta)$ then $(S+T)_* = S_* + T_*$ we have

THEOREM 1. The Sobolev functor $\xi \sim\to \{H^k(\xi)\}$ is an additive functor.

COROLLARY. If ξ_1 and ξ_2 are hermitian vector bundles over M then $\{H^k(\xi_1 \oplus \xi_2)\} = \{H^k(\xi_1)\} \oplus \{H^k(\xi_2)\}$.

PROOF. Whitney sums together with the natural injections and projections is the natural biproduct in the category of hermitian vector bundles over M.

Now let $\xi_1, \ldots, \xi_r$ and $\eta_1, \ldots, \eta_s$ be hermitian vector bundles over M, $\xi = \oplus_i \xi_i$ $\eta = \oplus_j \eta_j$. Let $\lambda_i\colon H^\infty(\xi_i) \to H^\infty(\xi)$ in $OP_0(\xi_i, \xi)$ denote the induced map of the injection $\xi_i \to \xi$ and let $\gamma_j\colon H^\infty(\eta) \to H^\infty(\eta_j)$ in $OP_0(\eta, \eta_j)$ denote the induced map of the projection $\eta \to \eta_j$. Given

$T\colon H^\infty(\xi) \to H^\infty(\eta)$ define $T_{ji}\colon H^\infty(\xi_i) \to H^\infty(\eta_j)$ by $T_{ji} = \gamma_j T \lambda_i$. We call the T_{ji} the components of T relative to the given Whitney sum decompositions of ξ and η, and we call the indexed set $\{T_{ji}\}$ the matrix of components of T. Needless to say, if $\zeta = \oplus_{k=1}^{\ell} \zeta_k$ and $S\colon H^\infty(\eta) \to H^\infty(\zeta)$ we have the usual matrix composition law:

$$(ST)_{ki} = \sum_{j=1}^{s} S_{kj}\, T_{ji} \quad .$$

If $T \in OP_r(\xi, \eta)$ then $T_{ji} \in OP_r(\xi_i, \eta_j)$ by [VIII, Theorem 3], or by §1 above. Moreover by the Theorem of §1 we have:

THEOREM 2. Let $\xi_1, \ldots, \xi_r$ and $\eta_1, \ldots, \eta_s$ be hermitian vector bundles over M. Then $T \to \{T_{ji}\}$ is a linear isomorphism of $OP_r(\oplus_i \xi_i, \oplus_j \eta_j)$ with $\oplus_{i,j} OP_r(\xi_i, \eta_j)$.

§3. Behaviour of $Smbl_k$ with respect to Whitney sums

Let M be a C^∞ manifold and let $\xi_1, \ldots, \xi_r; \eta_1, \ldots, \eta_s$ be C^∞ complex vector bundles over M. Let $\xi = \oplus_i \xi_i$ and $\eta = \oplus_j \eta_j$. Then $\pi^*\xi = \oplus_i \pi^*\xi_i$ and $\pi^*\eta = \oplus_j \pi^*\eta_j$, so $Hom(\pi^*\xi, \pi^*\eta) \approx \oplus_{ij} Hom(\pi^*\xi_i, \pi^*\eta_j)$ and we denote the natural isomorphism by $\sigma \to \{\sigma_{ji}\}$. Clearly if $\zeta = \oplus_k \zeta_k$ and $\tau \in Hom(\pi^*\eta, \pi^*\zeta)$ then $(\tau\sigma)_{ki} = \Sigma_{j=1}^{s} \tau_{kj}\sigma_{ji}$. If the ξ_i and η_i are hermitian, then $(\sigma^*)_{ij} = \sigma^*_{ji}$. If $r = s$ and $\sigma_{ji} = 0$ for $i \neq j$, then clearly $\sigma \in Iso(\pi^*\xi, \pi^*\eta)$ if and only if each $\sigma_{ii} \in Iso(\pi^*\xi_i, \pi^*\eta_i)$ and in this case $(\sigma^{-1})_{ij} = 0$ $i \neq j$ while $(\sigma^{-1})_{ii} = \sigma_{ii}^{-1}$. Finally, it is clear that $\sigma \in Smbl_k(\xi, \eta)$ if and only if each $\sigma_{ji} \in Smbl_k(\xi_i, \eta_j)$, hence

THEOREM. The map $\sigma \to \{\sigma_{ji}\}$ is a linear isomorphism of $Smbl_k(\oplus_i \xi_i, \oplus_j \eta_j)$ with $\oplus_{i,j} Smbl_k(\xi_i, \eta_j)$.

COROLLARY. If $\sigma \in Smbl_k(\oplus_{i=1}^{r} \xi_i, \oplus_{j=1}^{r} \eta_j)$ and $\sigma_{ji} = 0$ for $i \neq j$ then σ is elliptic if and only if σ_{ii} is elliptic.

§4. Behaviour of Int_k and σ_k under Whitney sums

Let M be a compact C^∞ manifold without boundary and with a strictly positive smooth measure. Let $\xi_1, \ldots, \xi_r$ and $\eta_1, \ldots, \eta_s$ be hermitian vector bundles over M and $\xi = \oplus_i \xi_i$, $\eta = \oplus_j \eta_j$. Let λ_i: $H^\infty(\xi_i) \to H^\infty(\xi)$ and γ_j: $H^\infty(\eta) \to H^\infty(\eta_j)$ be the induced maps of the natural injections $\xi_i \to \xi$ and projections $\eta \to \eta_j$. Since the latter are in $\mathrm{Hom}(\xi_i, \xi)$ and $\mathrm{Hom}(\eta, \eta_j)$ it follows [IV, §3, Corollary 2 of Theorem 1] that $\lambda_i \in \mathrm{Diff}_0(\xi_i, \xi) \subseteq \mathrm{Int}_0(\xi_i, \xi)$ and $\gamma_i \in \mathrm{Diff}_0(\eta, \eta_j)$. Then if $T \in \mathrm{Int}_k(\xi, \eta)$ it follows from (S3) of [XI] that the components $T_{ji} = \gamma_j T \lambda_i$ of T are in $\mathrm{Int}_k(\xi_i, \eta_j)$. Moreover, since $\sigma_0(\lambda_i)$ is clearly the injection of $\pi^*\xi_i$ into $\pi^*\xi$ and $\sigma_0(\gamma_j)$ is the projection of $\pi^*\eta$ onto $\pi^*\eta_j$ we have $\sigma_k(T_{ji}) = \sigma_0(\gamma_j)\sigma_k(T)\sigma_0(\lambda_i) = (\sigma_k(T))_{ji}$. Conversely, suppose T: $H^\infty(\xi) \to H^\infty(\eta)$ and that $T_{ji} = \gamma_j T \lambda_i \in \mathrm{Int}_k(\xi_i, \eta_j)$ for all i and j. Then letting $\bar{\gamma}_i$: $H^\infty(\xi) \to H^\infty(\xi_i)$ and $\bar{\lambda}_j$: $H(\eta_j) \to H(\eta)$ denote the maps induced by the projections $\xi \to \xi_i$ and inclusions $\eta_j \to \eta$ respectively, we have $T = \Sigma_{i,j} \bar{\lambda}_j T_{ji} \bar{\gamma}_i$ and since $\bar{\gamma}_i \in \mathrm{Int}_0(\xi, \xi_i)$ and $\bar{\lambda}_j \in \mathrm{Int}_0(\eta_j, \eta)$, $T \in \mathrm{Int}_k(\xi, \eta)$ by (S3) of [XI] again. This proves

THEOREM. The map $T \to \{T_{ji}\}$ is a linear isomorphism of $\mathrm{Int}_k(\oplus_i \xi_i, \oplus_j \eta_j)$ with $\oplus_{i,j} \mathrm{Int}_k(\xi_i, \eta_j)$. Moreover if $T \in \mathrm{Int}_k(\xi, \eta)$ then $(\sigma_k(T))_{ji} = \sigma_k(T_{ji})$.

COROLLARY. If $T \in \mathrm{Int}_k(\oplus_{i=1}^r \xi_i, \oplus_{j=1}^r \eta_j)$ and $T_{ji} = 0$ for $i \neq j$, then T is k^{th} order elliptic if and only if each T_{ii} is k^{th} order elliptic.

§5. Behaviour of the index under Whitney sums

LEMMA. Let $V_1, \ldots, V_r$ and $W_1, \ldots, W_r$ be Banach spaces, $V = \oplus_i V_i$ and $W = \oplus_i W_i$ and let T_i: $V_i \to W_i$ be an F-operator. Define T: $V \to W$ by $T(v_1, \ldots, v_r) = (T_1 v_1, \ldots, T_r v_r)$. Then T is an F-operator and $\mathrm{ind}(T) = \Sigma_{i=1}^r \mathrm{ind}(T_i)$.

PROOF. Trivial.

Now let M be a compact C^∞ manifold without boundary and with a smooth strictly positive measure. Let $\xi_1, \ldots, \xi_r$ and $\eta_1, \ldots, \eta_r$ be hermitian vector bundles over M.

THEOREM 1. Let $T_i \in E_k(\xi_i, \eta_i)$ $i = 1, \ldots, r$ and define T: $H^\infty(\oplus_i \xi_i) \to H^\infty(\oplus_i \eta_i)$ by $T(f_1, \ldots, f_r) = (T_1 f_1, \ldots, T_r f_r)$.

Then $T \in E_k(\oplus_i \xi_i, \oplus_i \eta_i)$ and $\operatorname{ind}(T) = \sum_{i=1}^r \operatorname{ind}(T_i)$.

PROOF. Immediate from the lemma and the Corollary of the Theorem of §4.

Now assume M is Riemannian. The notation in the following is that introduced in Chapter XII. If $\sigma_i \in C^0(I(\tilde{\xi}_i, \tilde{\eta}_i))$ $i = 1, \ldots, r$, then we get an element $\oplus_i \sigma_i$ of $C^0(I(\oplus_i \tilde{\xi}_i, \oplus_i \tilde{\eta}_i))$ by $(\oplus_i \sigma_i)(v, x)(e_1, \ldots, e_r) = (\sigma_1(v, x)e_1, \ldots, \sigma_r(v, x)e_r)$. The map $(\sigma_1, \ldots, \sigma_r) \to \oplus_i \sigma_i$ of $C^0(I(\tilde{\xi}_1, \tilde{\eta}_1)) \times \ldots \times C^0(I(\tilde{\xi}_r, \tilde{\eta}_r))$ into $C^0(I(\oplus_i \tilde{\xi}_i, \oplus_i \tilde{\eta}_i))$ so defined as clearly continuous, so by passage to arc components it induces a map $(\delta_1, \ldots, \delta_r) \to \oplus_i \delta_i$ of $\Delta(\xi_1, \eta_1) \times \ldots \times \Delta(\xi_r, \eta_r)$ into $\Delta(\oplus_i \xi_i, \oplus_i \eta_i)$.

THEOREM 2. If $\delta_i \in \Delta(\xi_i, \eta_i)$, then

$$\operatorname{ind}(\oplus_i \delta_i) = \sum_{i=1}^r \operatorname{ind}(\delta_i) \quad .$$

PROOF. Choose [XII, Theorem 4] $T_i \in E_0(\xi_i, \eta_i)$ so that $\delta(T_i) = \delta_i$, so $\operatorname{ind}(\delta_i) = \operatorname{ind}(T_i)$. Define $T\colon H(\oplus_i \xi_i) \to H(\oplus_i \eta_i)$ by $T(f_1, \ldots, f_r) = (T_1 f_1, \ldots, T_r f_r)$. Then by Theorem 1, $T \in E_0(\oplus_i \xi_i, \oplus_i \eta_i)$ and $\operatorname{ind}(T) = \sum_{i=1}^r \operatorname{ind}(\delta_i)$. But by the theorem of §4, $\tilde{\sigma}_0(T) = \oplus_i \tilde{\sigma}_0(T_i)$ hence $\delta(T) = \oplus_i[\tilde{\sigma}_0(T_i)] = \oplus_i \delta(T_i) = \oplus_i \delta_i$. Then $\operatorname{ind}(\oplus_i \delta_i) = \operatorname{ind}(\delta(T)) = \operatorname{ind}(T) = \sum_{i=1}^r \operatorname{ind}(\delta_i)$.

q.e.d.

COROLLARY (Stability of the index under "suspension"). Let ξ, η, ζ be hermitian vector bundles over M and let $I \in \operatorname{Iso}(\tilde{\zeta}, \tilde{\zeta})$ denote the identity automorphism of ζ. Then if $\delta \in \Delta(\xi, \eta)$ the element $\delta \oplus [I]$ of $\Delta(\xi \oplus \zeta, \eta \oplus \zeta)$ has the same index as δ.

PROOF. $I = \Sigma(I_\zeta)$ so $[I] = \delta(I_\zeta)$ hence $\operatorname{ind}([I]) = \operatorname{ind}(I_\zeta) = 0$, so by the theorem, $\operatorname{ind}(\delta \oplus [I]) = \operatorname{ind}(\delta) + \operatorname{ind}([I]) = \operatorname{ind}(\delta)$.

q.e.d.

CHAPTER XIV

TENSOR PRODUCTS

Richard S. Palais

§1. Tensor products of chains of hilbertian spaces

If H_1 and H_2 are two hilbert spaces then recall that there is a natural inner product on their algebraic tensor product $H_1 \otimes H_2$ characterized by $(e_1 \otimes f_1, e_2 \otimes f_2) = (e_1, e_2)(f_1, f_2)$. The completion of this prehilbert space is denoted by $H_1 \hat{\otimes} H_2$. if $\{e_n\}$ is a complete orthonormal basis for H_1 and $\{f_m\}$ a complete orthonormal basis for H_2 then $\{e_n \otimes f_m\}$ is a complete orthonormal basis for $H_1 \hat{\otimes} H_2$. We can also describe $H_1 \hat{\otimes} H_2$ as the space of Hilbert-Schmidt operators from the dual of H_2 into H_1, the element $e_1 \otimes e_2$ corresponding to the operator $f \to f(e_2)e_1$. If H_i is realized as $L^2(X_i)$ where X_1 and X_2 are measure spaces, then $H_1 \hat{\otimes} H_2$ is naturally isomorphic to $L^2(X_1 \times X_2)$; if e_i is represented by $f_i \in L^2(X_i)$ then $e_1 \otimes e_2$ corresponds to $f \in L^2(X_1 \times X_2)$ where $f(x_1, x_2) = f_1(x_1)f_2(x_2)$. If $k \in L^2(X_1 \times X_2)$, the corresponding Hilbert-Schmidt operator $K\colon L^2(X_2) \to L^2(X_1)$ (we are identifying the dual of $L^2(X_2)$ with $L^2(X_2)$ via the natural anti-isomorphism $f \to \bar{f}$) is given by $(Kg)(x_1) = \int k(x_1, x_2)g(x_2)dx_2$. If we change the inner products on H_1 and H_2 to equivalent inner products, then we get an equivalent inner product on $H_1 \otimes H_2$, so we get the same $H_1 \hat{\otimes} H_2$ with an equivalent inner product. Thus, $H_1 \hat{\otimes} H_2$ is defined when H_1 and H_2 are only hilbertian spaces. If H_1' and H_2' are hilbert spaces and $T_i\colon H_i \to H_i'$ is a bounded linear transformation, then it is easily seen that $T_1 \otimes T_2\colon H_1 \otimes H_2 \to H_1' \otimes H_2'$ is bounded and in fact $\|T_1 \otimes T_2\|_\infty = \|T_1\|_\infty \cdot \|T_2\|_\infty$, so $T_1 \otimes T_2$ extends to a bounded linear map $T_1 \hat{\otimes} T_2\colon H_1 \hat{\otimes} H_2 \to H_1' \hat{\otimes} H_2'$. If T_1 and T_2 are injective, then $T_1 \hat{\otimes} T_2$ is likewise injective. Indeed [VI, Theorem 10] $T_1^*(H_1)$ is dense in H_1' and $T_2^*(H_2)$ is dense in H_2'

and it follows that $T_1^* \otimes T_2^*(H_1 \otimes H_2)$ is dense in $H_1' \otimes H_2'$, hence in $H_1' \hat{\otimes} H_2'$, and *a fortiori* $T_1^* \hat{\otimes} T_2^*(H_1 \hat{\otimes} H_2)$ is dense in $H_1' \otimes H_2'$. Since clearly $(T_1 \hat{\otimes} T_2)^* = T_1^* \hat{\otimes} T_2^*$, the injectivity of $T_1 \hat{\otimes} T_2$ follows from [VI, Theorem 10].

We would now like to define a tensor product operation for discrete chains of hilbertian spaces. The *sine qua non* is of course that if ξ is an hermitian bundle over M and η an hermitian bundle over N then for the bundle $\xi \otimes \eta$ over $M \times N$ we should have $\{H^k(\xi \otimes \eta)\}$ naturally isomorphic to $\{H^k(\xi)\} \hat{\otimes} \{H^k(\eta)\}$. Now E. Nelson has pointed out that in fact $H^k(\xi \otimes \eta)$ is naturally isomorphic to $\cap_{\ell+m=k} H^\ell(\xi) \hat{\otimes} H^m(\eta)$, in a sense to be made precise, and this motivates the following definition.

Let $H_1 = \{H_1^k\}$ and $H_2 = \{H_2^k\}$ be discrete chains of hilbertian spaces. We proceed to construct a third chain $H = \{H^k\}$ which we shall define to be $H_1 \hat{\otimes} H_2$. First we note that if $k > \ell$ and $m > n$ and $j_{\ell k}^1 \colon H_1^k \to H_1^\ell$ and $j_{nm}^2 \colon H_2^m \to H_2^n$ are inclusions, then by the remark above $j_{\ell k}^1 \hat{\otimes} j_{nm}^2 \colon H_1^k \hat{\otimes} H_2^m \to H_1^\ell \hat{\otimes} H_2^n$ is injective. Moreover if $k' > k$ and $m' > m$ then $(j_{\ell k}^1 \hat{\otimes} j_{nm}^2)(j_{kk'}^1 \hat{\otimes} j_{mm'}^2) = (j_{\ell k}^1 j_{kk'}^1 \otimes j_{nm}^2 j_{mm'}^2) = (j_{\ell k'}^1 \otimes j_{nm'}^2)$ so we may consistently regard $H_1^k \hat{\otimes} H_2^m$ as included (as a vector space) in $H_1^\ell \hat{\otimes} H_2^n$ and $j_{\ell k}^1 \otimes j_{nm}^2$ as inclusion maps. In particular if $k, m \geq 0$ we can regard $H_1^k \otimes H_2^m$ as a linear subspace of $H_1^0 \hat{\otimes} H_2^0$. We define $H^0 = H_1^0 \hat{\otimes} H_2^0$. For $k > 0$ we define H^k as a vector space to be $\cap_{\ell+m \leq k} H_1^\ell \hat{\otimes} H_2^m$ $(\ell, m \geq 0)$, so in particular $H^k \subseteq H^0$. We topologize H^k as the finite inverse limit of $H_1^\ell \hat{\otimes} H_2^m$, i.e., with the weakest topology such that each inclusion $H^k \to H_1^\ell \hat{\otimes} H_2^m$ is continuous. It is easily seen that H^k is hilbertian. In fact a choice of admissible inner products for H_1^ℓ and H_2^m gives an inner product $(\ ,\ )_{\ell m}$ on $H_1^\ell \hat{\otimes} H_2^m$ as described at the beginning of this section and then $(\ ,\ )_k$ defined by $(f, g)_k = \Sigma_{\ell+m \leq k} (f, g)_{\ell m}$ gives an admissible inner product on H^k. Note that if $\ell + m < k$ then we can find $\ell' \geq \ell$ and $m' \geq m$ with $\ell' + m' = k$, so that $H_1^{\ell'} \hat{\otimes} H_2^{m'} \subseteq H_1^\ell \hat{\otimes} H_2^m$, so we may equally well regard H^k as the intersection of the $H_1^\ell \hat{\otimes} H_2^m$ with $\ell + m = k$.

It is immediate from the definition that if $k > k' \geq 0$ then $H^k \subseteq H^{k'}$ and the inclusion map is continuous. Since H_1^∞ is dense in each

H_1^m it follows that $H_1^\infty \otimes H_2^\infty$ is dense in each $H_1^\ell \otimes H_2^m$, hence in each $H_1^\ell \hat{\otimes} H_2^m$, hence in each H^k. Since $H^\infty = \varprojlim H^k$ is clearly also the inverse limit of the doubly indexed family $H_1^\ell \hat{\otimes} H_2^m$ $(\ell, m \geq 0)$, $H_1^\infty \otimes H_2^\infty$ is dense in H^∞ so of course H^∞ is dense in each H^k. It follows that $H = \{H^k\}$ is a chain of hilbertian spaces which we define to be the tensor product of the chains H_1 and H_2 and denote by $H_1 \hat{\otimes} H_2$ or $\{H_1^k\} \hat{\otimes} \{H_2^k\}$. We put $H_1^\infty \hat{\otimes} H_2^\infty = H^\infty = (H_1 \hat{\otimes} H_2)^\infty$.

Now suppose $f \in H_1^{-\ell} \hat{\otimes} H_2^{-m} \cong (H_1^\ell \hat{\otimes} H_2^m)^*$ where $\ell + m \leq k$. Then since the inclusion of H^k into $H_1^\ell \hat{\otimes} H_2^m$ is continuous, f gives, by restriction, a continuous functional on H^k. Now the $H_1^{-\ell} \hat{\otimes} H_2^{-m}$ where $\ell + m \leq k$ can be considered subspaces of $H_1^{-k} \hat{\otimes} H_2^{-k}$ and we can take their linear span $\Sigma_{\ell+m\leq k} H_1^{-\ell} \hat{\otimes} H_2^{-m}$. Then $f \to f|H^k$ gives a linear map of $\Sigma_{\ell+m\leq k} H_1^{-\ell} \hat{\otimes} H_2^{-m}$ into $(H^k)^* = H^{-k}$, and since $H_1^\infty \otimes H_2^\infty$ is dense in each $H_1^\ell \hat{\otimes} H_2^m$ it follows that this restriction mapping is injective. We now recall a theorem of G. W. Mackey concerning locally convex vector spaces. Let X be a complex vector space, $\hat{X}$ its algebraic dual, and given a pseudonorm N on X let $L(N) \subseteq \hat{X}$ denote the linear functionals on X which are N-bounded. Then Mackey's theorem [TAMS, vol. 57(1945), p. 199] states that if $N_1, \ldots, N_k$ are pseudonorms on X and if N is their supremum, then $L(N)$ is the linear span $\Sigma_{i=1}^k L(N_i)$ of the $L(N_i)$ in $\hat{X}$. If we apply this to the present situation, taking $X = H_1^\infty \otimes H_2^\infty$ and the N_i as the restrictions of admissible norms for the $H_1^\ell \hat{\otimes} H_2^m$, then we see that the above map of $\Sigma_{\ell+m\leq k} H_1^{-\ell} \hat{\otimes} H_2^{-m}$ into H^{-k} is in fact, bijective. However, we shall not in the sequel have occasion to refer to this realization of the H^k for $k < 0$.

THEOREM 1. Let H_i $(i = 1, 2, 3, 4)$ be discrete chains of hilbertian spaces and let $S\colon H_1^\infty \to H_3^\infty$ and $T\colon H_2^\infty \to H_4^\infty$ be linear maps such that $S \in OP_r(H_1, H_3)$ and $T \in OP_s(H_2, H_4)$ for some $r, s \in \mathbf{Z}$. Then $S \otimes T\colon H_1^\infty \otimes H_2^\infty \to H_3^\infty \otimes H_4^\infty$ extends uniquely to a map $S \hat{\otimes} T\colon H_1^\infty \hat{\otimes} H_2^\infty \to H_3^\infty \hat{\otimes} H_4^\infty$ and $(S, T) \to S \hat{\otimes} T$ is bilinear. Moreover $S^t \hat{\otimes} T^t$ is the transpose of $S \hat{\otimes} T$. If r and s are *non-negative* integers such that $S \in OP_r(H_1, H_3)$ and $T \in OP_s(H_2, H_4)$

then for all $k \geq r+s$, $S \hat{\otimes} T$ extends uniquely to a continuous linear map $(S \hat{\otimes} T)_k$: $(H_1 \hat{\otimes} H_2)^k \to (H_3 \hat{\otimes} H_4)^{k-r-s}$.

PROOF. Since $OP_r \subseteq OP_0$ if $r < 0$ we can certainly find non-negative integers r, s such that $S \in OP_r(H_1, H_3)$ and $T \in OP_s(H_2, H_4)$. Then let S_k: $H_1^k \to H_3^{k-r}$ and T_k: $H_2^k \to H_4^{k-s}$ be the unique continuous extensions of S and T. Note that if $k > \ell$ and $m > p$ then $S_k \hat{\otimes} T_m$ and $(S_\ell \hat{\otimes} T_p)|(H_1^k \hat{\otimes} H_2^m)$ are both continuous maps of $H_1^k \hat{\otimes} H_2^m$ into $H_1^{\ell-r} \hat{\otimes} H_2^{m-s}$ which agree with $S \otimes T$ on the dense set $H_1^\infty \otimes H_2^\infty$, hence they are equal. It follows that $(S_0 \hat{\otimes} T_0)|H_1^\infty \hat{\otimes} H_2^\infty$ is a continuous map of $H_1^\infty \hat{\otimes} H_2^\infty = \varprojlim H_1^k \hat{\otimes} H_2^\ell$ into $H_3^\infty \hat{\otimes} H_4^\infty = \varprojlim H_3^{k-r} \hat{\otimes} H_4^{\ell-s}$. This proves the existence of $S \hat{\otimes} T$ and uniqueness follows from the density of $H_1^\infty \otimes H_2^\infty$ in $H_1^\infty \hat{\otimes} H_2^\infty$. Bilinearity in turn follows from uniqueness. Since S^t and T^t exist and are respectively in $OP_r(H_3, H_1)$ and $OP_s(H_4, H_2)$ by [VIII, Theorem 4] the existence of $S^t \hat{\otimes} T^t$ now also follows. Recalling how the inner product in $(H_1 \hat{\otimes} H_2)^0 = H_1^0 \hat{\otimes} H_2^0$ and $H_3^0 \hat{\otimes} H_4^0$ are defined, it is immediate that if $f_i \in H_i^\infty$ then $((S \hat{\otimes} T)(f_1 \otimes f_2), f_3 \otimes f_4) = (f_1 \otimes f_2, (S^t \otimes T^t)(f_3 \otimes f_4))$ so $((S \hat{\otimes} T)f, g) = (f, (S^t \hat{\otimes} T^t)g)$ for $f \in H_1^\infty \otimes H_2^\infty$ and $g \in H_3^\infty \otimes H_4^\infty$, and then by continuity for $f \in H_1^\infty \hat{\otimes} H_2^\infty$ and $g \in H_3^\infty \hat{\otimes} H_4^\infty$; i.e., $S^t \hat{\otimes} T^t = (S \hat{\otimes} T)^t$. Now suppose $k \geq r+s$ and let $\ell, m \geq 0$ with $\ell+m \leq k-r-s$. Then $(S_0 \hat{\otimes} T_0)|(H_1^{\ell+r} \hat{\otimes} H_2^{m+s}) = S_{\ell+r} \hat{\otimes} T_{m+s}$ is a continuous map of $H_1^{\ell+r} \hat{\otimes} H_2^{m+s}$ into $H_3^\ell \hat{\otimes} H_4^m$, and since the inclusion $(H_1 \hat{\otimes} H_2)^k \to H_1^{\ell+r} \hat{\otimes} H_2^{m+s}$ is continuous (because $(\ell+r) + (m+s) \leq k$)) it follows that $(S_0 \otimes T_0)|(H_1 \hat{\otimes} H_2)^k = (S \hat{\otimes} T)_k$ is a continuous map of $(H_1 \hat{\otimes} H_2)^k$ into $H_3^\ell \hat{\otimes} H_4^m$. Since this holds for all $\ell, m \geq 0$ with $\ell+m \leq k-r-s$, $(S \hat{\otimes} T)_k$ is a continuous map of $(H_1 \hat{\otimes} H_2)^k$ into $(H_3 \hat{\otimes} H_4)^{k-r-s}$, which clearly extends $S \hat{\otimes} T$.

q.e.d.

COROLLARY 1. Let $r = 0$ or 1 and let $s = 0$ or 1. Then $(S, T) \to S \hat{\otimes} T$ is a bilinear map of $OP_r(H_1, H_3) \times OP_s(H_2, H_4)$ into $OP_{r+s}(H_1 \hat{\otimes} H_2, H_3 \hat{\otimes} H_4)$.

PROOF. If I_2 is the identity map of H_2^∞, an element of $OP_0(H_2, H_2)$ and $I_3 \in OP_0(H_3, H_3)$ is the identity map of H_3, then clearly

$S \hat{\otimes} T = (I_3 \hat{\otimes} T)(S \hat{\otimes} I_2)$, so by [VIII, Theorem 3] it will suffice to show that $S \hat{\otimes} I_2 \in OP_r(H_1 \hat{\otimes} H_2, H_3 \hat{\otimes} H_2)$ (and hence, symmetrically, that $I_s \hat{\otimes} T \in OP_s(H_3 \hat{\otimes} H_2, H_3 \hat{\otimes} H_4)$). But this follows from the theorem and the two corollaries of [VIII, Theorem 5].

COROLLARY 2. Let M_i be a C^∞ compact manifold without boundary and with a strictly positive smooth measure and ξ_i an hermitian vector bundle over M_i $(i = 1, 2, 3, 4)$. Then if r and s are *non-negative* integers, $S \in OP_r(\xi_1, \xi_3)$ and $T \in OP_s(\xi_2, \xi_4)$ then $S \hat{\otimes} T \in OP_{r+s}(\{H^k(\xi_1)\} \hat{\otimes} \{H^k(\xi_2)\}, \{H_3^k\} \hat{\otimes} \{H_4^k\})$.

PROOF. By Corollary 1 we can proceed inductively and assume the theorem true for smaller values of r and s. Choose $\Lambda_i \in E_1(\xi_i, \xi_i)$ satisfying Theorem 1 of Chapter XII. Then $S \hat{\otimes} T = (S\Lambda_1^{-1} \hat{\otimes} T\Lambda_2^{-1})(\Lambda_1 \hat{\otimes} \Lambda_2)$. Since $S\Lambda_1^{-1} \in OP_{r-1}(H_1, H_3)$ and $T\Lambda_2^{-1} \in OP_{s-1}(H_2, H_4)$ the corollary follows from the inductive hypothesis and [VIII, Theorem 3].

q.e.d.

In view of [VIII, Theorem 1] if we take $r = s = 0$ in Corollary 1 above, we get:

THEOREM 2. If C denotes the additive category of discrete chains of hilbertian spaces, then $\hat{\otimes}$ is a covariant functor from $C \times C$ into C which is additive in each variable separately.

COROLLARY. There are natural equivalences of functors $(H_1 \oplus H_2) \hat{\otimes} H_3 \cong (H_1 \hat{\otimes} H_3) \oplus (H_2 \hat{\otimes} H_3)$ and $H_1 \hat{\otimes} (H_2 \oplus H_3) \cong (H_1 \hat{\otimes} H_2) \oplus (H_1 \hat{\otimes} H_3)$.

Remark. Clearly there are also natural equivalences of $H_1 \hat{\otimes} H_2$ with $H_2 \hat{\otimes} H_1$ and of $H_1 \hat{\otimes} (H_2 \hat{\otimes} H_3)$ with $(H_1 \hat{\otimes} H_2) \hat{\otimes} H_3$, i.e., to within natural equivalence, $\hat{\otimes}$ is commutative, associative, and distributive.

§2. The Sobolev chain of a tensor product of bundles

Let M_1 and M_2 be compact C^∞ manifolds without boundary and with strictly positive smooth measures. Integration on $M_1 \times M_2$ will be with respect to the product measure which is likewise strictly positive and smooth. If ξ_i is an hermitian vector bundle over M_i then [VI, §8] $\xi_1 \otimes \xi_2$ is a vector bundle over $M_1 \times M_2$ with an hermitian structure characterized by $((e_1 \otimes e_2), (e_1' \otimes e_2'))_{\xi_1 \otimes \xi_2} = (e_1, e_1')_{\xi_1}(e_2, e_2')_{\xi_2}$ for $e_1, e_1' \in (\xi_1)_p$ and $e_2, e_2' \in (\xi_2)_p$. We recall that we identity $H^\infty(\xi_1) \otimes H^\infty(\xi_2)$ with subspace of $H^\infty(\xi_1 \otimes \xi_2)$; namely if $f_i \in H^\infty(\xi_i)$ then $f_1 \otimes f_2$ is the element of $H^\infty(\xi_1 \otimes \xi_2)$ whose value at (p, q) is $f_1(p) \otimes f_2(q)$. In the same way the prehilbert space $H^0(\xi_1) \otimes H^0(\xi_2)$ is identified with a subspace of $H^0(\xi_1 \otimes \xi_2)$. Moreover, if $f_i, f_i' \in H^0(\xi_i)$ then

$$
\begin{aligned}
< f_1 \otimes f_2, f_1' \otimes f_2' >_{\xi_1 \otimes \xi_2} &= \int_{M_1 \times M_2} (f_1 \otimes f_2, f_1' \otimes f_2')_{\xi_1 \otimes \xi_2} \\
&= \int_{M_1 \times M_2} (f_1, f_1')_{\xi_1}(f_2, f_2')_{\xi_2} \\
&= \Big(\int_{M_1} (f_1, f_1')_{\xi_1}\Big)\Big(\int_{M_2} (f_2, f_2')_{\xi_2}\Big) \\
&= < f_1, f_1' >_{\xi_1} < f_2, f_2' >_{\xi_2}
\end{aligned}
$$

so that the inclusion of $H^0(\xi_1) \otimes H^0(\xi_2)$ into $H^0(\xi_1 \otimes \xi_2)$ is even isometric. Now $H^\infty(\xi_1) \otimes H^\infty(\xi_2)$ is C^∞ dense in $H^\infty(\xi_1 \otimes \xi_2)$ hence *a fortiori* H^0-dense. On the other hand $H^\infty(\xi_1 \otimes \xi_2)$ is dense in $H^0(\xi_1 \otimes \xi_2)$ so $H^0(\xi_1) \otimes H^0(\xi_2) \supseteq H^\infty(\xi_1) \otimes H^\infty(\xi_2)$ is dense in $H^0(\xi_1 \otimes \xi_2)$ and, since by definition, $H^0(\xi_1) \hat{\otimes} H^0(\xi_2)$ is the completion of $H^0(\xi_1) \otimes H^0(\xi_2)$ we have

LEMMA 1. $H^0(\xi_1) \hat{\otimes} H^0(\xi_2) = H^0(\xi_1 \otimes \xi_2)$, hence if $\ell, m \geq 0$ we have more generally $H^0(J^\ell(\xi_1)) \otimes H^0(J^m(\xi_2)) = H^0(J^\ell(\xi_1) \otimes J^m(\xi_2))$.

LEMMA 2. If k is a non-negative integer and ℓ, m are non-negative integers with $\ell+m = k$ then there is a unique $T_{(\ell,m)} \in \mathrm{Hom}(J^k(\xi_1 \otimes \xi_2), J^\ell(\xi_1) \otimes J^m(\xi_2))$ such that $T_{(\ell,m)} j_k(f_1 \otimes f_2)_{(p,q)} = j_\ell(f_1)_p \otimes j_m(f_2)_q$ if $f_i \in H^\infty(\xi_i)$. Moreover if $T_{(\ell,m)}(j) = 0$ for all $\ell, m \geq 0$ with $\ell+m = k$ then $j = 0$, hence

$$\lambda_k \in \mathrm{Hom}(J^k(\xi_1 \otimes \xi_2), \bigoplus_{\ell+m=k} J^\ell(\xi_1) \otimes J^m(\xi_2))$$

defined by $\lambda_k(j) = \{T_{(\ell,m)}(j)\}_{\ell+m=k}$ gives a canonical identification of $J^k(\xi_1 \otimes \xi_2)$ with a sub-bundle of $\oplus_{\ell+m=k} J^\ell(\xi_1) \otimes J^m(\xi_2)$.

PROOF. By the theorem of [IV, §8] the map $j_\ell \otimes j_m\colon H^\infty(\xi_1) \otimes H^\infty(\xi_2) \to H^\infty(J^\ell(\xi_1)) \otimes H^\infty(J^m(\xi_2))$ extends uniquely to a map, still denoted by $j_\ell \otimes j_m\colon H^\infty(\xi_1 \otimes \xi_2) \to H^\infty(J^\ell(\xi_1) \otimes J^m(\xi_2))$ which belongs to $\mathrm{Diff}_k(\xi_1 \otimes \xi_2, J^\ell(\xi_1) \otimes J^m(\xi_2))$ and by [IV, §3, Corollary 1 of Theorem 1] there is a unique $T_{(\ell,m)} \in \mathrm{Hom}(J^k(\xi_1 \otimes \xi_2), J^\ell(\xi_1) \otimes J^m(\xi_2))$ such that $(j_\ell \otimes j_m)(f)_{(p,q)} = T_{(\ell,m)} j_k(f)_{(p,q)}$. It remains to show that if $f \in H^\infty(\xi_1 \otimes \xi_2)$ and if $(j_\ell \otimes j_m)(f)_{(p,q)} = 0$ for all $\ell+m = k$ then $j_k(f)_{(p,q)} = 0$. Since this is a local question we can assume that $M_i = \mathbf{R}^{n_i}$ and $\xi_i = R^{n_i} \times V_i$ so that $f \in H^\infty(\mathbf{R}^{n_1} \times \mathbf{R}^{n_2}, V_1 \otimes V_2)$ and we must show that if γ_0 is an $(n_1 + n_2)$-multi-index with $|\gamma_0| \leq k$ then $(D^\gamma f)(p, q) = 0$. We can write γ_0 uniquely as $\alpha_0 \otimes \beta_0$ where α_0 is an n_1-multi-index and β_0 is an n_2-multi-index and $|\alpha_0| + |\beta_0| = |\gamma_0|$ (the notation is that of the proof of the theorem of [IV, §8]). Choose $\ell+m = k$ with $|\alpha_0| \leq \ell$ and $|\beta_0| \leq m$. Then the proof of the cited theorem gives $(j_\ell \otimes j_m)(f)_{(p,q)} = \{D^{\alpha\otimes\beta} f(p, q)\}_{\substack{|\alpha|\leq\ell \\ |\beta|\leq m}}$ so in particular $(j_\ell \otimes j_m)(f)_{(p,q)} = 0$ implies $D^\gamma f(p, q) = D^{\alpha_0\otimes\beta_0} f(p, q) = 0$.

q.e.d.

THEOREM. The canonical inclusion of $H^\infty(\xi_1) \otimes H^\infty(\xi_2)$ into $H^\infty(\xi_1 \otimes \xi_2)$ extends uniquely to an isomorphism of the chain $\{H^k(\xi_1)\} \hat{\otimes} \{H^k(\xi_2)\}$ with the chain $\{H^k(\xi_1 \otimes \xi_2)\}$.

PROOF. Since $H^\infty(\xi_1) \otimes H^\infty(\xi_2)$ is dense in all the hilbertian spaces $H^\ell(\xi_1) \hat{\otimes} H^m(\xi_2)$ and $H^k(\xi_1 \otimes \xi_2)$, it will suffice to show that if we denote $H^\infty(\xi_1) \otimes H^\infty(\xi_2)$ as a subspace of $H^k(\xi_1 \otimes \xi_2)$ by $(H^\infty(\xi_1) \otimes H^\infty(\xi_2))_{[k]}$, and as a subspace of $H^\ell(\xi_1) \hat{\otimes} H^m(\xi_2)$ by $(H^\infty(\xi_1) \otimes H^\infty(\xi_2))_{[\ell,m]}$, then the topology of $(H^\infty(\xi_1) \otimes H^\infty(\xi_2))_{[k]}$ is just the least fine topology which is finer than each of the topologies of $(H^\infty(\xi_1) \otimes H^\infty(\xi_2))_{[\ell,m]}$ with $\ell+m = k$. Now by definition $j_k\colon (H^\infty(\xi_1) \otimes H^\infty(\xi_2))_{[k]} \to H^0(J^k(\xi_1 \otimes \xi_2))$ is a homeomorphism into, and similarly, using Lemma 1, $j_\ell \otimes j_m: (H^\infty(\xi_1) \otimes H^\infty(\xi_2))_{[\ell,m]} \to H^0(J^\ell(\xi_1) \otimes J^m(\xi_2))$ is also a homeomorphism into. Now, if $T_{(\ell,m)}$ is as in Lemma 2, then $T_{(\ell,m)*} j_k = j_\ell \otimes j_m$ or $(j_\ell \otimes j_m)^{-1} \circ T_{(\ell,m)*} j_k$ is the identity map of $H^\infty(\xi_1) \otimes H(\xi_2)$. Since by [IX, §3, Theorem 2] $T_{(\ell,m)*}: H^0(J^k(\xi_1 \otimes \xi_2)) \to H^0(J^\ell(\xi_1) \otimes J^m(\xi_2))$ is continuous it follows that the identity map of $(H^\infty(\xi_1) \otimes H^\infty(\xi_2))_{[k]}$ into $(H^\infty(\xi_1) \otimes H^\infty(\xi_2))_{[\ell,m]}$ is continuous, i.e., that the topology of $(H^\infty(\xi_1) \otimes H^\infty(\xi_2))_{[k]}$ is finer than that of $(H^\infty(\xi_1) \otimes H^\infty(\xi_2))_{[\ell,m]}$ if $\ell+m = k$. Since exact sequences of vector bundles split we can by Lemma 2 find a projection $\pi_k \in \mathrm{Hom}(\oplus_{\ell+m=k} J^k(\xi_1) \otimes J^m(\xi_2), J^k(\xi_1 \otimes \xi_2))$ such that $\pi_k\lambda_k$ is the identity map of $J^k(\xi_1 \otimes \xi_2)$. If $\pi_{(\ell,m)} \in \mathrm{Hom}(J^\ell(\xi_1) \otimes J^m(\xi_2), J^k(\xi_1 \otimes \xi_2))$ is the restriction of π_k to $J^\ell(\xi_1) \otimes J^m(\xi_2)$ then $\Sigma_{\ell+m=k}\, \pi_{(\ell,m)}T_{(\ell,m)}$ is the identity map of $J^k(\xi_1 \otimes \xi_2)$ so $\Sigma_{\ell+m=k}\, \pi_{(\ell,m)*}T_{(\ell,m)*}$ is the identity map of $H^0(J^k(\xi_1 \otimes \xi_2))$. Now suppose $\{f_n\}$ is a sequence in $H^\infty(\xi_1) \otimes H^\infty(\xi_2)$ which converges to zero in each $(H^\infty(\xi_1) \otimes H^\infty(\xi_2))_{[\ell,m]}$, i.e., such that $(j_\ell \otimes j_m)(f_n) \to 0$ in $H^0(J^\ell(\xi_1) \otimes J^m(\xi_2))$ if $\ell + m = k$. Then

$$j_k(f_n) = \sum_{\ell+m=k} \pi_{(\ell,m)*}T_{(\ell,m)*}j_k(f_n) = \sum_{\ell+m=k} \pi_{(\ell,m)*}(j_\ell \otimes j_m)(f_n)$$

so since $\pi_{(\ell,m)*}: H^0(J^\ell(\xi_1) \otimes J^m(\xi_2)) \to H^0(J^k(\xi_1 \otimes \xi_2))$ is continuous, by [IX, Theorem 2] again, it follows that $j_k(f_n) \to 0$ in $H^0(J^k(\xi_1 \otimes \xi_2))$, i e., that $f_n \to 0$ in $(H^\infty(\xi_1) \otimes H^\infty(\xi_2))_{[k]}$. Hence the topology for $(H^\infty(\xi_1) \otimes H^\infty(\xi_2))_{[k]}$ is less fine than any topology which is finer than that of all the $(H^\infty(\xi_1) \otimes H^\infty(\xi_2))_{[\ell,m]}$ with $\ell+m = k$.

q.e.d.

Remark. Henceforth we will identity $\{H^k(\xi_1 \otimes \xi_2)\}$ with $\{H^k(\xi_1)\} \hat{\otimes} \{H^k(\xi_2)\}$.

COROLLARY 1. Let ξ_i and η_i be hermitian vector bundles over M_i (i=1, 2) and let r, s be non-negative integers. Then $(S, T) \to S \hat{\otimes} T$ is a bilinear map of $OP_r(\xi_1, \eta_1) \times OP_s(\xi_2, \eta_2)$ into $OP_{r+s}(\xi_1 \otimes \xi_2, \eta_1 \otimes \eta_2)$ and also of $\mathrm{Int}(\xi_1, \eta_1) \times \mathrm{Int}(\xi_2, \eta_2)$ into $\mathrm{Int}(\xi_1 \otimes \xi_2, \eta_1 \otimes \eta_2)$.

PROOF. The first conclusion is immediate from Corollary 2 of Theorem 1 of the preceding section. If $S \in \mathrm{Int}(\xi_1, \eta_1)$ then [XI, Theorem 1] $S \in OP_r(\xi_1, \eta_1)$ for some $r \in \mathbf{Z}$ and if $r < 0$ then $S \in OP_0(\xi_1, \eta_1)$ [VIII, Theorem 2] so $S \in OP_r(\xi_1, \eta_1)$ for some non-negative r. Similarly, if $T \in \mathrm{Int}(\xi_2, \eta_2)$ then $T \in OP_s(\xi_2, \eta_2)$ for some non-negative s and hence $S \hat{\otimes} T \in OP_{r+s}(\xi_1 \otimes \xi_2, \eta_1 \otimes \eta_2)$ and [XI, Theorem 1] completes the proof.

q.e.d.

COROLLARY 2. Let $S_i \in E_1(\xi_i, \eta_i)$ $i = 1, 2$ so that $C = S_1^t S_1 \hat{\otimes} I_{\xi_2} + I_{\xi_1} \hat{\otimes} S_2^t S_2$ is in $OP_2(\xi_1 \otimes \xi_2, \xi_1 \otimes \xi_2)$. Then

$$C_k: H^k(\xi_1 \otimes \xi_2) \to H^{k-2}(\xi_1 \otimes \xi_2)$$

is for each $k \in \mathbf{Z}$ an F-operator. Moreover, $\ker C_k = \ker C \subseteq H^\infty(\xi_1) \otimes H^\infty(\xi_2)$ and $\dim \ker C_k = (\dim \ker S_1)(\dim \ker S_2)$.

PROOF. By [XI, Corollary of Theorem 14] we can find an orthonormal basis $\{f_n^i\}$ for $H^0(\xi_i)$ where $f_n^i \in H^\infty(\xi_i)$ is an eigenvector of $S_i^t S_i$ corresponding to a non-negative eigenvalue $\lambda_n^{(i)}$, and then $\{(1+\lambda_n^{(i)})^{-\ell/2} f_n^i\}$ is an orthonormal basis with respect to an admissible inner product for $H^\ell(\xi_i)$ and hence $\{(1+\lambda_n^{(1)})^{-\ell/2}(1+\lambda_p^{(2)})^{-m/2} f_n^1 \otimes f_p^2\}$ is an orthonormal basis for $H^\ell(\xi_1) \hat{\otimes} H^m(\xi_2)$. Recalling that $H^k(\xi_1 \otimes \xi_2) = \cap_{\ell+m=k} H^\ell(\xi_1) \hat{\otimes} H^m(\xi_2)$ with the weakest topology making each inclusion $H^k(\xi_1 \otimes \xi_2) \to H^\ell(\xi_1) \hat{\otimes} H^m(\xi_2)$ continuous, it follows that

$$\left\{ \sum_{\ell+m=k} \binom{k}{\ell} (1 + \lambda_n^{(1)})^{-\ell/2} (1 + \lambda_p^{(2)})^{-m/2} f_n^1 \otimes f_p^2 \right\}$$

is an orthonormal basis with respect to an admissible inner product for $H^k(\xi_1 \otimes \xi_2)$. Now $\Sigma_{\ell+m=k} \binom{k}{\ell}(1+|x|)^\ell(1+|y|)^m = (2+|x| + |y|)^k \geq (1+|x|\cdot|y|)^k$ while on the other hand

$$\begin{aligned}(1 + |x| + |y|)^k &= \frac{1}{2^k}((1 + 2|x|) + (1 + 2|y|))^k \\ &\geq \frac{1}{2^k}((1 + |x|) + (1 + |y|))^k \\ &= \frac{1}{2^k} \sum_{\ell+m=k} \binom{k}{\ell}(1 + |x|)^\ell (1 + |y|)^m\end{aligned}$$

when $k > 0$, and it follows that $\{\varphi_{n,p}^{(k)}\} = \{1+\lambda_n^{(1)} + \lambda_p^{(2)})^{-k/2} f_n^1 \otimes f_p^2\}$ is equally well an orthonormal basis with respect to an admissible inner product for $H^k(\xi_1 \otimes \xi_2)$ if $k > 0$. Since

$$< \varphi_{n,p}^{(-k)}, \varphi_{\ell,m}^{(k)} >_{\xi_1\otimes\xi_2} = < f_n^1 \otimes f_p^2, f_\ell^1 \otimes f_m^2 >_{\xi_1\otimes\xi_2} = < f_n^1, f_\ell^1 >_{\xi_1} < f_p^2, f_m^2 >_{\xi_2}$$

it follows that $\{\varphi_{n,p}^{(-k)}\}$ is an orthonormal basis for $H^{-k}(\xi_1 \otimes \xi_2)$. Next note that

$$C_k\varphi_{\ell,m}^{(k)} = (\lambda_\ell^{(1)} + \lambda_m^{(2)})\varphi_{\ell,m}^{(k)} = \frac{\lambda_\ell^{(1)} + \lambda_m^{(2)}}{1+\lambda_\ell^{(1)}+\lambda_m^2} \varphi_{\ell,m}^{(k-2)}$$

Recalling from [XI, Corollary of Theorem 14] that $\lambda_\ell^{(i)} \to \infty$, it follows that

$$\frac{\lambda_\ell^{(1)}+ \lambda_m^{(2)}}{1+\lambda_\ell^{(1)}+\lambda_m^{(2)}} \to 1 ,$$

from which it follows that the range of C_k is the closed linear span of the $\varphi_{\ell,m}^{(k-2)}$ such that $\lambda_\ell^{(1)}+ \lambda_m^{(2)} \neq 0$. Also $\ker C_k$ is the linear span of the $\varphi_{\ell,m}^{(k)}$ such that $\lambda_\ell^{(1)}+ \lambda_m^{(2)} = 0$ or, since $\lambda_n^{(i)} \geq 0$, such that $\lambda_\ell^{(1)} = \lambda_m^{(2)} = 0$, hence $\dim \ker C_k$ = (number of ℓ such that $\lambda_\ell^{(1)} = 0$) $\times$ (number of m such that $\lambda_m^{(2)} = 0$) = $(\dim \ker S_1^t S_1) \times (\dim \ker S_2^t S_2)$ = $(\dim \ker S_1) \times (\dim \ker S_2)$. Also since $\varphi_{\ell,m}^{(k)} \in H^\infty(\xi_1) \otimes H^\infty(\xi_2)$ it follows that $\ker C_k \subseteq H^\infty(\xi_1) \otimes H^\infty(\xi_2)$ and so $\ker C_k = \ker C$.

q.e.d.

§3. The # operation

The following notation will be maintained for the remainder of this chapter. For $i = 1, 2$, M_i will denote a compact Riemannian manifold without boundary and ξ_i and η_i hermitian vector bundles over M_i. M will denote the Riemannian manifold $M_1 \times M_2$ and ξ and η the hermitian bundles over M defined by

$$\xi = (\xi_1 \otimes \xi_2) \oplus (\eta_1 \otimes \eta_2)$$

$$\eta = (\eta_1 \otimes \xi_2) \oplus (\xi_1 \otimes \eta_2)$$

$I_{\xi_i} \in \mathrm{Hom}(\xi_i, \xi_i)$ and $I_{\eta_i} \in \mathrm{Hom}(\eta_i, \eta_i)$ will denote the obvious identity maps.

If $\sigma \in C^0(L(\pi^*\xi_i, \pi^*\eta_i))$ and $r \in \mathbf{R}$ we shall say that σ is homogeneous of degree r if $\sigma(\rho v, x) = \rho^r\sigma(v, x)$ for $\rho > 0$ (so that $\mathrm{Smbl}_k(\xi_i, \eta_i)$, $k \in \mathbf{Z}$, is precisely the set of $\sigma \in C^0(L(\pi^*\xi_i, \pi^*\eta_i))$ which are C^∞ and homogeneous of degree k). We note that if $r > 0$, then such a σ extends to be continuous on $T(M_i)$ if we define $\sigma(0, x)$ to be the zero map of ξ_x into η_x, while if $r < 0$ (and also for $r = 0$ unless $\sigma(v, x)$ is independent of v) no continuous extension of σ over $T(M)$ is possible.

Given $\sigma \in C^0(L(\pi^*\xi_1, \pi^*\eta_1))$ homogeneous of degree $r > 0$ we define $(\sigma \otimes \sigma_0(I_{\xi_2}))((v_1, v_2), (x_1, x_2)) = \sigma(v_1, x_1) \otimes \sigma_0(I_{\xi_2})(v_2, x_2)$ if $v_1 \neq 0$ and to be the zero map of $(\xi_1)_{x_1} \otimes (\xi_2)_{x_2}$ into $(\eta_1)_{x_1} \otimes (\xi_2)_{x_2}$ if $v_1 = 0$. Then from what has just been said it follows that

$$\sigma \otimes \sigma_0(I_{\xi_2}) \in C^0(L(\pi^*(\xi_1 \otimes \xi_2), \pi^*(\eta_1 \otimes \xi_2))$$

and in fact is homogeneous of degree r. [Note that even if $\sigma \in \mathrm{Smbl}_r(\xi_1,\eta_1)$, $\sigma \otimes \sigma_0(I_{\xi_2})$ will not necessarily be in $\mathrm{Smbl}_r(\xi_1 \otimes \xi_2, \eta_1 \otimes \eta_2)$ since it will in general be only continuous, not C^∞, at elements $((v_1, v_2), (x_1, x_2))$ of $T'(M)$ such that $v_1 = 0$. As we saw in [IV, §8] if $\sigma \in \mathrm{Smbl}_r^d(\xi_1, \eta_1)$ then $\sigma \otimes \sigma_0(I_{\xi_2}) \in \mathrm{Smbl}_r^d(\xi_1 \otimes \xi_2, \eta_1 \otimes \xi_2)$ and it is easily seen that except in this case $\sigma \otimes \sigma_0(I_{\xi_2})$ *cannot* be in $\mathrm{Smbl}_r(\xi_1 \otimes \xi_2, \eta_1 \otimes \xi_2)$.] More generally if $r, s > 0$ and $\sigma \in C^0(L(\pi^*\xi_1, \pi^*\eta_1))$ is homogeneous of degree r and $\tau \in C^0(L(\pi^*\xi_2, \pi^*\eta_2))$ is homogeneous of degree s then $\sigma \otimes \tau = (\sigma_0(I_{\eta_2}) \otimes \tau)(\sigma \otimes \sigma_0(I_{\xi_1}))$ is in $C^0(L(\pi^*\xi_1 \otimes \xi_2), \pi^*(\eta_1 \otimes \eta_2))$ and is homogeneous of degree $r+s$. In case $r = s$ we define an element $\sigma \# \tau$ of $C^0(L(\pi^*\xi, \pi^*\eta))$, which again is homogeneous of degree r; namely the matrix of components of $\sigma \# \tau$ [XIII, §3] is

$$\begin{pmatrix} \sigma \otimes \sigma_0(I_{\xi_2}) & -\sigma_0(I_{\eta_1}) \otimes (-1)^r\tau^* \\ \sigma_0(I_{\xi_1}) \otimes \tau & (-1)^r\sigma^* \otimes \sigma_0(I_{\eta_2}) \end{pmatrix}$$

where $(-1)^r = e^{ir\pi}$. Recall that the matrix of $(\sigma \# \tau)^*$ is obtained by reflecting the matrix of $\sigma \# \tau$ in the main diagonal and taking the adjoint of each entry. Since $\overline{(-1)^r} = (-1)^{-r}$ this gives

$$\begin{pmatrix} \sigma^* \otimes \sigma_0(I_{\xi_2}) & \sigma_0(I_{\xi_1}) \otimes \tau^* \\ -\sigma_0(I_{\eta_1}) \otimes (-1)^{-r}\tau & (-1)^{-r}\sigma \otimes \sigma_0(I_{\eta_2}) \end{pmatrix}$$

hence $(\sigma \# \tau)^*(\sigma \# \tau)$ has the matrix

$$\begin{pmatrix} \sigma^*\sigma \otimes \sigma_0(I_{\xi_2}) + \sigma_0(I_{\xi_1}) \otimes \tau^*\tau & 0 \\ 0 & \sigma_0(I_{\eta_1}) \otimes \tau\tau^* + \sigma\sigma^* \otimes \sigma_0(I_{\eta_2}) \end{pmatrix}$$

which is clearly a strictly positive endomorphism of $\xi_{(x_1,x_2)}$ at each point $((v_1, v_2), (x_1, x_2))$ of $T'(M)$ where at least one of the maps $\sigma(v_1, x_1):(\xi_1)_{x_1} \to (\eta_1)_{x_1}$ or $\tau(v_2, x_2):(\xi_2)_{x_2} \to (\eta_2)_{x_2}$ is non-singular, and hence $\sigma \# \tau$ is non-singular at such a point. It follows that if $\sigma \in C^0(I(\pi^*\xi_1, \pi^*\eta_1))$ and $\tau \in C^0(I(\pi^*\xi_2, \pi^*\eta_2))$ (which implies $\dim \xi_i = \dim \eta_i$ and hence that $\dim \xi = \dim \eta$) then

$$(\sigma \# \tau)((v_1, v_2), (x_1, x_2)): \xi_{(x_1,x_2)} \to \eta_{(x_1,x_2)}$$

is a monomorphism and hence an isomorphism for all $((v_1, v_2), (x_1, x_2)) \in T'(M)$. This proves:

THEOREM 1. If $\sigma_i \in C^0(I(\pi^*\xi_i, \pi^*\eta_i))$ is homogeneous of degree $r > 0$, then $\sigma_1 \# \sigma_2$ is in $C^0(I(\pi^*\xi, \pi^*\eta))$ and is homogeneous of degree r.

Recall from Chapter XII that $\tilde{\xi}_i$ is defined as the restriction of $\pi^*\xi_i$ to the unit sphere bundle of $T(M_i)$. Recall also that for any $r \in \mathbf{R}$ the restriction mapping is a bijection of the set of elements of $C^0(L(\pi^*\xi_i, \pi^*\eta_i))$ which are homogeneous of degree r with $C^0(L(\tilde{\xi}_i, \tilde{\eta}_i))$, the inverse map $\sigma \to \sigma^{(r)}$ being of course defined by

$$\sigma^{(r)}(v, x) = \|v\|^r \sigma(v/\|v\|, x) \quad .$$

Finally, recall that $\Delta(\xi_i, \eta_i)$ is the set of arc components of $C^0(I(\tilde{\xi}_i, \tilde{\eta}_i))$.

THEOREM 2. There is a uniquely determined map $(\delta_1, \delta_2) \to \delta_1 \# \delta_2$ of $\Delta(\xi_1, \eta_1) \times \Delta(\xi_2, \eta_2) \to \Delta(\xi, \eta)$ such that if $\sigma_i \in \delta_i \in \Delta(\xi_i, \eta_i)$ and $r > 0$ then

$$(\sigma_1^{(r)} \# \sigma_2^{(r)})|S(M) \in \delta_1 \# \delta_2 \quad .$$

PROOF. If $\sigma_i \in C^0(I(\tilde{\xi}_i, \tilde{\eta}_i))$ then $\sigma_i^{(r)} \in C^0(I(\pi^*\xi_i, \pi^*\eta_i))$ and is homogeneous of degree r for any $r > 0$, so by Theorem 1, $\sigma_1^{(r)} \# \sigma_2^{(r)} \in C^0(I(\pi^*\xi, \pi^*\eta))$ and hence $(\sigma_1^{(r)} \# \sigma_2^{(r)})|S(M) \in C^0(I(\tilde{\xi}, \tilde{\eta}))$. Moreover the map $(\sigma_1, \sigma_2) \to (\sigma_1^{(r)} \# \sigma_2^{(r)})|S(M)$ of $C^0(I(\tilde{\xi}_1, \tilde{\eta}_1)) \times C^0(I(\tilde{\xi}_2, \tilde{\eta}_2))$ into $C^0(I(\tilde{\xi}, \tilde{\eta})$ is clearly continuous and hence induces a map $\Delta(\xi_1, \eta_1) \times \Delta(\xi_2, \eta_2) \to \Delta(\xi, \eta)$. If $s > 0$ then as t varies from zero to unity $\lambda(t) = ts + (1-t)r$ varies from r to s and $(\sigma_1^{\lambda(t)} \# \sigma_2^{\lambda(t)})|S(M)$ is a continuous arc in $C^0(I(\tilde{\xi}, \tilde{\eta}))$ from $(\sigma_1^{(r)} \# \sigma_2^{(r)})|S(M)$ to $(\sigma_1^{(s)} \# \sigma_2^{(s)})|S(M)$ hence the above map $\Delta(\xi_1, \eta_1) \times \Delta(\xi_2, \eta_2) \to \Delta(\xi, \eta)$ is independent of r and it is clearly the unique map having the property stated in the theorem.

q.e.d.

Recall that in Chapter XII we defined an index map ind: $\Delta(\xi_i, \eta_i) \to \mathbf{Z}$. Our goal in the rest of this chapter is to prove its "multiplicativity," i.e., that

$$\text{ind}(\delta_1 \# \delta_2) = (\text{ind}(\delta_1))(\text{ind}(\delta_2)) \quad .$$

§4. The property (S6) of the Seeley Algebra

If k is a non-negative integer, $D \in \text{Diff}_k(\xi_1, \eta_1)$ then [IV, §8] $D \otimes I_{\xi_2} \in \text{Diff}_k(\xi_1 \otimes \xi_2, \eta_1 \otimes \xi_2)$ and $\sigma_k(D \otimes I_{\xi_2}) = \sigma_k(D) \otimes \sigma_0(I_{\xi_2})$. One might hope naively that analogously if $T \in \text{Int}_k(\xi_1, \eta_1)$ then $T \hat{\otimes} I_{\xi_2}$ (which by Corollary 1 of the Theorem of §2 is in $\text{OP}_k(\xi_1 \otimes \xi_2, \eta_1 \otimes \xi_2)$) would be in $\text{Int}_k(\xi_1 \otimes \xi_2, \eta_1 \otimes \xi_2)$) and its symbol would be $\sigma_k(T) \otimes \sigma_0(I_{\xi_2})$. However, as pointed out in the preceding section, $\sigma_k(T) \otimes \sigma_0(I_{\xi_2})$ is not even in $\text{Smbl}_k(\xi_1 \otimes \xi_2, \eta_1 \otimes \xi_2)$ unless $T \in \text{Smbl}_k^d(\xi_1, \eta_1)$, so this hope must be disappointed. If k is positive, then at least we know that $\sigma_k(T) \otimes \sigma_0(I_{\xi_2}) \in C^0(L(\pi^*(\xi_1 \otimes \xi_2), \pi^*(\eta_1 \otimes \eta_2))$ and is homogeneous of degree k so we can clearly uniformly approximate it on any compact set by an element of $\text{Smbl}_k(\xi_1 \otimes \xi_2, \eta_1 \otimes \xi_2)$. Not so obvious is the fact shown by Seeley that we can approximate $T \otimes I_{\xi_2}$ in $\text{OP}_k(\xi_1 \otimes \xi_2, \eta_1 \otimes \xi_2)$ by elements A in $\text{Int}_k(\xi_1 \otimes \xi_2, \eta_1 \otimes \xi_2)$ so that $\sigma_k(A)$ approximates

$\sigma_k(T) \otimes \sigma_0(I_{\xi_2})$ in the compact open topology. This is a basic fact on a par with the properties (S1)-(S5) listed in Chapter XI. We state it formally as (S6) and will prove it along with (S1)-(S5) when we give the explicit construction of the Seeley algebra.

(S6) Let M_1 and M_2 be compact C^∞ manifolds without boundary and with strictly positive smooth measures. Let ξ_1 and η_1 be hermitian vector bundles over M_1 and ξ_2 an hermitian vector bundle over M_2, and let $T \in \mathrm{Int}_k(\xi_1, \eta_1)$, $k > 0$. Then there is a sequence $\{A_n\}$ in $\mathrm{Int}_k(\xi_1 \otimes \xi_2, \eta_1 \otimes \xi_2)$ such that A_n converges to $T \hat{\otimes} I_{\xi_2}$ in $OP_k(\xi_1 \otimes \xi_2, \eta_1 \otimes \xi_2)$ and such that $\sigma_k(A_n)$ converges to $\sigma_k(T) \otimes \sigma_0(I_{\xi_2})$ in the compact-open topology.

§5. Multiplicativity of the index

Given $S_i \in \mathrm{Int}(\xi_i, \eta_i) (i = 1, 2)$ we define $S_1 \# S_2$ to be the element of $OP(\xi, \eta)$ whose matrix of components [XIII, §2] is

$$\begin{pmatrix} S_1 \hat{\otimes} I_{\xi_2} & -I_{\eta_1} \hat{\otimes} S_2^t \\ I_{\xi_1} \hat{\otimes} S_2 & S_1^t \hat{\otimes} I_{\eta_2} \end{pmatrix}$$

THEOREM 1. If $k \geq 0$ then $S_i \in OP_k(\xi_i, \eta_i)$ implies $S_1 \# S_2 \in OP_k(\xi, \eta)$. If $k > 0$ and $S_i \in \mathrm{Int}_k(\xi_i, \eta_i)$ then there is a sequence $\{A_n\}$ in $\mathrm{Int}_k(\xi, \eta)$ such that A_n converges to $S_1 \# S_2$ in $OP_k(\xi, \eta)$ and $\sigma_k(A_n)$ converges to $\sigma_k(S_1) \# \sigma_k(S_2)$ in the compact-open topology.

PROOF. Since $I_{\xi_i} \in OP_0(\xi_i, \xi_i)$, $I_{\eta_i} \in OP_0(\eta_i, \eta_i)$ and $S_i^t \in OP_k(\eta_i, \xi_i)$ the first statement is a consequence of [XIII, Theorem 2] and Corollary 1 of the theorem of §2 above. If $S_i \in \mathrm{Int}_k(\xi_i, \eta_i)$, $k > 0$, then by (S6) of the preceding section we can find a sequence $\{B_n\}$ in $\mathrm{Int}_k(\xi_1 \otimes \xi_2, \eta_1 \otimes \xi_2)$ converging to $S_1 \hat{\otimes} I_{\xi_2}$ in $OP_k(\xi_1 \otimes \xi_2, \eta_1 \otimes \xi_2)$ with $\sigma_k(B_n)$ converging to $\sigma_k(S_1) \otimes \sigma_0(I_{\xi_2})$ in the compact-open topology. Similarly, we can find sequences $\{C_n\}$, $\{D_n\}$, and $\{E_n\}$ in

$\mathrm{Int}_k(\eta_1' \otimes \eta_2, \eta_1 \otimes \xi_2)$, $\mathrm{Int}_k(\xi_1 \otimes \xi_2, \xi_1 \otimes \eta_2)$, and $\mathrm{Int}_k(\eta_1 \otimes \eta_2, \xi_1 \otimes \eta_2)$ respectively, converging in the respective OP_k's to $I_{\eta_1} \hat{\otimes} S_2^t$, $I_{\xi_1} \hat{\otimes} S_2$ and $S_1^t \hat{\otimes} I_{\eta_2}$ and with the corresponding sequences of symbols converging in the compact-open topology respectively to $\sigma_0(I_{\eta_1}) \otimes (-1)^k \sigma_k(S_2)^*$, $\sigma_0(I_{\xi_1}) \otimes \sigma_k(S_2)$, and $(-1)^k \sigma_k(S_1)^* \otimes \sigma_0(I_{\eta_2})$. Then by [XIII, §4, Theorem]

$$A_n = \begin{pmatrix} B_n & -C_n \\ D_n & E_n \end{pmatrix}$$

is in $\mathrm{Int}_k(\xi, \eta)$ and clearly, A_n converges in $OP_k(\xi, \eta)$ to $S_1 \# S_2$ while $\sigma_k(A_n)$ converges to $\sigma_k(S_1) \# \sigma_k(S_2)$ in the compact-open topology.

q.e.d.

THEOREM 2. $(S_1 \# S_2)^t = S_1^t \# (-S_2)$.

PROOF. The matrix of $(S_1 \# S_2)^t$ is obtained from that of $S_1 \# S_2$ by reflecting in the main diagonal and replacing each entry by its transpose, i.e.,

$$\begin{pmatrix} S_1^t \hat{\otimes} I_{\xi_2} & I_{\xi_1} \hat{\otimes} S_2^t \\ -I_{\eta_1} \hat{\otimes} S_2 & S_1 \hat{\otimes} I_{\eta_2} \end{pmatrix}$$

which is also clearly the matrix of $S_1^t \# (-S_2)$.

q.e.d.

COROLLARY 1. The matrix of $(S_1 \# S_2)^t(S_1 \# S_2)$ is $\begin{pmatrix} C & 0 \\ 0 & D \end{pmatrix}$ where $C = S_1^t S_1 \hat{\otimes} I_{\xi_2} + I_{\xi_1} \hat{\otimes} S_2^t S_2$ and $D = I_{\eta_1} \hat{\otimes} S_2 S_2^t + S_1 S_1^t \hat{\otimes} I_{\eta_2}$.

COROLLARY 2. If $S_i \in E_1(\xi_i, \eta_i)$ then for all $k \in \mathbf{Z}$ $\ker(S_1 \# S_2)_k = \ker(S_1 \# S_2)$ and has dimension $(\dim \ker S_1)(\dim \ker S_2) + (\dim \ker S_1^t)(\dim \ker S_2^t)$.

PROOF. We first note that for any $T \in OP_1(\xi, \eta)$

(a) $\ker T \subseteq \ker T_k$;

(b) $\ker T^t T = \ker T$;

(c) $(T^t T)_k = T_{k-1}^t T_k$.

Applying (a) and (c) with $T = S_1 \# S_2$ gives $\ker(S_1 \# S_2) \subseteq \ker(S_1 \# S_2)_k \subseteq \ker((S_1 \# S_2)^t(S_1 \# S_2))_k$. And applying (b) gives $\ker(S_1 \# S_2) = \ker(S_1 \# S_2)^t(S_1 \# S_2)$. Hence it will suffice to prove that

$$\ker((S_1 \# S_2)^t(S_1 \# S_2))_k = \ker(S_1 \# S_2)^t(S_1 \# S_2) \quad .$$

and has the required dimension. Now by Corollary 1 it follows that $\ker((S_1 \# S_2)^t(S_1 \# S_2))_k = \ker C_k \oplus \ker D_k$. By Corollary 2 of the theorem of §2, $\ker C_k = \ker C$ and has dimension $(\dim \ker S_1)(\dim \ker S_2)$. Interchanging the roles of ξ_i and η_i and of S_i and S_i^t, it follows that $\ker D_k = \ker D$ and has dimension $(\dim \ker S_1^t)(\dim \ker S_2^t)$. It follows that $\ker((S_1 \# S_2)^t(S_1 \# S_2))_k = \ker C \oplus \ker D = \ker(S_1 \# S_2)^t(S_1 \# S_2)$ and has the right dimension.

q.e.d.

LEMMA 1. Let X and Y be hilbert spaces and $T: X \to Y$ a continuous linear map. If T^*T has closed range, then so does T.

PROOF. Let $V = (\ker T)^\perp = (\ker T^*T)^\perp$. Then T^*T maps V bijectively with the range of T^*T so by [VI, Theorem 1] $T^*Tv_n \to 0$ implies $v_n \to 0$ if $\{v_n\}$ is a sequence in V. Now $Tv_n \to 0$ implies $T^*Tv_n \to 0$, hence T maps V isomorphically onto $T(V) = T(X)$. Hence $T(X)$, being isomorphic to V, is a hilbert space, hence closed in Y.

q.e.d.

LEMMA 2. Let H_1 and H_2 be chains of hilbertian spaces, $A \in OP_k(H_1, H_2)$ and suppose that $(A^tA)_k: H_1^k \to H_1^{-k}$ has closed range. Then $A_k: H_1^k \to H_2^0$ has closed range.

PROOF. A choice of admissible inner product for H_1^k gives rise to an isomorphism $j: H_1^{-k} \cong H_1^k$. Now $(A^tA)_k = A_0^tA_k$ and by [VIII, Theorem 4] $jA_0^t: H_2^0 \to H_1^k$ is the adjoint of A_k, so $j(A^tA)_k = A_k^*A_k$ has closed range and, by Lemma 1, so does A_k.

q.e.d.

THEOREM 3. Let $S_i \in E_1(\xi_i, \eta_i)$ so that (by Theorem 1) $S_1 \# S_2 \in OP_1(\xi, \eta)$. Then $(S_1 \# S_2)_1 : H^1(\xi) \to H^0(\eta)$ is an F-operator and $\operatorname{ind}(S_1 \# S_2)_1 = (\operatorname{ind} S_1)(\operatorname{ind} S_2)$.

PROOF. Writing $\nu = \dim \ker$ we have $\nu((S_1 \# S_2)_1) = \nu(S_1)\nu(S_2) + \nu(S_1^t)\nu(S_2^t)$ by Corollary 2 of Theorem 2. Since [VIII, Theorem 4] $(S_1 \# S_2)_1^* = (S_1 \# S_2)_0^t$, from Theorem 2 and its second corollary we have

$$\begin{aligned}\nu((S_1 \# S_2)_1^*) &= \nu(S_1^t \# -S_2)\\ &= \nu(S_1^t)\nu(S_2) + \nu(S_1)\nu(S_2^t) \quad .\end{aligned}$$

Then

$$\begin{aligned}\nu((S_1 \# S_2)_1) - \nu((S_1 \# S_2)_1^*) &= (\nu(S_1) - \nu(S_1^t))\nu(S_2) - \nu(S_2^t))\\ &= (\operatorname{ind}(S_1))(\operatorname{ind}(S_2)) \quad .\end{aligned}$$

Hence (cf. [VI, Corollary 2 of Theorem 10] it will suffice to prove that $(S_1 \# S_2)_1$ has closed range, and by Lemma 2 above it will suffice to prove that $((S_1 \# S_2)^t(S_1 \# S_2))_1$ has closed range. By Corollary 1 of Theorem 2 above $((S_1 \# S_2)^t(S_1 \# S_2))_1 = \begin{pmatrix} C_1 & 0 \\ 0 & D_1 \end{pmatrix}$ where C_1 has closed range by Corollary 2 of the theorem of §2. Interchanging the roles of ξ_i and η_i and of S_i and S_i^t it follows that D_1 has closed range, hence the range of $((S_1 \# S_2)^t(S_1 \# S_2))_1$ which is the direct sum of the range of C_1 and that of D_1 is also closed.

q.e.d.

THEOREM 4. (Multiplicativity of the index) If $\delta_i \in \Delta(\xi_i, \eta_i)$ then

$$\operatorname{ind}(\delta_1 \# \delta_2) = (\operatorname{ind} \delta_1)(\operatorname{ind} \delta_2).$$

PROOF. By [XII, Theorem 4] we can choose $S_i \in E_1(\xi_i, \eta_i)$ with $\delta_i = \delta(S_i) = [\tilde{\sigma}_1(S_i)]$ so $\delta_1 \# \delta_2 = [(\sigma_1(S_1) \# \sigma_1(S_2)) | S(M)]$. If we choose $\{A_n\}$ as in Theorem 1 then $\tilde{\sigma}_1(A_n) = \sigma_1(A_n) | S(M)$ converges uniformly to $(\sigma_1(S_1) \# \sigma_1(S_2)) | S(M)$. Recalling (see proof of the lemma of [XII, Theorem 4]) that $\delta_1 \# \delta_2$ is a neighborhood of $(\sigma_1(S_1) \# \sigma_2(S_2)) | S(M)$ in $C^0(I(\xi, \eta)$ it follows that for n large, $\tilde{\sigma}_1(A_n)$ is in $\delta_1 \# \delta_2$, hence $A_n \in E_1(\xi, \eta)$ and $\delta_1 \# \delta_2 = \delta(A_n)$ so that $\operatorname{ind}(\delta_1 \# \delta_2) = \operatorname{ind} A_n$. On the other hand, A_n converges to $S_1 \# S_2$ in $OP_1(\xi, \eta)$ so that $(A_n)_1$ converges to $(S_1 \# S_2)_1$

in $L(H^1(\xi), H^0(\eta))$. Hence for n large, $\text{ind } A_n = \text{ind}(A_n)_1 = (\text{ind}(S_1))(\text{ind}(S_2))$ by Theorem 3 above and [VII, Theorem 4].

q.e.d.

CHAPTER XV

DEFINITION OF i_a AND i_t ON K(M)

Robert M. Solovay

In §1, we show that $i_a(D)$ depends only on $\gamma(D) \in K(B(M), S(M))$. Paragraphs 2 and 3 are devoted to a study of the multiplicative properties of i_t. In §4, we associate to each vector bundle η over the even-dimensional manifold M, an operator $D_M \otimes 1_\eta$. Putting

$$i(M, \eta) = i(D_M \otimes 1_\eta) \quad ,$$

for $i = i_t$ or i_a, we may consider i to be defined on K(M). §5 summarizes the principal properties of i_a and i_t on K(M). For the most part these properties are proved in §§5—7, though one property will be established (after much labor) in XVII.

§1. Definition of the analytical index on K(B(M), S(M))

Let M be a closed oriented Riemannian manifold. Let B(M) (resp. S(M)) be the unit ball-bundle (resp. unit sphere bundle) of M. Let $\pi: B(M) \to M$ be the projection map. If ζ is a bundle over M, $\tilde{\zeta}$ shall denote the restriction of $\pi^*\zeta$ to S(M).

Now let ζ and η be complex vector bundles over M, and $D: C^\infty(\zeta) \to C^\infty(\eta)$ an elliptic operator. The symbol of D gives an isomorphism

$$\sigma(D): \tilde{\zeta} \cong \tilde{\eta} \quad .$$

The difference construction yields an element $\gamma(D) \in K(B(M), S(M))$;

$$\gamma(D) = d(\pi^*\zeta, \pi^*\eta, \sigma(D)) \quad .$$

THEOREM 1. There is a homomorphism

(1) $$i_a\colon K(B(M), S(M) \to \mathbf{Z}$$

such that

(2) $$i_a(D) = i_a(\gamma(D))$$

for each elliptic operator D. (Thus the analytical index of D depends only on $\gamma(D)$.) If $\gamma_0 \in K(B(M), S(M))$, then $\gamma_0 = \gamma(D)$, for some elliptic operator D.

PROOF. We prove the last assertion first. Since $\pi\colon B(M) \to M$ is a homotopy equivalence, every complex vector bundle over B(M) is isomorphic to one of the form $\pi^*\zeta$, where ζ is a smooth vector bundle over M. Thus [II, Theorem 2] shows that for suitable ζ, η, and σ_0,

$$\gamma_0 = d(\pi^*\zeta, \pi^*\eta, \sigma_0) \quad ,$$

where $\sigma_0 \in \mathrm{Iso}(\tilde{\zeta}, \tilde{\eta})$.* By [XII, Theorem 4] there is an elliptic operator $D\colon C^\infty(\zeta) \to C^\infty(\eta)$ with $\sigma(D)$ homotopic to σ_0. Then $\gamma(D) = \gamma_0$, and the last sentence of the theorem is proved.

Accoriing to [XII, Theorem 4] $i_a(D)$ depends only on the homotopy class of $\sigma(D)$ in $\mathrm{Iso}(\tilde{\zeta}, \tilde{\eta})$. Moreover $\sigma(D) = \sigma(D')$ for some elliptic operator D' of order zero. For the remainder of the proof, we shall consider only elliptic operators, D, of order zero.

Case 1. The automorphism $\sigma(D)$ extends to an automorphism of $\pi^*\zeta \cong \pi^*\eta$ over all of B(M).

By [II, Lemma 1] $\gamma(D) = 0$. We show that $i_a(D) = 0$. Since $\pi\colon B(M) \to M$ is a homotopy equivalence, $\sigma(D)$ is homotopic in $\pi^*\psi$ where $\psi\colon \zeta \cong \eta$. On the other hand, $\psi_*\colon C(\zeta) \to C(\eta)$ is an elliptic differential operator of order zero, and $\sigma(\psi_*) = \pi^*\psi|S(M)$. Thus $i_a(D) = i_a(\psi_*) = 0$, since ψ_* is an isomorphism.

Case 2. D is an elliptic operator of order zero, with $\gamma(D) = 0$.

---

* We allow the dimension of the fibres of ζ to differ on different connectedness components of M.

We show $i_a(D) = 0$. By [II, Lemma 1(v)] there is a bundle ω over M such that

$$\sigma(D) + 1_{\tilde{\omega}} : \tilde{\zeta} \oplus \tilde{\omega} \cong \tilde{\eta} \oplus \tilde{\omega}$$

extends to an isomorphism over all of B(M). Now $\sigma(D) \oplus 1_{\tilde{\omega}} = \sigma(D \oplus 1_{\omega})$ (cf. XIII, §4). By Case 1, $i_a(D \oplus 1_{\omega}) = 0$. On the other hand,

$$i_a(D \oplus 1_{\omega}) = i_a(D) + i_a(1_{\omega}) = i_a(D) \quad .$$

Thus $i_a(D) = 0$.

Case 3. D_1, D_2 are elliptic operators with $\gamma(D_1) = \gamma(D_2)$.

We show $i_a(D_1) = i_a(D_2)$. Let D_3 be elliptic of order zero with $\gamma(D_3) = -\gamma(D_1)$. By [XIII, §4] $\sigma(D_1 \oplus D_3) = \sigma(D_1) \oplus \sigma(D_3)$. By the additivity of the difference construction [II, Lemma 1 (vi)] $\gamma(D_1 \oplus D_3) = \gamma(D_1) + \gamma(D_3) = 0$. Similarly, $\gamma(D_2 + D_3) = 0$. By [XIII, Theorem 1] and Case 2, $0 = i_a(D_1 \oplus D_3) = i_a(D_1) + i_a(D_3)$; similarly, $0 = i_a(D_2) + i_a(D_3)$. Thus $i_a(D_1) = i_a(D_2)$.

By Case 3, i_a is well-defined on K(B(M), S(M)) by (2). In view of [XIII, Theorem 1] and the additivity of the difference construction, i_a is a homomorphism. This completes the proof of Theorem 1.

Remark. The definition of the topological index makes it clear, *a priori*, that $i_t(D)$ depends only on $\gamma(D)$. Thus i_t defines a homomorphism

$$i_t : K(B(M), S(M)) \to Q$$

such that $i_t(D) = i_t(\gamma(D))$. To prove the index theorem for all elliptic operators on M, it suffices to show that i_a and i_t agree on K(B(M), S(M)).

§2. Multiplicative properties of i_t

2.1. We review the results on tensor products that we need from Chapter XIV. For $i = 1, 2$, M_i is a closed oriented Riemannian manifold and ξ_i and η_i are hermitian bundles over M_i. Let $M = M_1 \times M_2$; define hermitian bundles ξ and η over M by

$$\xi = (\xi_1 \otimes \xi_2) \oplus (\eta_1 \otimes \eta_2)$$
$$\eta = (\eta_1 \otimes \xi_2) \oplus (\xi_1 \otimes \eta_2)$$

Let $S_i: C^\infty(\xi_i) \to C^\infty(\eta_i)$ be elliptic or order $r > 0$ for $i = 1, 2$. Define $S_1 \# S_2 \in OP_r(\xi, \eta)$ by the matrix

$$\begin{pmatrix} S_1 \hat{\otimes} I_{\xi_2} & -I_{\eta_1} \hat{\otimes} S_2^* \\ I_{\xi_1} \hat{\otimes} S_2 & S_1^* \hat{\otimes} I_{\eta_2} \end{pmatrix} \tag{3}$$

If S_1 and S_2 are differential operators, then $S_1 \# S_2$ is an elliptic differential operator of order r. However, in general, $S_1 \# S_2$ will not be elliptic of order r.

The symbol of S_i, $\sigma(S_i)$ is, *a priori* defined only on the non-zero tangent vectors of M_i, $T'(M_i)$. Since $\sigma(S_i)$ is homogeneous of degree $r > 0$, it has a continuous extension to all of $T(M_i)$: let $\sigma(0, x)$ be the zero map.

We define $\sigma(S_1 \# S_2) \in C^0(L(\pi^*\xi, \pi^*\eta)$ by giving its matrix components

$$\begin{pmatrix} \sigma(S_1) \otimes \sigma_0(I_{\xi_2}) & -\sigma_0(I_{\eta_1}) \otimes (-1)^r\sigma(S_2)^*) \\ \sigma_0(I_{\xi_1}) \otimes \sigma(S_2) & (-1)^r\sigma(S_1)^* \otimes \sigma_0(I_{\eta_2}) \end{pmatrix} \tag{4}$$

If S_1 and S_2 are differential operators, $\sigma(S_1 \# S_2)$ is the usual symbol. In general, $\sigma(S_1 \# S_2)$ will be homogeneous of degree r and elliptic. (I.e., if $(v, x) \in T(M)$, $v \neq 0$, then $\sigma(S_1 \# S_2)(v, x) \in \mathrm{Iso}(\xi_x, \eta_x)$.)

Finally, we remark that the analytical index enjoys the following multiplicative property: let $S: C^\infty(\xi) \to C^\infty(\eta)$ be elliptic of order r. Suppose that $\sigma(S)$ is homotopic to $\sigma(S_1 \# S_2)$ in $C^0(\mathrm{Iso}(\pi^*\xi, \pi^*\eta))$ $(\pi: T'(M) \to M)$. Then

$$i_a(S) = i_a(S_1 \# S_2) = i_a(S_1) \cdot i_a(S_2) \quad . \tag{5}$$

($S_1 \# S_2$ is an F-operator, so $i_a(S_1 \# S_2)$ is defined.)

2.2. We recall the definition of the topological index of an elliptic operator

$$S: C^\infty(\xi) \to C^\infty(\eta) \quad .$$

(Here ξ and η are complex vector bundles over M. For the moment, M is an arbitrary closed oriented Riemannian manifold.)

Let m be the dimension of M, and let $U \in H^m(B(M), S(M); \mathbf{Q})$ be the Thom class of M determined by its orientation. Let $\varphi_*: H^*(M, \mathbf{Q}) \cong H^*(B(M), S(M); \mathbf{Q})$ be the Thom isomorphism:

$$\varphi_*(a) = \pi^* a \cup U \qquad (\pi: B(M) \to M) \quad .$$

Since S is elliptic, the element $\gamma(S) \in K(B(M), S(M))$ is defined (cf. §1). We put

$$\text{(6)} \qquad \mathrm{Ch}(S) = -1^{\varepsilon(m)} \varphi_*^{-1} \mathrm{ch}(\gamma(S))$$

where

$$\text{(7)} \qquad \varepsilon(m) = \frac{m(m+1)}{2} \quad .$$

Next recall the definition of $\mathcal{T}(M) \in H^*(M, \mathbf{Q})$. Let ξ be a real vector bundle over M; we view the rational Pontrjagin classes of ξ as elementary symmetric functions in $y_1^2, \dots, y_n^2$ (n large): $1 + p_1(\xi) + \dots + p_m(\xi) = \prod_{i=1}^n (1+y_i^2)$. Then

$$\text{(8)} \qquad \mathcal{T}(\xi) = \prod_{i=1}^{n} \frac{y_i}{1-e^{-y_i}} \cdot \frac{-y_i}{1-e^{y_i}}$$

Finally, $\mathcal{T}(M) = \mathcal{T}(T(M))$.

The following formula results from (8):

$$\text{(9)} \qquad \mathcal{T}(\xi_1 \oplus \xi_2) = \mathcal{T}(\xi_1) \cdot \mathcal{T}(\xi_2) \quad .$$

We recall the argument. Write

$$p(\xi_1) = \prod_{i=1}^{r} (1+y_i^2) \quad \text{and} \quad p(\xi_2) = \prod_{i=r+1}^{s} (1+y_i^2)$$

(where the y_i's are indeterminates and r, $s-r$ are large). The product formula for Pontrjagin classes says that $p(\xi_1 \oplus \xi_2) = p(\xi_1) \cdot p(\xi_2) = \prod_{i=1}^s (1+y_i^2)$. Now (9) follows easily from (8):

$$\mathcal{T}(\xi_1 \oplus \xi_2) = \prod_{i=1}^{s} \left(\frac{y_i}{1-e^{-y_i}} \cdot \frac{-y_i}{1-e^{y_i}} \right) = \prod_{i=1}^{r} (\dots) \cdot \prod_{i=r+1}^{s} (\dots) = \mathcal{T}(\xi_1) \cdot \mathcal{T}\xi_2) .$$

Finally, if $a \in H^*(M, \mathbf{Q})$, $a[M]$ is the result of evaluating the top-dimensional component of a on the fundamental cycle determined by the orientation on M. The topological index of S is given by

(10) $$i_t(S) = Ch(S)\ \mathcal{T}(M)[M]$$

2.3. We return to the notation of 2.1. Let $m_i = \dim M_i$. We define $\gamma(S_1\# S_2) \in K(B(M), S(M))$ by $\gamma(S_1\# S_2) = d(\pi^*\xi, \pi^*\eta, \sigma(S_1\# S_2)|S(M))$. Define $i_t(S_1\# S_2) \in \mathbf{Q}$ by (6) and (10).

THEOREM 2. The topological index is multiplicative:

$$i_t(S_1 \# S_2) = i_t(S_1) \cdot i_t(S_2) \quad .$$

PROOF. The basic point is that all the "ingredients" of i_t have multiplicative properties. The sign in (6) will serve to compensate for signs arising from the skew-commutativity of the cup-product.

We shall first show that

(11) $$\mathcal{T}(M) = \mathcal{T}(M_1) \times \mathcal{T}(M_2) \quad .$$

In fact, we have a direct sum decomposition $T(M) = \pi_1^*\ T(M_1) \oplus \pi_2^* T(M_2)$. By (9), $\overline{\mathcal{T}}(M) = \pi_1^*\ \mathcal{T}(M_1) \cup \pi_2^*\mathcal{T}(M_2) = \overline{\mathcal{T}}(M_1) \times \overline{\mathcal{T}}(M_2)$.

We shall eventually show that

(12) $$Ch(S_1\# S_2) = Ch(S_1) \times Ch(S_2) \quad .$$

Granting (12), Theorem 2 follows from the well-known identity:

(13) $$\alpha_1 \times \alpha_2[M_1 \times M_2] = \alpha_1[M_1] \cdot \alpha_2[M_2]$$

($\alpha_i \in H^*(M_i, \mathbf{Q})$.) In fact, $Ch(S_1 \# S_2)\ \overline{\mathcal{T}}(M) = (Ch(S_1) \times Ch(S_2)) \cdot (\overline{\mathcal{T}}(M_1) \times \overline{\mathcal{T}}(M_2)) = (Ch(S_1) \cdot \overline{\mathcal{T}}(M_1)) \times (Ch(S_2) \cdot \overline{\mathcal{T}}(M_2))$; thus $i_t(S_1 \# S_2) = Ch(S_1 \# S_2) \cdot \overline{\mathcal{T}}(M)[M] = (Ch(S_1) \cdot \overline{\mathcal{T}}(M_1)) \times (Ch(S_2) \cdot \overline{\mathcal{T}}(M_2))[M] = i_t(M_1) \cdot i_t(M_2)$ (by (13)).

The proof of (12) will use a homotopy equivalence

$$r\colon (B(M_1) \times B(M_2);\ B(M_1) \times S(M_2) \cup S(M_1) \times B(M_2)) \rightarrow$$
$$\rightarrow (B(M_1 \times M_2);\ S(M_1 \times M_2))$$

defined as follows: we have

$$B(M_1 \times M_2) \subseteq B(M_1) \times B(M_2) \quad .$$

The map r will be the identity on $B(M_1 \times M_2)$; on the exterior of

$B(M_1 \times M_2)$, r is a radial retraction onto $S(M_1 \times M_2)$:

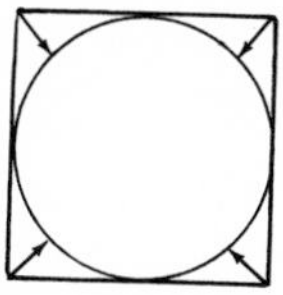

Figure 1

Figure 1 shows the map r on a typical fibre when $m_1 = m_2 = 1$.

Let $U_i \in H^{m_i}(B(M_i), S(M_i); \mathbf{Q})$ be the Thom class of M_i, and let $U \in H^{m_1+m_2}(B(M), S(M); \mathbf{Q})$ be the Thom class of M. Then $(r^*)^{-1}(U_1 \times U_2)$ restricts to a generator of $H^*(B(M)_x, S(M)_x)$ for each $x \in M$. Since this characterizes the Thom class U (cf. III §1.0), we have

$$r^*(U) = U_1 \times U_2 \quad . \tag{14}$$

The following lemma will be proved in §3:

LEMMA 1. The operation γ is multiplicative:

$$r^!\gamma(S_1 \# S_2) = \gamma(S_1 \times \gamma(S_2) \quad .$$

From Lemma 1, we get

$$r^*(ch(\gamma(S_1 \# S_2))) = ch(\gamma(S_1)) \times ch(\gamma(S_2)) \quad . \tag{15}$$

On the other hand, (6) implies

$$\begin{aligned} ch(\gamma(S_i)) &= -1^{\varepsilon(m_i)} \pi^* Ch(S_i) \cup U_i \\ ch(\gamma(S_1 \# S_2) &= -1^{\varepsilon(m_1+m_2)} \pi^* Ch(S_1 \# S_2) \cup U \quad . \end{aligned} \tag{16}$$

From (14), (15), and (16), we get

$$-1^{\varepsilon_1} Ch(S_1 \# S_2) = -1^{\varepsilon_2} Ch(S_1) \times Ch(S_2) \tag{17}$$

where $\varepsilon_1 = \varepsilon(m_1 + m_2)$ and $\varepsilon_2 = \varepsilon(m_1) + \varepsilon(m_2) + m_1 m_2$. (The factor $-1^{m_1 m_2}$ arises in the following way: $Ch(S_2) \cup U_2$ $(= \pm ch(\gamma(S_2)))$ consists of even-dimensional terms. Thus, $Ch(S_2)$ consists of terms of parity m_2 (= grading of U_2). To get (17), one has to bring $Ch(S_2)$ past U_1, and the factor $(-1)^{m_1 m_2}$ results.)

Finally, (12) follows from (17) and the following verified identity.

$$\varepsilon(m_1 + m_2) = \varepsilon(m_1) + \varepsilon(m_2) + m_1 m_2$$

§3. Proof of Lemma 1

We keep the notations of §2. Thus for $i = 1, 2$, we have bundles ξ_i and η_i over M_i, and bundle maps,

$$\sigma(S_i): \pi^* \xi_i \to \pi^* \eta_i \quad ,$$

defined over $B(M_i)$. (Here $\pi: B(M_i) \to M_i$ is the projection map,* and the symbol, $\sigma(S_i)$, is extended to the whole of $B(M_i)$ by continuity. By definition,

(18) $$\gamma(S_i) = d(\pi^* \xi_i, \pi^* \eta_i, \sigma(S_i) | S(M_i)) \quad .$$

As in §2.1, there are bundles ξ and η defined over M ($= M_1 \times M_2$) and a bundle map

(19) $$\sigma(S_1 \# S_2): \pi^* \xi \to \pi^* \eta \ (\pi: B(M_1) \times B(M_2) \to M)$$

defined over $B(M_1) \times B(M_2)$. The map (19) is an isomorphism off the zero cross-sections of $B(M_1) \times B(M_2)$. By definition,

(20) $$\gamma(S_1 \# S_2) = d(\pi^* \xi, \pi^* \eta, \sigma(S_1 \# S_2) | S(M)) \quad ;$$

here π is the projection of $B(M)$ onto M, and $\gamma(S_1 \# S_2)$ lies in $K(B(M), S(M))$.

We now apply Theorem 8 of Chapter II. We put: $X_i = B(M_i)$, $Y_i = S(M_i)$, $E_i = \pi^* \xi_i$, $F_i = \pi^* \eta_i$, $\tilde{\sigma}_i = \sigma(S_i)$. A comparison of the definitions given in [II, §5 and §2.1] of this lecture shows that

$$E = \pi^* \xi, \quad F = \pi^* \eta, \quad \tilde{\sigma}_1 \# \tilde{\sigma}_2 = \sigma(S_1 \# S_2) \quad ,$$

(where $\pi: B(M_1) \times B(M_2) \to M$).

---

* We use the symbol π to denote several different bundle projections. Its meaning will be clear from context.

We put, for brevity,

$$\partial(B(M_1) \times B(M_2)) = B(M_1) \times S(M_2) \cup S(M_1) \times B(M_2) \quad .$$

Then [II, Theorem 8] together with (18), shows that

$$\gamma(S_1) \times \gamma(S_2) = d(\pi^*\xi,\ \pi^*\eta,\ \sigma(S_1 \# S_2) | \partial(B(M_1) \times B(M_2))) \quad . \tag{21}$$

(Both sides of (21) lie in

$$K(B(M_1) \times B(M_2),\ \partial(B(M_1) \times B(M_2))).)$$

We shall deduce Lemma 1 from (20) and (21). Let $\|x\|$ denote the length of x, and let

$$E(M) = \{(x_1, x_2) \in B(M_1) \times B(M_2) : \ \|(x_1, x_2)\| \geq 1\} \quad .$$

Thus $E(M)$ is the part of $B(M_1) \times B(M_2)$ lying between $S(M)$ and $\partial(B(M_1) \times B(M_2))$. (Cf. Figure 1 of §2.) We have a homotopy commutative diagram of homotopy equivalences;

$$\begin{array}{ccc} (B(M_1) \times B(M_2),\ \partial(B(M_1) \times B(M_2))) & & \\ \big\downarrow r & \searrow^{i_1} & \\ (B(M),\ S(M)) & \xrightarrow{\ i_2\ } & (B(M_1) \times B(M_2),\ E(M)) \end{array} \quad . \tag{22}$$

Here i_1 and i_2 are inclusions and r is as in Lemma 1 (cf. Figure 1).

The map $\sigma(S_1 \# S_2) | E(M)$ is an isomorphism since $E(M)$ consists of non-zero vectors. Define $\gamma^* \in K(B(M_1) \times B(M_2),\ E(M))$ by

$$\gamma^* = d(\pi^*\xi,\ \pi^*\eta,\ \sigma(S_1 \# S_2) | E(M)) \quad .$$

Then by (22), $r^! i_2^!(\gamma^*) = i_1^!(\gamma^*)$. Now $i_1^!(\gamma^*) = \gamma(S_1) \times \gamma(S_2)$ by (21); by (20), $i_2^!(\gamma^*) = \gamma(S_1 \# S_2)$. Thus

$$r^! \gamma(S_1 \# S_2) = \gamma(S_1) \times \gamma(S_2) \quad ,$$

and Lemma 1 is proved.

§4. Definition of i_t and i_a on $K(M)$

4.1. We shall need the following material from [V, §3]. Let M be a closed oriented even-dimensional manifold; $\dim M = 2m$. Let $\xi = \Lambda^*(T^*(M)) \otimes \mathbf{C}$ be the bundle of complex-valued exterior differential forms. Then there is a canonical direct sum decomposition: $\xi = \xi^+ \oplus \xi^-$. The elliptic differential operator

$$d + \delta \colon C^\infty(\xi) \to C^\infty(\xi)$$

restricts to an elliptic differential operator

$$D_M \colon C^\infty(\xi^+) \to C^\infty(\xi^-) \quad .$$

The character of D_M may be computed using the results of [III, §6]. To state the result, we view the Pontrjagin classes of M as the elementary symmetric functions of $y_1^2, \ldots, y_m^2$, in the usual way: $1 + p_1(M) + \ldots + p_m(M) = \prod_{i=1}^m (1+y_i^2)$. Then

$$\text{(23)} \qquad Ch(D_M) = \prod_{i=1}^{m} \left(\frac{e^{y_i} - e^{-y_i}}{y_i} \right) \quad .$$

The element y_i is of formal degree 2. Since

$$(e^{y_i} - e^{-y_i})/y_i = 2 + \text{positive-dimensional terms},$$

(23) implies

$$\text{(24)} \qquad Ch(D_M) = 2^m + \text{positive-dimensional terms.}$$

4.2. Let η be a complex vector bundle over M. Let $\pi \colon T^*(M) \to M$ be the projection map. Then

$$\sigma(D_M) \otimes 1_{\pi^*\eta} \colon \pi^*(\xi^+ \otimes \eta) \to \pi^*(\xi^- \otimes \eta)$$

lies in $\mathrm{Symb}_1^d(\xi^+ \otimes \eta, \xi^- \otimes \eta)$. It is elliptic of order one since $\sigma(D_M)$ is. By the symbol exact sequence for differential operators [IV, §3, Theorem 2] there is a first order elliptic differential operator,

$$D_M \otimes 1_\eta \colon C^\infty(\xi^+ \otimes \eta) \to C^\infty(\xi^- \otimes \eta) \quad ,$$

whose symbol is $\sigma(D_M) \otimes 1_{\pi^*\eta}$. ($D_M \otimes 1_\eta$ is not uniquely determined; however, the ambiguity will not matter in what follows.)

Recall that $K(B(M), S(M))$ is a $K(M)$ module under the action:

$$\alpha \cdot \beta = \pi^*\alpha \otimes \beta (\alpha \in K(M), \beta \in K(B(M), S(M)).)$$

We compute $\gamma(D_M \otimes 1_\eta)$ as follows: $\gamma(D_M \otimes 1_\eta) = d(\pi^*(\xi^+ \otimes \eta), \pi^*(\xi^- \otimes \eta), \sigma(D_M) \otimes 1_\eta) = d(\pi^*\xi^+, \pi^*\xi^-, \sigma(D_M)) \cup [\pi^*\eta]$ by [II, Lemma 1(viii)]. In other words,

$$\text{(25)} \qquad \gamma(D_M \otimes 1_\eta) = [\eta] \cdot \gamma(D_M) \quad .$$

An immediate consequence is

$$\mathrm{Ch}(D_M \otimes 1_\eta) = \mathrm{Ch}(D_M) \cdot \mathrm{ch}(\eta) \quad . \tag{26}$$

4.3. For the following remarks, let i denote either i_a or i_t. In §1, we defined $i\colon K(B(M), S(M)) \to \mathbf{Q}$ so that

$$i(D) = i(\gamma(D)) \quad ,$$

where D is an elliptic operator over M. For M even-dimensional, we define

$$i : K(M) \to \mathbf{Q}$$

by

$$i(\alpha) = i(\alpha \cdot \gamma(D_M)) \quad .$$

In view of (25), we have

$$i([\eta]) = i(D_M \otimes 1_\eta) \quad .$$

4.4. The following theorem says, in effect, that there are sufficiently many elliptic operators of the form $D_M \otimes 1_\eta$.

THEOREM 3. Let M be even-dimensional. If i_a and i_t agree on $K(M)$, then

$$i_a(D) = i_t(D)$$

for all elliptic operators D over M.

PROOF. Let $\varphi = i_a - i_t$. We are given that φ vanishes on $K(M) \cdot \gamma(D_M)$; we have to show φ vanishes on the whole of $K(B(M), S(M))$.

Define the group J by the exact sequence

$$0 \to K(M) \cdot \gamma(D_M) \xrightarrow{i} K(B(M), S(M)) \to J \to 0 \quad . \tag{27}$$

(Here i is the inclusion map.) The map φ defines by passage to quotients a map $\bar{\varphi}\colon J \to \mathbf{Q}$; we have to show $\bar{\varphi} = 0$. It suffices to show that J is a torsion group, since $\mathbf{Q}$ is torsion free. (We shall see in fact that J is a finitely generated torsion group, and so is finite.) In other words, we must prove that $J \otimes \mathbf{Q} = 0$.

The proof will be based on the following facts which were recalled in Chapter II. Let (X, Y) be a finite CW complex. Then:

1) $K(X, Y)$ is a finitely generated abelian group;

2) the Chern character gives an isomorphism of rings:

(28) $$\mathrm{ch}\colon K(X, Y) \otimes \mathbf{Q} = \bigoplus_{i \equiv 0 \pmod 2} H^i(X, Y; \mathbf{Q}) = H^{ev}(X, Y; \mathbf{Q}) .$$

From 1) it follows that J is finitely generated.

We now write down a chain of equivalent propositions:

a) $J \otimes \mathbf{Q} = 0$

b) $[K(M) \cdot \gamma(D_M)] \otimes \mathbf{Q} = K(B(M), S(M)) \otimes \mathbf{Q}$

(Apply the exact functor, $\otimes \mathbf{Q}$, to (27).)

c) $H^{ev}(M, Q) \cdot \mathrm{ch}(\gamma(D_M)) = H^{ev}(B(M), S(M); \mathbf{Q})$.

(Apply (28) to b).)

d) $H^{ev}(M; Q) \cdot \mathrm{Ch}(D_M) = H^{ev}(M; \mathbf{Q})$

(Apply the Thom isomorphism to c).)

e) $\mathrm{Ch}(D_M)$ is a unit for the ring $H^{ev}(M, \mathbf{Q})$.

We now prove e). By (24), we can write

$$2^{-m}\mathrm{Ch}(D_M) = 1 - x ,$$

where $x \in H^{ev}(M; \mathbf{Q})$ is a sum of positive-dimensional terms. Since M is finite-dimensional, x is nilpotent. (In fact, $x^{2m+1} = 0$.) Thus

$$(1-x)(1+x+x^2+\ldots+x^{2m}) = 1 - x^{2m+1} = 1 ,$$

and $\mathrm{Ch}(D_M)$ has the inverse

$$2^{-m}(1+x+\ldots+x^{2m}) .$$

This shows that $\mathrm{Ch}(D_M)$ is a unit in $H^{ev}(M; \mathbf{Q})$. The proof is complete.

§5. Summary of the properties of i_a and i_t on $K(M)$

We change notation slightly from the preceding paragraph. If M is an even-dimensional closed oriented manifold, and $\alpha \in K(M)$, we write $i(M, \alpha)$ in place of $i(\alpha)$ when we wish to indicate explicitly the dependence on M. (Here i is either i_t or i_a.)

The following theorem lists properties shared by i_a and i_t. Part of the proof will be postponed to a later chapter.

THEOREM 4. Let i denote either i_a or i_t. Then considered as a function defined on $K(M)$, i has the following properties:

a) $i(X+Y, a+b) = i(X, a) + i(Y, b)$;
$i(X, a \oplus b) = i(X, a) + i(X, b)$ where $+$ is disjoint sum, $\oplus$ is Whitney sum. (We suppose here that $\dim X = \dim Y$.)

b) $i(X \times Y, a \otimes b) = i(X, a) \cdot i(Y, b)$.

c) $i(X, a) = 0$ if (X, a) is a boundary, i.e., if there exists a compact oriented manifold Y with boundary $X = \partial Y$, and an element $a' \in K(Y)$ whose restriction to X is equal to a.

d) $i(CP(2m), 1) = 1$; $i(S^{2m}, V_m) = 2^m$, where $V_m \in K(S^{2m})$ is characterized as follows: $ch(V_m)$ is the generator of $H^{2m}(S^{2m}, \mathbf{Q})$ determined by the orientation on S^{2m}; i.e.,

$$ch(V^m)[S^{2m}] = 1 \quad .$$

Remark. It will be shown in Chapter XVIII that properties (a) through (d) uniquely characterize the real valued function i. In view of Theorem 3, this result will prove the index theorem for even-dimensional manifolds.

The proof of (c) for i_a requires the theory of elliptic boundary value problems. It will be given in Chapter XVII.

PROOF of a). It was shown in §1 that $i_a\colon K(B(X), S(X)) \to Z$ is a group homomorphism. That $i_t\colon K(B(X), S(X)) \to \mathbf{Q}$ is a homomorphism is clear from its definition. Thus if i is i_a or i_t,

$$i(X, a \oplus b) = i([a+b] \cdot \gamma(D_X)) = i([a] \cdot \gamma(D_X)) + i([b] \cdot \gamma(D_X))$$
$$= i(X, a) + i(X, b) \quad .$$

The additivity of i_t with respect to disjoint unions is trivial. For i_a, let S and T be elliptic operators of order zero on X and Y such that

$$\gamma(S) = a \cdot \gamma(D_X), \; \gamma(T) = b \cdot \gamma(D_Y) \quad .$$

Then if we define the disjoint sum, $S + T$, in the obvious way, we have $\gamma(S+T) = \gamma(S) + \gamma(T)$ (disjoint sum!).* Thus $i_a(S+T) = i_a(a+b)$. But clearly $i_a(S+T) = i_a(S) + i_a(T)$.

PROOF of c) for i_t. If $X = \partial Y$, then $T(Y)|X$ splits as a direct sum of $T(X)$ plus a trivial one dimensional bundle. It follows that if $j : X \to Y$ is the inclusion map, then

$$j^* p_i(Y) = p_i(X) \quad .$$

Here p_i is the ith Pontrjagin class. Thus

$$Ch(D_X) \text{ and } \mathcal{T}(X) \text{ lie in } \operatorname{im} j^* \quad .$$

Let $D_X \otimes 1_a$ be an elliptic operator with $\gamma(D_X \otimes 1_a) = a \cdot \gamma(D_X)$. Then $Ch(D_X \otimes 1_a) = Ch(D_X)ch(a) = Ch(D_X)j^* ch(a')$; this lies in $\operatorname{im} j^*$.

Now if $\lambda \in H^*(X, \mathbf{Q})$, and $\lambda = j^*\lambda'$, we have $\lambda[X] = 0$. To see this, we assume as we may that $\dim \lambda = \dim X$. Let $\mu_X \in H_{2m}(X; \mathbf{Q})$ and $\mu_Y \in H_{2m+1}(Y, X; \mathbf{Q})$ be the orientation classes of X and Y. Then $\partial\mu_Y = \mu_X$, and

$$\lambda[X] = < \lambda, \mu_X > = < \lambda, \partial\mu_Y > = < \delta\lambda, \mu_Y > = < \delta j^*\lambda', \mu_Y > \quad .$$

However $\delta j^* = 0$, by the exact sequence in cohomology for the pair (X, Y). If we take $\lambda = Ch(D_X \otimes 1_a)\mathcal{T}(X)$, we get $i_t(X, a) = 0$.

In §6, we shall prove (b). Paragraph §7 will contain the proof of (d).

§6. Multiplicative properties of i on $K(X)$

Let M_1, M_2 be even-dimensional closed oriented Riemannian manifolds, and let $M = M_1 \times M_2$. The proof of (b) will be based on the following theorem.

> THEOREM 5. Let ξ_i be the bundle of complex valued exterior-differential forms over M_i, and let ξ be the corresponding bundle over M. Let

---

* This is not listed among the properties (S1)—(S5), but it is a trivial consequence of the construction of the Seeley algebra.

$$D_{M_i} : C^\infty(\xi_i^+) \to C^\infty(\xi_i^-) \quad \text{and} \quad D_M : C^\infty(\xi^+) \to C^\infty(\xi^-) \quad ,$$

be as in §4. Then, up to canonical isomorphism, we have

a) $\xi = \xi_1 \otimes \xi_2$;

b) $\xi^+ = \xi_1^+ \otimes \xi_2^+ \oplus \xi_1^- \otimes \xi_2^-$; $\xi^- = \xi_1^- \otimes \xi_2^+ \oplus \xi_1^+ \otimes \xi_2^-$;

(Thus $D_{M_1} \# D_{M_2} : C^\infty(\xi^+) \to C^\infty(\xi^-)$.)

c) The operators,

$$D_M, D_{M_1} \# D_{M_2} : C^\infty(\xi^+) \to C^\infty(\xi^-) \quad ,$$

have homotopic symbols.

We first show how Theorem 5 implies Theorem 4 b). Let $a_i \in K(M_i)$. Since i is additive with respect to Whitney sum, we may as well assume that $a_i = [\eta_i]$. Inspection of the definition of # shows that

(29) $$(D_{M_1} \otimes 1_{\eta_1}) \# (D_{M_2} \otimes 1_{\eta_2}) = (D_{M_1} \# D_{M_2}) \otimes 1_{\eta_1 \otimes \eta_2} \quad .$$

In view of Theorem 5 c), the right hand side of (29) has symbol homotopic to $D_M \otimes 1_{\eta_1 \otimes \eta_2}$.

Now apply i to both sides of (29). The index of the left side is $i(M_1, [\eta_1]) \cdot i(M_2, [\eta_2])$. (By Theorem 2, if $i = i_t$; if $i = i_a$ by the results of Chapter XIV.) On the other hand, the index of the right hand side is $i(M, [\eta_1 \otimes \eta_2])$ by the remark of the previous paragraph. Since $[\eta_1 \otimes \eta_2] = [\eta_1] \times [\eta_2]$, the proof that Theorem 5 implies Theorem 4 b) is complete.

We turn now to the proof of Theorem 5. If V is a finite-dimensional real vector space, we denote by $\Lambda_{\mathbf{C}}^*(V)$ the complexification of the exterior algebra of V. If $V = V_1 \oplus V_2$, there is a canonical vector space isomorphism,

(30) $$\Lambda_{\mathbf{C}}^*(V_1) \otimes_{\mathbf{C}} \Lambda_{\mathbf{C}}^*(V_2) \cong \Lambda_{\mathbf{C}}^*(V) \quad ,$$

which sends $v_1 \otimes 1 + 1 \otimes v_2$ into $v_1 \oplus v_2$, $(v_i \in V_i)$, and sends $\lambda_1 \otimes \lambda_2$ into $\lambda_1 \wedge \lambda_2$ (for $\lambda_i \in \Lambda_{\mathbf{C}}^*(V_i)$).

Since $M = M_1 \times M_2$, we have

(31) $$T(M) = \pi_1^* T(M_1) \oplus \pi_2^* T(M_2) \quad .$$

If we apply (30) at each point of $M_1 \times M_2$, we get an isomorphism $\psi: \xi_1 \otimes \xi_2 \to \xi$, such that if $\varphi_i \in H^\infty(\xi_i)$, we have

(32) $$\psi(\varphi_1 \otimes \varphi_2) = \pi_1^* \varphi_1 \wedge \pi_2^* \varphi_2 \quad ,$$

(In the future, we shall identify $\xi_1 \otimes \xi_2$ with ξ via ψ.) We have proved a).

Now let V be an even-dimensional real vector space. In [II, §6.1], we defined a canonical map

$$\alpha: \Lambda_{\mathbf{C}}^* (V) \cong \Lambda_{\mathbf{C}}^* (V) \quad ,$$

whose square is 1; $\Lambda_{\pm}(V)$ is the eigenspace of α for the eigenvalue ± 1. Let w be multiplication by $(-1)^k$ on $\Lambda_{\mathbf{C}}^k (V)$. Then w commutes with α, since α does not change the parity of a homogeneous element: $\alpha: \Lambda^k(V) \to \Lambda^{2\ell-k}(V)$. It follows that w maps the eigenspaces, $\Lambda_{\pm}$, of α into themselves. Since $w^2 = 1$, w is an automorphism of $\Lambda_{\pm}$.

The maps w and α will therefore commute on the bundle level, and w will induce automorphism of $\xi_i^{\pm}$. Later we shall need to know that $w: \xi_i^{\pm} \to \xi_i^{\pm}$ is homotopic to the identity automorphism. To see this define $w_\theta: \Lambda_{\mathbf{C}}^* (V) \to \Lambda_{\mathbf{C}}^* (V)$, by

$$w_\theta(\varphi) = \varphi \quad \text{if} \quad \varphi \in \Lambda_{\mathbf{C}}^k (V), \quad k \text{ even}$$

$$w_\theta(V) = e^{\pi i\theta}\varphi \quad \text{if} \quad \varphi \in \Lambda_{\mathbf{C}}^k (V), \quad k \text{ odd} .$$

Then w_θ commutes with α and induces an automorphism of $\xi_i^{\pm}$; moreover, $w_0 = 1$, $w_1 = w$, so w_θ provides the desired homotopy.

Next let V and W be even-dimensional vector spaces. If $a \in \Lambda_{\mathbf{C}}^* (V)$ and $b \in \Lambda_{\mathbf{C}}^* (W)$, then

$$\alpha_{V \oplus W}(a \otimes b) = \alpha_V(a) \otimes \alpha_W(b)$$

(cf. III, §6.1). From this it follows that

(33) $$\begin{aligned} \Lambda_+(V \oplus W) &= (\Lambda_+(V) \otimes \Lambda_+(W)) \oplus (\Lambda_-(V) \otimes \Lambda_-(W)) \\ \Lambda_-(V \oplus W) &= (\Lambda_-(V) \otimes \Lambda_+(W)) \oplus (\Lambda_+(V) \otimes \Lambda_-(W)) \end{aligned}$$

Taking (33) on the bundle level, we get (b) of Theorem 5.

We write D for $d+\delta$. Thus

(34) $$D|\xi_i^+ = D_{M_i} \quad ; \quad D|\xi_i^- = D_{M_i}^*$$

as recalled in §4.

LEMMA 2. Let φ_i $C(\xi_i)$, $i = 1, 2$. Then $D(\varphi_1 \otimes \varphi_2) = D\varphi_1 \otimes \varphi_2 + w(\varphi_1) \otimes D\varphi_2$.

PROOF. We may assume that φ_i is homogeneous of degree k_i. Since d is a derivation,

(35) $$d(\varphi_1 \otimes \varphi_2) = D\varphi_1 \otimes \varphi_2 + (-1)^{k_1}\varphi_1 \otimes d\varphi_2 \quad .$$

Taken on the bundle level, (24) of Chapter III becomes:

(36) $$*(\varphi_1 \otimes \varphi_2) = (-1)^{k_1 k_2} *\varphi_1 \otimes *\varphi_2 \quad .$$

On the other hand, since M_1, M_2, and M are even-dimensional,

(37) $$\delta = -*d* \quad .$$

Thus
$$\begin{aligned}\delta(\varphi_1 \otimes \varphi_2) &= (-1)^{k_1 k_2}(-*d(*\varphi_1 \otimes *\varphi_2)\\ &= (-1)^{k_1 k_2}(-1)^{(k_1+1)k_2}(-*d*\varphi_1 \otimes *^2\varphi_2)\\ &+ (-1)^{k_1 k_2}(-1)^{k_1(k_2+1)}((-1)^{k_1}*^2\varphi_1 \otimes (-*d*\varphi_2))\\ &= \delta\varphi_1 \otimes \varphi_2 + (-1)^{k_1}\varphi_1 \otimes \delta\varphi_2 \quad .\end{aligned}$$

(We have used the facts that $*^2 = (-1)^k$ on Λ^k, and $*\varphi$ has the same parity as φ; both facts are valid for even-dimensional manifolds.)

Lemma 2 results now from (35) and the corresponding result for δ proved in the preceding paragraph.

Using Lemma 2 and (34) we see that the matrix of D_M relative to the direct sum decomposition of (b) is:

(38) $$\begin{pmatrix} D_{M_1} \otimes I_{\xi_2^+} & w \circ I_{\xi_1^-} \otimes D_{M_2}^* \\ w \circ I_{\xi_1^+} \otimes D_{M_2} & D_{M_1}^* \otimes I_{\xi_2^-} \end{pmatrix} \quad .$$

On the other hand, the matrix for $D_{M_1} \# D_{M_2}$ is:

$$(39)\qquad \begin{pmatrix} D_{M_1} \otimes I_{\xi_2^+} & -I_{\xi_1^-} \otimes D_{M_2}^* \\ I_{\xi_1^+} \otimes D_{M_2} & D_{M_1}^* \otimes I_{\xi_2^-} \end{pmatrix}$$

(cf. (3)).

To relate (38) and (39) we need the identities:

$$Dw = -wD; \quad w^2 = 1 \quad .$$

The first follows from the fact that D changes parities, and the second is trivial. Using these identities we see that the matrix product

$$\begin{pmatrix} -w \circ I_{\xi_1^-} \otimes I_{\xi_2^+} & 0 \\ 0 & I_{\xi_1^+} \otimes I_{\xi_2^-} \end{pmatrix} \cdot \begin{pmatrix} D_{M_1} \otimes I_{\xi_2^+} & w \circ I_{\xi_1^-} \otimes D_{M_2}^* \\ w \circ I_{\xi_1^+} \otimes D_{M_2} & D_{M_1}^* \otimes I_{\xi_2^-} \end{pmatrix}$$

$$\cdot \begin{pmatrix} w \circ I_{\xi_1^+} \otimes I_{\xi_2^+} & 0 \\ 0 & I_{\xi_1^-} \otimes I_{\xi_2^-} \end{pmatrix}$$

is equal to (39).

Since $w: \xi_i^{\pm} \to \xi_i^{\pm}$ is homotopic to the identity through bundle automorphisms, the first and third matrices of the matrix product can be deformed through bundle automorphisms to the identity. This yields a homotopy from $D_{M_1} \# D_{M_2}$ to D_M through elliptic operators. Taking symbols, we get the homotopy of symbols asserted in c).

Remark. For the application of Theorem 5, it would suffice to know that $\gamma(D_M) \otimes 1 = \gamma(D_{M_1} \# D_{M_2}) \otimes 1$ in $K(B(M), S(M)) \otimes \mathbf{Q}$. This can easily be verified by a character computation, using (23).

§7. Direct check that $i_a = i_t$ in some special cases

The fact that $i_a(\mathbf{C}P(2m), 1) = i_t(\mathbf{C}P(2m), 1)) = 1$ follows from [V, Proposition 7]. We now consider $i(S^{2m}, V_m)$. Since the Pontrjagin classes of S^{2m} are zero (in fact S^{2m} is stably parallelizable), (23) implies that

$$Ch(D_{S^{2m}}) = 2^m$$

(cf. also (24)). It follows that

$$ch(\gamma(D_{S^{2m}})) = (-1)^m 2^m \cup U$$

where $U \in H^{2m}(B(S^{2m}), S(S^{2m}))$ is the Thom class. Now let $\sigma \in H^{2m}(S^{2m}, \mathbf{Q})$ be the generator determined by the orientation: $\sigma[S^{2m}] = 1$. Let $V_m \in K(S^{2m})$ be determined by $ch(V_m) = \sigma$. Then by (25),

$$ch(\gamma(D_{S^{2m}} \otimes 1_{V^m})) = (-1)^m 2^m \sigma \cup U \quad . \tag{40}$$

Next consider the operator

$$d+\delta: \quad C^\infty(\xi^e) \to C^\infty(\xi^o)$$

of [V, §2]. For brevity, call this operator D_0. The analytical and topological indices of D_0 are equal to the Euler characteristic of S^{2m}, which is 2. (V, Proposition 1 and Corollary 2.)

On the other hand, the character of D_0 may be computed using Proposition 5.1 of Chapter III. We have

$$Ch(D_0)\mathscr{T}(S^{2m}) = \chi(S^{2m})$$

where $\chi(S^{2m})$ is the Euler class. Since the Pontrjagin classes of S^{2m} are zero, $\mathscr{T}(S^{2m}) = 1$ and $Ch(D_0) = \chi(S^{2m}) = 2\sigma$. (The Euler class equals the Euler characteristic times the generator.) It follows that

$$ch(\gamma(D_0)) = (-1)^m 2\sigma \cup U \quad . \tag{41}$$

Now if (X, Y) is a finite CW pair, ch induces an isomorphism of $K(X, Y) \otimes \mathbf{Q}$ with $H^{ev}(X, Y; \mathbf{Q})$. It follows that the kernel of ch is the torsion subgroup of K(X, Y). Thus (40) and (41) imply

$$\gamma(D_{S^{2m}} \otimes 1_{V^m}) = 2^{m-1}\gamma(D_0) + \text{torsion.} \tag{42}$$

Now i_a and i_t map into Q and thus annihilate torsion. Moreover, as recalled above,

$$i_a(\gamma(D_0)) = i_t(\gamma\ D_0)) = 2 \quad .$$

Thus $i(S^{2m}, V^m) = i(\gamma(D_{S^{2m}} \otimes 1_{V^m})) = 2^m$. (Here $i = i_a$ or i_t.) This completes the proof of (d).

CHAPTER XVI

CONSTRUCTION OF Int_k

R. S. Palais and R. T. Seeley

§1. The Fourier Transform.

For $1 \le p < \infty$ $L^p(\mathbf{R}^n)$ will denote the measurable complex valued functions f on $\mathbf{R}^n$ such that $\|f\|_{L^p} = (\int |f(x)|^p dx)^{1/p} < \infty$ and $L^\infty(\mathbf{R}^n)$ will denote the measurable complex valued functions f on $\mathbf{R}^n$ such that $\|f\|_{L^\infty} = \mathrm{Inf}\{M \big| |f(x)| < M \text{ a.e.}\} < \infty$ and we recall that if we identify functions which are equal almost everywhere then the $L^p(\mathbf{R}^n)$ are Banach spaces with $\| \ \|_p$ as norm. Moreover if $1 \le p < \infty$ and $\frac{1}{p} + \frac{1}{q} = 1$ then $L^q(\mathbf{R}^n)$ is the dual space of $L^p(\mathbf{R}^n)$, the pairing being given by

$$< f, g > = \int f(x)g(x)dx \qquad f \in L^p, \quad g \in L^q \quad .$$

If f and g are non-negative measurable functions on $\mathbf{R}^n$ then it is easily shown that the function $f*g$ on $\mathbf{R}^n$ defined by $f*g(x) = \int f(x-y)g(y)dy$ satisfies

$$\|f*g\|_{L^p} \le \|f\|_{L^1} \|g\|_{L^p} \qquad 1 \le p \le \infty \quad .$$

(See Loomis, *Abstract Harmonic Analysis*, p. 121.) It follows that

THEOREM 1 (Young's Theorem). Let $1 \le p \le \infty$ and let $f \in L^1(\mathbf{R}^n)$ and $g \in L^p(\mathbf{R}^n)$. Then $f(x-y)g(y)$ is summable as a function of y for almost all x and $f*g$, defined by

$$f*g(x) = \int f(x-y)g(y)dy$$

belongs to $L^p(\mathbf{R}^n)$ and in fact

$$\|f*g\|_{L^p} \leq \|f\|_{L^1} \|g\|_{L^p} \quad .$$

An easy application of Fubini's Theorem gives that $*$ is associative and commutative and it follows that

COROLLARY. $L^1(\mathbf{R}^n)$ is a commutative Banach algebra under $*$ and each $L^p(\mathbf{R}^n)$ is an $L^1(\mathbf{R}^n)$ module.

If $f \in L^1(\mathbf{R}^n)$ we define its Fourier transform $\hat{f} = \mathscr{F}(f): \mathbf{R}^n \to \mathbf{C}$ by

$$\hat{f}(y) = \int e^{-ix\cdot y} f(x)dx \quad .$$

We note that clearly $|\hat{f}(y)| \leq \|f\|_{L^1}$. Also if $y_n \to y$ then $|e^{-ix\cdot y_n} f(x)| = |f(x)|$ and for each $x \in \mathbf{R}^n$

$$e^{-ix\cdot y_n} f(x) \to e^{-ix\cdot y} f(x)$$

so, by the Lebesque dominated convergence theorem $\hat{f}(y_n) \to \hat{f}(y)$, i.e., $\hat{f}$ *is continuous*. If also $g \in L^1(\mathbf{R}^n)$

$$\begin{aligned}(f*g)\hat{\ }(y) &= \int dx \int f(x-z)g(z)e^{-ix\cdot y}\, dz \\ &= \int dx \int f(x)g(z)e^{-i(x+z)\cdot y}\, dz \\ &= \hat{f}(y)\hat{g}(y) \quad .\end{aligned}$$

THEOREM 2. If $f, g \in L^1(\mathbf{R}^n)$ then $(f*g)\hat{\ } = \hat{f}\hat{g}$.

DEFINITION. $S(\mathbf{R}^n)$ denotes the space of C^∞ maps $f: \mathbf{R}^n \to \mathbf{C}$ such that for each pair of n-multi-indices α, β $|x^\alpha D^\beta f(x)|$ is bounded on $\mathbf{R}^n$. We topologize $S(\mathbf{R}^n)$ by means of the family of pseudonorms

$$N_{\alpha,\beta}(f) = \mathrm{Sup}\{|x^\alpha D^\beta f(x)| \,\big|\, x \in \mathbf{R}^n\} \quad .$$

We note that if $P: \mathbf{R}^n \to \mathbf{C}$ is a polynomial map and D a differential operator on $\mathbf{R}^n$ with constant coefficients then

$$N_{P,D}(f) = \mathrm{Sup}\{|P(x)Df(x)| \,\big|\, x \in \mathbf{R}^n\}$$

is likewise a continuous pseudonorm on $S(\mathbf{R}^n)$. In particular $S(\mathbf{R}^n)$ is stable under differential operators with constant coefficients and multiplication by polynomials. If $f \in S(\mathbf{R}^n)$ and k is a positive integer then there exists $M_k > 0$ so that $|(1 + \|x\|^2)^k f(x)| \leq M_k$ or

$$|f(x)| \leq M_k(1 + \|x\|^2)^k \quad .$$

Now

$$\int \frac{dx}{(1+\|x\|^2)^k} = \Omega \int_0^\infty \frac{\rho^{n-1}d\rho}{(1+\rho^2)^k}$$
$$\leq \Omega\left[\int_0^1 \frac{\rho^{n-1}d\rho}{(1+\rho^2)^k}\right] + \Omega \int_1^\infty \frac{d\rho}{\rho^{2k-n-1}}$$

which is finite if $2k-n-1 > -1$, i.e., if $k > n/2$. It follows that $S(\mathbf{R}^n) \subseteq L^1(\mathbf{R}^n)$ and in particular the Fourier transform of an element of $S(\mathbf{R}^n)$ is defined.

Let $e_j = (\delta_{1j}, \ldots, \delta_{nj}) \in \mathbf{R}^n$ $j = 1, \ldots, n$ denote the standard base for $\mathbf{R}^n$.

$$e^{-ix\cdot(y+te_j)} = e^{-ix\cdot y}\, e^{-itx_j}$$
$$= e^{-ix\cdot y}\,(1 - itx_j - t^2x_j^2 g(tx))$$

where by Taylor's Theorem $g(tx) = 2e^{i\theta x_j}$ with $0 \leq \theta \leq t$ and hence $|g(tx)| \leq 2$. If $f \in L^1(\mathbf{R}^n)$ then

$$\frac{1}{t}(\hat{f}(y+te_j) - \hat{f}(y)) = \int e^{-ix\cdot y}\,(-ix_j)f(x)dx$$
$$- t\int e^{-ix\cdot y}\, g(tx)x_j^2 f(x)dx \quad .$$

Now if $f \in S(\mathbf{R}^n)$ then $x_j^2 f \in S(\mathbf{R}^n) \subseteq L^1(\mathbf{R}^n)$, and since $|e^{-ix\cdot y}g(tx)| \leq 2$ we have $|\int e^{-ix\cdot y}g(tx)x_j^2 f(x)dx| \leq 2\|x_j^2 f\|_{L_1}$. Letting $t \to 0$ we get

$$\frac{\partial\hat{f}}{\partial y_j}(y) = \int e^{-ix\cdot y}\,(-ix_j)f(x)dx \quad .$$

Then by induction

LEMMA 1. If $f \in S(\mathbf{R}^n)$ then $\hat{f}$ is C^∞ and

$$(D^\beta\hat{f})(y) = \int e^{-ix\cdot y}\,(-ix)^\beta f(x)dx$$
$$= (-i)^{|\beta|}(x^\beta f)^\wedge(y) \quad .$$

Assume again that $f \in S(\mathbf{R}^n)$. Then we can choose M_k so that

$$|(1+x_n^2)(1+x_1^2 + \ldots + x_{n-1}^2)^k f(x)| \leq M_k \quad .$$

As we saw above if $k > \frac{n-1}{2}$ then

$$\int_{\mathbf{R}^{n-1}} (1+x_1^2 + \ldots + x_{n-1}^2)^{-k}\, dx = C_k < \infty, \quad \text{hence}$$

$$\left| \int_{\mathbf{R}^{n-1}} f(x_1, \ldots, x_n) dx_1 \ldots dx_{n-1} \right| \leq \frac{C_k M_k}{1+x_n^2}$$

hence

$$\left| \int_{\mathbf{R}^{n-1}} dx_1 \ldots dx_{n-1} \int_{-T}^{T} \frac{\partial f}{\partial x_n}\, dx_n \right| \leq \frac{2C_k M_k}{1+T^2}$$

and letting $T \to \infty$ we get $\int \frac{\partial f}{\partial x_n}\, dx = 0$. Similarly, $\int \frac{\partial f}{\partial x_j}\, dx = 0 \quad j = 1, \ldots, n$. Now if $y \in \mathbf{R}^n$ then $D^\alpha(e^{-ix\cdot y}) = (-iy)^\alpha e^{-ix\cdot y}$ and it follows that $e^{-ix\cdot y} f(x)$ is, for each y, in $S(\mathbf{R}^n)$, hence

$$\int \frac{\partial}{\partial x_j} (e^{-ix\cdot y}\, f(x))dx = 0$$

or

$$\left(\frac{\partial f}{\partial x_j}\right)^{\wedge}(y) = (iy_j)\hat{f}(y)$$

and inductively

LEMMA 2. If $f \in S(\mathbf{R}^n)$ then

$$(D^\alpha f)^{\wedge}(y) = (i)^{|\alpha|} y^\alpha \hat{f}(y) \quad .$$

THEOREM 3. The Fourier transform $f \to \hat{f}$ is a continuous linear map of $S(\mathbf{R}^n)$ into itself. Moreover if $f \in S(\mathbf{R}^n)$ then

$$y^\alpha (D^\beta \hat{f})(y) = (-1)^{|\beta|} (i)^{|\alpha+\beta|} (D^\alpha x^\beta f)^{\wedge}(y) \quad .$$

PROOF. The latter formula is immediate from Lemmas 1 and 2. Choose $k > n/2$ so that as was shown above $\int (1+\|x\|^2)^{-k} dx = C < \infty$. Then

$$\begin{aligned}(D^\alpha x^\beta f)^{\wedge}(y) &= \int e^{-ix\cdot y} (D^\alpha x^\beta f)(x) dx \\ &= \int (1+\|x\|^2)^k (D^\alpha x^\beta f)(x) e^{-ix\cdot y} (1+\|x\|^2)^{-k} dx,\end{aligned}$$

hence

$$\operatorname{Sup} |y^{\alpha}(D^{\beta}\hat{f})(y)| \leq C \operatorname{Sup} |(1+\|x\|^2)^k (D^{\alpha}x^{\beta}f)(x)| .$$

Since $\operatorname{Sup}|(1+\|x\|^2)^k (D^{\alpha}x^{\beta}f)(x)|$ is a continuous pseudonorm on $S(\mathbf{R}^n)$ the theorem follows.

q.e.d.

We recall the value of the definite integral $I = \int_{-\infty}^{\infty} e^{-t^2/2}dt$. Recalling that Fubini's Theorem is valid for positive integrands:

$$I^2 = \int_{-\infty}^{\infty} e^{-x_1^2/2} dx_1 \int_{-\infty}^{\infty} e^{-x_2^2/2} dx_2$$

$$= \int_{\mathbf{R}^2} e^{-\|x\|^2/2} dx = \int_0^{2\pi} d\theta \int_0^{\infty} e^{-\rho^2/2} d(\tfrac{\rho^2}{2}) = 2\pi .$$

It follows that

$$\int_{\mathbf{R}^n} e^{-\|x\|^2/2} dx = \int_{\mathbf{R}^n} \prod_{i=1}^{n} e^{-x_i^2/2} dx = \prod_{i=1}^{n} \int_{-\infty}^{\infty} e^{-x_i^2/2} dx_i$$

$$= I^n = (I^2)^{n/2} = (2\pi)^{n/2} .$$

LEMMA. If we define $g\colon \mathbf{R}^n \to \mathbf{C}$ by $g(x) = \exp(-\|x\|^2/2)$ then $g \in S(\mathbf{R}^n)$ and $\hat{g} = (2\pi)^{n/2}g$.

PROOF. By an easy induction $(D^{\alpha}g(x) = P_{\alpha}(x)g(x)$ where P_{α} is a polynomial of degree less that $|\alpha|$. It follows that

$$|x^{\beta}(D^{\alpha}g)(x)| \leq C_{\alpha,\beta}(1+\|x\|^2)^{|\alpha+\beta|} g(x)$$

for some constant $C_{\alpha,\beta}$ and it then follows from L'Hospital's rule that $|x^{\beta}(D^{\alpha}g)(x)|$ tends to zero as $\|x\|$ tends to ∞, so *a fortiori* $|x^{\beta}(D^{\alpha}g)(x)|$ is bounded. Now

$$\hat{g}(y) = \int \exp\Big(-\frac{\|x\|^2}{2} - ix\cdot y\Big)dx$$

$$= \int \exp\Big(-\frac{\|x+iy\|^2}{2} - \frac{\|y\|^2}{2}\Big) dx$$

$$= g(y) \int \exp\Big(-\frac{\|x-iy\|^2}{2}\Big) dx$$

$$= g(y) \int e^{-\frac{\|x\|^2}{2}} dx = (2\pi)^{n/2}g(y)$$

q.e.d.

THEOREM 4 (Fourier Inversion Formula). If $f \in S(\mathbf{R}^n)$ then $\hat{\hat{f}}(x) = (2\pi)^n f(-x)$.

PROOF. Let $h \in S(\mathbf{R}^n) \subseteq L^1(\mathbf{R}^n)$. Then since $f \in L^1(\mathbf{R}^n)$, $(y, z) \to h(y)f(z)$ is in $L^1(\mathbf{R}^n \times \mathbf{R}^n)$ by Fubini's Theorem and hence $(y, z) \to e^{-ix\cdot y} h(y)f(z)e^{-iz\cdot y}$ is likewise in $L^1(\mathbf{R}^n \times \mathbf{R}^n)$, and by Fubini:

$$\int e^{-ix\cdot y} h(y)\hat{f}(y)dy = \int e^{-ix\cdot y} h(y)dy \int f(z)e^{-iz\cdot y} dz$$
$$= \int \hat{h}(x+z)f(z)dz$$
$$= \int \hat{h}(z)f(z-x)dz \quad .$$

Replacing h by h_ε , where for $\varepsilon > 0$ $h_\varepsilon(x) = h(\varepsilon x)$, we have $(h_\varepsilon)\hat{}(z) = \varepsilon^{-n} \hat{h}(z/\varepsilon)$ so

$$\int e^{-ix\cdot y} h(\varepsilon y)\hat{f}(y)dy = \int \hat{h}(z/\varepsilon)f(z-x)d(\tfrac{z}{\varepsilon})$$
$$= \int \hat{h}(w)f(\varepsilon w-x)dw \quad .$$

Now h, f, $\hat{h}$ and $\hat{f}$ are all continuous and bounded, so by the Lebesgue dominated convergence theorem, if $\varepsilon \to 0$ we find

$$h(0) \int e^{-ix\cdot y} \hat{f}(y)dy = f(-x) \int \hat{h}(w)dw \quad .$$

Choosing h to be the function g of the Lemma, $h(x) = \exp(-\|x\|^2/2)$, $h(0) = 1$, $\hat{h}(w) = (2\pi)^{n/2}h(w)$ and

$$\int \hat{h}(w)dw = (2\pi)^{n/2} \int h(w)dw = (2\pi)^n.$$

q.e.d.

COROLLARY. The Fourier transform restricted to $S(\mathbf{R}^n)$ is an automorphism of $S(\mathbf{R}^n)$.

PROOF. Let $\mathscr{F}_S$ denote the restriction of the Fourier transform to $S(\mathbf{R}^n)$. By Theorem 3, $\mathscr{F}_S$ is a continuous endomorphism of $S(\mathbf{R}^n)$ and hence so is $T = (2\pi)^{-2n}\mathscr{F}_S^3$. By Theorem 4, $\mathscr{F}_S T = T\,\mathscr{F}_S$ is the identity map of $S(\mathbf{R}^n)$.

q.e.d.

We write $<,>_0$ for the inner product in the hilbert space $L^2(\mathbf{R}^n)$

$$< f, g >_0 = \int f(x)\bar{g}(x)\,dx$$

and

$$\|f\|_0^2 = < f, f >_0 = \|f\|_{L_2}^2 \quad .$$

If $f \in S(\mathbf{R}^n)$ then $M = \mathrm{Sup}|f(x)| < \infty$ and $\|f\|_{L^1} < \infty$ hence

$$\|f\|_0^2 = \int |f(x)|^2 dx \leq M \int |f(x)|\,dx \leq M\|f\|_{L^1} < \infty$$

so $S(\mathbf{R}^n) \subseteq L^2(\mathbf{R}^n)$. It is well known that $C_0^\infty(\mathbf{R}^n)$ is dense in $L^2(\mathbf{R}^n)$ so *a fortiori* $S(\mathbf{R}^n)$ is dense in $L^2(\mathbf{R}^n)$.

THEOREM 5. (Plancherel Theorem) The Fourier transform on $S(\mathbf{R}^n)$ extends uniquely to a continuous linear automorphism $f \to \hat{f}$ of $L^2(\mathbf{R}^n)$. Moreover, for $f, g \in L^2(\mathbf{R}^n)$ Parseval's formula holds, i.e.,

$$< f, g >_0 = (2\pi)^n < \hat{f}, \hat{g} >_0$$

or in other words, $f \to (2\pi)^{-n/2}\hat{f}$ is an isometry of $L^2(\mathbf{R}^n)$ with itself.

PROOF. If $f, g \in S(\mathbf{R}^n)$ then by Schwarz's inequality

$$\int |e^{-iz\cdot y} f(z)\overline{\hat{g}(y)}|\,dy\,dz \leq \|f\|_{L^1} \|\hat{g}\|_{L^1} < \infty$$

and Fubini's Theorem gives

$$\begin{aligned} < \hat{f}, \hat{g} >_0 &= \int \hat{f}(y)\overline{\hat{g}(y)}\,dy \\ &= \int dy \int e^{-iz\cdot y} f(z)\overline{\hat{g}(y)}\,dz \\ &= \int f(z)\Big(\int e^{iz\cdot y} \hat{g}(y)\,dy\Big)dz \\ &= \int f(z)\hat{\hat{g}}(-z)\,dz \quad . \end{aligned}$$

But by Theorem 4 $\hat{\hat{g}}(-z) = (2\pi)^n g(z)$, so Parseval's formula holds for $f, g \in S(\mathbf{R}^n)$. Thus $f \to (2\pi)^{-n/2}\hat{f}$ is an isometry of the dense subspace $S(\mathbf{R}^n)$ of $L^2(\mathbf{R}^n)$ onto itself and extends uniquely to an isometry of $L^2(\mathbf{R}^n)$.

q.e.d.

DEFINITION. We denote by $\{\hat{H}^k(\mathbf{R}^n)\}$ the continuous chain of hilbert spaces $\{L^2_{\hat{k}}(\mathbf{R}^n, \mathbf{C}, (1+\|x\|^2))\}$ where the measure on $\mathbf{R}^n$ is taken to be $(2\pi)^{-n}$ times Lebesque measure. Thus the norm $\| \ \|_{\hat{k}}$ on $\hat{H}^k(\mathbf{R}^n)$ is given by

$$\|f\|^2_{\hat{k}} = (2\pi)^{-n} \int |f(x)|^2 (1+\|x\|^2)^k \, dx \quad .$$

Remark. The definition of $L^2_{\hat{k}}(\mathbf{R}^n, \mathbf{C}, (1+\|x\|^2))$ is given in Chapter VIII, §4. By Theorem 2 of that section it follows that $\{\hat{H}^k(\mathbf{R}^n)\}$ is a scale. Note that $\hat{H}^0(\mathbf{R}^n) = L^2(\mathbf{R}^n)$ hence $S(\mathbf{R}^n)$ is dense in $\hat{H}^0(\mathbf{R}^n)$. Also $f(x) \mapsto (1+\|x\|^2)^{-k/z} f(x)$ is an isometry of $\hat{H}^0(\mathbf{R}^n)$ onto $\hat{H}^k(\mathbf{R}^n)$ and since $S(\mathbf{R}^n)$ is stable under multiplication by $(1+\|x\|^2)^k$ it follows that $S(\mathbf{R}^n)$ is dense in each $\hat{H}^k(\mathbf{R}^n)$, hence in $\hat{H}^\infty(\mathbf{R}^n)$.

DEFINITION. For each non-negative integer k we define $H^k(\mathbf{R}^n)$ to be the hilbert space obtained by completing $S(\mathbf{R}^n)$ with respect to the norm

$$\|f\|^2_k = \sum_{|\alpha| \leq k} c^k_\alpha \|D^\alpha f\|^2_0 \qquad \text{(cf. [X, §2])} \quad .$$

LEMMA. If k is a non-negative integer then for $f \in S(\mathbf{R}^n)$ we have

$$\|\hat{f}\|_{\hat{k}} = \|f\|_k \quad .$$

PROOF. Immediate from Theorems 3 and 5.

THEOREM 6. $\{H^k(\mathbf{R}^n)\}$ is a scale of hilbert spaces. Moreover the Fourier transform on $S(\mathbf{R}^n)$ extends uniquely to an isomorphism of $\{H^k(\mathbf{R}^n)\}$ with $\{\hat{H}^k(\mathbf{R}^n)\}$ and of $\{\hat{H}^k(\mathbf{R}^n)\}$ with $\{H^k(\mathbf{R}^n)\}$, both of which we continue to denote by $f \mapsto \hat{f}$. If $f \in H^k(\mathbf{R}^n)$ then $\|f\|_k = \|\hat{f}\|_{\hat{k}}$ and $\hat{\hat{f}}(x) = (2\pi)^n f(-x)$.

DEFINITION. We define $OP_r(\mathbf{R}^n) = OP_r(\{H^k(\mathbf{R}^n)\}, \{H^k(\mathbf{R}^n)\})$ and $OP_{-\infty}(\mathbf{R}^n) = \bigcap_{r \in \mathbf{Z}} OP_r(\mathbf{R}^n)$.

§2. Calderon-Zygmund Operators

DEFINITION 1. We denote by $\mathrm{Smbl}_r(\mathbf{R}^n)$ the linear space of C^∞ maps $a: \mathbf{R}^n \times (\mathbf{R}^n - \{0\}) \to \mathbf{C}$ such that $a(x, t\zeta) = t^r a(x, \zeta)$ for $t > 0$ and such that for all positive integers k and n-multi-indices α, β $\mathrm{Sup}\,\{\,|\,\|x\|^k (D_x)^\alpha (D_\zeta)^\beta\, a(x, \zeta)\,|\;\big|\; x \in \mathbf{R}^n,\ \zeta \in S^{n-1}\} < \infty$.

We topologize $\mathrm{Smbl}_r(\mathbf{R}^n)$ by this family of semi-norms.

DEFINITION 2. A *patch function* on $\mathbf{R}^n$ is a C^∞ map $\theta: \mathbf{R}^n \to [0, 1]$ such that θ is identically zero near the origin and identically one near infinity.

DEFINITION 3. If $a \in \mathrm{Smbl}_r(\mathbf{R}^n)$ and θ is a patch function on $\mathbf{R}^n$ we define a linear map $A(\theta, a)$: $S(\mathbf{R}^n) \to S(\mathbf{R}^n)$ by

$$[A(\theta, a)f](x) = (2\pi)^{-n} \int e^{ix\cdot\zeta}\, \theta(\zeta) a(x, \zeta) \hat{f}(\zeta)\, d\zeta \quad .$$

We have the following results which will be proved below.

THEOREM 1. For each patch function θ on $\mathbf{R}^n$, real number s, and integer r there is a constant $C(\theta, s, r)$ such that

$$\|A(\theta, a)f\|_s \le \|f\|_{r+s}\, C(\theta, s, r)\ \mathrm{Sup} \int \left| \left[1 - \sum_{i=1}^{n} \frac{\partial}{\partial x_i}^2\right]^p a(x, \zeta) \right| dx$$

for each $f \in S(\mathbf{R}^n)$ and $a \in \mathrm{Smbl}_r(\mathbf{R}^n)$. Here p is an integer $> (|s|/2) + (n/2)$ and the Sup is over all $\zeta \in S^{n-1}$. In particular we can regard $A(\theta, a)$ as an element of $OP_r(\mathbf{R}^n)$ and the map $a \mapsto A(\theta, a)$ is then a continuous linear map of $\mathrm{Smbl}_r(\mathbf{R}^n)$ into $OP_r(\mathbf{R}^n)$. Finally if θ' is also a patch function on $\mathbf{R}^n$ then $A(\theta, a) - A(\theta', a) \in OP_{-\infty}(\mathbf{R}^n)$ for all $a \in \mathrm{Smbl}_r(\mathbf{R}^n)$.

THEOREM 2. Given $x_0 \in \mathbf{R}^n$ and $\zeta_0 \in S^{n-1}$ there is a sequence $\{\varphi_m\}$ in $S(\mathbf{R}^n)$ such that:

(i) $\varphi_m(x) = 0$ if $\|x-x_0\| > \frac{1}{m}$;

(ii) $\|\varphi_m\|_0 = 1$ and for $s < 0$ $\lim_{m \to \infty} \|\varphi_m\|_s = 0$;

(iii) if $a \in \mathrm{Smbl}_0(\mathbf{R}^n)$ and θ is a patch function on $\mathbf{R}^n$ then

$\|A(\theta, a)\varphi_m - a(x_0, \zeta_0)\varphi_m\|_0 \to 0$.

COROLLARY. If $a \in \mathrm{Smbl}_r(\mathbf{R}^n)$ is not identically zero and θ is a patch function on $\mathbf{R}^n$ then $A(\theta, a)$ does not belong to $\mathrm{OP}_{r'}(\mathbf{R}^n)$ for any integer $r' < r$.

DEFINITION 4. We denote by $\Sigma(\mathbf{R}^n)$ the complex vector space of all formal sums $\sigma = \Sigma_{k\in \mathbf{Z}}\, a_k$ where $a_k \in \mathrm{Smbl}_k(\mathbf{R}^n)$ and $a_k = 0$ for k sufficiently large; and we filter $\Sigma(\mathbf{R}^n)$ by the subspaces $\Sigma_r(\mathbf{R}^n)$ consisting of such σ with $a_k = 0$ for $k > r$.

Remark. If $a_k \in \mathrm{Smbl}_k(\mathbf{R}^n)$ then clearly $D_x^\alpha a_k(x, \zeta)$ is an element of $\mathrm{Smbl}_k(\mathbf{R}^n)$ which we denote by $D_x^\alpha a_k$, and similarly $D_\zeta^\alpha a_k(x, \zeta)$ is an element of $\mathrm{Smbl}_{k-|\alpha|}(\mathbf{R}^n)$ which we denote by $D_\zeta^\alpha a_k$. Let $\sigma = \Sigma_k\, a_k \in \Sigma_r(\mathbf{R}^n)$ and $\sigma' = \Sigma_k\, b_k \in \Sigma_s(\mathbf{R}^n)$. Then $D_\zeta^\alpha a_{k+|\alpha|} \neq 0$ only if $|\alpha| \leq r-k$, hence *a fortiori* $D_x^\alpha D_\zeta^\alpha a_{k+|\alpha|} \neq 0$ only if $|\alpha| \leq r-k$, and it follows that for each $k \in \mathbf{Z}$

$$\sum_{|\alpha| \geq 0} \frac{1}{\alpha!} D_x^\alpha D_\zeta^\alpha \overline{a_{k+|\alpha|}}$$

is a finite sum of elements of $\mathrm{Smbl}_k(\mathbf{R}^n)$ and is zero if $k > r$ (the $\overline{}$ denotes complex conjugate). Similarly $(D_\zeta^\alpha a_{k-\ell+|\alpha|})((\frac{1}{i} D_x)^\alpha b_\ell)$ is an element of $\mathrm{Smbl}_k(\mathbf{R}^n)$ which is zero unless $\ell \leq s$ and $0 \leq |\alpha| \leq r - k+\ell$, hence unless $|\alpha| \leq r + s-k$ and $k - r \leq \ell \leq s$. Hence for each $k \in \mathbf{Z}$

$$\sum_{\ell\in\mathbf{Z}} \sum_{|\alpha| \geq 0} \frac{1}{\alpha!} (D_\zeta^\alpha a_{k-\ell+|\alpha|})((\frac{1}{i} D_x)^\alpha b_\ell)$$

is a finite sum of elements of $\mathrm{Smbl}_k(\mathbf{R}^n)$ and is zero for $k > r + s$. It follows that we have well-defined elements σ^* and $\sigma\sigma'$ of $\Sigma(\mathbf{R}^n)$ belonging to $\Sigma_r(\mathbf{R}^n)$ and $\Sigma_{r+s}(\mathbf{R}^n)$ respectively, given by the following definition.

DEFINITION 5. If $\sigma = \Sigma_k a_k$ and $\sigma' = \Sigma_k b_k$ are elements of $\Sigma(\mathbf{R}^n)$ (belonging to $\Sigma_r(\mathbf{R}^n)$ and $\Sigma_s(\mathbf{R}^n)$ respectively) then we define σ^* and $\sigma\sigma'$ in $\Sigma(\mathbf{R}^n)$ (belonging to $\Sigma_r(\mathbf{R}^n)$ and $\Sigma_{r+s}(\mathbf{R}^n)$ respectively) by

$$\sigma^* = \sum_{|\alpha| \geq 0} \frac{1}{\alpha!} (\tfrac{1}{i} D_x)^\alpha (D_\zeta^\alpha \bar{\sigma})$$

$$= \sum_{k \in \mathbf{Z}} \sum_{|\alpha| \geq 0} \frac{1}{\alpha!} D_x^\alpha D_\zeta^\alpha \bar{a}_{k+|\alpha|} \quad ,$$

$$\sigma\sigma' = \sum_{|\alpha| \geq 0} \frac{1}{\alpha!} (D_\zeta^\alpha \sigma)((\tfrac{1}{i} D_x)^\alpha \sigma')$$

$$= \sum_{k \in \mathbf{Z}} \sum_{\ell \in \mathbf{Z}} \sum_{|\alpha| \geq 0} \frac{1}{\alpha!} (D_\zeta^\alpha a_{k-\ell+|\alpha|})((\tfrac{1}{i} D_x)^\alpha b_\ell) .$$

THEOREM 3. With respect to the operations introduced in Definition 5, $\Sigma(\mathbf{R}^n)$ is a filtered *-algebra.

DEFINITION 6. A linear map $A\colon S(\mathbf{R}^n) \to S(\mathbf{R}^n)$ will be called a Calderón-Zymund operator of order r if there exists $\sigma = \Sigma_{k\in\mathbf{Z}} a_k$ in $\Sigma_r(\mathbf{R}^n)$ such that for each integer $m \geq 0$ there is a patch function θ on $\mathbf{R}^n$ such that

$$A - \sum_{k=r-m}^{r} A(\theta, a_k) \in OP_{r-m-1}(\mathbf{R}^n) \quad .$$

The collection of such A will be denoted by $CZ_r(\mathbf{R}^n)$ and we define $CZ(\mathbf{R}^n) = \bigcup_{r\in\mathbf{Z}} CZ_r(\mathbf{R}^n)$. We define $\sigma(A) = \sigma$.

Remark. It follows from the last statement of Theorem 1 and from the corollary of Theorem 2 that $\sigma(A)$ is well-defined.

If $A \in CZ_r(\mathbf{R}^n)$ and $\sigma(A) = \Sigma_k a_k$ then $A - A(\theta, a_r) \in OP_{r-1}(\mathbf{R}^n)$ and since $A(\theta, a_r) \in OP_r(\mathbf{R}^n)$, it follows that $A \in OP_r(\mathbf{R}^n)$. Moreover, if $a_r \neq 0$ then by the corollary of Theorem 2 $A(\theta, r) \notin OP_{r-1}(\mathbf{R}^n)$ hence $A \notin OP_{r-1}(\mathbf{R}^n)$. Thus

$$CZ_r(\mathbf{R}^n) = \{A \in CZ(\mathbf{R}^n) \mid \sigma(A) \in \Sigma_r(\mathbf{R}^n)\} = CZ(\mathbf{R}^n) \cap OP_r(\mathbf{R}^n) \quad .$$

It is immediate from the definition that $OP_{-\infty}(\mathbf{R}^n) \subseteq CZ_r(\mathbf{R}^n)$ and that $\sigma(A) = 0$ for $A \in OP_{-\infty}(\mathbf{R}^n)$. By the preceding remark it follows that in fact $OP_{-\infty}(\mathbf{R}^n) = \bigcap_r CZ_r(\mathbf{R}^n) = \{A \in CZ(\mathbf{R}^n) \mid \sigma(A) = 0\}$.

Since $CZ_r(\mathbf{R}^n) \subseteq OP_r(\mathbf{R}^n)$ it follows from [VIII, Theorem 4] that if $A \in CZ_r(\mathbf{R}^n)$ then A has a transpose $A^t \in OP_r(\mathbf{R}^n)$.

The following theorem states the basic algebraic facts about the collection of Calderón-Zygmund operators and the mapping σ.

THEOREM 4. The collection $CZ(\mathbf{R}^n)$ of Calderón-Zygmund operators for $\mathbf{R}^n$ is closed under sums, products and $A \mapsto A^t$ and hence forms a *-algebra. The $CZ_r(\mathbf{R}^n)$ are subspaces of $CZ(\mathbf{R}^n)$ and give $CZ(\mathbf{R}^n)$ the structure of a filtered *-algebra. Moreover the mapping $\sigma\colon CZ(\mathbf{R}^n) \to \Sigma(\mathbf{R}^n)$ is a *-homomorphism and $\sigma(A) \in \Sigma_r(\mathbf{R}^n)$ if and only if $A \in CZ_r(\mathbf{R}^n)$. Finally the sequence

$$0 \to OP_{-\infty}(\mathbf{R}^n) \to CZ(\mathbf{R}^n) \to \Sigma(\mathbf{R}^n) \to 0$$

is exact.

DEFINITION 7. If $A \in CZ_r(\mathbf{R}^n)$ and $\sigma(A) = \Sigma_k a_k$, $a_k \in \mathrm{Smbl}_k(\mathbf{R}^n)$, then we define

$$\sigma_r(A) = (-i)^r a_r \quad .$$

COROLLARY OF THEOREM 4. σ_r is a linear map of $CZ_r(\mathbf{R}^n)$ into $\mathrm{Smbl}_r(\mathbf{R}^n)$ and if $A \in CZ_r(\mathbf{R}^n)$ then

$$\sigma_r(A^t) = (-i)^r \overline{\sigma_r(A)} \quad .$$

Moreover the sequence

$$0 \to CZ_{r-1}(\mathbf{R}^n) \to CZ_r(\mathbf{R}^n) \to \mathrm{Smbl}_r(\mathbf{R}^n) \to 0$$

is exact.

If $A \in CZ_r(\mathbf{R}^n)$ and $B \in CZ_s(\mathbf{R}^n)$ then $AB \in CZ_{r+s}(\mathbf{R}^n)$ and for all $(x, \zeta) \in \mathbf{R}^n \times (\mathbf{R}^n - \{0\})$

$$\sigma_{r+s}(AB)(x, \zeta) = [\sigma_r(A)(x, \zeta)][\sigma_s(B)(x, \zeta)] \quad .$$

DEFINITION 8. If $\psi \in S(\mathbf{R}^n)$ we define $M_\psi\colon S(\mathbf{R}^n) \to S(\mathbf{R}^n)$ by

$$(M_\psi f)(x) = \psi(x)f(x) \quad .$$

THEOREM 5. Let $\psi \in S(\mathbf{R}^n)$ and define $D\colon S(\mathbf{R}^n) \to S(\mathbf{R}^n)$ by $D = M_\psi D^\alpha$. Then $D \in CZ_{|\alpha|}(\mathbf{R}^n)$ and $\sigma_{|\alpha|}(D)(x, \zeta) = \psi(x)\zeta^\alpha$.

THEOREM 6. Let $A \in CZ_r(\mathbf{R}^n)$ $r > 0$, and let $\psi \in S(\mathbf{R}^n)$. There is a sequence $\{B_\nu\}$ in $CZ_r(\mathbf{R}^n \times \mathbf{R}^m)$ and a K in $OP_0(\mathbf{R}^n \times \mathbf{R}^m)$ such that B_ν converges in $OP_r(\mathbf{R}^n \times \mathbf{R}^m)$ to $A \otimes M_\psi - K$ and $\sigma_r(B_\nu)((x_1, x_2)(\zeta_1, \zeta_2))$ converges uniformly on $\mathbf{R}^{n+m} \times S^{n+m-1}$ to $\sigma_r(A)(x_1, \zeta_1)\psi(x_2)$.

Finally we consider coordinate transformations. If U is an open set in $\mathbf{R}^n$ then we shall consider $C_0^\infty(U)$ as a subspace of $S(\mathbf{R}^n)$ by extending an element f of $C_0^\infty(U)$ to be identically zero outside U. If $\psi\colon U \to \mathbf{R}^n$ is a C^∞ diffeomorphism then we define $\psi_*\colon C_0^\infty(U) \to C_0^\infty(\psi(U))$ by $\psi_*(f) = f \circ \psi^{-1}$ and we define $\psi^*\colon S(\mathbf{R}^n) \to C^\infty(U)$ by $\psi^*(f) = f \circ \psi$. Note that if φ is an element of $C_0^\infty(U)$ then M_φ maps $S(\mathbf{R}^n)$ into $C_0^\infty(U)$ and maps $C^\infty(U)$ into $C_0^\infty(U) \subseteq S(\mathbf{R}^n)$. It follows that if φ_1 and φ_2 are in $C_0^\infty(U)$ and A maps $S(\mathbf{R}^n)$ into itself then $M_{\varphi_1} \circ \psi^* \circ A \circ \psi_* \circ M_{\varphi_2}$ maps $S(\mathbf{R}^n)$ into itself.

THEOREM 7. Let U be an open set in $\mathbf{R}^n$, $\psi\colon U \to \mathbf{R}^n$ a C^∞ diffeomorphism and $\varphi_1, \varphi_2 \in C_0^\infty(U)$. Then if $A \in CZ_r(\mathbf{R}^n)$ so is $B = M_{\varphi_1} \circ \psi^* \circ A \circ \psi_* \circ M_{\varphi_2}$ and

$$\sigma_r(B)(x, \zeta) = \varphi_1(x)\sigma_r(A)(\psi(x), J^{-1}(x)\zeta)\varphi_2(x)$$

where $J(x)$ is the adjoint of the differential of ψ at x.

We now proceed to the proof of the above theorems.

LEMMA 1. For each real number s

$$(1+\|\xi\|^2)^s(1+\|\eta\|^2)^{-s} \leq 2^{|s|}(1+\|\xi-\eta\|^2)^{|s|}$$

for all $\xi, \eta \in \mathbf{R}^n$.

PROOF. It will suffice to prove

$$(*) \qquad 1 + \|\xi\|^2 \leq 2(1+\|\xi-\eta\|^2)(1+\|\eta\|^2) \quad .$$

Indeed the desired inequality is immediate from (*) when $s \geq 0$ while the case $s < 0$ follows from $s > 0$ by interchanging ξ and η and replacing s by $-s$. To prove (*) we put $\|\xi\| = a$, $\|\eta\| = b$ and note that $\|\xi-\eta\|^2 \geq (\|\xi\| - \|\eta\|)^2 = a^2 - 2ab + b^2$ so

$$2(1+\|\xi-\eta\|^2)(1+\|\eta\|^2) - (1+\|\xi\|^2) =$$

$$= 1 + a^2 + 4b^2 - 4ab + 2a^2b^2 + 2b^4 - 4ab^3 = f(a, b) \quad .$$

Since $f \to \infty$ as $a, b \to \infty$, the minimum of f is assumed when $\frac{\partial f}{\partial a} = \frac{\partial f}{\partial b} = 0$. Now $2\frac{\partial f}{\partial a} + \frac{\partial f}{\partial b} = 4ab(a-b)$ and it follows that at the minimum of f either $a = b$ or else one of a and b is zero. If $a = b$ then $f(a, b) = 1 + a^2$, while $f(a, 0) = 1 + a^2$ and $f(0, b) = 1 + 4b^2 + 2b^4$, hence $f(a, b) \geq 1 > 0$

q.e.d.

LEMMA 2. Let $k \in C^\infty(\mathbf{R}^n \times \mathbf{R}^n)$ and suppose that for each positive integer p there is a constant C_p with $|k(\xi, \zeta)| \leq C_p(1+\|\zeta\|^2)^{t/2}(1+\|\xi-\zeta\|^2)^{-p}$. Then there is an (obviously unique) operator K in $OP_t(\mathbf{R}^n)$ such that for $f \in S(\mathbf{R}^n)$

$$(Kf)^\wedge(\xi) = \int k(\xi, \zeta)\hat{f}(\zeta)d\zeta$$

and moreover for each real number s there is a constant $C(s)$ such that

$$\|Kf\|_s \leq C_pC(s)\|f\|_{s+t}$$

whenever p is an integer $> \frac{|s|}{2} + \frac{n}{2}$.

PROOF. By [§1, Theorem 6] if we define

$$\Lambda^r: S(\mathbf{R}^n) \to S(\mathbf{R}^n) \quad \text{by} \quad (\Lambda^r f)^\wedge(\xi) = (1+\|\xi\|^2)^{r/2}\hat{f}(\xi)$$

then Λ^{r} extends to an isometry of $H^q(\mathbf{R}^n)$ onto $H^{q-r}(\mathbf{R}^n)$, hence the norm of K from $H^{s+t}(\mathbf{R}^n)$ to $H^s(\mathbf{R}^n)$ is the same as the norm of $A = \Lambda^s K \Lambda^{-(s+t)}$ from $H^0(\mathbf{R}^n)$ to $H^0(\mathbf{R}^n)$. But

$$(Af)^\wedge(\xi) = \int a(\xi, \zeta)\hat{f}(\zeta)d\zeta$$

where $a(\xi, \zeta) = (1+\|\xi\|^2)^{s/2} k(\xi, \zeta)(1+\|\zeta\|^2)^{-(s+t)/2}$, and by Lemma 1 and the assumption on k,

$$|a(\xi, \zeta)| \leq C_p 2^{|s|/2} (1+\|\xi-\zeta\|^2)^{-p+|s|/2} .$$

Then by [§1, Theorem 1] (recalling $L^2 = H^0$)

$$\|Af\|_0 \leq C_p 2^{|s|/2} \left(\int (1+\|\xi\|^2)^{-p+|s|/2} d\xi\right)\|f\|_0$$

provided $(1+\|\xi\|^2)^{-p+|s|/2} \in L^1(\mathbf{R}^n)$, which as we saw in §1 happens as soon as $\frac{|s|}{2} - p < -\frac{n}{2}$.

q.e.d.

PROOF of Theorem 1. We have

$$[A(\theta, a)f]^\wedge(\xi) = (2\pi)^{-n} \int a^\wedge(\xi-\zeta, \zeta)\theta(\zeta)\hat{f}(\zeta)d\zeta$$

where $a^\wedge(\xi, \zeta) = \int e^{-ix\cdot\xi} a(x, \zeta)dx$.

Since

$$(1+\|\xi-\zeta\|^2)^p a^\wedge(\xi-\zeta, \zeta) = \int e^{ix\cdot(\xi-\zeta)}\left[1 - \sum_{j=1}^{n} \left(\frac{\partial}{\partial x_j}\right)^2\right]^p a(x, \zeta)dx$$

and $a(x, t\zeta) = t^r a(x, \zeta)$, Theorem 1 follows directly from Lemma 2.

PROOF of Theorem 2. By translation we may take $x_0 = 0$. Take any φ in $S(\mathbf{R}^n)$ with $\|\varphi\|_0 = 1$, and the support of φ in $\{x \in \mathbf{R}^n \mid \|x\| < 1\}$.

Define an isometry T_m of $H^0(\mathbf{R}^n)$ onto itself by $(T_m f)(x) = m^{n/2} f(mx)$, and set $\varphi_m = T_m e^{im(\zeta_0, \cdot)} \varphi$. Then condition (i) of Theorem 2 holds. To obtain (ii), we have $\|\varphi_m\|_s^2 = \int (1+\|\xi\|^2)^s |\varphi_m(\xi)|^2 d\xi = \int (1+\|m\zeta + m^2\zeta_0\|^2)^s |\varphi(\zeta)|^2 d\zeta$, which tends to zero as $m \to \infty$ by the dominated convergence theorem. Since T_m and multiplication by $e^{im(\zeta_0, \cdot)}$ are isometries of $H^0(\mathbf{R}^n)$, we may establish (iii) by showing that

$e^{-im(\zeta_0,\cdot)} T_m^{-1} A(\theta, a)\varphi_m = \psi_m$ approaches $a(0, \zeta_0)\varphi$ in $H^0(\mathbf{R}^n)$.

We have

$$\psi_m(x) = m^{-n}(2\pi)^{-n} \int e^{i(\zeta - m^2\zeta_0,\, x/m)} \theta(\zeta)a(x/m, \zeta)\varphi(\zeta/m - m\zeta_0)d\zeta \quad .$$

Setting $\xi = \zeta/m - m\zeta_0$ and using the homogeneity of a, we get

$$\psi_m(x) = (2\pi)^{-n} \int e^{i(\xi,x)} \theta(m\zeta + m^2\zeta_0)a(x/m, \xi/m + \zeta_0)\varphi(\xi)d\xi \quad .$$

By the Lebesgue dominated convergence theorem, for each $x \in \mathbf{R}^n$,

$$\psi_m(x) \to \psi(x) = (2\pi)^{-n} \int e^{i(\xi,x)} a(0, \zeta_0)\varphi(\xi)d\xi = a(0, \zeta_0)\varphi(x) \quad .$$

We show that this convergence is in L^2 by showing that for each α, $x^\alpha\psi_m(x)$ is bounded on $\mathbf{R}^n$. In fact, again using the homogeneity of a, we have

$$|x^\alpha\psi_m(x)| = (2\pi)^{-n}\left| \int [D_\xi^\alpha e^{i(\xi,x)}]\, \theta a(x/m, m\xi + m^2\zeta_0)\varphi(\xi) \right| d\xi \le$$

$$(*) \qquad (2\pi)^{-n} \int |D_\xi^\alpha [\theta a(x/m, m\xi + m^2\zeta_0)\varphi(\xi)]|d\xi \ ,$$

after an integration by parts. If we let $(\theta a)^{(\beta)}(y, \zeta) = D_\zeta^\beta[\theta(\zeta)a(y, \zeta)]$, and choose R so that $\theta(\zeta) = 0$ for $\|\zeta\| \le R$, then (*) is a sum of terms of the form

$$C_{\alpha\beta}m^{|\beta|} \int_{\|m\xi + m^2\zeta_0\| > R} |(\theta a)^{(\beta)}(x/m, m\xi + m^2\zeta_0)|\cdot|\varphi^{(\gamma)}(\xi)|d\xi$$

$$\le \text{const.} \int_{\|\xi + m\zeta_0\| > R/m} \|\xi + m\zeta_0\|^{-|\beta|} \cdot |\varphi^{(\gamma)}(\xi)|d\xi \quad .$$

In this last expression, the integral for $\|\xi + m\zeta_0\| \ge 1$ is dominated by $\int|\varphi^{(\gamma)}(\xi)|d\xi$. The integral for $R/m < \|\xi + m\zeta_0\| < 1$ is

$$\le \text{const.} \int_{R/m < \|\eta\| < 1} \|\eta\|^{-|\beta|} \cdot |\varphi^{(\gamma)}(\eta - m\zeta_0)|d\eta \quad .$$

Since $\varphi^{(\gamma)} \in S(\mathbf{R}^n)$, for any positive integer k we have

$$|\varphi^{(\gamma)}(\xi)| \le \text{const.}(1 + \|\xi\|^2)^{-k} \quad ,$$

so since $\|\zeta_0\| = 1$, $\|\eta\| < 1$ implies $\|\eta - m\zeta_0\| \ge m-1$ and evaluating the above integral in polar coordinates yields

$$\leq \text{const.} \int_{R/m}^{1} \rho^{n-1-|\beta|}(1 + (m-1)^2)^{-k}\, d\rho$$

$$\leq \text{const.} \left[1 - \left(\tfrac{R}{m}\right)^{n-|\beta|}\right](1 + (m-1)^2)^{-k}$$

(the first factor is $\log(\frac{R}{m})$ if $|\beta| = n$). Choosing $k > \frac{1}{2}(|\beta| - n)$ gives a bound independent of m. Now we have $\psi_m \to \psi$ pointwise and $|\psi_m(x)| \leq \text{const.}(1 + \|x\|)^{-n} \in L^2$ so the dominated convergence theorem gives $\int |\psi_m - \psi|^2 \to 0$.

q.e.d.

Remark. Multiplication of φ by $e^{im(\zeta_0, \cdot)}$ translates $\hat{\varphi}$ by $m\zeta_0$, so that $\hat{\varphi}$ becomes more and more concentrated in a small sector in the direction of ζ_0. Application of T_m concentrates the support of φ near the origin.

PROOF of Theorem 3. Since the homomorphic image of a *-algebra is a *-algebra, Theorem 3 will follow from Theorem 4.

PROOF of Theorem 4. We consider only the product AB of two elements of $CZ(\mathbf{R}^n)$, since it is clear that σ is linear and since the proof for the adjoint is similar to (but simpler than) that for the product.

It suffices to consider $A = A(\theta_1, a)$ and $B = A(\theta_2, b)$ with $a \in \mathrm{Smbl}_r(\mathbf{R}^n)$ and $b \in \mathrm{Smbl}_s(\mathbf{R}^n)$, and we may assume that $\theta_1 = 1$ on the support of θ_2. To simplify notation let $\tilde{a}(x, \zeta) = a(x, \zeta)\theta_1(\zeta)$ and let $\tilde{b}(x, \zeta) = b(x, \zeta)\theta_2(\zeta)$. By the first formula in the proof of Theorem 1

$$(ABf)^\wedge(\tau) = (2\pi)^{-2n} \int \tilde{a}^\wedge(\tau-\xi, \xi) \int \tilde{b}^\wedge(\xi-\zeta, \zeta)\hat{f}(\zeta)\,d\zeta\, d\xi$$

$$= (2\pi)^{-2n} \int \tilde{a}^\wedge(\tau-\xi, \xi) \int \tilde{b}^\wedge(\xi-\zeta, \zeta)\hat{f}(\zeta)\,d\xi\, d\zeta \quad .$$

If we set $\tilde{a}^{(\alpha)}(x, \zeta) = D_\zeta^\alpha \tilde{a}(x, \zeta)$ and $\tilde{b}_{(\alpha)}(x, \zeta) = (\frac{1}{i} D_x)^\alpha \tilde{b}(x, \zeta)$, we have

$$\tilde{a}^\wedge(\tau-\xi, \xi) = \sum_{|\alpha| \leq m} \tilde{a}^{(\alpha)}(\tau-\xi, \zeta)\, \frac{(\xi-\zeta)^\alpha}{\alpha!} + R_m(\tau, \xi, \zeta)$$

and

$$(ABf)\hat{}(\tau) = (2\pi)^{-n}\int \sum_{|\alpha|\leq m} \frac{1}{\alpha!}\left((\tilde{a}^{(\alpha)}\tilde{b}_{(\alpha)})\right)\hat{}(\tau-\zeta,\ \zeta)\hat{f}(\zeta)d\zeta$$

$$+ \int\int R_m(\tau,\ \xi,\ \eta)\tilde{b}\hat{}(\xi-\zeta,\ \zeta)\hat{f}(\zeta)d\zeta d\xi$$

where in the above we have used Theorem 2 and Theorem 3 of §1.

Since all derivatives of θ_1 vanish on the support of θ_2 and $\theta_1\theta_2 = \theta_2$, we have

$$\tilde{a}^{(\alpha)}(x,\ \zeta)\tilde{b}_{(\alpha)}(x,\ \zeta) = \theta_2(\zeta)a^{(\alpha)}(x,\ \zeta)b_{(\alpha)}(x,\ \zeta) \quad ,$$

and

$$K = AB - \sum_{|\alpha|\leq m} A(\theta_2,\ a^{(\alpha)}b_{(\alpha)})\Big/\alpha!$$

is the operator

$$(Kf)\hat{}(\tau) = \int k(\tau,\ \zeta)\hat{f}(\zeta)d\zeta$$

with

$$k(\tau,\ \zeta) = \int R_m(\tau,\ \xi,\ \zeta)\tilde{b}\hat{}(\xi-\zeta,\ \zeta)d\xi \quad .$$

We will show that when $m+1 \geq r$, Lemma 2 applies to K, with the t of that lemma equal to $r + s - m - 1$, so that $K \in OP_t(\mathbf{R}^n)$.

From

$$R_m(\tau,\ \xi,\ \zeta) = (m+1)\sum_{|\alpha|=m+1} \frac{1}{\alpha!}(\xi-\zeta)^{(\alpha)}\int_0^1 (1-t)^m\tilde{a}^{(\alpha)}\hat{}(\tau-\xi,\ \zeta+t(\xi-\zeta))dt$$

we get

$$|R_m(\tau,\ \xi,\ \zeta)| \leq C_p\|\xi-\zeta\|^{m+1}(1+\|\tau-\xi\|^2)^{-p/2}(1+\mathrm{Inf}(\|\zeta\|,\ \|\xi\|))^{r-m-1}$$

because $\tilde{a}^{(\alpha)}(x,\ \zeta)$ is homogeneous of degree $r-m-1$ in ζ for large $\|\zeta\|$. Since

$$|\tilde{b}\hat{}(\xi-\zeta,\ \zeta)| \leq C_q(1+\|\zeta\|)^s(1+\|\xi-\zeta\|^2)^{-q/2}$$

we get

$$|k(\tau,\ \zeta)| \leq \mathrm{Const.}(1+\|\zeta\|)^s \int_{\|\xi\|\leq\|\zeta\|} (1+\|\xi-\zeta\|)^{m+1-q}(1+\|\tau-\xi\|)^{-p}(1+\|\xi\|)^{r-m-1}d\xi$$

$$+ \mathrm{Const.}(1+\|\zeta\|)^{s+r-m-1}\int_{\|\xi\|\geq\|\zeta\|} (1+\|\xi-\zeta\|)^{m+1-q}(1+\|\tau-\xi\|)^{-p}d\xi \quad ,$$

since $(1+\|\zeta\|^2)^{1/2} \sim (1+\|\zeta\|)$. Call the expression $\int_{\|\xi\| \leq \|\zeta\|}$, k_1, and the other k_2. In k_2 take $m + 1 - q = -p$ where $p > n$. Then by integrating separately over the two half spaces $\|\xi-\tau\| < \|\xi-\zeta\|$ and $\|\xi-\tau\| > \|\xi-\zeta\|$ we get $k_2(\tau, \zeta) \leq \text{Const.}(1+\|\zeta\|)^{s+r-m-1}(1+\frac{1}{2}\|\tau-\zeta\|)^{-p}$ since in each half space one of the factors in

$$\int_{\|\xi\| \geq \|\zeta\|} (1+\|\xi-\zeta\|)^{m+1-q}(1+\|\tau-\xi\|)^{-p}d\xi \quad \text{is} \leq \quad (1+\tfrac{1}{2}\|\tau-\zeta\|)^{-p}$$

and the other is integrable.

For k_1 we have

$$(1+\|\xi\|)^{r-m-1} \leq \text{Const.}(1+\|\zeta\|)^{r-m-1}(1+\|\xi-\zeta\|)^{|r-m-1|}$$

by Lemma 1 above, and we get as before

$$k_1(\tau, \zeta) \leq \text{Const.}(1+\|\zeta\|)^{s+r-m-1}(1 + \tfrac{1}{2}\|\tau-\zeta\|)^{-p} \quad .$$

Thus Lemma 2 applies and $K \in OP_t(\mathbf{R}^n)$. It follows that $AB \in CZ(\mathbf{R}^n)$ and that

$$\sigma(AB) = \sigma(A)\sigma(B) \quad .$$

To complete the proof of Theorem 4 we must show that $\sigma\colon CZ(\mathbf{R}^n) \to \Sigma(\mathbf{R}^n)$ is surjective. Let $\Sigma_j a_j \in \Sigma_r(\mathbf{R}^n)$, so $a_j \in \mathrm{Smbl}_j(\mathbf{R}^n)$ and $a_j = 0$ for $j > r$. Choose patch function θ_j so that for $j < 0$

$$|(1+\|x\|^2)^{-j} D_x^\alpha a_j(x, \zeta)\theta_j(\zeta)| < 2^j$$

for $|\alpha| \leq |j|$. This is possible since $(1+\|x\|^2)^{-j} D_x^\alpha a_j(x, \zeta)$ converges to zero uniformly as $\|\zeta\| \to \infty$, because $a_j(x, \zeta)$ is homogeneous of degree $j < 0$.

Let $a(x, \zeta) = \Sigma_j a_j(x, \zeta)\theta_j(\zeta)$. The series converges uniformly on $\mathbf{R}^n \times \mathbf{R}^n$ and has the properties:

(i) $(1+\|x\|^2)^k D_x^\alpha a(x, \zeta)(1+\|\zeta\|)^{-r}$ is bounded on $\mathbf{R}^n \times \mathbf{R}^n$ for each k, α.

(ii) $(1+\|x\|^2)^k D_x^\alpha [a(x, \zeta) - \Sigma_{j=-m}^r a_j(x, \zeta)\theta_j(\zeta)](1+\|\zeta\|)^{m+1}$ is bounded on $\mathbf{R}^n \times \mathbf{R}^n$ for each k, α.

From (i) it follows that if for $f \in S(\mathbf{R}^n)$ we define $(Af)(x) = (2\pi)^{-n} \int e^{i(x,\zeta)} a(x, \zeta)\hat{f}(\zeta)d\zeta$ then A maps $S(\mathbf{R}^n)$ linearly into itself; from (ii) and Lemma 2 it follows that

$$A - \sum_{j=-m}^{r} A(\theta_j, a_j) \in OP_{-m-1}(\mathbf{R}^n) \quad .$$

Thus $A \in CZ(\mathbf{R}^n)$ and

$$\sigma(A) = \sum_{j=-\infty}^{r} a_j \quad .$$

q.e.d.

For the proof of Theorems 5 and 6 we will need

LEMMA 3. If $a \in Smbl_r(\mathbf{R}^n)$, $r \geq 0$, then the estimates of Theorem 1 apply when θ is replaced by the constant 1. Moreover if θ is any patch function $A(\theta, a) - A(1, a) \in OP_{-\infty}(\mathbf{R}^n)$ and hence $A(1, a) \in CZ_r(\mathbf{R}^n)$ and $\sigma_r(A(1, a)) = (-i)^r a$.

PROOF. We need only invoke Lemma 2; because if $r \geq 0$ then

$$\int \left| \left(1 - \sum_{j=1}^{n} \left(\frac{\partial}{\partial x_j}\right)^2\right)^p a(x, \zeta) \right| dx \leq \text{Const.}(1+\|\zeta\|^2)^{r/2} \quad ,$$

and because $\theta - 1$ vanishes outside a compact set

$$\int \left| \left(1 - \sum_{j=1}^{n} \left(\frac{\partial}{\partial x_j}\right)^2\right)^p a(x, \zeta)[\theta(\zeta)-1] \right| dx \leq \text{Const.}(1+\|\zeta\|^2)^s$$

for every real number s.

PROOF of Theorem 5. By Theorem 3 of §1

$$(D^\alpha f)^\wedge(\zeta) = (i\zeta)^\alpha \hat{f}(\zeta)$$

so by Theorem 4 of §1

$$(Df)(x) = (2\pi)^{-n} \int e^{ix\cdot\zeta} \psi(x)(i\zeta)^\alpha \hat{f}(\zeta)d\zeta$$

or in other words $D = A(1, a)$ where $a \in Smbl_{|\alpha|}(\mathbf{R}^n)$ is defined by $a(x, \zeta) = \psi(x)(i\zeta)^\alpha$. Since $|\alpha| \geq 0$ Theorem 5 is an immediate consequence of Lemma 3.

PROOF of Theorem 6. Because the norm of $A \otimes M_\psi$ as an operator from $H^{s+r}(\mathbf{R}^n \times \mathbf{R}^m)$ to $H^s(\mathbf{R}^n \times \mathbf{R}^m)$ is, for $r \geq 0$, dominated by the norm of A from $H^{s+r}(\mathbf{R}^n)$ to $H^s(\mathbf{R}^n)$ it suffices to consider A of the form $A(\theta, a)$ with $a \in \text{Smbl}_r(\mathbf{R}^n)$, $r > 0$. Because of Lemma 3 it suffices to approximate $A(1, a) \otimes M_\psi$ by $A(1, b_k)$, with $b_k \in \text{Smbl}_r(\mathbf{R}^n \times \mathbf{R}^m)$. Let x and ζ denote points in $\mathbf{R}^n$ and y, η points of $\mathbf{R}^m$. Choose a φ in $C^\infty(\mathbf{R}^n \times \mathbf{R}^m)$ with $\varphi(x, y)$ vanishing for $\|x\|^2 + \|y\|^2 \geq \frac{1}{4}$ and $\int \varphi(x, y)dxdy = 1$.

Define $b_k \in \text{Smbl}_r(\mathbf{R}^n \times \mathbf{R}^m)$ by

$$b_k(x, y; \xi, \eta) = \psi(y) \int a(x, \tilde{\xi}) k^{n+m} \varphi(k(\xi-\tilde{\xi}, \eta-\tilde{\eta}))d\tilde{\xi}d\tilde{\eta}$$

when $\|\xi\|^2 + \|\eta\|^2 = 1$. For $\|\xi\|^2 + \|\eta\|^2 = t^2$ define $b_k(x, y, \xi, \eta) = t^r b(x, y; \frac{\xi}{t}, \frac{\eta}{t})$. Since $x^\alpha y^\beta (D_x)^\gamma (D_y)^\delta (\partial/\partial\xi_j)\psi(y)a(x, \xi)$ is bounded for every α, β, γ, δ and j on $\|\xi\| \leq 2$, we have

$$x^\alpha y^\beta (D_x)^\gamma (D_y)^\delta [b_k(x, y; \xi, \eta) - \psi(y)a(x, \xi))] \to 0$$

uniformly on $\mathbf{R}^{n+m} \times S^{n+m-1}$. Thus $\sigma(A(1, b_k)) \to \sigma(A(1, a)) \otimes \sigma(M_\psi)$ uniformly on $\mathbf{R}^{n+m} \times S^{n+m-1}$ as desired. That $A(1, b_k)$ converges to $A(1, a) \otimes M_\psi$ in $OP_r(\mathbf{R}^n \times \mathbf{R}^m)$ follows as in the proof of Theorem 1.

PROOF of Theorem 7. Since $\psi_* M_{\varphi_2}$ and $M_{\varphi_1}\psi^*$ are in $OP_0(\mathbf{R}^n)$ it suffices to consider the case $A = A(\theta, a)$ where $a \in \text{Smbl}_r(\mathbf{R}^n)$. Then we have

$$(1) \qquad (A\psi_* M_{\varphi_2} f)(\bar{x}) = (2\pi)^{-n} \int\int e^{i(\bar{x}-\bar{y},\zeta)} a(\bar{x}, \zeta)\theta(\zeta)\varphi_2(y)f(y)d\bar{y}d\zeta$$

where $y = \psi^{-1}(\bar{y})$, $x = \psi^{-1}(\bar{x})$. Replace $\theta(\zeta)$ by $\theta(J(x)\zeta)$ and set $a(\psi(x), \zeta) = a'(x, J(x)\zeta)$, $J(x)\zeta = \xi$, and $v(x) = |\det J(x)|$. Then

$$(2) \qquad M_{\varphi_1}\psi^* A\psi_* M_{\varphi_2} - A' = S \in OP_{-\infty}(\mathbf{R}^n)$$

where

(3) $(A'f)(x) =$

$$(2\pi)^{-n} \varphi_1(x)v(x)^{-1} \int\int e^{i(\psi(x)-\psi(y), J(x)^{-1}\xi)} a'(x, \xi)\theta(\xi)(\varphi_2 fv)(y)dyd\xi.$$

We use the expansion

$$e^z = \sum_{j=0}^{k} z^j/j! + z^{k+1}\int_0^1 (1-t)^k e^{zt}\, dt/k! \quad ,$$

and

$$\psi(y) - \psi(x) = d\psi_x(y-x) + \sum_{|\alpha|=2}^{m} \psi^{(\alpha)}(x)(y-x)^\alpha/\alpha! + R_m(x, y)$$

or

$$d\psi_x^{-1}(\psi(x)-\psi(y)) = x-y + \sum_{|\alpha|=2}^{m} Q_\alpha(x)(x-y)^\alpha + R_m'(x, y)$$

where $d\psi_x$ is the differential of ψ at x. By multiplying by a partition of unity we can suppose that where $\varphi_1(x)\varphi_2(y) \neq 0$ we have

(4) $$\|d\psi_x(y-x) + tR_1(x, y)\| \geq C\|y-x\| \qquad 0 \leq t \leq 1$$

where $R_1(x, y) = O(\|x-y\|^2)$. Note that

$$e^{i(\psi(x)-\psi(y), J(x)^{-1}\xi)} = e^{i(x-y,\xi)}\, e^{i(R_1'(x,y),\xi)} \quad .$$

Set $z = i(R_1'(x, y), \xi)$ in the above expansion of e^z. Using the expansion of ψ to m terms and of e^z to k terms, and neglecting all remainders we get

(5) $(A_{m,k}f)(x) =$

$$(2\pi)^{-n}\varphi_1(x)v(x)^{-1}\int\int e^{i(x-y,\xi)} \sum_{j=0}^{k} \Big(i\sum_{|\alpha|=2}^{m} Q_\alpha(x)(y-x)^\alpha, \xi\Big)^j \Big/ j!$$

$$a'(x, \xi)\theta(\xi)(\varphi_2 fv)(y)dyd\xi \quad .$$

If in the sum $\Sigma_{j=0}^{k}$ we take only the term $j = 0$ we obtain

$$(2\pi)^{-n}\varphi_1(x)v(x)^{-1}\int\int e^{i(x-y,\xi)} a'(x, \xi)\theta(\xi)(\varphi_2 fv)(y)dyd\xi \quad ,$$

which by Theorem 4 is in $CZ_r(\mathbf{R}^n)$ and has the desired symbol. The terms corresponding to $1 \leq j \leq k$ give rise to integrals of the form

$$\varphi_3(x)\int\int e^{i(x-y,\xi)}(x-y)^\beta \xi^\gamma\, a'(x, \xi)\theta(\xi)\varphi_4(y)f(y)dyd\xi$$

with $|\beta| > |\gamma|$. Writing

$$(x-y)^{\beta} e^{i(x-y,\xi)} = \left(-i \frac{\partial}{\partial\xi}\right)^{\beta} e^{i(x-y,\xi)} ,$$

interchanging $\partial/\partial\xi$ with $\int dy$, and integrating by parts we obtain an element of $CZ_t(\mathbf{R}^n)$ with $t = r + |\gamma| - |\beta| < r$, since for large ξ $(\partial/\partial\xi)^{\beta}\, \xi^{\gamma} a'(x, \xi)\theta(\xi)$ is homogeneous of degree $r + |\gamma| - |\beta|$ in ξ. Thus $A_{m,k}$ is an element of $CZ_r(\mathbf{R}^n)$ with the desired σ_r; and if $m^1 > m$, $k^1 > k$, then $A_{m,k}$ and A_{m^1,k^1} agree within elements of $CZ_t(\mathbf{R}^n)$ with $t \leq r - \min(m, k+1)$.

Now consider the terms that arise from the remainders in the above Taylor expansions. We find that:

$$((A' - A_{m,k})f(x) = (6) + \text{terms of the form } (7) \text{ where}$$

$$(6) = \varphi_3(x) \int\int e^{i(x-y),\xi)} \int_0^1 (1-t)^k e^{i(R_1',\xi)t}\, dt (R_1', \xi)^{k+1}\, a'(x, \xi)\theta(\xi)\, \varphi_4(y)f(y)\,dy\,d\xi$$

and

$$(7) = \varphi_3(x) \int\int e^{i(x-y,\xi)} (y-x)^{\alpha} R_m(x, y)^{\beta} \xi^{\gamma}\, a'(x, \xi)\theta(\xi)\varphi_4(y)f(y)\,dy\,d\xi \quad ;$$

here $\varphi_3, \varphi_4 \in C_0^{\infty}(\mathbf{R}^n)$, and $|\gamma| \leq k$, $|\beta| \geq 1$. We shall show the following two facts.

LEMMA 4. Given $s > 0$, k and m can be chosen arbitrarily large so that (6) and (7) have the form

$$\int K(x, y)f(y)\,dy \quad , \tag{8}$$

where the support of K is a compact subset of $\mathbf{R}^n \times \mathbf{R}^n$ and K has continuous derivatives of order $\leq 4s$.

LEMMA 5. Let $T\colon S(\mathbf{R}^n) \to S(\mathbf{R}^n)$ be a linear map and suppose there exists an even integer $2s \geq 0$ and a K in $C^{4s}(\mathbf{R}^n \times \mathbf{R}^n)$, with compact support so that

$$(Tf)(x) = \int K(x, y)f(y)\,dy \quad .$$

Then if $j \geq -2s$ and $t \leq 2s$, T extends to a continuous linear map of $H^j(\mathbf{R}^n)$ into $H^t(\mathbf{R}^n)$.

Granted this, Theorem 7 is concluded by showing that $A'-A_{\ell,\ell-1}$ has order $\leq r-\ell$, and hence that the expansion for A' to order $r-\ell+1$ is obtained from that of $A_{\ell,\ell-1}$. To check the order of $A'-A_{\ell,\ell-1}$, we show that for each j $\|A'f - A_{\ell,\ell-1}f\|_{j-r+\ell} \leq c_j\|f\|_j$, where $\|f\|_k$ = the norm of f in $H^k(\mathbf{R}^n)$. Let s be an integer with $2s \geq \max(|j|, |j-r+\ell|)$. Then by Lemmas 4 and 5, we may choose $m > \ell$ and $k > \ell-1$ so that $A'-A_{m,k}$ maps H^j continuously into $H^{j-r+\ell}$. Since $A_{m,k} - A_{\ell,\ell-1}$ has order $\leq r-\ell$, we obtain by the triangle inequality that $\|A'f - A_{\ell,\ell-1}f\|_{j-r+\ell} \leq c_j\|f\|_j$.

PROOF of Lemma 4. Take k so large that there is an even integer 2ℓ satisfying

$$(9) \qquad 2k - 4s + 2 > 2\ell > r + k + 1 + 4s + n \quad .$$

Since $\Delta_\xi\, e^{i(z,\xi)} = -\|z\|^2 e^{i(z,\eta)}$ (where $\Delta_\xi = \Sigma_{i=1}^n \frac{\partial^2}{2\xi_i^2}$) we can write (6) as a sum of terms of the form

$$(10) \qquad \varphi_3(x)\int\int\int_0^1 \left[(\Delta_\xi)^\ell\, e^{i(x-y+tR_1',\xi)}\right](1-t)^k(R_1')^\gamma$$
$$\|x-y+tR_1'\|^{-2\ell}\,\xi^\gamma\, a'(x,\xi)\theta(\xi)\varphi_4(y)f(y)\,dt\,dy\,d\xi$$

with $|\gamma| = k+1$. Interchanging $(\Delta_\xi)^\ell$ with the two inner integrals and integrating by parts yields again

$$(10') \qquad \varphi_3(x)\int\int\int_0^1 e^{i(x-y+tR_1',\xi)}(1-t)^k(R_1')^\gamma$$
$$\|x-y+tR_1'\|^{-2\ell}\,(\Delta_\xi)^\ell[\xi^\gamma a'(x,\xi)\theta(\xi)]\varphi_4(y)f(y)\,dt\,dy\,d\xi \quad .$$

Since a' is homogeneous of degree r in ξ and since $|\gamma| = k+1$ we have from (9) that $(\Delta_\xi)^\ell[\xi^\gamma a'(x,\xi)\theta(\xi)]$ is homogeneous of degree $r + k + 1 - 2\ell < -4s - n$ for large $\|\xi\|$, and hence is integrable. Applying Fubini's Theorem, (10') has the form (8) with

$$K(x,y) = \varphi_3(x)\varphi_4(y)\int\int_0^1 e^{i(x-y+tR_1',\xi)}(1-t)^k R_1{}^\gamma$$
$$\|x-y+tR_1'\|^{-2\ell}\,(\Delta_\xi)^\ell[\xi^\gamma a'(x,\xi)\theta(\xi)]\,dt\,d\xi \quad .$$

Since the derivatives of R_1 of order $\leq j$ are $O(\|x-y\|^{2-j})$, and $|\gamma| = k+1$, we find from (4) and (9) that $R_1^\gamma\|x-y+tR_1'\|^{-2\ell}$ has derivatives of order $\leq 4s$, continuous in (x, y, t) from (9); in fact the derivatives of order $4s$ are $O(\|x-y\|^{2k+2-2\ell-4s})$ and $2k + 2 - 2\ell - 4s > 0$. Moreover, the derivatives of $e^{i(x-y+tR_1, \xi)}$ of order $\leq 4s$ introduce powers of ξ of degree $\leq 4s$, which do not destroy the integrability in ξ. Thus $K(x, y)$ has continuous derivatives of order $\leq 4s$.

We have analogously for the other remainder terms

$$(7) = \varphi_3(x)\int\int e^{i(x-y,\xi)}(y-x)^\alpha R_m(x, y)^\beta\|x-y\|^{-2\ell} (\Delta_\xi)^\ell[\xi^\gamma a'(x, \xi)\theta(\xi)]\varphi_4(y)f(y)dyd\xi$$

with $|\beta| \geq 1$ and $|\gamma| \leq k$. Choosing $m > 1 + 8s + r + k + n$ and then choosing ℓ so that

$$r + |\gamma| + 4s + n < 2\ell < |\alpha| + (m+1)|\beta| - 4s$$

we may interchange dy and $d\xi$ and differentiate the resulting kernel continuously $4s$ times.

PROOF of Lemma 5.(T is continuous from $H^j(R^n)$ to $H^t(R^n)$ for $j \geq -2s$ and $t \leq 2s$). It suffices to take $j = -2s$ and $t = 2s$, because of the continuous injections of H^j into H^{-2s} and H^{2s} into H^t. But then we need only show that for f in $S(\mathbf{R}^n)$ $\|\Lambda^{2s}T\,\Lambda^{2s}f\|_{H^0} \leq$ Const.$\|f\|_{H^0}$ with $\Lambda^{2s} = (1 - \Sigma_1^n\,\partial^2/\partial x_j^2)^s$. This follows from integration by parts, differentiation under the integral, and Hölder's inequality. In fact

$$\int|\Lambda^{2s}T\,\Lambda^{2s}f|^2 = \int|\Lambda_x^{2s}\int K(x, y)\,\Lambda^{2s}f(y)dy|^2dx = \int|\int[\Lambda_x^{2s}\,\Lambda_y^{2s}\,K(x, y)]f(y)dy|^2dx$$
$$\leq \int|f(y)|^2dy\int|\max_y\Lambda_x^{2s}\,\Lambda_y^{2s}\,K(x, y)|^2\,dx\,.$$

q.e.d.

§3. Calderón-Zygmund operators for a compact manifold

In this section M will denote a compact n-dimensional manifold without boundary. We will write $H^k(M)$ for the hilbertian space $H^k(\mathbf{C}_M)$ where $\mathbf{C}_M$ denotes the trivial complex line bundle over M. Similarly, we define $\mathrm{OP}_k(M) = \mathrm{OP}_k(\mathbf{C}_M, \mathbf{C}_M)$, $\mathrm{Smbl}_k(M) = \mathrm{Smbl}_k(\mathbf{C}_M, \mathbf{C}_M)$, and $\mathrm{Diff}_k(M) = \mathrm{Diff}_k(\mathbf{C}_M, \mathbf{C}_M)$.

If $T: C^\infty(M) \to C^\infty(M)$ is a linear map then T is called *local* if whenever $f \in C^\infty(M)$ vanishes on an open set $\mathcal{O}$, Tf also vanishes on $\mathcal{O}$. For example, as we saw in Chapter IV, §3, elements of $\mathrm{Diff}_k(M)$ are local. It is easily seen that T is local if and only if whenever φ_1 and φ_2 are two elements of $C^\infty(M)$ with disjoint supports, $M_{\varphi_1} T M_{\varphi_2} = 0$, where $M_{\varphi_1} \in \mathrm{Diff}_0(M)$ is the map $f \mapsto \varphi_i f$.

DEFINITION 1. A linear map $T: C^\infty(M) \to C^\infty(M)$ is called *quasi-local* if and only if whenever φ_1, φ_2 are elements of $C^\infty(M)$ with disjoint supports $M_{\varphi_1} T M_{\varphi_2} \in OP_{-\infty}(M)$.

Remark. If $A \in CZ_r(\mathbf{R}^n)$ and φ_1, φ_2 are elements of $S(\mathbf{R}^n)$ with disjoint support, then it follows from Theorem 5 of §2 (with $|\alpha| = 0$) that $M_{\varphi_i} \in CZ_0(\mathbf{R}^n)$ and $\sigma(M_{\varphi_i})(x, \zeta) = \varphi_i(x)$. It then follows from Theorem 4 of §2 that $M_{\varphi_i} A M_{\varphi_2} \in CZ_r(\mathbf{R}^n)$ and $\sigma(M_{\varphi_1} A M_{\varphi_2}) = 0$, and hence by that same theorem $M_{\varphi_1} A M_{\varphi_2} \in OP_{-\infty}(\mathbf{R}^n)$. In other words elements of $CZ(\mathbf{R}^n)$ are quasi-local operators.

DEFINITION 2. If $T: C^\infty(M) \to C^\infty(M)$ is a linear map we define the *support of* T to be the complement of the largest open set $\mathcal{O}$ such that

1) $Tf(x) = 0$ if $x \in \mathcal{O}$;

2) $Tf = 0$ if support $f \subseteq \mathcal{O}$.

Remark. If $\varphi \in C^\infty(M)$ has its support disjoint from the support of T then clearly $M_\varphi T = TM_\varphi = 0$. If $\varphi \in C^\infty(M)$ is identically one on a neighborhood of support T then $M_{(1-\varphi)}T = 0$ so $T = M_\varphi T$ and similarly $TM_\varphi = T$. Clearly if $\varphi_1, \varphi_2 \in C^\infty(M)$ then for any $T: C^\infty(M) \to C^\infty(M)$, support $(M_{\varphi_1} T M_{\varphi_2}) \subseteq$ support $\varphi_1 \cup$ support φ_2.

DEFINITION 3. Let $\psi: \mathcal{O} \to \mathbf{R}^n$ be a chart for M and let $T: C^\infty(M) \to C^\infty(M)$ be a linear map with support $T \subseteq \mathcal{O}$. We define a linear map $A(T, \psi)$: $S(\mathbf{R}^n) \to C_0(\mathbf{R}^n)$, called the transfer of T by ψ, as follows: let $\varphi \in C_0^\infty(\mathcal{O})$ be identically one on a neighborhood of support T and for $f \in S(\mathbf{R}^n)$

define

$$A(T, \psi)f = A(\varphi(f \circ \psi)) \circ \psi^{-1}$$

extended to be zero outside $\psi(\mathcal{O})$.

Remark. We note that $A(T, \psi)$ has its support in $\psi(\mathcal{O})$, and in fact its support is $\psi(\text{support } T)$. Conversely if $S: S(\mathbf{R}^n) \to C_0(\mathbf{R}^n)$ has compact support in $\psi(U)$ then S is of the form $A(T, \psi)$ for some $T: C^\infty(M) \to C^\infty(M)$ with support in U; in fact for such S we can define $A(S, \psi^{-1}): C^\infty(M) \to C^\infty(M)$ having support in $\mathcal{O}$ and the maps $T \mapsto A(T, \psi)$ and $S \mapsto A(S, \psi^{-1})$ are mutually inverse one-to-one maps between linear maps $T: C^\infty(M) \to C^\infty(M)$ with support in $\mathcal{O}$ and linear maps $S: S(\mathbf{R}^n) \to C_0^\infty(\mathbf{R})$ with compact support in $\psi(\mathcal{O})$.

THEOREM 1. Let $\psi: U \to \mathbf{R}^n$ be a chart for M and let $\mathcal{O}$ be open in M with $\overline{\mathcal{O}} \subseteq U$. Then the map $T \mapsto A(T, \psi)$ is bicontinuous linear isomorphism of the subspace of elements of $OP_k(M)$ having support in $\mathcal{O}$ with the subspace of $OP_k(\mathbf{R}^n)$ having support in $\psi(\mathcal{O})$.

PROOF. Let Ω be a compact submanifold of $\mathbf{R}^n$ with $\overline{\psi(\mathcal{O})} \subseteq \text{int } \Omega \subseteq \Omega \subseteq \psi(U)$, and let $\varphi \in C^\infty(M)$ be identically one on $\mathcal{O}$ and have its support in $\psi^{-1}(\text{int } \Omega)$. Then we can write $A(T,\psi) = i \circ \nu \circ T \circ \mu \circ \lambda$ where $i: C_0^\infty(\Omega) \to C_0^\infty(\mathbf{R}^n)$ is the inclusion, $\nu: C^\infty(M) \to C_0^\infty(\Omega)$ is the map $f \mapsto (\varphi f) \circ \psi^{-1}$, $\mu: C_0^\infty(\Omega) \to C^\infty(M)$ is the map $f \mapsto f \circ \psi$ ($f \circ \psi$ is extended to be zero outside U) and $\lambda: S(\mathbf{R}^n) \to C_0^\infty(\Omega)$ is the map $f \mapsto (\varphi \circ \psi^{-1})f$. If we define $H_0^k(\Omega)$ to be the closure of $C_0^\infty(\Omega)$ in $H^k(\Omega)$ then it is easily seen (for example from Chapter X, §4) that $i \in OP_0(\{H_0^k(\Omega)\}, \{H^k(\mathbf{R}^n)\})$ and that $\lambda \in OP_0(\{H^k(\mathbf{R}^n)\}, \{H_0^k(\Omega)\})$. On the other hand it is obvious that $\mu \in OP_0(\{H_0^k(\Omega)\}, \{H^k(M)\})$ and that $\nu \in OP_0(\{H^k(M)\}, \{H_0^k(\Omega)\})$ and the continuity of $T \mapsto A(T, \psi)$ follows. The continuity of $S \to A(S, \psi^{-1})$ is proved similarly, and in fact $A(S, \psi^{-1}) = \mu \circ S \circ i \circ \nu$.

q.e.d.

DEFINITION 4. Let $T\colon C^\infty(M) \to C^\infty(M)$ be a linear map. If for each chart $\psi\colon \mathcal{O} \to \mathbf{R}^n$ for M and $\varphi_1, \varphi_2 \in C_0^\infty(\mathcal{O})$, $A(M_{\varphi_1} TM_{\varphi_2}, \psi)$, the transfer of $M_{\varphi_1} TM_{\varphi_2}$ by ψ, is in $CZ_r(\mathbf{R}^n)$ then we say that T is locally in CZ_r. We define $CZ_r(M)$ to be the set of all linear maps $T\colon C^\infty(M) \to C^\infty(M)$ which are quasi-local and are locally in CZ_r. For $T \in CZ_r(M)$ we define $\sigma_r(T) \in \mathrm{Smbl}_r(M)$ as follows: given $\psi, \varphi_1, \varphi_2$ as above put $A = A(M_{\varphi_1} TM_{\varphi_2}, \psi)$. Then

$$\varphi_1(p)\sigma_r(T)(v, p)\varphi_2(p) = \sigma_r(A)(\psi(p), (d\psi_p^*)^{-1}(v)) .$$

Remark. It is immediate from Theorem 7 of §2 that $\sigma_r(T)$ is well-defined, and that it is in $\mathrm{Smbl}_r(M)$ is an easy consequence of $\sigma_r(A) \in \mathrm{Smbl}_r(\mathbf{R}^n)$.

Recall that $OP_r(M)$ has two distinct $C^\infty(M)$ module structures, the "left" and the "right" defined by letting $\varphi \in C^\infty(M)$ act on $T \in OP_r(M)$ either by $M_\varphi T$ or TM_φ.

THEOREM 2. For each $r \in \mathbf{Z}$ $CZ_r(M)$ is both a left and a right $C^\infty(M)$ submodule of $OP_r(M)$ and $\sigma_r\colon CZ_r(M) \to \mathrm{Smbl}_r(M)$ is a module homomorphism with respect to each of these structures. The kernel of σ_r is $CZ_{r-1}(M)$. If $r \geq 0$ then $\mathrm{Diff}_r(M) \subseteq CZ_r(M)$ and σ_r extends the symbol map $\sigma_r\colon \mathrm{Diff}_r(M) \to \mathrm{Smbl}_r^d(M)$ of Chapter IV. Finally if $T \in CZ_r(M)$ and $S \in CZ_s(M)$ then $ST \in CZ_{s+r}(M)$ and $\sigma_{s+r}(ST) = \sigma_s(S)\sigma_r(T)$.

PROOF. Let $\{\varphi_i\}$ $i = 1, \ldots, \ell$ be a C^∞ partition of unity for M such that if support $\varphi_i \cap$ support $\varphi_j \neq \emptyset$ then there exists a chart $\psi\colon \mathcal{O} \to \mathbf{R}^n$ for M with support $\varphi_i \cup$ support $\varphi_j \subseteq \mathcal{O}$; existence follows from an easy Lebesgue number argument. If $T \in CZ_r(M)$ then $T = \Sigma_{i,j} M_{\varphi_i} TM_{\varphi_j}$. Now if support $\varphi_i \cap$ support $\varphi_j = \emptyset$ then $M_{\varphi_i} TM_{\varphi_j} \in OP_{-\infty}(M) \subseteq OP_r(M)$. If support $\varphi_i \cap$ support $\varphi_j \neq \emptyset$ then, choosing ψ as above, $A(M_{\varphi_i} TM_{\varphi_j}, \psi) \in$

$CZ_r(\mathbf{R}^n) \subseteq OP_r(\mathbf{R}^n)$ so again, this time by Theorem 1, $M_{\varphi_i} T M_{\varphi_j} \in OP_r(M)$. Hence $T = \Sigma_{i,j} M_{\varphi_i} T M_{\varphi_j} \in OP_r(M)$ and we have proved $CZ_r(M) \subseteq OP_r(M)$. It is clear that the sum of two quasi-local operators on $C^\infty(M)$ is again quasi-local since $M_{\varphi_1}(S+T)M_{\varphi_2} = M_{\varphi_1} S M_{\varphi_2} + M_{\varphi_1} T M_2$ which is in $OP_{-\infty}(M)$ if both $M_{\varphi_1} S M_{\varphi_2}$ and $M_{\varphi_1} T M_{\varphi_2}$ are. Also if $T\colon C^\infty(M) \to C^\infty(M)$ is quasi-local and $\varphi \in C^\infty(M)$, then since $M_{\varphi_1} M_\varphi T M_{\varphi_2} = M_\varphi(M_{\varphi_1} T M_{\varphi_2})$ and $M_{\varphi_1} T M_\varphi M_{\varphi_2} = (M_{\varphi_1} T M_{\varphi_2}) M_\varphi$ and since $OP_{-\infty}(M)$ is a left and right $C^\infty(M)$ module, it follows that the quasi-local operators on $C^\infty(M)$ form a left and right $C^\infty(M)$ module. Suppose S and T map $C^\infty(M)$ into itself, $\psi\colon \mathcal{O} \to \mathbf{R}^n$ is a chart for M, $\varphi_1, \varphi_2 \in C_0^\infty(M)$ and $\lambda, \mu \in C^\infty(M)$. Then

$$A(M_{\varphi_1}(M_\lambda S + M_\mu T)M_{\varphi_2}, \psi) = M_{\bar\lambda} A(M_{\varphi_1} S M_{\varphi_2}, \psi) + M_{\bar\mu} A(M_{\varphi_1} T M_{\varphi_2}, \psi)$$

where $\bar\lambda$ and $\bar\mu$ are any elements of $C_0^\infty(\psi(\mathcal{O}))$ equal to $\lambda \circ \psi^{-1}$ and $\mu \circ \psi^{-1}$ respectively on a neighborhood of ψ (support $\varphi_1 \cup$ support φ_2). Since by Theorem 4 and Theorem 5 (with $|\alpha| = 0$) of §2 if A_1 and A_2 are in $CZ_r(\mathbf{R}^n)$ and $\bar\lambda, \bar\mu \in S(\mathbf{R}^n)$ then $M_{\bar\lambda} A_1 + M_{\bar\mu} A_2$ is in $CZ_r(\mathbf{R}^n)$ and

$$\sigma_r(M_{\bar\lambda} A_1 + M_{\bar\mu} A_2)(x, \zeta) = \bar\lambda(x)\sigma_r(A_1)(x, \zeta) + \bar\mu(x)\sigma_r(A_2)(x, \zeta)$$

it is now immediate that $CZ_r(M)$ is a left $C^\infty(M)$ module and that σ_r is a module homomorphism, and similarly for the right module structure. That $\ker(\sigma_r) = CZ_{r-1}(M)$ is immediate from the corollary of Theorem 4, §2. That $\mathrm{Diff}_r(M) \subseteq CZ_r(M)$ for $r \geq 0$ and that σ_r extends the symbol map of Chapter IV follows from Theorem 5 of §2 and its corollary, together with the fact that differential operators are local and *a fortiori* quasi-local.

Finally suppose $T \in CZ_r(M)$ and $S \in CZ_s(M)$. Let $\varphi_1, \varphi_2 \in C^\infty(M)$ have disjoint supports and choose $\varphi_3 \in C^\infty(M)$ which is identically one on a neighborhood of support φ_1 and identically zero on a neighborhood of support φ_2 and let $\varphi_4 = 1-\varphi_3$, so $\varphi_3 + \varphi_4 = 1$ and $M_{\varphi_1} S T M_{\varphi_2} = (M_{\varphi_1} S M_{\varphi_4}) T M_{\varphi_2} + M_{\varphi_1} S(M_{\varphi_3} T M_{\varphi_2})$. Now $M_{\varphi_1} S M_{\varphi_4} \in OP_{-\infty}(M)$ and $M_{\varphi_3} T M_{\varphi_2} \in OP_{-\infty}(M)$ while $T M_{\varphi_2} \in CZ_r(M) \subseteq OP_r(M)$ and $M_{\varphi_1} S \in CZ_s(M) \subseteq OP_s(M)$ and it follows that $M_{\varphi_1} S T M_{\varphi_2} \in OP_{-\infty}(M)$, hence ST is quasi-local.

Let $\psi: \mathcal{O} \to \mathbf{R}^n$ be a chart for M and $\varphi_1, \varphi_2 \in C_0^\infty(\mathcal{O})$. Choose $\varphi \in C_0^\infty(\mathcal{O})$ identically one on a neighborhood of support $\varphi_1 \cup$ support φ_2. Clearly $M_{\varphi_1} S T M_{\varphi_2} = (M_{\varphi_1} S M_\varphi)(M_\varphi T M_{\varphi_2}) + B$ where

$$B = (M_{\varphi_1} S M_{1-\varphi})(M_\varphi T M_{\varphi_2}) + (M_{\varphi_1} S M_\varphi)(M_{1-\varphi} T M_{\varphi_2}) + (M_{\varphi_1} S M_{1-\varphi})(M_{1-\varphi} T M_{\varphi_2})$$

is clearly in $OP_{-\infty}(M)$. Then

$$A(M_{\varphi_1} S T M_{\varphi_2}, \psi) = A(M_{\varphi_1} S M_\varphi, \psi) A(M_\varphi T M_{\varphi_2}, \psi) + A(B, \psi) \quad .$$

Since $B \in OP_{-\infty}(M)$, by Theorem 1 $A(B, \psi) \in OP_{-\infty}(\mathbf{R}^n)$. That $ST \in CZ_{r+s}(M)$ and that $\sigma_{r+s}(ST) = \sigma_s(S)\sigma_r(T)$ is now an easy consequence of Theorem 4 of §2 and its corollary.

q.e.d.

THEOREM 3. Let $\psi: \mathcal{O} \to \mathbf{R}$ be a chart for M and let $T \in CZ_r(\mathbf{R}^n)$ have compact support in $\psi(\mathcal{O})$. Then $A(T, \psi^{-1}) \in CZ_r(M)$ and $\sigma_r(A(T, \psi^{-1}))(v, x) = \sigma_r(T)(\psi(x), (d\psi_x^*)^{-1}(v))$ for $x \in \mathcal{O}$ and $\sigma_r(A(T, \psi^{-1}))(v, x) = 0$ for $x \notin \mathcal{O}$.

PROOF. Immediate from Theorem 7 of §2 (to calculate the symbol of $A(T, \psi^{-1})$ use $\varphi_1, \varphi_2 \in C_0^\infty(\mathcal{O})$ which are identically one on a neighborhood of ψ^{-1} (support T) = support $A(T, \psi^{-1})$).

COROLLARY. Let $S: C^\infty(M) \to C^\infty(M)$ be a quasi-local linear map and suppose that for each $p \in M$ there is a chart $\psi: \mathcal{O} \to \mathbf{R}^n$ at p and $\varphi_1, \varphi_2 \in C_0^\infty(M)$ with $\varphi_i(p) \neq 0$ such that $A(M_{\varphi_1} S M_{\varphi_2}, \psi) \in CZ_r(\mathbf{R}^n)$. Then $S \in CZ_r(M)$.

PROOF. By an easy partition of unity argument we can write such an operator S as a sum of operators of the form $A(T, \psi^{-1})$ of the theorem, plus operators in $OP_{-\infty}(M) \subseteq CZ_r(M)$.

THEOREM 4. Suppose M has a strictly positive smooth measure μ. Then if $T \in CZ_r(M)$ its transpose T^t is also in $CZ_r(M)$ and $\sigma_r(T^t) = (-1)^r \overline{\sigma_r(T)}$.

PROOF. Given $p \in M$ choose a chart $\psi\colon \mathcal{O} \to \mathbf{R}^n$ at p which carries μ into Lebesgue measure on $\psi(\mathcal{O})$, and let $\varphi_1, \varphi_2 \in C_0^\infty(M)$ with $\varphi_i(p) \neq 0$. Then $A(M_{\varphi_1} T^t M_{\varphi_2}, \psi) = A(M_{\varphi_1} TM_{\varphi_2}, \psi)^t$. The theorem is then immediate from the corollary of Theorem 4 of §2 and the above corollary.

q.e.d.

THEOREM 5. There is a continuous linear map $\chi_r\colon \mathrm{Smbl}_r(M) \to \mathrm{OP}_r(M)$ such that for each $\sigma \in \mathrm{Smbl}_r(M)$ $\chi_r(\sigma) \in \mathrm{CZ}_r(M)$ and $\sigma_r(\chi_r(\sigma)) = \sigma$.

PROOF. As in the proof of Theorem 1 let $\{\varphi_i\}$ $i = 1, \ldots, \ell$ be a C^∞ partition of unity for M such that if support $\varphi_i \cap$ support $\varphi_j \neq \emptyset$ then there is a chart $\psi_{ij}\colon \mathcal{O}_{ij} \to \mathbf{R}^n$ with support $\varphi_i \cup$ support $\varphi_j \subseteq \mathcal{O}_{ij}$. For each such pair i, j and $\sigma \in \mathrm{Smbl}_r(M)$ define $\sigma_{ij} \in \mathrm{Smbl}_r(\mathbf{R}^n)$ by $\sigma_{ij}(x, \zeta) = 0$ for $x \notin \psi_{ij}(\mathcal{O}_{ij})$ and $\sigma_{ij}(\psi_{ij}(p), (d\psi_{ij}^*)_p^{-1}(v)) = \varphi_i(p)\varphi_j(p)\sigma(v, p)$. Then clearly $\sigma \to \sigma_{ij}$ is a continuous linear map of $\mathrm{Smbl}_r(M)$ into $\mathrm{Smbl}_r(\mathbf{R}^n)$. Let θ be a patch function on $\mathbf{R}^n$. Then by Theorem 1 of §2

$$\sigma \mapsto A(\theta, \sigma_{ij})$$

is a continuous linear map of $\mathrm{Smbl}_r(\mathbf{R}^n)$ into $\mathrm{OP}_r(\mathbf{R}^n)$ with image in $\mathrm{CZ}_r(\mathbf{R}^n)$ and $\sigma_r(A(\theta, \sigma_{ij})) = \sigma_{ij}$ by Definitions 6 and 7 of §2. Then by Theorems 1 and 3 above $\sigma \mapsto A_{ij}(\sigma) = A(A(\theta, \sigma_{ij}), \psi_{ij}^{-1})$ is a continuous linear map of $\mathrm{Smbl}_r(M)$ into $\mathrm{OP}_r(M)$, and $A_{ij}(\sigma) \in \mathrm{CZ}_r(M)$ and

$$\sigma_r(A_{ij}(\sigma))(v, p) = \varphi_i(p)\varphi_j(p)\sigma(v, p) \quad .$$

It follows that $\chi_r(\sigma) = \Sigma_{ij} A_{ij}(\sigma)$, where the sum is over all pairs i, j such that support $\varphi_i \cap$ support $\varphi_j \neq \emptyset$, satisfies the requirements of the theorem.

q.e.d.

COROLLARY. The sequence

$$0 \to \mathrm{CZ}_{r-1}(M) \to \mathrm{CZ}_r(M) \xrightarrow{\sigma_r} \mathrm{Smbl}_r(M) \to 0$$

is exact.

THEOREM 6. Let M_1 at M_2 be compact Riemannian manifolds without boundary and let $A \in CZ_r(M_1)$ $r > 0$. There is a sequence $\{B_\nu\}$ in $CZ_r(M_1 \times M_2)$ and a $K \in OP_0(M_1 \times M_2)$ such that B_ν converges to $A \otimes I - K$ in $OP_r(M_1 \times M_2)$ and $\sigma_r(B_\nu)((v_1, v_2), (x_1, x_2))$ converges uniformly to $\sigma_r(A)(v_1, x_1)$ on the unit sphere bundle of $M_1 \times M_2$.

PROOF. If A is of the form $A(T, \psi^{-1})$ where $\psi\colon \mathcal{O} \to \mathbf{R}^n$ is a chart for M_1 and $T \in CZ_r(\mathbf{R}^n)$ has its support in $\psi(\mathcal{O})$, then the theorem is an easy consequence of Theorem 6 of §2 (taking for the ψ of that theorem the elements of a partition of unity for M_2 subordinate to a covering by coordinate patches). Since any $A \in CZ_r(M_1)$ can be written as a sum of such $A(T, \psi^{-1})$ and elements of $OP_{-\infty}(M_1)$ and since $A \in OP_{-\infty}$ implies $A \in OP_0$ implies $A \otimes I \in OP_0$ the theorem follows.

q.e.d.

§4. Calderón-Zygmund operators for vector bundles.

Let M be as in Section 3 and let ξ, η, ζ be hermitian vector bundles over M.

DEFINITION 1. For each $h \in C^\infty(\xi)$ we define $M_h\colon C^\infty(M) \to C^\infty(\xi)$ by $M_h(f) = fh$ and for each $\ell \in C^\infty(\eta^*)$ we define $\ell_*\colon C^\infty(\eta) \to C^\infty(M)$ by $\ell_*(g)(x) = \ell(g(x))$.

THEOREM 1. For each $h \in C^\infty(\xi)$ $M_h \in \mathrm{Diff}_0(\mathbf{C}_M, \xi)$ and $\sigma_0(M_h)(v, x)e = eh(x)$. For each $\ell \in C^\infty(\eta)$, $\ell_* \in \mathrm{Diff}_0(\eta, \mathbf{C}_M)$ and $\sigma_0(\ell_*)(v, x)e = \ell(e)$.

PROOF. Trivial.

DEFINITION 2. We define $CZ_r(\xi, \eta)$ to be the set of linear maps $T\colon C^\infty(\xi) \to C^\infty(\eta)$ such that $\ell_* \circ T \circ M_h \in CZ_r(M)$ for each $h \in C^\infty(\xi)$ and $\ell \in C^\infty(\eta^*)$.

THEOREM 2. If $T \in CZ_r(\xi, \eta)$ there is a unique element $\sigma_r(T)$ of $\mathrm{Smbl}_r(\xi, \eta)$ such that

$$\sigma_r(\ell_* \circ T \circ M_h)(v, x) = \ell(\sigma_r(T)(v, x)h(x))$$

for all $h \in C^\infty(\xi)$ and $\ell \in C^\infty(\eta^*)$.

PROOF. Since uniqueness is clear it suffices to prove existence locally and we can assume that ξ and η are trivial bundles. Let $h_1, \ldots, h_m$ be a basis of C^∞ sections for ξ, $g_1, \ldots, g_n$ a basis of C^∞ sections for η and $\ell^1, \ldots, \ell^n$ the dual basis of sections for η^*. Let $T_{ij} = \ell^i_* \circ T \circ M_{h_j}$ and define $\sigma_r(T) \in \mathrm{Smbl}_r(\xi, \eta)$ by requiring that the matrix of $\sigma_r(T)(v, x)$ with respect to the bases

$$(h_1(x), \ldots, h_m(x)) \text{ for } \xi_x \text{ and } (g_1(x), \ldots, g_n(x))$$

for η_x is $\sigma_r(T_{ij})(v, x)$. Then if $h \in C^\infty(\xi)$ and $\ell \in C^\infty(\eta^*)$ then $h = \Sigma\, b_j h_j$ and $\ell = \Sigma\, a_i \ell^i$ where $a_i, b_j \in C^\infty(M)$ and $\ell_* \circ T \circ M_h = \Sigma_{i,j} M_{a_i} T_{ij} M_{b_j}$ so that by Theorem 2 of §3

$$\sigma_r(\ell_* \circ T \circ M_h)(v, x) = \sum_{i,j} a_i(x)\sigma_r(T_{ij})(v, x)b_j(x)$$

$$= \ell(\sigma_r(T)(v, x)h(x)) \quad .$$

q.e.d.

THEOREM 3. If $g \in C^\infty(\eta)$ and $\lambda \in C^\infty(\xi^*)$ and $T \in CZ_r(M)$ then $M_g \circ T \circ \lambda_* \in CZ_r(\xi, \eta)$ and $\sigma_r(M_g \circ T \circ \lambda_*)(v, x)e = \sigma_r(T)(v, x)\lambda(e)g(x)$. Moreover every element of $CZ_r(\xi, \eta)$ is a finite sum of operators of the form $M_g \circ T \circ \lambda_*$ and an operator in $OP_{-\infty}(\xi, \eta)$.

PROOF. If $\ell \in C^\infty(\eta^*)$ and $h \in C^\infty(\xi)$ then $\ell_*(M_g \circ T \circ \lambda_*) \circ M_h = M_{\ell(g)} \circ T \circ M_{\lambda(h)}$ which by Theorem 2 of §3 is in $CZ_r(M)$ and $\sigma_r(\ell_*(M_g \circ T \circ \lambda_*) \circ M_h)(v, x) = \ell(g(x))\lambda(h(x))\sigma_r(T)(v, x)$. This proves that $M_g \circ T \circ \lambda_*$ is in $CZ_r(\xi, \eta)$ and has the right symbol. Given $A \in CZ_r(\xi, \eta)$ let $\{\varphi_i\}$ be a partition of unity for M such that if support $\varphi_i \cap$ support $\varphi_j \neq \emptyset$ then (support $\varphi_i \cup$ support φ_j) is included in an open set over which ξ and η are trivial. Then $A = \Sigma_{i,j} M_{\varphi_i} A M_{\varphi_j}$ and since $M_{\varphi_i} A M_{\varphi_j} \in OP_{-\infty}(\xi, \eta)$ if φ_i and φ_j have disjoint support, we can assume that the support of A is in an open set $\mathcal{O}$ over which ξ and η are trivial. Let $h_1, \ldots, h_m$ be a basis of sections for ξ over $\mathcal{O}$ and $g_1, \ldots, g_m$ a basis of sections for η over $\mathcal{O}$. Let $\lambda^1, \ldots, \lambda^n$ and $\ell^1, \ldots, \ell^m$ be the dual sections. Then if we define $A_{ij} \in CZ_r(M)$ by $A_{ij} = \ell^i_* \circ A \circ M_{h_j}$ then

$$A = \sum M_{g_i} \circ A_{ij} \circ \lambda^j_* \quad .$$

q.e.d.

THEOREM 4. For each $r \in \mathbf{Z}$ $CZ_r(\xi, \eta)$ is a linear subspace of $OP_r(\xi, \eta)$ and $\sigma_r\colon CZ_r(\xi, \eta) \to \mathrm{Smbl}_r(\xi, \eta)$ is a linear map with kernel $CZ_{r-1}(\xi, \eta)$. If $r \geq 0$ then $\mathrm{Diff}_r(\xi, \eta) \subseteq CZ_r(\xi, \eta)$ and σ_r extends the symbol map $\sigma_r\colon \mathrm{Diff}_r(\xi, \eta) \to \mathrm{Smbl}^d_r(\xi, \eta)$ of Chapter IV. If $T \in CZ_r(\xi, \eta)$ and $S \in CZ_s(\eta, \zeta)$ then $ST \in CZ_{r+s}(\xi, \zeta)$ and $\sigma_{r+s}(ST) = \sigma_s(S)\sigma_r(T)$.

PROOF. If $T \in CZ_r(M) \subseteq OP_r(\mathbf{C}_M, \mathbf{C}_M)$, $g \in C^\infty(\eta)$, and $\lambda \in C^\infty(\xi^*)$ then $M_g \in \mathrm{Diff}_0(\mathbf{C}_M, \eta) \subseteq OP_0(\mathbf{C}_M, \eta)$ and $\lambda_* \in \mathrm{Diff}_0(\xi, \mathbf{C}_M) \subseteq OP_0(\xi, \mathbf{C}_M)$, hence $M_g \circ T \circ \lambda_* \in OP_r(\xi, \eta)$ and it follows from Theorem 3 that $CZ_r(\xi, \eta) \subseteq OP_r(\xi, \eta)$. That $CZ_r(\xi, \eta)$ is a linear subspace of $OP_r(\xi, \eta)$ and that $\sigma_r\colon CZ_r(\xi, \eta) \to \mathrm{Smbl}_r(\xi, \eta)$ is a linear map with kernel $CZ_{r-1}(\xi, \eta)$ is immediate from the Definitions 1 and 2 above and Theorem 2 of §3. That for $r \geq 0$ $\mathrm{Diff}_r(\xi, \eta) \subseteq CZ_r(\xi, \eta)$ and σ_r extends the symbol map of Chapter IV follows from Theorem 2 of §2 together with the fact that if $T \in \mathrm{Diff}_r(\xi, \eta)$ then

$$\ell_* \circ T \circ M_g \in \mathrm{Diff}_r(\mathbf{C}_M, \mathbf{C}_M) = \mathrm{Diff}_r(M)$$

for any $g \in C^\infty(\xi)$ and $\ell \in C^\infty(\eta^*)$; because $M_g \in \mathrm{Diff}_0(\xi, \mathbf{C}_M)$ and $\ell_* \in \mathrm{Diff}_0(\mathbf{C}_M, \eta)$. Finally, by Theorem 3 above, to prove the facts about ST it suffices to consider the case $T = M_g \circ T' \circ \lambda_*$ and $S = M_h \circ S' \circ \ell_*$ where $T' \in CZ_r(M)$, $S' \in CZ_r(M)$, $\lambda \in C^\infty(\xi^*)$, $g \in C^\infty(\eta)$,

$\ell \in C^\infty(\eta^*)$, and $h \in C^\infty(\zeta)$. Then $ST = M_h(S'M_{\ell(g)}T')\lambda_*$ and since by Theorem 2 of §3, $S'M_{\ell(g)}T' \in CZ_{r+s}(M)$ and $\sigma_{r+s}(S'M_{\ell(g)}T')(v, x) = \ell(g(x))\sigma_s(S')\sigma_r(T')(v, x)$ it follows from Theorem 3 above that $ST \in CZ_{r+s}(\xi, \zeta)$ and $\sigma_{r+s}(ST) = \sigma_s(S)\sigma_r(T)$.

q.e.d.

THEOREM 5. There is a continuous linear map $\chi_r\colon \mathrm{Smbl}_r(\xi, \eta) \to OP_r(\xi, \eta)$ such that for each $\sigma \in \mathrm{Smbl}_r(\xi, \eta)$, $\chi_r(\sigma) \in CZ_r(\xi, \eta)$ and $\sigma_r(\chi_r(\sigma)) = \sigma$.

PROOF. By an obvious partition of unity argument it will suffice to show that if ξ and η are trivial over an open set $\mathcal{O}$ and $\varphi \in C_0^\infty(\mathcal{O})$ then there is a continuous linear map $\chi_r\colon \mathrm{Smbl}_r(\xi, \eta) \to OP_r(\xi, \eta)$ with each $\chi_r(\sigma) \in CZ_r(\xi, \eta)$ and $\sigma_r(\chi_r(\sigma))(v, x) = \varphi(x)\sigma(v, x)$. Let $h_1, \ldots, h_m$ be a basis of sections for ξ over $\mathcal{O}$, $g_1, \ldots, g_n$ a basis of sections for η over $\mathcal{O}$ and let $\lambda^1, \ldots, \lambda^m$ and $\ell^1, \ldots, \ell^n$ be the dual bases. Given $\sigma \in \mathrm{Smbl}_r(\xi, \eta)$ define $\sigma_{ij} \in \mathrm{Smbl}_r(M)$ by

$$\sigma_{ij}(v, x) = \varphi(x)\ell_i(\sigma(v, x)h_j(x))$$

and define

$$\chi_r^\varphi(\sigma) = \sum_{i,j} M_{g_i} \circ (\chi_r(\sigma_{ij})) \circ \lambda_*^j$$

where χ_r is as in Theorem 5 of §3. It is clear that χ_r^φ has the desired properties.

q.e.d.

COROLLARY. The sequence

$$0 \to CZ_{r-1}(\xi, \eta) \to CZ_r(\xi, \eta) \to \mathrm{Smbl}_r(\xi, \eta) \to 0$$

is exact.

THEOREM 6. If M has a strictly positive smooth measure μ and if ξ and η are hermitian vector bundles, then for each $T \in CZ_r(\xi, \eta)$, $T^t \in CZ_r(\eta, \xi)$ and $\sigma_r(T^t) = (-1)^r\sigma_r(T)^*$

PROOF. By Theorem 3 it suffices to consider the case $T = M_g \circ S \circ \lambda_*$ where $g \in C^\infty(\eta)$ and $\lambda \in C^\infty(\xi^*)$. Let $\hat{g} \in C^\infty(\eta^*)$ and $\hat{\lambda} \in C^\infty(\xi)$ be the sections dual to g and λ with respect to the Hermitian structures of η and ξ. Then a trivial computation shows that $M_g^t = \hat{g}_*$; namely if $f \in C^\infty(\eta)$ and $h \in C^\infty(M) = C^\infty(\mathbf{C}_M)$ then

$$\begin{aligned} \langle f, M_g h \rangle_\eta &= \int (f(x), h(x)g(x))_\eta d\mu(x) \\ &= \int (f(x), g(x))_\eta \bar{h}(x) d\mu(x) \\ &= \int \hat{g}(f(x))\bar{h}(x) d\mu(x) \\ &= \langle \hat{g}_*(f), h \rangle_{\mathbf{C}_M} , \end{aligned}$$

and similarly $(\lambda_*)^t = M_{\hat{\lambda}}$. Then

$$T^t = \lambda_*^t S^t M_g^t = M_\lambda S^t \hat{g}_*$$

and the theorem is now an easy consequence of Theorem 3 above and Theorem 4 of §3.

q.e.d.

THEOREM 7. Let M_1 and M_2 be compact Riemannian manifolds without boundary, ξ and η vector bundles over M_1, ζ a vector bundle over M_2 and let $T \in CZ_r(\xi, \eta)$, $r > 0$. Then there is a sequence $\{B_\nu\}$ in $CZ_r(\xi \otimes \zeta, \eta \otimes \zeta)$ and a $K \in OP_0(\xi \otimes \zeta, \eta \otimes \zeta)$ such that B_ν converges to $T \otimes I - K$ in $OP_r(\xi \otimes \zeta, \eta \otimes \zeta)$ and $\sigma_r(B_\nu)$ converges uniformly on the unit sphere bundle of $M_1 \times M_2$ to $\sigma_r(A) \otimes \sigma_0(I_\zeta)$.

PROOF. By Theorem 3 above we can assume $T = M_g \circ A \circ \lambda_*$ where $A \in CZ_r(M)$, $g \in C^\infty(\eta)$ and $\lambda \in C^\infty(\xi^*)$, and the theorem then follows easily from Theorem 6 of §3.

q.e.d.

§5. Definition and properties of $Int_r(\xi, \eta)$.

Again M is a compact manifold without boundary and ξ, η, ζ are vector bundles over M.

THEOREM 1. For each integer r

$$CZ_{r-1}(\xi, \eta) = CZ_r(\xi, \eta) \cap OP_{r-1}(\xi, \eta) \quad .$$

PROOF. As noted in the remark following Definition 6 of §2, $CZ_r(\mathbf{R}^n) = CZ(\mathbf{R}^n) \cap OP_r(\mathbf{R}^n)$ from which it follows that $CZ_{r-1}(\mathbf{R}^n) = CZ_r(\mathbf{R}^n) \cap OP_{r-1}(\mathbf{R}^n)$. It is then immediate from the definition of $CZ_r(M)$ and Theorem 1 of §3 that $CZ_{r-1}(M) = CZ_r(M) \cap OP_{r-1}(M)$, and the theorem follows directly from this and the definition of $CZ_r(\xi, \eta)$.

DEFINITION 1. We define

$$\mathrm{Int}_r(\xi, \eta) = CZ_r(\xi, \eta) + OP_{r-1}(\xi, \eta) \quad .$$

Given $T \in \mathrm{Int}_r(\xi, \eta)$ write $T = A + S$ where $A \in CZ_r(\xi, \eta)$ and $S \in OP_{r-1}(\xi, \eta)$ and define $\sigma_r(T) \in \mathrm{Smbl}_r(\xi, \eta)$ by $\sigma_r(T) = \sigma_r(A)$.

Remark. If $T = A' + S'$ where $A' \in CZ_r(\xi, \eta)$ and $S' \in OP_{r-1}(\xi, \eta)$ then $A - A' = S' - S$. Now $A - A' \in CZ_r(\xi, \eta)$ and $S' - S \in OP_{r-1}(\xi, \eta)$, hence

$$A - A' \in CZ_r(\xi, \eta) \cap OP_{r-1}(\xi, \eta) = CZ_{r-1}(\xi, \eta) \quad .$$

By Theorem 4 of §4 $\sigma_r(A) = \sigma_r(A')$, proving that σ_r is well defined. It is clearly linear.

Since $CZ_r(\xi, \eta) \subseteq OP_r(\xi, \eta)$ (Theorem 4 of §4) and $OP_{r-1}(\xi, \eta) \subseteq OP_r(\xi, \eta)$ it is clear that $\mathrm{Int}_r(\xi, \eta) \subseteq OP_r(\xi, \eta)$. Properties (S1), (S2) and (S3) of Chapter XI are also immediate consequences of Theorem 4 of §4 and Definition 1 above. Properties (S4) and (S5) of Chapter XI follow from Theorems 6 and 5 of §4 respectively. Finally, Property (S6) of Chapter XIV, §4 follows directly from Theorem 7 of §4. This completes the construction and verification of the properties of the Seeley Algebra.

§6. An element of $\mathrm{Int}_0(S^1)$ with analytical index -1

This section considers the situation in which analytical indices for singular integral operators were first computed, namely on the manifold $M = S^1$, realized as the unit circle $\{|z| = 1\}$ in the complex plane. Here we have standard coordinate systems $\lambda: z \to -i \log z$ sending $e^{ix} \to x$, and thus identify the cotangent bundle $T^*(S^1)$ with the infinite cylinder $S^1 \times \mathbf{R}^1$ by letting $(z, v) \in S^1 \times \mathbf{R}^1$ correspond to $v d\lambda_z$, with λ a standard coordinate system.

Let $\{\varphi_n\}_{-\infty}^{\infty} = \{z^n\}_{-\infty}^{\infty}$ be the usual orthogonal basis of $L^2(S^1)$.

For $f \in C^\infty(S^1)$ and $0 < r < 1$, set $P_r f(z) = \frac{1}{2\pi i} \int \frac{f(\zeta)}{\zeta - rz} d\zeta$, $|z| = 1$.

THEOREM 1. Let $f \in C^\infty(S^1)$. Then as $r \to 1-$, $P_r f$ converges uniformly to a limit, denoted Pf. The operator $P \in CZ_0(S^1)$ and $\sigma_0(P)(v d\lambda_z) = 1$ when $v > 0$, $= 0$ when $v < 0$. Further $P\varphi_n = \varphi_n$ if $n \geq 0$, $P\varphi_n = 0$ if $n < 0$.

PROOF. The first and last assertions depend on Cauchy's formula. For the first, $\frac{1}{2\pi i} \int_{|\zeta|=1} \frac{d\zeta}{\zeta - rz} = 1$ when $|rz| < 1$, so $P_r f(z) = f(z) + \frac{1}{2\pi i} \int_{|\zeta|=1} \frac{f(\zeta) - f(z)}{\zeta - rz} d\zeta$ converges uniformly as $r \to 1-$. For $P\varphi_n$ with $n \geq 0$ we have by Cauchy's formula $P_r \varphi_n(z) = r^n z^n \to z^n = \varphi_n(z)$; and for $n < 0$ $P_r \varphi_n(z) = \lim_{R \to \infty} \int_{|\zeta|=R} \frac{\zeta^n}{\zeta - rz} d\zeta = 0$.

To show that $P \in CZ_0(S^1)$, consider first φ and ψ with disjoint supports. Then $M_\varphi P M_\psi f(z) = \frac{1}{2\pi i} \int \frac{\varphi(z)\psi(\zeta)}{\zeta - z} f(\zeta) d\zeta = \int K(z,\zeta) f(\zeta) d\zeta$ with $K(z, \zeta) \in C^\infty(S^1 \times S^1)$, so $M_\varphi P M_\psi$ has order $-\infty$.

Finally, consider the representation of P in standard coordinates in a neighborhood of $\{z = 1\}$. Choose ψ in $C^\infty(\mathbf{R}^1)$ with $\psi = 1$ on $\{|x| < \pi/4\}$, $\psi = 0$ on $\{|x| > \pi/2\}$, $\varphi = 0$ on $\{|x| > \pi\}$. Then

$$M_\psi \lambda_* P \lambda^* M_\psi g(x) = \lim_{r \to 1-} \frac{1}{2\pi} \int_{-\pi}^{\pi} \frac{\psi(x) g(y) \psi(y)}{1 - re^{i(x-y)}} dy$$

$$= \lim_{r \to 1-} \frac{1}{2\pi} \int_{-\infty}^{\infty} \psi(x) g(y) \psi(y) \frac{\varphi(x-y)}{1 - re^{i(x-y)}} dy \quad ,$$

since $\varphi(x-y) = 1$ when $\psi(x)\psi(y) \neq 0$. Let $K_r(x) = \frac{1}{2\pi}\frac{\varphi(x)}{1-re^{ix}}$, and T be defined by $Tg(\xi) = 1/2(\frac{\xi}{|\xi|} + 1)g(\xi)$. We can conclude the proof of the theorem by showing that the map $g \mapsto \lim_{r->1-} K_r{*}g$ differs from $g \mapsto Tg$ by an operator of order $-\infty$. Now

$$K_r(\xi) = \frac{1}{2\pi}\int_{-\infty}^{\infty} e^{-i\xi x}\varphi(x) \sum_0^{\infty} r^n e^{inx}\, dx$$

$$= \frac{1}{2\pi}\sum_0^{\infty} \varphi(\xi-n)r^n$$

converges boundedly to

$$K(\xi) = \frac{1}{2\pi}\sum_0^{\infty}\varphi(\xi-n) \quad ,$$

and the theorem is thus reduced to the proof that

$$|K(\xi) - \frac{1}{2}(\frac{\xi}{|\xi|} + 1)| \leq C_k(1 + |\xi|)^{-k}$$

for each integer k. Taking first $\xi < 0$,

$$2\pi|K(\xi)| \leq \sum_0^{\infty} |\varphi(\xi-n)| \leq C_{k+1}\sum_0^{\infty}(1 + |\xi| + n)^{-k-1}$$

$$< C_{k+1}\int_0^{\infty}(|\xi| + t)^{-k-1}\, dt$$

$$= \frac{C_{k+1}}{k}|\xi|^{-k} \quad ,$$

which yields the desired estimate since K is bounded and $\xi/|\xi| + 1 = 0$ when $\xi < 0$. For $\xi > 0$ we have in the same way

$$|K(\xi) - \frac{1}{2\pi}\sum_{-\infty}^{\infty}\varphi(\xi-n)| \leq \frac{C_{k+1}}{k}|\xi|^{-k} \quad ,$$

and it remains only to show that, for $\xi > 0$,

$$\frac{1}{2\pi}\sum_{-\infty}^{\infty}\varphi(\xi-n) = \frac{1}{2}(\frac{\xi}{|\xi|} + 1) = 1 \quad .$$

But $\frac{1}{2\pi}\Sigma_{-\infty}^{\infty}\ \varphi(\xi-n)$ is a continuous function with period 1, and

$$\int_0^1 \frac{1}{2\pi}\sum_{-\infty}^{\infty}\varphi(\xi-n)e^{-2\pi i\xi k}\, d\xi = \frac{1}{2\pi}\int_{-\infty}^{\infty}\varphi(\xi)e^{-2\pi i\xi k}\, d\xi = \varphi(-2\pi k) = \delta_{ok} \, .$$

Since $\{e^{-2\pi i \xi k}\}$ is an orthonormal basis for the functions of period 1, we have

$$\frac{1}{2\pi} \sum_{-\infty}^{\infty} \varphi(\xi - n) = 1 ,$$

and Theorem 1 is proved.

THEOREM 2. Define σ in $\mathrm{Smbl}_0(S^1)$ by $\sigma(vd\lambda_z) = z$ if $v > 0$ and $\sigma(vd\lambda_z) = 1$ if $v < 0$. If $A \in \mathrm{Int}_0(S^1)$ has symbol σ, then A is elliptic and $\mathrm{ind}(A) = -1$.

PROOF. A is elliptic, by the definition following [XI, Theorem 3], since $|\sigma_0(A)| = 1$. Because $\mathrm{ind}(A)$ depends only on $\sigma_0(A)$ by [XI, Theorem 10], it suffices to exhibit an A_0 in $CZ_0(S^1)$ with $\sigma_0(A_0) = \sigma$ and $\mathrm{ind}(A_0) = -1$. Let P be the operator of Theorem 1, M denote multiplication by the function φ_1 $(\varphi_1(z) = z)$, and set $A_0 = MP + (I-P)$. Then $\sigma(A_0)(vd\lambda_z) = z\sigma_0(P)(vd\lambda_z) + 1 - \sigma_0(P)(vd\lambda_z) = \sigma$. Finally, if $\varphi_n(Z) = e^{inz}$ we have $A_0(\varphi_n) = \varphi_{n+1}$ if $n \geq 0$, $A_0(\varphi_n) = \varphi_n$ if $n < 0$; thus A_0 is an isometry of $L^2(S^1)$ onto the orthogonal complement of the constants, and $\mathrm{ind}(A_0) = -1$.

§7. The topological index of the operator of §6

Let (X, A) be a compact pair and let $\mathbf{C}_X^n$ denote the product complex n-plane bundle over X. A continuous map λ: $A \to GL(n, \mathbf{C})$ defines an isomorphism (also denoted by λ) of $\mathbf{C}_X^n|A$ with itself, defined by $(a, v) \to (a, \lambda(a)v)$, and hence a difference element $d(\mathbf{C}_X^n, \mathbf{C}_X^n, \lambda) \in K(X, A)$. We shall now derive a formula for $ch(d(\mathbf{C}_X^n, \mathbf{C}_X^n, \lambda)) \in H^{even}(X, A; \mathbf{Q})$.

Let κ_n denote the cone over U(n), i.e., $U(n) \times I$ with $U(n) \times \{1\}$ collapsed to a point and U(n) identified with $U(n) \times \{0\}$, and let $id_{(n)}$: $U(n) \to GL(n, \mathbf{C})$ denote the inclusion map. Since κ_n is contractible, in the exact cohomology sequence

$$H^{odd}(\kappa_n; \mathbf{Q}) \to H^{odd}(U(n); \mathbf{Q}) \xrightarrow{\delta} H^{even}(\kappa_n, U(n); \mathbf{Q}) \to H^{even}(\kappa_n; \mathbf{Q})$$

δ is an isomorphism, and we can make the following definition:

DEFINITION. We define $ch_{(n)}$ to be the unique element of $H^{odd}(U(n); \mathbf{Q})$ such that

$$ch(d(\mathbf{C}_{\kappa_n}^n, \mathbf{C}_{\kappa_n}^n, id_{(n)})) = \delta\, ch_{(n)} \quad .$$

Remark. Since U(n) is a strong deformation retract of GL(n), $id_{(n)}$ induces a canonical isomorphism $H^{odd}(GL(n, \mathbf{C}); \mathbf{Q}) \approx H^{odd}(U(n); \mathbf{C})$ so we may equally well regard $ch_{(n)}$ as an element of $H^{odd}(GL(n, \mathbf{C}); \mathbf{Q})$.

THEOREM 1. If (X, A) is a compact pair and λ: $A \to GL(n, \mathbf{C})$ is a continuous map then

$$ch(d(\mathbf{C}_X^n, \mathbf{C}_X^n, \lambda)) = \delta\lambda^*(ch_{(n)})$$

where δ: $H^{odd}(A; \mathbf{Q}) \to H^{even}(X, A; \mathbf{Q})$ is the coboundary map for the pair (X, A).

PROOF. Since $d(\mathbf{C}_X^n, \mathbf{C}_X^n, \lambda)$ depends only on the homotopy class of the map λ: $A \to GL(n, \mathbf{C})$ [II, §3, (ii) of Lemma 1] we can compose λ with a deformation retraction $GL(n, \mathbf{C}) \to U(n)$, i.e., we can suppose λ: $A \to U(n)$. Since U(n) is a differentiable manifold and hence an absolute neighborhood retract we can extend λ to a map $\tilde{\lambda}: \mathcal{O} \to U(n)$ where $\mathcal{O}$ is a neighborhood of A in X. By Urysohn's lemma we can find $g: X \to I$ with $g|A$ identically zero and $g|X - \mathcal{O}$ identically one. Then if $\pi: U(n) \times I \to \kappa_n$ is the canonical map, $x \to \pi(\tilde{\lambda}(x), g(x))$ defines a continuous map $f: X \to \kappa_n$ which extends λ, i.e., we have a map of pairs $(f, \lambda): (X, A) \to (\kappa_n, U(n))$. Then $id_{(n)} \circ \lambda = \lambda$ and $f^* \mathbf{C}^n_{\kappa_n} = \mathbf{C}^n_X$, hence by naturality of the difference construction [II, §3, (i) of Lemma 1]

$$d(\mathbf{C}^n_X, \mathbf{C}^n_X, \lambda) = f^* d(\mathbf{C}^n_{\kappa_n}, \mathbf{C}^n_{\kappa_n}, id_{(n)}) \quad .$$

Then by the naturality of ch and the definition of $ch_{(n)}$ we have

$$ch(d(\mathbf{C}^n_X, \mathbf{C}^n_X, \lambda)) = f^* \delta(ch_{(n)})$$

and finally by the naturality of the coboundary map for pairs with respect to maps of pairs $f^*\delta = \delta\lambda^*$.

q.e.d.

Now let M be a compact, oriented, n-dimensional Riemannian manifold without boundary and let $B(M)$ and $S(M)$ denote the unit ball bundle and unit sphere bundle of M respectively, and $\pi: B(M) \to M$ and $\tilde{\pi} = \pi|S(M)$ the bundle projections. If $(v, x) \in B(M)$ then $T(B(M))_{(v,x)}$ is canonically isomorphic to $T(M)_x \times T(T(M)_x)_v \cong T(M)_x \times T(M)_x$. Hence there is a "natural" complex structure for $T(B(M))_{(v,x)}$ defined by the condition that multiplication by i carries $((u, x), (w, x))$ into $((-w, x), (u, x))$. Thus $T(B(M))$ is a complex vector bundle (and hence $B(M)$ is an almost complex manifold). It is immediate from the definition that $T(B(M)) = \pi^*(T(M) \otimes \mathbf{C})$. Recall that the Todd class $\mathfrak{J}(M)$ is defined as $\mathfrak{J}(T(M) \otimes \mathbf{C})$, hence by the naturality of $\mathfrak{J}$, $\pi^*(\mathfrak{J}(M)) = \mathfrak{J}(T(B(M)) = \mathfrak{J}(B(M))$ (where the latter of course means the Todd class of $B(M)$ as an almost complex manifold, *not* as a real manifold).

Now let $\mathbf{C}^k_M$ denote the product complex k-plane bundle over M so that $\pi^* \mathbf{C}^k_M = \mathbf{C}^k_{B(m)}$, and let $A \in Int_r(\mathbf{C}^k_M, \mathbf{C}^k_M)$, and let $\tilde{\sigma}_r(A): S(M) \to GL(k, \mathbf{C})$ denote the restriction of the symbol of A to $S(M)$.

Then $\gamma(A)$, as defined in Chapter XV is just $d(\mathbf{C}^k_{B(M)}, \mathbf{C}^k_{B(M)}, \tilde{\sigma}_r(A))$, so by Theorem 1 above

$$\mathrm{ch}(\gamma(A)) = \delta(\tilde{\sigma}_r(A)^*(\mathrm{ch}_{(k)})) \quad .$$

Next given $a \in H^*(M; \mathbf{Q})$ and $b \in H^*(B(M), S(M); \mathbf{Q})$ define $a \cdot b \in H^*(B(M), S(M); Q)$ by $a \cdot b = \pi^*(a) \cup b$, where the product on the right is a relative cup product. Then according to the Thom Isomorphism Theorem this makes $H^*(B(M), S(M); \mathbf{Q})$ into a free $H^*(M: \mathbf{Q})$ module with one generator, the Thom class $U \in H^n(B(M), S(M); \mathbf{Q})$. The Thom isomorphism $\varphi_*: H^*(M; Q) \approx H^*(B(M), S(M); \mathbf{Q})$ is defined by $\varphi_*(a) = a \cdot U = \pi^*(a) \cup U$. It follows that if $b \in H^{even}(M; \mathbf{Q})$ then $\varphi_*(a \cup b) = \pi^*(a) \cup \pi^*(b) \cup U = \pi^*(a) \cup U \cup \pi^*(b) = \varphi_*(a) \cup \pi^*(b)$. In particular taking $b = \mathfrak{J}(M)$, so $\pi^*(b) = \mathfrak{J}(B(M))$, and taking

$$a = \mathrm{Ch}(A) = (-1)^{\frac{n(n+1)}{2}} \varphi_*^{-1}(\mathrm{ch}(\gamma(A)))$$

we get

$$\begin{aligned}\varphi_*(\mathrm{Ch}(A) \cup \mathfrak{J}(M)) &= (-1)^{\frac{n(n+1)}{2}} \mathrm{ch}(\gamma(A)) \cup \mathfrak{J}(B(M)) \\ &= (-1)^{\frac{n(n+1)}{2}} \delta(\tilde{\sigma}_r(A)^*(\mathrm{ch}_{(k)})) \cup \mathfrak{J}(B(M)) \quad .\end{aligned}$$

Now recall that the inclusion $S(M) \to B(M)$ induces a map $x \to x|S(M)$ of $H^*(B(M)) \to H^*(S(M))$ and that if for $a \in H^*(S(M))$ and $b \in H^*(B(M))$ we define $a \cdot b = a \cup (b|S(M))$, then this makes $H^*(S(M))$ a right $H^*(B(M))$ module and $\delta: H^*(S(M)) \to H^*(B(M), S(M))$ is an $H^*(B(M))$ module homomorphism. Hence

$$\varphi_*(\mathrm{Ch}(A) \cup T(M)) = (-1)^{\frac{n(n+1)}{2}} \delta((\tilde{\sigma}_r(A)^*(\mathrm{ch}_{(k)})) \cup (\mathfrak{J}(B(M))|S(M))) \quad .$$

Finally we recall that it is an elementary property of the Thom isomorphism that if $a \in H^*(M)$ and $[M]$ and $[B(M), S(M)]$ denote the fundamental classes of M and $(B(M), S(M))$ respectively then $a[M] = \varphi_*(a)[B(M), S(M)]$. Also if $x \in H^*(S(M))$ then $\delta x[B(M), S(M)] = x[S(M)]$ where $[S(M)]$ is the fundamental class of $S(M)$. Hence

THEOREM 2. Let M be a compact, oriented, n-dimensional Riemannian manifold without boundary and let $A \in$

$\mathrm{Int}_r(\mathbf{C}^k_M, \mathbf{C}^k_M)$ be elliptic. Then the topological index of A is given by the formula

$$i_t(A) = (-1)^{\frac{n(n+1)}{2}} (\sigma^*(ch_{(k)}) \cup (\mathfrak{J}(B(M))|S(M)))[S(M)]$$

where $\sigma\colon S(M) \to GL(k, \mathbf{C})$ is $\sigma_r(A)$ restricted to $S(M)$, $\mathfrak{J}(B(M))$ is the Todd class of the almost complex manifold $B(M)$, and $[S(M)]$ is the fundamental class of $S(M)$ (oriented as the boundary of the oriented manifold $B(M)$).

In order to apply Theorem 2 to compute the topological index of the operator of §6 it remains only to compute $ch_{(1)}$.

Let S^2 denote the Riemann sphere and g the generator of $H^2(S^2)$ from its orientation as a complex manifold. We put $D_0 = \{z \in S^2|\ |z| \leq 1\}$, $D_\infty = \{z \in S^2|\ |z| \geq 1\}$ and $S^1 = \{z \in S^2|\ |z| = 1\}$. We identify $U(1)$ with S^1 in the standard way and we identify D_0 with κ_1 by the map $z \to (z/|z|, 1 - |z|)$. By restriction and excision isomorphisms we can regard g as the generator of $H^2(S^2, D_\infty)$ and $H^2(D_0, S^1)$. We denote by μ the generator of $H^1(S^1)$ giving its standard orientation (i.e., as the boundary of D_0) so that $\delta\mu = g$ where $\delta\colon H^1(S^1) \to H^2(D_0, S^1)$.

We identify S^2 with the complex projective line $\mathbf{C}P_1$ in the standard way, i.e., $z \to [(z, 1)]$ for $z \neq \infty$ and $z \to [(1, 1/z)]$ for $z \neq 0$. Then over $\mathbf{C}P_1$ we have the standard universal bundle $\bar{H}$ whose fiber at x is the one-dimensional subspace x of $\mathbf{C}^2$. We recall (see references in the next section) that the first Chern class c_1 is defined so that $c_1(\bar{H}) = -g$. If $z \in D_\infty$ then the fiber of $\bar{H}$ at z is $\{(c, c/z)|c \in \mathbf{C}\}$ and we define an isomorphism θ of $\bar{H}|D_\infty$ with $\mathbf{C}_{S^2}|D_\infty = D_\infty \times \mathbf{C}$ by $\theta(c, c/z) = (z, c)$. This gives rise to a difference element $d(\bar{H}, \mathbf{C}_{S^2}, \theta) \in K(S^2, D_\infty)$. If f denotes the inclusion $S^2 \to (S^2, D_\infty)$ then by [II, §3, (iv) of Lemma 1]

$$f^* d(\bar{H}, \mathbf{C}_{S^2}, \theta) = \bar{H} - \mathbf{C}_{S^2} .$$

Then by the naturality of ch we have

$$f^*\mathrm{ch}(d(\bar{H}, \mathbf{C}_{S^2}, \theta)) = \mathrm{ch}(\bar{H}) - \mathrm{ch}(\mathbf{C}_{S^2})$$

$$= e^{-g} - 1 = -g.$$

On the other hand $f^*\colon H^*(S^2, D_\infty; \mathbf{Q}) \to H^*(S^2; \mathbf{Q})$ is an isomorphism and by our notational conventions above $f^*(g) = g$, hence

$$\mathrm{ch}(d(\bar{H}, \mathbf{C}_{S^2}, \theta)) = -g \quad .$$

Next we note that by excision the inclusion

$$j\colon \ (D_0, S^1) \to (S^2, D_\infty)$$

induces isomorphisms in cohomology and K-theory and that again by notational convention $j^*(g) = g$. Hence by [II, §3, (i) of Lemma 1] and the naturality of ch

$$\mathrm{ch}(d(\bar{H}|D_0, \mathbf{C}_{D_0}, \theta|S^1)) = -g \quad .$$

If $z \in D_0$ then the fiber of $\bar{H}$ at z is $\{(cz, c) | c \in \mathbf{C}\}$ and we define an isomorphism h of $\bar{H}|D_0$ with $\mathbf{C}_{D_0}$ by $h(cz, c) = (z, c)$. Now if $z \in S^1$ then we have

$$\theta(cz, c) = \theta(cz, \tfrac{cz}{z}) = (z, cz)$$

and

$$\mathrm{id}_{(1)}(z)h(cz, c) = \mathrm{id}_{(1)}(z)(z, c) = (z, cz)$$

i.e., we have commutativity in the diagram

$$\begin{array}{ccc}
(\bar{H}|D_0)|S^1 & \xrightarrow{\ \theta|S^1\ } & \mathbf{C}_{D_0}|S^1 \\
{\scriptstyle h|S^1}\downarrow & & \downarrow{\scriptstyle \text{identity}} \\
\mathbf{C}_{D_0}|S^1 & \xrightarrow[\ \mathrm{id}_{(1)}\ ]{} & \mathbf{C}_{D_0}|S^1
\end{array}$$

It follows (formally, by [II, §3, (v) and (ix) of Lemma 1]) that $d(\bar{H}|D_0, \mathbf{C}_{D_0}, \theta|S^1) = d(\mathbf{C}_{D_0}, \mathbf{C}_{D_0}, \mathrm{id}_{(1)})$ and hence

$$d(\mathbf{C}_{D_0}, \mathbf{C}_{D_0}, \mathrm{id}_{(1)}) = -g = \delta(-\mu) \quad .$$

Recalling our identifications $U(1) = S^1$ and $\kappa_1 = D_0$ we get the following result by comparing with Definition 1.

THEOREM 3. Identify $U(1)$ with $S^1 = \{z \in \mathbf{C} \mid |z| = 1\}$ in the standard fashion and let μ be the generator of $H^1(S^1; \mathbf{Q})$ corresponding to its standard orientation (i.e., as the boundary of $D_0 = \{z \in \mathbf{C} \mid |z| \leq 1\}$, the latter having its orientation as a complex manifold). Then

$$ch_{(1)} = -\mu \quad .$$

Remark. The idea of the above proof was suggested by R. Solovay. Note that we have nowhere used the explicit definition of the difference construction, just its functorial properties given in [II, §3, Lemma 1].

THEOREM 4. Let $A \in \mathrm{Int}_0(S^1)$ be an operator as in Theorem 2 of §6. Then the topological index, $i_t(A)$, of A is minus one.

PROOF. Since S^1 is parallelizable $\mathfrak{J}(B(S^1)) = 1$ so by Theorems 2 and 3 above

$$\begin{aligned} i_t(A) &= -\sigma^*(-\mu)[S(S^1)] \\ &= \sigma^*(\mu)[S(S^1)] \quad . \end{aligned}$$

Now $B(S^1) = S^1 \times [-1, 1]$ with the product orientation so $S(S^1) = (S^1 \times \{1\} \cup (S^1 \times \{-1\})$ with the "top" circle, $S^1 \times \{1\}$, oriented negatively, with respect to the usual orientation of S^1, and the "bottom" circle $S^1 \times \{-1\}$ oriented positively.

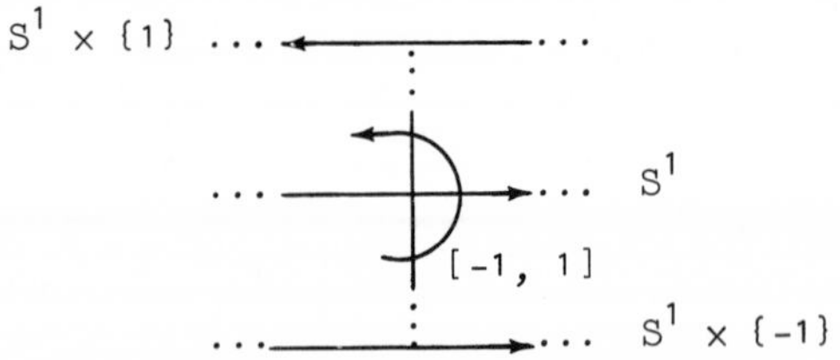

Since $\sigma|S^1 \times \{1\}$ is the projection $S^1 \times \{1\} \to S^1$ while $\sigma|S^1 \times \{-1\}$ is the constant map $z \to 1$ it follows that $\sigma^*(\mu)[S(S^1)] = \mu(-[S^1]) = -1$.

q.e.d.

§8. Sign conventions.

The definition of the topological index is replete with arbitrary choices, and a change in any one of these choices calls for a compensating multiplication by a power of -1. Since this has caused so many headaches already, it is perhaps in order to make these various choices explicit and remark on the effect of a change in each of them.

1. The definition of the Chern character, ch.

This is of course determined by the definition of the Chern classes c_i. The various possibilities are exhaustively considered in an appendix to Borel and Hirzebruch's paper "Characteristic Classes of Homogeneous Spaces, II," appearing in Vol. LXXXI, No. 2 of the American Journal of Mathematics. We have adopted the conventions of the body of that paper (the definitions ${}^1c_i = {}^2c_i = {}^3c_i$ of the appendix) and indeed since the appearance of the above paper and J. Milnor's "Lectures on Characteristic Classes" (Mimeographed, Princeton, 1957) these conventions have become almost universal.

2. The definition of the Thom isomorphism.

Here the question is whether to define the Thom isomorphism $\varphi_*\colon H^*(M) \to H^*(B(M), S(M))$ by $\varphi_*(a) = \pi^*(a) \cup U$ or $\varphi_*(a) = U \cup \pi^*(a)$ where U is the Thom class of $T(M)$. Equivalently shall we regard $H^*(B(M), S(M))$ as a right or left $H^*(M)$ module. We have adopted the first alternative which is also the convention in Milnor (loc. cit.). It is easily seen that a change to the second possibility will call for a compensating factor of $(-1)^{n^2} = (-1)^n$ in the definition of i_t (where $n = \dim M$).

3. The definition of the Fourier transform.

Here the question is whether to define

$$\hat{f}(\zeta) = \int e^{-i(x,\zeta)} f(x)dx \quad \text{so that} \quad f(x) = \frac{1}{(2\pi)^n} \int e^{i(x,\zeta)} \hat{f}(\zeta)\, d\zeta ,$$

or rather to define

$$\hat{f}(\zeta) = \int e^{i(x,\zeta)} f(x)dx \quad \text{so that} \quad f(x) = \frac{1}{(2\pi)^n} \int e^{-i(x,\zeta)} \hat{f}(\zeta)d\zeta \quad .$$

We have adopted the first of these alternatives, following L. Hörmander's *Linear Partial Differential Operators*, Academic Press, New York, 1963. It is easily seen that if one chooses the other alternative then the definition of the symbol of an element of $\mathrm{Int}_k(\xi, \eta)$ is changed to $\sigma'_k(A)$ related to our symbol by the equation $\sigma'_k(A)(v, x) = (-1)^k \sigma_k(A)(-v, x)$. Of course for $A \in \mathrm{Diff}_k(\xi, \eta)$ we have $\sigma_k(A)(-v, x) = (-1)^k \sigma_k(v, x)$ so that $\sigma'_k(A) = \sigma_k(A)$. This change in the symbol is easily seen to change $\gamma(A) \in K(B(M), S(M))$ by a factor of $(-1)^n$, and hence we must introduce a compensating factor of $(-1)^n$ in the definition of i_t.

4. The definition of the difference construction.

If we interchange the roles of E and F in the definition of $d(E, F, \alpha)$ then clearly the new difference element is minus the old one. This of course necessitates a compensating factor of -1 in the definition of i_t.

It is interesting to compare the present conventions with those of an earlier proof of the Index Theorem, namely that in R. Bott, M. Atiyah, and I. Singer, "Topology Seminar, Fall 1962" (Mimeographed, Harvard, 1963). The definition of ch is the same as here, however, in the definition of the Thom isomorphism, Fourier transforms and difference construction the opposite choices were made. Now the first two changes lead to a factor of $(-1)^n(-1)^n = 1$, i.e. they cancel out, whereas the third introduces an extra factor of (-1) in the topological index. That is why in their definition of i_t there appears the factor

$$(-1)^{\frac{n(n+1)}{2} + 1} \quad \text{rather than our} \quad (-1)^{\frac{n(n+1)}{2}} \quad .$$

9. Historical notes on singular integral operators.

Singular integral operators (i.e., elements of $CZ_0(R^n)$) have a long history of use in connection with elliptic partial differential equations. The first results related to solvability in the elliptic case appear to be due to Noether (see Mihlin [7] for references and some applications, particularly in the setting of Hölder continuous and L^2 functions). Calderón and Zygmund established the essential inequality for L^p functions [1] and began to exploit singular integrals systematically in investigating partial differential equations [2]. They worked modulo operators of lower order (as in the above exposition) whereas earlier work was generally done modulo compact operators (as in [7]). Their approach was carried over to manifolds by Seeley [8] where the effect of coordinate changes was given. Earlier work on manifolds was done by Giraud in the Hölder setting.

Operators of order greater than zero were first considered formally by Dynin [3], who obtained the regularity and solvability results in the elliptic case, apparently by generalizing the proofs for differential operators. The algebra was enlarged to contain operators of negative order by Seeley in [9], so that regularity and solvability results were direct corollaries of the basic properties of the algebra (see Chapter XI).

All the above work exploited only the "top order" symbol σ_r of operators of order r. The complete asymptotic expansion given here is due to Kohn and Nirenberg [6]; the definitions and proofs of Theorem 1 and 4 of §2 given above are taken from [6]. Theorem 2 of §2 and its applications are essentially due to Gohberg [4]. The proof of Theorem 7 of §2 is more or less new; in general outline, it resembles a proof of a weaker result in the Séminaire Cartan-Schwartz, 1963-64. Another proof has been given by I. M. Singer in lecture notes. Many of the results established here are stated in slightly different form in [10].

REFERENCES

[1] A. P. Calderon and A. Zygmund, " On Singular Integrals" Amer. Journ. Math., 78 (1956) pp. 289-309.

[2] _____, "Singular integral operators and differential equations," Am. Journ. Math., 79 (1957), 901-921.

[3] A. S. Dynin, "Singular integral operators of arbitrary order on a manifold," Dokl. Akad. Nauk 141 (1961), 21-23.

[4] I. C. Gohberg, "On the theory of multidimensional singular integral equations," Dokl. Akad. Nauk, 133 (1960), 1279-1282.

[5] L. Hörmander, Pseudo-differential operators," to appear.

[6] J. J. Kohn and L. Nirenberg, "On the algebra of pseudo-differential operators," to appear in Comm. Pure and Appl. Math.

[7] S. G. Mihlin, "Singular integral equations," Usp. Mat. Nauk, 3 (1948), 29-112, AMS translation 24 (1950).

[8] R. T. Seeley, "Singular Integrals on Compact Manifolds," Am. Journ. Math., 81 (1959), 6581690.

[9] _____, "Integro-differential operators on vector bundles," Trans. AMS, 117 (1965), pp. 167-204.

[10] A. Unterberger and J. Bokobza, Les opérateurs de Calderón-Zygmund precisés, C. R. Acad. Sc. Paris, vol. 259, 1612-1614.

CHAPTER XVII

COBORDISM INVARIANCE OF THE ANALYTICAL INDEX

R. S. Palais and R. T. Seeley

In this chapter M will denote a compact, oriented, n-dimensional Riemannian manifold which is the boundary of a compact, oriented, (n+1)-dimensional Riemannian manifold Y. X will denote an (n+1)-dimensional oriented Riemannian manifold without boundary which is the union of $X_+ = Y$ and X_-, with $X_+ \cap X_- = M$. A particular such X is the double of Y, with the Riemannian structures extended over X in some smooth way. As usual we use the Riemannian structure to identity $T(M)$ with $T^*(M)$ and $T(X)$ with $T^*(X)$. At each $x \in M$ we regard $T(M)$ as a subspace of $T(X)$ and we denote by $\nu(x)$, or simply ν, the unit normal to M at x pointing from X_- to X_+.

We begin with an explicit form of the Green-Stokes formula for a first order differential operator.

THEOREM 1. Let ξ and η be hermitian bundles over Y and let $L \in \mathrm{Diff}_1(\xi, \eta)$. Define $G \in \mathrm{Hom}(\xi|M, \eta|M)$ by

$$G(x) = \sigma_1(L)(\nu, x)$$

Then if $f \in C^\infty(\xi)$ and $g \in C^\infty(\eta)$

$$< Lf, g >_0 - < f, L^*g >_0 = - \int_M (G(f|M), g|M)_\eta$$

PROOF. By using a partition of unity we can suppose that f has its support in a coordinate neighborhood U of a point $p \in M$. Choose coordinates $x_1, \ldots, x_n$, t in U so that U is identified with

$\{(x, t) \in \mathbf{R}^{n+1} \mid -1 < x_i < 1$ and $0 \leq t < 1\}$ with p at the origin. It is well known that we can choose the coordinates to be "unimodular," i.e., so that the Riemannian measure is given in U by Lebesque measure. Also we can assume that $\nu = \partial/\partial t$. We can now regard $\xi|U$ and $\eta|U$ as trivial bundles with fiber hermitian vector spaces V_1 and V_2, the hermitian structures are then given by C^∞ maps A and B of U into the positive operators on V_1 and V_2 respectively (see [IV, §4, Lemma 4]). The operator L is given in U by $Lf(x, t) = G(x, t)\frac{\partial f}{\partial t} + \Sigma_{i=1}^n C_i(x, t)\frac{\partial f}{\partial x_i}$, (plus an operator of order zero which we can ignore) where $G(x, t) = \sigma_1(L)(dt, (x, t))$ and $C_i(x, t) = \sigma_1(L)(dx_i, (x, t))$, and in particular $G(x, 0) = G(x)$. Then by the proof of [IV, §4, Lemma 4] we have

$$L^*g(x, t) = -A^{-1}\frac{\partial}{\partial t}(G'(x, t)B(x, t)g(x, t)) - \sum_{i=1}^n A^{-1}\frac{\partial}{\partial x_i}(C_i'(x, t)B(x, t)g(x, t))$$

where G' and C_i' are the maps $V_2 \to V_1$ adjoint to G and C_i. Thus

$$(Lf, g)_\eta - (f, L^*g)_\xi = \left(BG\frac{\partial f}{\partial t}, g\right)_2 + \left(f, \frac{\partial}{\partial t}(G'Bg)\right)_1 + \sum_{i=1}^n\left[\left(BC_i\frac{\partial f}{\partial x_i}, g\right)_2 + \left(f, \frac{\partial}{\partial x_i}(C_i'Bg)\right)_1\right]$$
$$= \frac{\partial}{\partial t}(BGf, g)_1 + \sum_{i=1}^n \frac{\partial}{\partial x_i}(BC_if, g)_1 .$$

Then

$$< Lf, g >_0 - < f, L^*g >_0$$
$$= \int_{-1}^1 dx_1 \cdots \int_{-1}^1 dx_n \cdots \int_0^1 dt\left[\frac{\partial}{\partial t}(BGf, g)_1 + \sum_{i=1}^n \frac{\partial}{\partial x_i}(BC_if, g)_1\right]$$

and recalling that the support of f is included in U

$$< Lf, g >_0 - < f, L^*g >_0 = -\int_{-1}^1 dx_1 \cdots \int_{-1}^1 dx_n(B(x,0)G(x,0)f(x,0), g(x, 0))_1$$
$$= -\int_M (G(x)f(x), g(x))_\eta . \qquad \text{q.e.d.}$$

The following theorem is closely related to a theorem of A.P. Calderón in "Boundary value problems for elliptic equations," Outlines of the Joint Soviet-American Symposium on Partial Differential Equations, August, 1963, Novosibirsk, p. 303.

THEOREM 2. Let ζ be a hermitian bundle over X and $L \in \mathrm{Diff}_1(\zeta, \zeta)$ an elliptic operator such that $L: C^\infty(\zeta) \to C^\infty(\zeta)$ is bijective. Define subspaces H_+ and H_- of $C^\infty(\zeta|M)$ by

$$H_\pm = \{f|M \,\big|\, f \in C^\infty(\zeta|X_\pm) \text{ and } Lf = 0 \text{ in } X_\pm\} \quad .$$

Then H_+ and H_- are complementary subspaces of $C^\infty(\zeta|M)$ and hence there are complementary projections $P_\pm: C^\infty(\zeta|M) \to C^\infty(\zeta|M)$ defined by: $P_\pm$ is the projection on $H_\pm$ along $H_\mp$. Moreover $P_\pm \in CZ_0(\zeta|M, \zeta|M)$ and the symbol of P_+ can be characterized as follows: let $\lambda = \sigma_1(L)$ and given $v \in T^*(M)_x$ let $E^\pm(v)$ be the subspace of ζ_x which is the direct sum of the generalized eigenspaces of $-\lambda(\nu, x)^{-1}\lambda(v, x)$ corresponding to eigenvalues μ with $\mathrm{Im}(\mu) > 0$ (for $E^+(v)$) and $\mathrm{Im}(\mu) < 0$ (for $E^-(v)$). Then $\sigma(P_+)(v, x): \zeta_x \to \zeta_x$ is the projection on $E^+(v)$ along $E^-(v)$.

The proof of Theorem 2 is divided into a number of lemmas.

LEMMA A. $H_+ \cap H_- = 0$.

PROOF. Suppose $f_\pm \in C^\infty(\zeta|X_\pm)$, $Lf_\pm = 0$ in $X_\pm$, and $f_+|M = f_-|M$. Define a (continuous) f by: $f = f_\pm$ in $X_\pm$. We can show that $Lf = 0$ in X, hence f is C^∞, and thus $f = 0$ since L is bijective. A fortiori, $f_+|M = f|M = 0$. To see that $Lf = 0$, we have for $g \in C^\infty(\zeta)$ that $< Lf, g >_0 = < f, L^*g >_0 = < f_+, L^*g|X_+ >_0 + < f_-, L^*g|X_- >_0 = \int_M (G(f_+|M), g|M)_\zeta - \int_M (G(f_-|M), g|M)_\zeta = 0$, since $Lf_\pm = 0$ and $f_+|M = f_-|M$.

q.e.d.

Now let ρ be the metric on X, and define a function t on X by $t(x) = \rho(x, M)$ if $x \in X_+$, $t(x) = -\rho(x, M)$ if $x \in X_-$. Then t is a coordinate in a tubular neighborhood $\{|t| < \varepsilon_0\}$ of M. We may suppose that $\varepsilon_0 = 1$, and that $\zeta|\{|t| < 1\}$ is the product of $\zeta|M$ and the unit interval $(-1, 1)$. Then for $-1 < \varepsilon < 1$ there is a map R_ε: $C^\infty(\zeta|\{|t| < 1\}) \to C^\infty(\zeta|M)$ given by $(R_\varepsilon f)(m) = f(m, \varepsilon)$ for m in M. By [X, §4, Theorem 7], R_ε is continuous from $H^s(\zeta)$ to $H^{s-1/2}(\zeta|M)$ for $s > 1/2$. For $\varepsilon = 0$ we need also the adjoint $R_0{}^*$ defined by $< f, R_0{}^* g >_0 = \int_M (f|M, g)_\zeta$ for smooth g. By duality, $R_0{}^*$ extends to a continuous map of $H^s(\zeta|M)$ into $H^{s-1/2}(\zeta)$ for $s < 0$.

Define L_0: $C^\infty(\zeta|M) \to C^\infty(\zeta|M)$ by $(L_0 f)(x) = \lambda(\nu, x) f(x)$. Since $\lambda = \sigma_1(L)$ and L is elliptic, it follows that L_0 is bijective.

LEMMA B. If $g \in C^\infty(\zeta|M)$, then as $\varepsilon \to 0+$ $R_\varepsilon L^{-1} R_0{}^* L_0 g$ converges uniformly to a limit $P_+ g$, where $P_+ \in CZ_0(\zeta|M, \zeta|M)$ with the symbol described in Theorem 2. The same holds as $\varepsilon \to 0-$ when P_+ is replaced by $-P_-$. If D is any differential operator then also $R_\varepsilon D L^{-1} R_0{}^* L_0 g$ converges uniformly as $\varepsilon \to 0+$ or $\varepsilon \to 0-$.

The proof of Lemma B is postponed for a few paragraphs. It is the essential part of Theorem 2.

LEMMA C. If P_+ and P_- are the operators constructed in Lemma B, then $P_+ + P_- =$ identity.

PROOF. Let $f \in C^\infty(\zeta|M)$, and set $u = L^{-1} R_0{}^* L_0 f$. Then for any $\varphi \in C^\infty(\zeta)$, $\int_M (L_0 f, \varphi|M) = < L_0 f, R_0 \varphi >_0 = < R_0{}^* L_0 f, \varphi >_0 = < Lu, \varphi >_0 = < u, L^* \varphi >_0 = \lim_{\varepsilon \to 0} \int_{|t| > \varepsilon} (u, L^* \varphi)$. From Lemma B, $u|\{|t| > \varepsilon\}$ is C^∞, and since $Lu = R_0{}^* L_0 f$ has support in M, $Lu = 0$ in $\{|t| > \varepsilon\}$. Thus from Theorem 1

$$\int_M (L_0 f, \varphi|M) = \lim_{\varepsilon \to 0+} \int_{M_\varepsilon} (L_\varepsilon(u|M_\varepsilon), \varphi|M_\varepsilon)$$

$$- \lim_{\varepsilon \to 0+} \int_{M_{-\varepsilon}} (L_{-\varepsilon}(u|M_{-\varepsilon}), \varphi|M_{-\varepsilon}) \quad ,$$

where $M_\varepsilon = \{t = \varepsilon\}$ and L_ε is the appropriate analog of L_0. Since everything in sight is C^∞ in the right places, we may pass to the limit to obtain $\int_M (L_0 f, \varphi|M) = \int_M (L_0(P_+ f + P_- f), \varphi|M)$, since $P_\pm = \pm \lim_{\varepsilon \to 0+} R_\varepsilon L^{-1} R_0^*$. But every C^∞ section of $\zeta|M$ has the form $\varphi|M$ for a φ in ζ, so $L_0 f = L_0(P_+ f + P_- f)$. Finally, L_0 is bijective, so $f = P_+ f + P_- f$.

q.e.d.

PROOF of Theorem 2. Define $P_\pm$ as in Lemma B. In view of Lemmas A and C, it suffices to show that the range of $P_\pm$ lies in $H_\pm$, for then $f = P_+ f + P_- f$ is the unique decomposition of f into an element of H_+ plus an element of H_-. But Lemma B shows that if $f \in C^\infty(\zeta|M)$, then $u|X_+ = (L^{-1}R_0^* L_0 f)|X_+ \in C^\infty(\zeta|X_+)$. Since $Lu = R_0^* L_0 f$ is supported in M, $Lu = 0$ in the interior of X_+, and $P_+ f = u|M \in H_+$. Similarly $P_- f \in H_-$.

q.e.d.

The proof of Lemma B uses

LEMMA D. $L^{-1} \in CZ_{-1}(\zeta, \zeta)$.

PROOF. Choose $T \in CZ_{-1}(\zeta, \zeta)$ with $\sigma_{-1}(T) = \lambda^{-1} = \sigma_1(L)^{-1}$. Then $\sigma_0(TL) = \sigma_0(I_\zeta)$, so $TL = I - K$ with $K \in CZ_{-1}(\zeta, \zeta)$. Multiplying $(I + K + \dots + K^m)TL = I - K^{m+1}$ on the right by L^{-1} yields

$$L^{-1} = T + KT + \dots + K^m T + K^{m+1} L^{-1}$$

Now $K^j T \in CZ_{-j-1}(\zeta, \zeta)$, and $K^{m+1}L^{-1} \in OP_{-m-2}(\zeta, \zeta)$ since $L^{-1} \in OP_{-1}$. Thus L^{-1} can be approximated within arbitrarily low order by members of CZ_{-1}, and the lemma follows easily.

PROOF of Lemma B. It suffices to consider $M_{\varphi_1} L^{-1} M_{\varphi_2} R_0^* L_0 g$ when φ_1 and φ_2 have disjoint support, or are supported in an appropriate coordinate neighborhood. In the first case, $M_{\varphi_1} L^{-1} M_{\varphi_2} R_0^*$ is continuous from $H^s(M)$ to $H^\infty(X)$ for all $s < 0$, and a fortiori for all s whatsoever, Thus $R_\varepsilon D M_{\varphi_1} L^{-1} M_{\varphi_2} R_0^* L_0 g$ converge uniformly to a limit Hg, and H is of order $-\infty$.

Suppose now φ_1 and φ_2 have support in a neighborhood $U \subset X$ with coordinates $\psi\colon U \to \mathbf{R}^{n+1}$, and such that $\zeta|U$ is trivial. If U

does not intersect M, $M_{\varphi_2}R_0{}^*L_0g = 0$ and there is nothing to prove; so we suppose that $\psi = (\psi_1, \ldots, \psi_n, \psi_{n+1})$ with $\psi_{n+1} = t$. Let $\varphi = 1$ on the support of $|\varphi_1| + |\varphi_2|$, support $(\varphi) \subset U$. Then according to Lemma D, the operator

$$B = \psi_* M_\varphi L^{-1} M_\varphi \psi^* \in CZ_{-1} \quad .$$

It is crucial to know certain details about $\sigma(B)$, which we compute. Let $\sigma(B)(y, t; \eta, \tau) = \Sigma_{\ell < -1}\, b_\ell(y, t; \eta, \tau)$ and $\sigma(\psi^* M_\varphi L M_\varphi \psi_*)(y,t;\eta,\tau) = a_1 + a_0$, where a_j is homogeneous of degree j. Here $\eta \doteq (\eta_1, \ldots, \eta_n)$ are the variables "dual to" y, and τ is "dual to" t. Because $\zeta|U$ is trivial, we regard the a_j and b_ℓ as matrices of functions. Since for functions f with support $(f) \subset$ support $(|\varphi_1| + |\varphi_2|)$ we have $M_\varphi L^{-1} M_\varphi M_\varphi L M_\varphi g = g$, it follows from [XVI, §2, Theorem 3] that on $\psi(\text{support}(|\varphi_1| + |\varphi_2|))$ the b_ℓ satisfy

$$b_{-1}a_1 = \text{identity matrix}$$

(1) $$b_{-1}a_0 + b_{-2}a_1 - i(\partial b_{-1}/\partial\tau)(\partial a_1/\partial t) - i\Sigma(\partial b_{-1}/\partial\eta_j)(\partial a_1/\partial y_j) = 0 \quad \text{etc.}$$

Let θ be a patch function, and set

$$B_\ell = M_{\varphi_1} \psi^* A(\theta, b_\ell) \psi_* M_{\varphi_2} \quad ,$$

with $A(\theta, b_\ell)$ as in [XVI, §2, Definition 3]. Then if D has order $\leq k$, $D[M_{\varphi_1} L^{-1} M_{\varphi_2} - \Sigma_{\ell > \ell_0} B_\ell]$ has order $\leq \ell_0 + k$, so that for $\ell_0 < -1 - k - (n+1)/2$ Soboleff's theorem [X, §4, Theorem 4] and the continuity of $R_0{}^*: H^{-1/2}(\zeta|M) \to H^{-1}(\zeta)$ remarked above show that $D[M_{\varphi_1} L^{-1} M_{\varphi_2} - \Sigma_{\ell > \ell_0} B_\ell] R_0{}^* L_0$ is continuous from $H^{-1/2}(\zeta|M)$ to $C^0(\zeta)$. Hence $R_\varepsilon D[M_{\varphi_1} L^{-1} M_{\varphi_2} - \Sigma_{\ell > \ell_0} B_\ell] R_0{}^* L_0 g$ converges uniformly as $\varepsilon \to 0$, and it remains to prove a like result for $R_\varepsilon D B_\ell R_0{}^* L_0 g$.

Let $\alpha \in C^\infty(R^1)$, $\alpha(s)$ vanish except for $-1 < s < -\frac{1}{2}$, and $\int \alpha = 1$. Set $\alpha_m(s) = m\alpha(ms)$. Then as $m \to +\infty$ we have $\alpha_m \otimes g \to R_0{}^* g$ weakly in $H^s(X)$ for each $s < -\frac{1}{2}$, i.e., $\int\int(\alpha_m(t)g(y), \varphi(y, t))dydt \to \int (g(y), \varphi(y, 0))dy$ for φ in H^{-s}. Thus with

$$f = \psi_* \varphi_2 g \quad \text{and} \quad \varphi_{1*} = \psi_* \varphi_1 \quad ,$$

we have

(2) $(\psi_* B_\ell R_0{}^* g)(y, t)$

$$= (2\pi)^{-n-1} \varphi_{1*} \lim_{m->\infty} \int_{\mathbf{R}^n} \int_{-\infty}^{\infty} \theta\hat{\alpha}(\tau/m)\hat{f}b_\ell e^{it\tau} d\tau \; e^{i<y, \eta>} \, d\eta$$

on every open set where this expression converges uniformly as $m \to \infty$. Here we assume $\theta(\eta, \tau) = 1$ for $|\eta|^2 + |\tau|^2 \geq 1$, $\theta = 0$ for $|\eta|^2 + |\tau|^2 < \frac{1}{2}$. We obtain an integral in which $\lim_{m->\infty}$ may be taken under the integral sign by replacing $\int_{-\infty}^{\infty} d\tau$ with an integral over a finite path in $\{\mathrm{Im}(\tau) \geq 0\}$. To see that this is possible, consider the equations (1) for the b_ℓ. There $a_1(y, t; \eta, \tau)$ is a linear function of (η, τ) which is non-singular for $|\eta|^2 + |\tau|^2 > 0$, η and τ real, because of the ellipticity of L. Thus there is a compact set C in the complex plane, not intersecting the real axis, such that for $|\eta| = 1$ and $(y, t) \in \mathrm{support}(\psi(|\varphi_1| + |\varphi_2|))$ the (complex) values of τ for which a_1 is not invertible lie in C. Thus $b_1 = (a_1)^{-1}$ has a holomorphic extension to the complement of C, for such η and (y, t). It follows by induction, using (i), that all the b_ℓ, and all their derivatives, have such extensions, each of which is bounded by some polynomial in $|\tau|$. Let C lie in $\{|\tau| \leq R\}$, and set

$$\Gamma(\eta) = \text{boundary of } \{|\tau| \leq \max(1, R|\eta|)\} \cap \{\mathrm{Im}(\tau) > 0\} \quad .$$

Extend θ to $\mathbf{R}^n \times \mathbf{C}$ so that $\theta(\eta, \tau) = 1$ still for $|\eta|^2 + |\tau|^2 \geq 1$. Since $\alpha(\tau) = \int^{-1/2} e^{-it\tau} \alpha(t)dt$ decays exponentially as $|\tau| \to \infty$ in $\{\mathrm{Im}(\tau) \geq 0\}^{-1}$, and $e^{it\tau}$ is bounded for $t \geq 0$ and $\mathrm{Im}(\tau) \geq 0$, and the integrand in (2) is holomorphic between $\Gamma(\eta)$ and $\{\mathrm{Im}(\tau) = 0\}$, $\int_{-\infty}^{\infty} d\tau$ may be replaced by $\int_{\Gamma(\eta)} d\tau$. Then $\lim_{m->\infty}$ may pass inside the integrals, yielding for (2) the expression

$$(3) \qquad (2\pi)^{-n-1}\varphi_{1*} \int_{\mathbf{R}^n} \int_{\Gamma(\eta)} \theta\hat{f}b_\ell e^{it\tau} d\tau \; e^{i<y, \eta>} \, d\eta \quad ,$$

since $\hat{\alpha}(\tau/m)$ converges boundedly to $\hat{\alpha}(0) = \int \alpha = 1$ as $m \to \infty$. It is immediate that the expression (3) is C^∞ for $t > 0$, and all its derivatives in y and t extend continuously to $\{t \geq 0\}$. This establishes the uniform convergence of $R_\varepsilon D B_\ell R_0{}^* g$. Further

$$\lim_{\varepsilon -> 0+} R_\varepsilon B_\ell R_0^{*} \in CZ_{\ell+1}(\zeta|M) \quad ;$$

for if $|\eta| \geq 1$ and $R|\eta| \geq 1$ then the function

$$\frac{1}{2\pi}\int_{\Gamma(\eta)} \theta(\eta, \tau) b_\ell(y, 0; \eta, \tau)\, d\tau$$

is homogeneous of degree $\ell+1$ in η. (Note that the homogeneity of b_ℓ is preserved in its holomorphic extension, and for the given η $\theta(\eta, \tau) = 1$ and $\Gamma(\eta)$ is the boundary of $\{|\tau| \leq R|\eta|\} \cap \{\mathrm{Im}(\tau) > 0\}$.)

It remains only to compute $\sigma_0(\lim_{\varepsilon -> 0+} R_\varepsilon B_{-1} R_0^{*})$, and hence $\sigma_0(P_+) = \sigma_0(\lim_{\varepsilon -> 0+} R_\varepsilon B_{-1} R_0^{*} L_0)$. We have for x in M and $(y, 0) = \psi(x)$ that

(4) $$\left(\lim_{\varepsilon \to 0+} R_\varepsilon B_{-1} R_0^{*} g\right)(x)$$

$$= \varphi_1(x)(2\pi)^{-n}\int (\psi_*\varphi_2 g)(\eta) e^{i<y,\eta>}\left[\frac{1}{2\pi}\int_{\Gamma(\eta)} \frac{1}{a_1(y,0;\eta,\tau)}\, d\tau\right] d\eta.$$

Since $\lambda = \sigma_1(L)$ we have from [XVI, §2, Definition 7 and §3, Definition 4] that $a_1(y, 0; \eta, \tau) = i\tau\lambda(\nu, x) + i\lambda(v, x)$ when $v = (d\psi^{*})(\eta)$, so the symbol of (4) is

(5) $$\frac{1}{2\pi}\int_{\Gamma(\eta)} [\lambda(\nu, x)\tau + \lambda(v, x)]^{-1} d\tau$$

on the interior of the set where $\varphi_1 = 1$ and $\varphi_2 = 1$; here $\Gamma(\eta)$ surrounds the generalized eigenvalues of $-\lambda(\nu, x)^{-1}\lambda(v, x)$ lying in $\{\mathrm{Im}(\tau) > 0\}$. From (4) and the fact that $\sigma_{-1}(B_{-1}) = \sigma_{-1}(L^{-1})$ on the set where $\varphi_1 = 1$ and $\varphi_2 = 1$, it is immediate that (5) gives

$$\sigma_0(P_+)(v, x) = \frac{1}{2\pi i}\int_{\Gamma(\eta)} [\lambda(\nu, x)\tau + \lambda(v, x)]^{-1}\, d\tau\, \sigma_0(L_0)$$

$$= \frac{1}{2\pi i}\int_{\Gamma(\eta)} [\tau + \lambda(\nu, x)^{-1}\lambda(v, x)]^{-1}\, d\tau \quad ,$$

since $\sigma_0(L_0)(v, x) = \lambda(\nu, x)$. It follows from the properties of holomorphic maps of elements of Banach algebras (or in this case from the Jordan canonical form) that (5) is the projection onto the generalized eigenspace of $-\lambda(\nu, x)^{-1}\lambda(v, x)$ with eigenvalues in $\{\mathrm{Im}(\tau) > 0\}$, and parallel to the generalized eigenspace with eigenvalues in $\{\mathrm{Im}(\tau) < 0\}$.

q.e.d.

THEOREM 3. Let X be the double of Y and let ζ be an hermitian bundle over X. Let $\lambda \in \mathrm{Smbl}_1^d(\zeta, \zeta)$ satisfy $\lambda(v, x)^* = -\lambda(v, x)$ for all $v \in T^*(X)_x$ and $\lambda(v, x)^2 = -1$ if $\|v\| = 1$. Define bundles ξ^+ and ξ^- over M by

$$\xi_x^{\pm} = \{e \in \zeta_x | \lambda(\nu, x)e = \pm ie\}$$

Then $\zeta|M$ is the orthogonal direct sum $\xi^+ \oplus \xi^-$. Moreover if $v \in T(M)_x$ then $\lambda(v, x)$ maps ξ_x^+ isomorphically onto ξ_x^-, and hence there is an elliptic symbol $\sigma \in \mathrm{Smbl}_1^d(\xi^+, \xi^-)$ defined by $\sigma(v, x) = \lambda(v, x)|\xi^+$. The analytical index of σ is zero. More generally if η is any bundle over M which is the restriction of a bundle over Y and if we define $\tilde{\sigma} \in \mathrm{Smbl}_1^d(\xi^+ \otimes \eta, \xi^- \otimes \eta)$ by $\tilde{\sigma} = \sigma \otimes I_\eta$ then $\tilde{\sigma}$ has analytical index zero.

PROOF. We note that since $\lambda(v, x)$ is linear in v it follows from $\lambda(v, x)^2 = -1$ when $\|v\| = 1$ that more generally $\lambda(v, x)^2 = -\|v\|^2$ (so if $v \neq 0$ then $\lambda(v, x)^{-1} = -(1/\|v\|^2)\,\lambda(v, x)$ which incidentally proves that λ is elliptic). Using the linearity of $\lambda(v, x)$ in v once again we get

$$\begin{aligned}-\|v_1\|^2 - \|v_2\|^2 - 2(v_1 v_2) &= -\|v_1 + v_2\|^2 = \lambda(v_1 + v_2, x)^2 \\ &= \lambda(v_1, x)^2 + \lambda(v_2, x)^2 + \lambda(v_1, x)\lambda(v_2, x) + \lambda(v_2, x)\lambda(v_1, x) \\ &= -\|v_1\|^2 - \|v_2\|^2 + \lambda(v_1, x)\lambda(v_2, x) + \lambda(v_2, x)\lambda(v_1, x)\end{aligned}$$

hence $\lambda(v_1, x)\lambda(v_2, x) + \lambda(v_2, x)\lambda(v_1, x) = -2(v_1, v_2)$. In particular if v_1 and v_2 are orthogonal then $\lambda(v_1, x)$ and $\lambda(v_2, x)$ anti-commute. If $x \in M$ then since $\lambda(\nu, x)$ is skew adjoint and satisfies $\lambda(\nu, x)^2 = -1$ it follows that ζ_x is the orthogonal direct sum of the $+i$ and $-i$ eigenspaces of $\lambda(\nu, x)$, i.e., of ξ_x^+ and ξ_x^-. If $v \in T(M)_x$ then v is orthogonal to ν, hence $\lambda(v, x)$ and $\lambda(\nu, x)$ anti-commute, and it follows that $\lambda(v, x)$ maps ξ_x^+ into ξ_x^- and ξ_x^- into

ξ_x^+. If $v \neq 0$ then $\lambda(v, x)$ is an automorphism of ζ_x so that in this case $\lambda(v, x)$ maps $\xi_x^{\pm}$ isomorphically onto $\xi_x^{\mp}$. This shows that σ is a well defined elliptic symbol. We now note a few facts for later reference. If T is a skew adjoint operator satisfying $T^2 = -1$ then the projection on the $+i$ eigenspace along the $-i$ eigenspace is just $\frac{1}{2}(I - iT)$ and the complementary projection is $\frac{1}{2}(I + iT)$. In particular the orthogonal projections of ζ_x on $\xi_x^{\pm}$ are $\frac{1}{2}(I \mp i\lambda(\nu, x))$. Also if $v \in T^*(M)$ has norm one, then since $\lambda(v, x)$ and $\lambda(\nu, x)$ have the properties of T and anticommute, so does $\lambda(\nu, x)\lambda(v, x)$ and the projection on the $\pm i$ eigenspace along the $\mp i$ eigenspace is $\frac{1}{2}(I \mp i\lambda(\nu, x)\lambda(v, x))$.

Now choose $D \in \mathrm{Diff}_1(\zeta, \zeta)$ with $\sigma_1(D) = \lambda$. Then $\sigma_1(D^*) = -\lambda^* = \lambda$, so if we put $L = \frac{1}{2}(D + D^*)$ then $L = L^*$ and $\sigma_1(L) = \lambda$. Since λ is elliptic, by [XI, Theorem 14] there is a sequence $\{f_n\}$ in $C^\infty(\zeta)$, forming an orthonormal base for $H^0(\zeta)$, and a sequence of real numbers $\{\lambda_n\}$ such that $Lf_n = \lambda_n f_n$. If we now replace L by $L-\mu I$, where μ is a real number distinct from λ_n, then again $L = L^*$, $\sigma_1(L) = \lambda$, but now in addition $\ker L = 0$ and hence by [XI, Theorems 9 and 12] $L\colon C^\infty(\zeta) \to C^\infty(\zeta)$ is bijective, hence the hypotheses of Theorem 2 are satisfied.

Let $B^+(x)$ and $B^-(x)$ denote respectively the orthogonal projections of ζ_x on ξ_x^+ and ξ_x^- $(x \in M)$, so that $\lambda(\nu, x) = i(B^+(x) - B^-(x))$ and $B^+(x) + B^-(x) = \text{identity}$. Define $B^{\pm}\colon C^\infty(\zeta|M) \to C^\infty(\zeta|M)$ by

$$(B^{\pm} f)(x) = B^{\pm}(x)f(x) \quad .$$

Then by Theorem 1 if $u, v \in C^\infty(\zeta|X_{\pm})$ we have the following Green-Stokes Formula:

$$(1) \qquad \int_{X_{\pm}} [Lu, v)-(u, Lv)] = \mp i \int_M (B^+(u|M) - B^-(u|M), v|M) \quad .$$

Now let $\mathcal{H}_+$ and $\mathcal{H}_-$ denote the subspaces of $C^\infty(\zeta|X_+)$ and $C^\infty(\zeta|X_-)$ respectively defined by

$$\mathcal{H}_{\pm} = \{u \in C^\infty(\zeta|X_{\pm})|Lu = 0\}$$

and let $H_{\pm}$ denote the subspaces of $C^\infty(\zeta|M)$ which are boundary values of elements of $\mathscr{H}_{\pm}$ respectively

$$H_{\pm} = \{f \in C^\infty(\zeta|M) \,\big|\, f = u|M, \quad u \in \mathscr{H}_{\pm}\} \quad ,$$

so that by Theorem 2 H_+ and H_- are complementary subspaces of $C^\infty(\zeta|M)$. Define $P_{\pm}: C^\infty(\zeta|M) \to C^\infty(\zeta|M)$ by $P_{\pm}$ = projection on $H_{\pm}$ along $H_{\mp}$. Then, again by Theorem 2, $P_{\pm} \in CZ_0(\zeta|M, \zeta|M)$ and if $v \in T^*(M)_x$ has norm one, then $\sigma_0(P_+)(v, x)$ is the projection on the direct sum of the generalized eigenspaces of $-\lambda(\nu, x)^{-1}\lambda(v, x)$ with positive imaginary part along the direct sum of the remaining generalized eigenspaces. Since $\lambda(\nu, x)^{-1} = -\lambda(\nu, x)$, by what was remarked above we have $\sigma_0(P_{\pm})(v, x) = \frac{1}{2}(I \mp i\lambda(\nu, x)\lambda(v, x))$. We also have $\sigma_0(B^{\pm})(v, x) = B^{\pm}(x) = \frac{1}{2}(I \mp i\lambda(\nu, x))$. Keeping in mind that $\lambda(v, x)$ and $\lambda(\nu, x)$ anticommute and have square -1 a straightforward computation gives

$$\sigma_0(B^+P_+)(v, x) = \tfrac{1}{4}(I - i\lambda(\nu, x) - i\lambda(\nu, x)\lambda(v, x) + \lambda(v, x))$$

$$\sigma_0(B^-P_-)(v, x) = \tfrac{1}{4}(I + i\lambda(\nu, x) + i\lambda(\nu, x)\lambda(v, x) + \lambda(v, x)) \ .$$

So if we define $C \in CZ_0(\zeta|M, \zeta|M)$ by $C = B^+P_+ + B^-P_-$ then

$$\sigma_0(C)(v, x) = \tfrac{1}{2}(I + \lambda(v, x)) \quad .$$

Since $\lambda(v, x)^2 = -I$ and $\lambda(v, x)^* = -\lambda(v, x)$

$$\sigma_0(C)^*(v, x) = \tfrac{1}{2}(I - \lambda(v, x))$$

and

$$\sigma_0(C)^{-1}(v, x) = (I - \lambda(v, x))$$

so in particular C is elliptic. Now $\sigma_0(C^2)(v, x) = \frac{1}{2}\lambda(v, x)$ is skew-adjoint so by XI, Corollary of Theorem 9, C^2 has index zero. Since $\text{index}(C^2) = 2\ \text{index}\ (C)$ it follows that C has index zero. On the other hand $\ker(C) = 0$. Indeed suppose $0 = Cf = B^+P_+f + B^-P_-f$. Since B^+ and B^- are orthogonal projections it follows that

$$B^+P_+f = B^-P_-f = 0.$$

Let $P_+ f = u|M$, $u \in \mathscr{H}_+$. Then by the Green-Stokes formula (1) with $u = v$ we have (since $Lu = 0$)

$$0 = \int_M (B^-\hat{P}_+ f, P_+ f) = \int_M \|B^- P_+ f\|^2_-$$

so $B^- P_+ f = 0$, hence $P_+ f = B^+ P_+ f + B^- P_+ f = 0$. A similar argument shows that $P_- f = 0$ hence $f = P_+ f + P_- f = 0$. Since C has kernel and index zero it is bijective and, by an argument similar to that of Lemma D, $C^{-1} \in CZ_0(\zeta|M, \zeta|M)$, and of course

$$\sigma_0(C^{-1})(v, x) = \sigma_0(C)^{-1}(v, x) = (I - \lambda(v, x)) .$$

Now define $T \in CZ_0(\xi^+, \xi^-)$ by

$$T = B^- P_+ C^{-1} i_+$$

where $i_+ \in \mathrm{Diff}_0(\xi^+, \zeta|M)$ is the inclusion of $C^\infty(\xi^+)$ into $C^\infty(\zeta|M)$. Then

$$\begin{aligned}\sigma_0(B^- P_+)(v, x) &= \tfrac{1}{4}(I + i\lambda(\nu, x))(I - i\lambda(\nu, x)\lambda(v, x)) \\ &= \tfrac{1}{4}(I + i\lambda(\nu, x) - i\lambda(\nu, x)\lambda(v, x) - \lambda(v, x)) \\ &= \tfrac{1}{4}(I + i\lambda(\nu, x))(I - \lambda(v, x))\end{aligned}$$

so

$$\begin{aligned}\sigma_0(B^- P_+ C^{-1})(v, x) &= \tfrac{1}{4}(I + i\lambda(\nu, x))(I - \lambda(v, x))^2 \\ &= -\tfrac{1}{2}(I + i\lambda(\nu, x))\lambda(v, x) \\ &= -\tfrac{1}{2}\lambda(v, x)(I - i\lambda(\nu, x))\end{aligned}$$

Now on ξ^+_x, $\lambda(\nu, x)$ is multiplication by i, hence $I - i\lambda(\nu, x)$ is multiplication by two, so

$$\sigma_0(T)(v, x) = \sigma_0(B^- P_+ C^{-1} i_+)(v, x) = -\lambda(v, x)|\xi^+_x = -\sigma(v, \dot{x}) .$$

Thus $\sigma_0(T)$ agrees with $-\sigma$ on the unit sphere bundle of M, so T is elliptic and by [VII, Theorem 3] the analytical index of σ is equal to the analytical index of T. Thus to complete the proof that σ has analytical index zero it will suffice to show that $T\colon C^\infty(\xi^+) \to C^\infty(\xi^-)$ is bijective.

Define a linear map U as follows: if $g \in H_+$ then U maps B^+g into B^-g. To see that U is well-defined we must show that if $B^+g = 0$ then $B^-g = 0$. Let $u \in \mathbf{H}_+$ with $u|M = g$. Since $Lu = 0$ if we take $u = v$ in the Green-Stokes Formula (1)

$$0 = \int_M (B^+g - B^-g, g) = \int_M (\|B^+g\|^2 - \|B^-g\|^2)$$

so $\|B^+g\|_0 = \|B^-g\|_0$ which proves that U is not only well defined, but also preserves H^0 norms. We claim next that in fact $T = U$ so that T is injective. Indeed given $f \in C^\infty(\xi^+)$ let $h = C^{-1}i_+f = C^{-1}f$. Then $f = Ch = (B^+P_+ + B^-P_-)h$. Applying B^+; $f = B^+f = B^+(B^+P_+ + B^-P_-)h = B^+P_+h = B^+g$ where $g = P_+h \in H_+$. Then

$$Uf = B^-g = B^-P_+h = B^-P_+C^{-1}i_+f = Tf .$$

It remains to show that T is surjective. For this we will show that if $h \in H^0(\xi^-)$ is orthogonal to the range of T then $h = 0$.

Since $T \in CZ_0(\xi^+, \xi^-) \subseteq Int_0(\xi^+, \xi^-)$ is elliptic it follows from [XI, Theorem 7] that $h \in C^\infty(\xi^-)$. We have the three equalities

$$\text{(i)} \quad \langle B^+P_+h, h\rangle_0 = 0 \quad ;$$
$$\text{(ii)} \quad \langle B^+P_-h, h\rangle_0 = 0 \quad ;$$
$$\text{(iii)} \quad \langle B^-P_+h, h\rangle_0 = 0 \quad .$$

The first and second because $B^+h = 0$ and $\langle B^+P_\pm h, h\rangle_0 = \langle P_\pm h, B^+h\rangle_0$ and the third because $B^-P_+h = U(B^+P_+h) = T(B^+P_+h)$ is in the range of T, hence orthogonal to h. Then

$$\|h\|_0^2 = \langle (B^+ + B^-)(P^+ + P^-)h, h\rangle_0 = \langle B^-P_-h, h\rangle_0$$
$$= \langle B^-P_-h - B^+P_-h, h\rangle_0 \quad .$$

Now $P_-h \in H_-$, say $P_-h = v|M$ with $v \in \mathbf{H}_-$. Since $Lv = 0$ if we take $u = v$ in the Green-Stokes Formula (1) we get

$$0 = \langle B^-P_-h - B^+P_-h, h\rangle_0 = \|h\|_0^2 \quad \text{so} \quad h = 0 \quad ,$$

which completes the proof that the analytical index of σ is zero.

To prove the final statement of the Theorem we note that by [X, §4, Theorem 5] η is the restriction to M of a bundle $\tilde{\eta}$ over X. Let $\tilde{\zeta} = \zeta \hat{\otimes} \tilde{\eta}$ and define $\tilde{\lambda} \in \mathrm{Smbl}_1^d(\tilde{\zeta}, \tilde{\zeta})$ by $\tilde{\lambda} = \lambda \otimes I_\eta$. Clearly $\tilde{\lambda}$ is skew-adjoint and satisfies $\tilde{\lambda}(v, x)^2 = -1$ if $\|v\| = 1$. Moreover, if we put $\tilde{\xi}_x^{\pm} = \{e \in \tilde{\zeta}_x | \tilde{\lambda}(v, x)e = \pm ie\}$ for $x \in M$ then clearly $\tilde{\xi}_x^{\pm} = \xi_x^{\pm} \otimes \eta_x$. Moreover it is clear that $\tilde{\lambda}(v, x)|\tilde{\xi}^+ = \tilde{\sigma}(v, x)$. The proof that the analytical index of σ is zero now implies the same for the analytical index of $\tilde{\sigma}$. q.e.d.

We now show how Theorem 3 leads to the main goal of this chapter; namely the proof of part c) of Theorem 4 of [XV, §5] for the analytical index. We assume that M has dimension $n = 2m$, so Y has dimension $2m+1$, and we let X be the double of Y. As usual we put

$$\Lambda^*(T^*(X) \otimes \mathbf{C}) = \sum_{p=0}^{2m+1} \Lambda^p(T^*(X) \otimes \mathbf{C}) ,$$

$$\Lambda^{even}(T^*(X) \otimes \mathbf{C}) = \sum_{p=0}^{m} \Lambda^{2p}(T^*(X) \otimes \mathbf{C}),$$

and

$$\Lambda^{odd}(T^*(X) \otimes \mathbf{C}) = \sum_{p=0}^{m} \Lambda^{2p+1}(T^*(X) \otimes \mathbf{C}) .$$

We recall certain linear maps. First for each $v \in T(X)$ we have the exterior multiplication map $e \to v \wedge e$ of $\Lambda^*(T^*(X) \otimes \mathbf{C})_x$ into itself (recall the identification of $T(X)_x$ with $T^*(X)_x$), which carries Λ^p into Λ^{p+1} and hence interchanges Λ^{even} and Λ^{odd}. Secondly, there is the interior multiplication by v, i_v, identified by

$$i_v\theta(v_1, \ldots, v_{p-1}) = \theta(v, v_1, \ldots, v_{p-1})$$

for $\theta \in \Lambda^p(T^*(X) \otimes \mathbf{C})_x$. We recall [IV, §6c] that i_v is the adjoint of $e \mapsto v \wedge e$. Since i_v maps Λ^p into Λ^{p-1} it likewise interchanges Λ^{even} and Λ^{odd}. If we define $u_v\colon \Lambda^*(T(X) \otimes \mathbf{C})_x \to \Lambda^*(T(X) \otimes \mathbf{C})_x$ by $u_v e = v \wedge e - i_v e$, then u_v is skew adjoint and interchanges Λ^{even} and Λ^{odd}. We also recall from [IV, §6c] that $\sigma_1(d)(v, x)e = v \wedge e$, hence that $\sigma_1(\delta)(v, x)e = -i_v e$ and so $\sigma_1(d+\delta)(v, x) = u_v$. Also $\sigma_2(\Delta)(v, x)$

$= \sigma_2((d+\delta)^2)(v, x) = u_v^2$ which we computed to be multiplication by $-\|v\|^2$. Since $v \to u_v$ is linear the argument at the beginning of the proof of Theorem 3 shows that

$$u_{v_1} u_{v_2} + u_{v_2} u_{v_1} = -2(v_1, v_2)$$

and in particular *if* v_1 *and* v_2 *are orthogonal then* u_{v_1} *and* u_{v_2} *anticommute*.

We also have a bundle automorphism $*_X$ of $\Lambda^*(T^*(X) \otimes \mathbf{C})$ mapping Λ^p into Λ^{2m+1-p} and hence again interchanging Λ^{even} and Λ^{odd}. We recall the explicit definition of $*_X$. There is a canonical basis element (the volume element) for $\Lambda^{2m+1}(T^*(X) \otimes \mathbf{C})_x$, denoted by ω_x, and defined by $\omega_x = v_1 \wedge \ldots \wedge v_{2m+1}$, where $v_1, \ldots, v_{2m+1}$ is any oriented orthonormal basis for $T^*(X)_x$. Then if $e \in \Lambda^p$, $*_X e$ is the unique element of Λ^{2m+1-p} such that $f \wedge *_X e = (f, \bar{e})\omega_x$, for all $f \in \Lambda^p$, where (f, e) is the hermitian structure for Λ^p induced by that in $T^*(X)_x \otimes \mathbf{C}$ and $\bar{e}$ is the complex conjugate of e. In particular it follows that if $v_1, \ldots, v_{2m+1}$ is an oriented orthonormal base for $T(X)_x$ then $*_X(v_1 \wedge \ldots \wedge v_p) = v_{p+1} \wedge \ldots \wedge v_{2m+1}$. In particular since the elements of $\Lambda^*(T^*(X) \otimes \mathbf{C})_x$ of the form $v_{j_1} \wedge \ldots \wedge v_{j_p}$ with $j_1 < \ldots < j_p$ form an orthonormal basis for $\Lambda^*(T^*(X) \otimes \mathbf{C})_x$ it follows that $*_X$ is a unitary map. It also follows that on Λ^p we have $*_X^2 = (-1)^{p(2m+1-p)} = 1$ i.e., that $*_X^2$ is the identity. If $e \in \Lambda^p$ then because interior and exterior multiplication by v are adjoint maps we have for any $f \in \Lambda^{p-1}$

$$f \wedge v \wedge *_X e = (f \wedge v, \bar{e})\omega_x = (-1)^{p-1}(v \wedge f, \bar{e})\omega_x$$

$$= (-1)^{p-1}(f, i_v\bar{e})\omega_x = (-1)^{p-1} f \wedge *_X(i_v e)$$

and hence $v \wedge *_X e = (-1)^{p-1} *_X(i_v e)$.

Define a bundle automorphism α_X of $\Lambda^*(T^*(X) \otimes \mathbf{C})$ by $\alpha_X = i^{p(p-1)-m+1} *_X$ on Λ^p. Then clearly α_X interchanges Λ^{odd} and Λ^{even} and is a unitary map satisfying $\alpha_X^2 = -1$. It follows that $\alpha_X^* = \alpha_X^{-1} = -\alpha_X$, i.e., α_X *is skew-adjoint*. Also if $e \in \Lambda^p$ then multiplying the equation $v \wedge *_X e = (-1)^{p-1} *_X(i_v e) = -(i)^{-2p} *_X(i_v e)$ by $i^{p(p-1)-m+1}$ we get

$v \wedge \alpha_X e = \alpha_X i_v e$. Replacing e by $\alpha_X e$ and applying α_X to both sides of the latter equation gives $\alpha_X(v \wedge e) = i_v \alpha_X e$. Hence $\alpha_X u_v e = \alpha_X v \wedge e - \alpha_X i_v e = i_v e = i_v \alpha_X e - v \wedge \alpha_X e = -u_v \alpha_X e$. In other words α_X *and* u_v *anti-commute*.

We now define the bundle ζ over X by $\zeta = \Lambda^{even}(T^*(X) \otimes \mathbf{C})$. Recalling that both α_X and u_v interchange Λ^{even} and Λ^{odd} it follows that we can define an element $\lambda \in \mathrm{Smbl}_1^d(\zeta, \zeta)$ by the formula $\lambda(v, x)e = u_v \alpha_X e$, and in fact λ is the symbol of the operator $(d+\delta)\alpha_X$ considered as an element of $\mathrm{Diff}_1(\zeta, \zeta)$.

We note that

$$\lambda(v, x)^2 = u_v \alpha_X u_v \alpha_X = -u_v^2 \alpha_X^2 = -\|v\|^2 \quad .$$

Also since u_v and α_X are skew adjoint we have

$$\lambda(v, x)^* = \alpha_X^* u_v^* = \alpha_X u_v = -u_v \alpha_X = -\lambda(v, x) \quad .$$

Thus the hypotheses of Theorem 3 are satisfied and we can define bundles ξ^+ and ξ^- over M by $\xi^+ = \{e \in \zeta_x | \lambda(\nu, x)e = \pm ie\}$, and an elliptic symbol $\sigma \in \mathrm{Smbl}_1^d(\xi^+, \xi^-)$ by $\sigma(v, x) = \lambda(v, x)|\xi_x^+$, and the analytical index of σ is zero.

We now define a bundle ξ over M by $\xi = \Lambda^*(T^*(M) \otimes \mathbf{C})$. Since we are regarding $T^*(M)$ as a sub-bundle of $T^*(X)|M$ (via the Riemannian structure) it follows that ξ is a sub-bundle of $\Lambda^*(T^*(X) \otimes \mathbf{C})|M$. We note that if $v \in T(M)_x$ then the exterior multiplication map $e \mapsto v \wedge e$ on ξ_x, its adjoint the interior multiplication map i_v, and their difference u_v, are just the restrictions to ξ_x of the corresponding maps on $\Lambda^*(T^*(X) \otimes \mathbf{C})_x$ when we regard v as an element of $T(X)_x$.

There is a canonical isomorphism $f\colon\ \xi \approx \zeta|M = \xi^+ \oplus \xi^-$ defined by $f(e) = e$ if $e \in \Lambda^{even}(T^*(M) \otimes \mathbf{C})$ and $f(e) = u_\nu e = -e \wedge \nu$ if $e \in \Lambda^{odd}(T^*(M) \otimes \mathbf{C})$. If $v \in T(M)_x$ then it is easily seen that $f(u_v e) = u_\nu u_v f(e)$ by considering the two cases $e \in \Lambda^{even}$ and $e \in \Lambda^{odd}$.

The bundle automorphism $*_M$ of ξ analogous to $*_X$ satisfies $*_M^2 = (-1)^{p(2m-p)} = (-1)^p$ and if we define $\alpha_M = i^{p(p-1)-m} *_M$ on

$\Lambda^p(T^*(M) \otimes \mathbf{C})$ then α_M is a unitary and self adjoint automorphism of ξ satisfying $\alpha_M^2 = 1$.

Given $x \in M$ let $v_2, \ldots, v_{2m+1}$ be an oriented orthonormal basis for $T(M)_x$, so that if we put $v_1 = -\nu$ then $v_1, \ldots, v_{2m+1}$ is an oriented orthonormal basis for $T(X)_x$. Checking on elements of the form $e = v_{j_1} \wedge \ldots \wedge v_{j_p}$ with $1 < j_1 < j_2 < \ldots < j_p$ we verify the formula $f(*_M e) = (-1)^p u_\nu *_X f(e)$ if $e \in \Lambda^p(T^*(M) \otimes \mathbf{C})$ and multiplying the latter by $i^{p(p-1)-m}$ we get

$$f(\alpha_M e) = \frac{1}{i} u_\nu \alpha_X f(e) = \frac{1}{i}\lambda(\nu, x) f(e)$$

or finally

$$f\alpha_M f^{-1} = \frac{1}{i}\lambda(\nu, x) \quad .$$

In particular since $\xi_x^{\pm}$ is the set of $e \in \zeta_x$ such that $\lambda(\nu, x)e = \pm ie$, we have

(1) $$\xi^{\pm} = \{e \in \zeta|M \,|\, f\alpha_M f^{-1}e = \pm e\} \quad .$$

Now if $\omega \in \xi$ we have seen that $fu_v\omega = u_\nu u_v f\omega$ for any $v \in T(M)$. If $\omega = f^{-1}e$, where $e \in \xi^+$, then $\alpha_M\omega = \omega$, so $f\omega = f(\alpha_M\omega) = \frac{1}{i} u_\nu \alpha_X f\omega$, hence since $u_\nu^2 = -1$ we get $fu_v\omega = -iu_v\alpha_X f(\omega) = -i\sigma(v, x)f(\omega)$. Thus

(2) $$fu_v f^{-1}e = \sigma(v, x)e \qquad e \in \xi^+ \quad .$$

Now by Theorem 3, if η is any bundle over M which is the restriction of a bundle over Y, then $\sigma \otimes I_\eta$ is an elliptic element of $\mathrm{Smbl}_1^d(\xi^+ \otimes \eta, \xi^- \otimes \eta)$ with analytical index zero. Since $f\colon \xi \approx \xi^+ \oplus \xi^-$ is an isomorphism it follows from (1) and (2) that if we redefine $\xi^{\pm}$ by $\xi^{\pm} = \{e \in \xi | \alpha_M e = \pm e\}$ and redefine σ by $\sigma(v, x) = u_v$, then the same result holds. To recapitulate we have the following theorem whose proof was the main goal of this chapter.

THEOREM 4. Let $\xi^{\pm} = \{e \in \Lambda^*(T^*(M) \otimes \mathbf{C}) | \alpha_M e = \pm e\}$ and define $\sigma \in \mathrm{Smbl}_1^d(\xi^+, \xi^-)$ by $\sigma = \sigma_1(d+\delta)|\xi^+$, i.e., $\sigma(v, x) = u_v$.

If η is any bundle over M which is the restriction of a bundle over Y, then $\sigma \otimes I_\eta \in \mathrm{Smbl}_1^d(\xi^+ \hat{\otimes} \eta, \xi^- \hat{\otimes} \eta)$ is an elliptic symbol with analytical index zero. In other words c) of Theorem 4 of [XV, §5] holds for the analytical index.

CHAPTER XVIII

BORDISM GROUPS OF BUNDLES

E. E. Floyd

§1. Introductory remarks

The purpose of this chapter is to prove the uniqueness theorem for index functions stated in Chapter I. The proof can be based directly upon the results of Conner and myself in our Ergebnisse tract [2]. In view of the fact that torsion does not enter into the proof, it is also possible to give the following complete proof based directly upon Thom's work [4].

We first collect some definitions and elementary remarks, beginning with Thom's L-equivalence classes. Fix a differentiable n-manifold X without boundary and an integer k with $0 \leq k \leq n$. Two closed differentiable k-dimensional submanifolds M_0, M_1 with oriented normal bundle are L-*equivalent* if there exists a compact differentiable submanifold W of $X \times I$ such that W intersects $X \times 0$, $X \times 1$ transversally in $M_0 \times 0$, $M_1 \times 1$ respectively and such that W has no other boundary, and if the normal bundle of W can be oriented so as to extend the orientation of the normal bundle of $M_0 \times 0$, $M_1 \times 1$ in $X \times 0$, $X \times 1$ respectively. Denote by $L_k(X)$ the set of L-equivalence classes of closed k-manifolds in X with oriented normal bundle. There are the following remarks.

(1) If X is oriented, there is a one-to-one correspondence between orientations for the normal bundle of $M \subset X$ and orientations for the tangent bundle of M. In this case, in the definition of L-equivalence we suppose the tangent bundle oriented instead of the normal bundle.

(2) Given an M_0 with oriented normal bundle and a smooth isotopy of M_0 with $M_1 \subset X$, then the normal bundle of M_1 receives an orientation and M_0 and M_1 are L-equivalent.

(3) If $k < \dim X/2$, given M_0 and M_1 there is an M_1' smoothly isotopic to M_1 with M_0 and M_1' disjoint. Hence in this case we can define an abelian operation in $L_k(X)$ by disjoint union.

Since $L_k(X)$ is defined only for manifolds, does not always have a natural operation, etc., it is natural to consider also more functional constructs (see Atiyah [1], Conner-Floyd [2]).

Let X be a space, and n a non-negative integer. Consider pairs (M, f) where M is a closed oriented differentiable n-manifold and $f: M \to X$ is a map. Two pairs (M_0, f_0), (M_1, f_1) are *bordant* if there exists a compact oriented differentiable manifold W with boundary the disjoint union $M_0 \cup -M_1$ and a map $F: W \to X$ with $F|M_0 = f_0$, $F|M_1 = f_1$. There results an equivalence relation. Denote by $[M, f]$ the class represented by (M, f), and by $\Omega_n(X)$ the set of all $[M, f]$. Then $\Omega_n(X)$ is an abelian group under disjoint union. For X = point, $\Omega_n(X)$ is the Thom group Ω_n consisting of all bordism classes of closed oriented differentiable n-manifolds. There are the following straightforward remarks.

(4) A map $\varphi: X \to Y$ gives a homomorphism $\varphi_*: \Omega_k(X) \to \Omega_k(Y)$ defined by $\varphi_*[M, f] = [M, \varphi f]$. Moreover, $(\varphi_2\varphi_1)_* = \varphi_{2*}\varphi_{1*}$; if $\varphi_0, \varphi_1: X \to Y$ are homotopic then $\varphi_{0*} = \varphi_{1*}$. Hence if $\varphi: X \to Y$ is a homotopy equivalence, then $\varphi_*: \Omega_n(X) \approx \Omega_n(Y)$.

(5) If X is an oriented differentiable manifold without boundary and if $2k + 2 \leq \dim X$, there is the natural homomorphism $L_k(X) \to \Omega_k(X)$ which takes the L-equivalence class represented by the closed oriented submanifold M into $[M, i] \subseteq \Omega_k(X)$, where i is the inclusion map. It follows from the Whitney embedding theorem that this is an isomorphism $L_k(X) \approx \Omega_k(X)$.

(6) Let X be a finite complex embedded as a subcomplex of S^n. Denote by N the closed regular neighborhood of X and by ∂N its boundary. Then (4) implies $\Omega_k(X) \approx \Omega_k(N-\partial N)$, and for $2k+2 \leq n$, (5) implies that $\Omega_k(X) \approx L_k(N-\partial N)$.

(7) Given $f: M \to X$, where M is a closed oriented differentiable k-manifold, there are the *Pontrjagin numbers of* f [2]. Namely, given a cup product $p_{i_1} \cdots p_{i_r} \in H^p(M)$ of Pontrjagin classes of the tangent

bundle of M and $x \in H^q(X)$ with $r(i_1 + \ldots + i_r) + q = k$, there is the integer

$$p_{i_1} \cdots p_{i_r} f^*(x)[M] \quad ,$$

the value of $p_{i_1} \cdots p_{i_r} f^*(x) \in H^k(M)$ on the orientation class of M in $H_k(M)$. These numbers are functions only of the bordism class $[M, f] \in \Omega_k(X)$, and are the Pontrjagin numbers of $[M, f]$. We may also let $x \in H^q(X; \mathbf{Q})$, in which case the Pontrjagin number is a rational number.

Consider now $\Omega_k(BG)$, where G is a compact Lie group. We can reinterpret this group in the following way. Consider pairs (M, α) where M is a closed oriented differentiable k-manifold and α is a principal G-bundle over M. Two pairs (M_0, α_0) and (M_1, α_1) are *bordant* if there exists a compact oriented differentiable manifold W with ∂W the disjoint union $M_0 \cup -M_1$, and a principal G-bundle β over W which restricts to α_i on M_i, $i = 0, 1$. This is an equivalence relation; we see that the set of equivalence classes is in one-to-one correspondence with $\Omega_k(BG)$. In fact, given (M, α) there is a classifying map $f: M \to BG$ for α. Letting the bordism class represented by (M, α) map into $[M, f] \in \Omega_k(BG)$, we get the one-to-one correspondence. It is seen that we may use for BG any classifying space for G in dimensions $\leq k + 1$. Hence we may consider BG a finite complex.

In a similar fashion, we can consider bordism of pairs (M, a) where M is a closed oriented differentiable manifold, and $a \in K(M)$. Two pairs (M_0, a_0) and (M_1, a_1) are *bordant* if there exists a compact oriented differentiable manifold W with boundary the disjoint union $M_0 \cup -M_1$, and $b \in K(W)$ with the restriction $K(W) \to K(M_i)$ sending b into a_i for $i = 0, 1$. It can be seen that this is an equivalence relation, using, in proving transitivity, exactness of

$$K(W_1 \cup W_2) \to K(W_1) + K(W_2) \to K(W_1 \cap W_2) \quad .$$

We are thus lead to an abelian group of bordism classes. But $K(M)$ is in one-to-one correspondence with homotopy classes of maps $M \to \mathbf{Z} \times BU$ (base points not considered). Hence, as above, the bordism group is in one-to-one correspondence with $\Omega_k(\mathbf{Z} \times BU)$.

§2. The computation of $\Omega_k(X) \otimes \mathbf{Q}$

We first recall some well-known facts about homotopy theory. Given spaces X, Y with base point, denote by [X, Y] the set of homotopy classes of maps $X \to Y$ which preserve base point. We suppose always that X is a finite CW-complex and that Y is a CW-complex whose skeletons are finite.

If Y is (n-1)-connected and $\dim X \leq 2n - 2$ (i.e., in the stable range), then [X, Y] is an abelian group, also finitely generated [3]. In the stable range there is a homomorphism

$$[X, Y] \to \mathrm{Hom}[H_*(X), H_*(Y)] \quad ,$$

where $\mathrm{Hom}[H_*(X), H_*(Y)]$ is the group of degree preserving homomorphisms $H_*(X) \to H_*(Y)$, which sends the homotopy class of f into $f_*: H_*(X) \to H_*(Y)$. This is an isomorphism modulo the class of torsion groups [3]. It is equally true that

$$[X, Y] \to \mathrm{Hom}[H^*(Y), H^*(X)]$$

is an isomorphism modulo torsion. Here homology and cohomology are taken to be reduced.

Let $A \to BSO(n)$ be a universal SO(n)-bundle with fiber the closed n-ball, and let $\partial A \subset A$ denote the union of the boundary spheres. Then $MSO(n) = A/\partial A$ is the universal Thom space; it is (n-1)-connected. The cohomology is given by the Thom isomorphism

$$\psi: H^i(BSO(k)) \approx \tilde{H}^{k+i}(MSO(k)) \quad ,$$

where $H^*(BSO(k))$ is, up to torsion, the polynomial algebra generated by the Pontrjagin classes.

The fundamental theorem of Thom is now assumed [4].

(2.1) THOM. Let (X, B) be a finite CW-pair so that X - B is a differentiable n-manifold without boundary. There is a canonical one-to-one correspondence $L_k(X-B) \approx [X/B, MSO(n-k)]$. In the stable range $2k+2 \leq n$, this is a group isomorphism.

There are the following consequences of (2.1).

(8) We have $\Omega_k \approx L_k(S^n)$ for $k < n/2$. Hence by (2.1), $\Omega_k \approx [S^n, MSO(n-k)] \approx H^n(MSO(n-k))$ mod torsion.

(9) For a finite complex X, the groups $\Omega_k(X)$ and $\Sigma_{i+j=k} H_i(X) \otimes \Omega_j$ have the same rank. For embed X in S^n, $2k+2 \leq n$, and let N be a closed regular neighborhood of X. Then $\Omega_k(X) \approx L_k(N-\partial N)$ by (6), and hence

$$\Omega_k(X) \approx \mathrm{Hom}[H^*(MSO(n-k)), \quad H^*(N/\partial N)]$$

modulo torsion by (2.1). Using Poincaré duality,

$$H^i(N/\partial N) \approx H_{n-i}(N-\partial N) \approx H_{n-i}(X) \quad .$$

Hence

$$\begin{aligned} \text{rank } \Omega_k(X) &= \sum_i \text{rank } H_{n-i}(X) \cdot \text{rank } H^i(MSO(n-k)) \\ &= \sum \text{rank } H_{n-i}(X) \cdot \text{rank } \Omega_{i-n+k} \\ &= \text{rank} \sum_{i+j=k} H_i(X) \otimes \Omega_j \quad . \end{aligned}$$

For a more detailed analysis of $\Omega_k(X)$ see Conner-Floyd [2].

§3. The bordism ring of bundles

We shall now consider $\Omega_*(\mathbf{Z} \times BU)$. Recall that an element of $\Omega_k(\mathbf{Z} \times BU)$ is a bordism class $[M, a]$ where M is a closed oriented manifold and $a \in K(M)$. Addition is by disjoint union; there is a multiplication given by $[M, a] \cdot [M', a'] = [M \times M', a \otimes a']$, so that $\Omega_*(\mathbf{Z} \times BU)$ is a ring. There is the subring $\Omega_*(1 \times BU)$ consisting of all $[M, a]$ with a of virtual dimension one. Also $\Omega_k(1 \times BU) = \Omega_k(BU) \approx \Omega_k(BU(n))$ for $n > k$; choosing a classifying space $BU(n)$ in dimensions $\leq N$ to be a finite complex, we may apply (9) to compute rank $\Omega_k(1 \times BU)$. It is the number of pairs (ω, ω') of partitions $\omega = (i_1, i_2, \ldots)$, $\omega' = (j_1, j_2, \ldots)$ with $4(i_1 + i_2 + \ldots) + 2(j_1 + j_2 + \ldots) = k$.

For $a \in K(X)$, let $ch\, a = \Sigma\, ch_q\, a$ where $ch_q\, a$ is the $2q$-dimensional component. Writing $\Sigma\, t_i^q$ as a polynomial in elementary symmetric functions we obtain,

$$\mathrm{ch}_q a = (-1)^{n-1} \frac{c_q}{(q-1)!} + \omega(c_1, \ldots, c_{q-1}) .$$

Denote by $\mathrm{ch}_q \in H^{2q}(BU; \mathbf{Q})$ the class $\mathrm{ch}_q a$ where a is the universal bundle. It is seen that $H^*(BU; \mathbf{Q})$ is the polynomial algebra generated by ch_q, $q > 0$. Given a sequence $\tau = (v_1, v_2, \ldots)$ of non-negative integers with $v_i = 0$ for almost all i, let

$$\mathrm{ch}_\tau = (\mathrm{ch}_1)^{v_1} \cdot (\mathrm{ch}_2)^{v_2} \ldots .$$

If $a \in K(X)$ and $b \in K(Y)$ are virtual dimension one, then $\mathrm{ch}(a \otimes b) = \mathrm{ch}\, a \otimes \mathrm{ch}\, b$ implies that

$$\mathrm{ch}_n(a \otimes b) = \sum_{p+q=n} \mathrm{ch}_p a \otimes \mathrm{ch}_q b$$

where $\mathrm{ch}_0 = 1$.

Consider now S^{2k}, and the element $V_k \in K(S^{2k})$ with $\mathrm{ch}_k V_k$ a generator g of $H^{2k}(S^{2k}; \mathbf{Z}) \subset H^{2k}(S^{2k}; \mathbf{Q})$, with V_k of virtual dimension one. In $K((S^{2k})v)$, let $(V_k)^v = V_k \otimes \ldots \otimes V_k$. Then

$$\mathrm{ch}(V_k)^v = (1 + g) \otimes \ldots \otimes (1 + g)$$
$$\mathrm{ch}_k(V_k)^v = g \otimes 1 \otimes \ldots \otimes 1 + \ldots + 1 \otimes 1 \otimes \ldots \otimes 1 \otimes g,$$
$$(\mathrm{ch}_k)^v(V_k)^v = v!\ g \otimes \ldots \otimes g .$$

Denote $g \otimes \ldots \otimes g$ by $g_{k,v}$. Note also that $\mathrm{ch}_i(V_k)^v = 0$ if $i < k$.

Consider again the sequences τ as above. For each τ, let $S_\tau = (S^2)^{v_1} \times \ldots \times (S^{2k})^{v_k}$ where $v_i = 0$ for $i > k$, and let $V_\tau \in K(S_\tau)$ be given by $V_\tau = (V_1)^{v_1} \otimes \ldots \otimes (V_k)^{v_k}$. Write elements of $H^*(S_\tau)$ as linear combinations of elements $x_1 \otimes \ldots \otimes x_k$ where $x_i \in H^*((S^{2i})^{v_i})$. Then

$$(\mathrm{ch}_1)^{v_1} V_\tau = v_1!\ g_{1,v_1} \otimes 1 \otimes \ldots \otimes 1$$

$$(\mathrm{ch}_2)^{v_2} V_\tau = v_2!\ 1 \otimes g_{2,v_2} \otimes 1 \otimes \ldots \otimes 1 + \Sigma\, x_i \otimes y_i \otimes 1 \otimes \ldots \otimes 1,$$
$$\deg x_i > 0,$$

$$\vdots$$

Order the partitions τ as follows. Let $\deg \tau = 2v_1 + 4v_2 + \dots + 2kv_k$. If $\tau' = (v_1', v_2', \dots)$ has $\deg \tau' = \deg \tau$, let $\tau' < \tau$ if there exists k with $v_i' = v_i$ for $i > k$ while $v_k' < v_k$. Computation as above shows

$$\text{(11)} \quad ch_\tau V_{\tau'} = 0 \text{ if } \deg \tau' = \deg \tau \text{ and } \tau' < \tau .$$

Consider now elements $[M, \alpha] \in \Omega_k(BU)$, and consider the characteristic numbers of such elements as in (7) except that $x \in H^*(BU; \mathbf{Q})$. given finite sequences $\omega = (s_1, s_2, \dots)$, $\tau = (v_1, v_2, \dots)$, let $p_\omega = (p_1)^{s_1}(p_2)^{s_2} \dots$ be the appropriate cup product of Pontrjagin classes of M and let

$$p_\omega ch_\tau [M, \alpha] = p_\omega \cdot ch_\tau(\alpha)[M] .$$

These rational numbers are functions only of the bordism class $[M, \alpha]$. They are zero unless

$$(4s_1 + 8s_2 + 12s_3 + \dots) + (2v_1 + 4v_2 + 6v_3 + \dots) = k .$$

(3.1) THEOREM. Consider $\Omega_*(BU)$ as the ring of bordism classes $[M, \alpha]$ where M is a closed oriented differentiable manifold and $a \in K(M)$ is of virtual dimension one. Then $\Omega_*(BU) \otimes \mathbf{Q}$ is the polynomial algebra generated by $[P_{2i}(\mathbf{C}), 1]$, $i = 1, 2, \dots$, and $[S^{2j}, v_j]$, $j = 1, 2, \dots$, where $V_j \in K(S^{2j})$ has $ch_j V_j$ a generator of $H^{2j}(S^{2j}; \mathbf{Z}) \subset H^{2j}(S^{2j}; \mathbf{Q})$.

PROOF. Consider finite sequences $\omega = (s_1, s_2, \dots)$, $\tau = (v_1, v_2, \dots)$ of non-negative integers. Let $P_\omega = (P_2(\mathbf{C}))^{s_1} \times (P_4(\mathbf{C}))^{s_2} \times \dots$, and consider $[P_\omega \times S_\tau, 1 \otimes V_\tau] \in \Omega_*(BU)$. Note that since the Pontrjagin classes of S_τ are all zero, we have

$$p_{\omega'} \cdot ch_{\tau'}[P_\omega \times S_\tau, 1 \otimes V_\tau] = p_{\omega'}[P_\omega] \cdot (ch_{\tau'} V_\tau)[S_\tau] .$$

Hence, $p_{\omega'} \cdot ch_{\tau'}[P_\omega \times S_\tau, 1 \otimes V_\tau] = 0$ unless $\deg \omega' = \deg \omega$, $\deg \tau' = \deg \tau$ and $\tau' \leq \tau$.

Suppose the characteristic numbers of a linear combination

$$[M, a] = \Sigma\, n_{\omega,\tau}[P_\omega \times S_\tau, 1 \otimes V_\tau]$$

are all zero. We show inductively that $n_{\omega,\tau} = 0$ for all ω, τ. Suppose

$n_{\omega,\tau} = 0$ for all ω, τ with $\deg \tau = \deg \tau_0$ and $\tau < \tau_0$. Then

$$0 = p_{\omega'} \cdot ch_{\tau_0}[M, a] = \sum n_{\omega,\tau} p_{\omega'}[P_\omega] \cdot ch_{\tau_0} V_\tau [S_\tau]$$

$$= \sum_\omega n_{\omega,\tau_0} p_{\omega'}[P_\omega] \cdot ch_{\tau_0} V_{\tau_0} [S_{\tau_0}]$$

$$= v_1! \dots v_k! \sum_\omega n_{\omega,\tau_0} p_{\omega'}[P_\omega]$$

where $\tau_0 = (v_1, v_2, \dots)$. Since the Pontrjagin numbers of $\sum n_{\omega,\tau_0}[P_\omega] \in \Omega_*$ are all zero, it follows from Thom that $n_{\omega,\tau_0} = 0$ for all ω. Hence, inductively, $n_{\omega,\tau} = 0$ for all ω, τ.

The elements $[P_\omega \times S_\tau, 1 \otimes V_\tau] \otimes 1$ are then linearly independent in $\Omega_*(BU) \otimes \mathbf{Q}$. Since there are exactly enough such elements to provide a basis for $\Omega_*(BU) \otimes \mathbf{Q}$ in each dimension, the theorem follows.

(3.2) COROLLARY. Consider a ring homomorphism $I: \Omega_*(BU) \to \mathbf{Q}$, where $\Omega_*(BU)$ is the ring of $[M, a]$ with $a \in K(M)$ of virtual dimension one. Then I is determined by its values on $[P_{2i}(\mathbf{C}), 1]$ and $[S^{2j}, V_j]$ for $i, j = 1, 2, \dots$. If $I: \Omega_*(\mathbf{Z} \times BU) \to \mathbf{Q}$ is a ring homomorphism with $I[M, a+b] = I[M, a] + I[M, b]$, then I is determined by its values on $[P_{2i}(\mathbf{C}), 1]$, $i = 1, 2, \dots$ and on $[S^2, V_1]$.

PROOF. We have only to consider the second proposition. Let $V_j = 1 + W_j$. We shall see that $[S^2 \times S^2 \times \dots \times S^2, 1 + W_1 \otimes W_1 \otimes \dots \otimes W_1] \otimes 1 = [S^{2n}, 1 + W_n] \otimes 1$ in $\Omega_*(\mathbf{Z} \times BU) \otimes \mathbf{Q}$. Both $S^2 \times \dots \times S^2$ and S^{2n} have trivial Pontrjagin classes. Also

$$ch(1 + W_1 \otimes \dots \otimes W_1) = 1 + g \quad ,$$

g a generator of $H^{2n}(S^2 \times \dots \times S^2; \mathbf{Q})$, and similarly, for $ch(1 + W_n)$. Hence $[(S^2)^n, 1 + W_1 \otimes \dots \otimes W_1]$ and $[S^{2n}, 1 + W_n]$ have the same rational Pontrjagin numbers. It follows from the proof of (3.1) that

$$[(S^2)^n, 1 + W_1 \otimes \dots \otimes W_1] \otimes 1 = [S^{2n}, 1 + W_n] \otimes 1 \quad .$$

Then

$$I[S^{2n}, V_n] = I[(S^2)^n, 1] + I[(S^2)^n, W_1 \otimes \ldots \otimes W_1]$$
$$= (I[S^2, W_1])^n, \quad \text{since } S^2 \text{ bords}$$
$$= (I[S^2, V_1])^n \quad .$$

Also if $a \in K(M)$ is of virtual dimension k, then

$$I[M, a] = I[M, a-(k-1)] + (k-1)I[M, 1]$$

where the bundles on the right hand side are all of virtual dimension one. The corollary follows.

The uniqueness theorem for index functions given in Chapter I is now proved.

REFERENCES

[1] M. F. Atiyah, "Bordism and cobordism," Proc. Camb. Philos. Soc. 57 (1961), pp. 200-208.

[2] P. E. Conner and E. E. Floyd, "Differentiable Periodic Maps," Erg. d. Math. u. Grenzgeb. N. F. 33, Springer Verlag, Berlin 1964.

[3] E. H. Spanier, "Duality and the suspension category," Symposium International de Topología Algebraica, 1958, pp. 259-272.

[4] R. Thom, "Quelques propriétés globales des variétés differentiables," Comment. Math. Helv. 28 (1954), pp. 17-86.

CHAPTER XIX

THE INDEX THEOREM: APPLICATIONS

Robert M. Solovay

The different steps of the proof of the index theorem, as outlines in Chapter I, have been carried out in Chapters V and XI to XVIII. For the sake of completeness, we recapitulate this briefly in §1.

Section 2 is devoted to a reformulation of the index theorem, due to Atiyah, which makes sense on non-oriented, or non-orientable, manifolds, and §3 to a reduction of the non-orientable case to the oriented case. We have made use of an unpublished manuscript of Atiyah's. Underlying this new form of the index theorem is a simpler definition of the topological index which, besides the greater generality, has also the advantage of making the sign factor disappear.

Sections 4-6 give some of the main applications of the index theorem: the Riemann-Roch-Hirzebruch formula for arbitrary compact complex manifolds (§4), and the integrality theorems of algebraic topology (§§ 5, 6).

§1. Proof of the index theorem

THEOREM 1. Let X be a compact oriented smooth manifold without boundary, ξ, η two complex vector bundles on X, and $S \in E_k(\xi, \eta)$ an elliptic operator from ξ to η (see XI). Then the analytical index $i_a(S)$ and the topological index $i_t(S)$ are equal.

PROOF. By applying the difference construction to the symbol of S, we get an element $\gamma(S) \in K(B(X), S(X))$. According to [XV, Theorem 1] $i_t(S)$ depends only on $\gamma(S)$; moreover, each element $a \in K(B(X), S(X))$ has the form $\gamma(S)$ for some elliptic operator S. In this way, i_a induces a homomorphism of $K(B(X), S(X))$ into $\mathbf{Z}$. On the other hand, by its definition, i_t may be viewed as a homomorphism of $K(B(X), S(X))$ into $\mathbf{Q}$.

Let now X be even dimensional and let D_X be the differential operator constructed in V, §2, such that $i_a(D_X)$ is the signature of X and $i_t(D_X)$ the L-genus of X. We define homomorphisms $i_a^!$, $i_t^!$ of $K(X)$ into $\mathbf{Q}$ by putting $i_a^!(b) = i_a(b \cdot D_X)$, $i_t^!(b) = i_t(b \cdot D_X)$. By Theorem 3 of XV, the index theorem for X is equivalent to the equality $i_t^!(b) = i_a^!(b)$ for all $b \in K(X)$.

Both $i_a^!$ and $i_t^!$ satisfy (a), (b), (c) and (d) of I, §4, as follows from Theorem 4 of XV and from XVII. They are therefore equal by 3.2 of XVIII, which proves the index theorem for even-dimensional manifolds.

Let A be the elliptic scalar operator on the circle, whose two indices are equal to -1, constructed in XVI. Let S be an elliptic operator on an odd-dimensional manifold X. By XIV, there is an elliptic operator C on $X \times S^1$ such that

$$i_a(C) = i_a(A) \cdot i_a(S) \qquad i_t(C) = i_t(A) \cdot i_t(S) \quad .$$

Since the theorem is already proved for $X \times S^1$, we have $i_a(C) = i_t(C)$, whence also $i_a(S) = i_t(S)$.

Remark. Let S, T be elliptic operators on odd-dimensional manifolds X, Y. The index theorem for even-dimensional manifolds and the multiplicativity properties of i_a, i_t already imply that

$$i_a(S) \cdot i_a(T) = i_t(S) \cdot i_t(T) \quad ,$$

and consequently that we have either $i_a(S) = i_t(S)$ or $i_a(S) = -i_t(S)$ for all elliptic operators on odd-dimensional manifolds. In particular, since the topological index of a *differential* operator on an odd-dimensional manifold vanishes (Chapter V), this is enough to show that $i_a(S)$ is also zero in that case. However, in order to get the full theorem, it seems necessary to exhibit one operator on an odd-dimensional manifold for which both indices are equal and not zero.

§2. An alternative formulation of the index theorem

Let X be a closed smooth manifold, not necessarily oriented, and let $T^*(X)$ denote its cotangent bundle, with projection $\pi: T^*(X) \to X$. We are going to see that $T^*(X)$ is an almost-complex manifold in a natural way.

LEMMA 2.1. Let E be a differentiable real vector bundle over X, with projection $\pi: E \to X$. Then there is an exact sequence of vector bundles:

(1) $$0 \to \pi^* E \to T(E) \xrightarrow{\pi_*} \pi^* T(X) \to 0 \quad .$$

PROOF. The map π_* is the map induced by the differential of the projection map $d\pi: T(E) \to T(X)$. It is clearly surjective, and its kernel consists of the vectors tangent to the fibres of E. Now if V is any real vector space, and $x \in V$, then the tangent space to V at x is canonically isomorphic to V. If we apply this remark to the fibres of E, we see that the bundle of vectors tangent to the fibres of E is canonically isomorphic to $\pi^* E$. This completes the proof.

If we apply this lemma to $T^*(X)$, we get the exact sequence of vector bundles over $T^*(X)$:

(2) $$0 \to \pi^* T^*(X) \to T(T^*(X)) \to \pi^* T(X) \to 0 \quad .$$

A choice of a Riemannian metric on X determines an isomorphism $T(X) \cong T^*(X)$; moreover, the Riemannian connection induces a splitting of (2). Thus we get an isomorphism

(3) $$T(T^*(X)) \cong \pi^*(T^*(X) \oplus T(X)) \cong \pi^*(T(X) \oplus T(X)) \quad .$$

Now $T(X) \oplus T(X)$ is the underlying real vector bundle of $T(X) \otimes \mathbf{C}$: the complex structure on $T(X) \oplus T(X)$ is given by $J(\langle u, v \rangle) = \langle -v, u \rangle$.

By (3), $T(T^*(X))$ inherits a complex structure (in which the real part is "vertical" and the imaginary part is "horizontal"); in this way, $T^*(X)$ becomes an almost-complex manifold. By construction, we have an isomorphism of complex vector bundles:

$$T(T^*(X)) \cong \pi^*(T(X) \otimes \mathbf{C}) \quad . \tag{4}$$

Remark. The almost-complex structure on $T^*(X)$ depends on the choice of a Riemannian metric; however, it is well-defined up to a homotopy since any two Riemannian structures on X are homotopic.

Let $B(X)$ be the unit ball bundle of $T^*(X)$ determined by some fixed Riemannian structure on X. $B(X)$ inherits an almost-complex structure from $T^*(X)$; we give $B(X)$ the orientation determined by its almost-complex structure. Let $n = \dim X$, and let $[B(X), S(X)] \in H_{2n}(B(X), S(X); \mathbf{Q})$ be the fundamental class determined by the orientation of $B(X)$. Finally, let $\mathcal{T}(B(X)) = \mathcal{T}(T(B(X)))$ be the Todd class of the *almost-complex* manifold $B(X)$.

THEOREM 2. Let X be a compact differentiable manifold, *not necessarily oriented*; let

$$S\colon\ C^\infty(\xi) \to C^\infty(\eta)$$

be an elliptic operator on X. Then

$$i_a(S) = ch(\gamma(S)) \cdot \mathcal{T}(B(X))[B(X), S(X)] \quad . \tag{5}$$

(Note the absence of signs!)

PROOF. We consider first the case when X is oriented. Let $[X] \in H_n(X; \mathbf{Q})$ be the fundamental class determined by some fixed orientation of X. Let $U \in H^n(B(X), S(X); \mathbf{Q})$ be the Thom class associated to this orientation. (From now on, rational coefficients are understood.) Let

$$\varphi_*\colon\ H^{j+n}(B(X), S(X)) \to H^j(X)$$

be the Thom isomorphism: $\varphi_*^{-1}(a) = \pi^* a \cup U$.

LEMMA 2.2. Let $x \in H^*(B(X), S(X))$. Then

$$x[B(X), S(X)] = (-1)^{n(n+1)/2} \varphi_*(x)[X] \quad .$$

PROOF. We recall that the orientation of X determines an orientation of each of the fibres of $B(X)$. A local chart

$$\psi: \pi^{-1}(U) \cong U \times D^n \tag{6}$$

is oriented if it induces the correct orientation of the fibres of $\pi^{-1}(U)$. Orient $B(X)$ so that for each oriented local chart ψ, (6) is an orientation preserving diffeomorphism. (We shall call this the *fibre-bundle* orientation of $B(X)$ to distinguish it from the almost-complex orientation previously introduced.) Let $[B(X), S(X)]^{\#}$ be the fundamental class corresponding to this orientation. Then the following formula is an elementary property of the Thom isomorphism:

$$\varphi_*(x)[X] = x[B(X), S(X)]^{\#} \qquad (x \in H^*(B(X), S(X)) \quad .$$

So it suffices to show that

$$[B(X), S(X)]^{\#} = (-1)^{n(n+1)/2} [B(X), S(X)] \quad . \tag{7}$$

Let $p \in T^*(X)$ and let $\{e_1, \ldots, e_n\}$ be an oriented base for the tangent space to the fibre at p. Then by the definition of the almost-complex structure J on $T^*(X)$,

$$\{Je_1, \ldots, Je_n\}$$

projects onto an oriented base for the tangent space of X at $\pi(p)$. Thus $\{Je_1, \ldots, Je_n, e_1, \ldots, e_n\}$ is an oriented base for the tangent space at p for the fibre-bundle orientation; $\{e_1, Je_1, \ldots, e_n, Je_n\}$ is an oriented base for the almost-complex orientation. These two bases differ by a permutation of parity $n + (n-1) + \ldots + 1 = n(n+1)/2$. This establishes (7) and completes the proof of Lemma 2.2.

PROOF of Theorem 2 (X oriented). By (4),

$$\pi^* \mathcal{T}(X) = \mathcal{T}(B(X)) \quad . \tag{8}$$

Recall that

(9) $\varphi_*(\pi^* a \cup b) = a \cdot \varphi_*(b)$ (for all $a \in H^*(X)$, $b \in H^*(B(X), S(X))$).

Let $\varepsilon = (-1)^{n(n+1)/2}$. We have the following chain of equalities:

$$
\begin{aligned}
(10) \qquad i_t(S) &= \varepsilon\, \varphi_*(\mathrm{ch}(\gamma(S)))\ \mathscr{T}(X)[X] \quad \text{(by definition)} \\
&= \varepsilon\, \varphi_*(\mathrm{ch}(\gamma(S))\ \mathscr{T}(B(X)))[X] \quad \text{(by (8) and (9))} \\
&= \mathrm{ch}(\gamma(S))\ \mathscr{T}(B(X))[B(X), S(X)] \quad \text{(by Lemma 2.2)}\ .
\end{aligned}
$$

(We have used implicitly that $\mathscr{T}(X)$ lies in the center of $H^*(X)$ since it is even-dimensional.)

Theorem 2 (for X oriented) now results from Theorem 1 and (10).

§3. The non-orientable case of Theorem 2

3.1. Let X be a closed smooth manifold, not necessarily orientable. We are going to check Theorem 2 for elliptic operators on X. Our procedure will be as follows: X has a two-sheeted cover $\tilde{X}$ which is orientable. Thus, Theorem 2 is known for elliptic operators on $\tilde{X}$ (cf. §2). To each complex vector bundle, ξ, on $\tilde{X}$, we shall associate a vector bundle $\pi_*\xi$ on X such that

$$(11) \qquad C^\infty(\xi) \cong C^\infty(\pi_*\xi) \quad .$$

In view of (11), each elliptic operator $S \in E_k(\xi, \eta)$ determines an operator $\pi_*S\colon C^\infty(\pi_*\xi) \to C^\infty(\pi_*\eta)$ such that $i_a(S) = i_a(\pi_*S)$. We shall show that $\pi_*S \in E_k(\pi_*\xi, \pi_*\eta)$, and that $i_t(S) = i_t(\pi_*S)$. It follows that $i_a(\pi_*S) = i_t(\pi_*S)$. It turns out that the subgroup of $K(B(X), S(X))$ generated by elements of the form $\gamma(\pi_*S)$ has finite index in $K(B(X), S(X))$. Since $i_a = i_t$ on this subgroup, $i_a = i_t$ on $K(B(X), S(X))$, and the index theorem holds on X.

3.2. Let X be a closed C^∞-manifold (possibly with boundary), and let $\tilde{X}$ be a double covering of X. $\tilde{X}$ may be thought of as a fibre bundle over X with fibre a two-element set. Let ξ be a complex vector bundle on $\tilde{X}$. We define a complex vector bundle $\pi_*\xi$ on X as follows: let $x \in X$, and let y_1, y_2 be the points of $\tilde{X}$ lying over x. Then the fiber of $\pi_* \xi$ at x is given by

$$(\pi_* \xi)_x = \xi_{y_1} \oplus \xi_{y_2} \quad . \tag{13}$$

Let U be a simply connected open subset of X. The portion of X lying over U is a trivial double covering of U. Let j_1, j_2: $U \to \pi^{-1}(U)$ be the two sections. From (13) we get an isomorphism

$$\pi_* \xi | U \cong j_1^* \xi \oplus j_2^* \xi \quad . \tag{14}$$

We use (14) to make $\pi_* \xi$ into a smooth vector bundle. If $f \in C^\infty(\xi)$, then by (13), f determines a section of $\pi_* \xi$. In this way, we get (11); details are left to the reader.

Since the map $\{\xi \to \pi_* \xi\}$ is additive, there is an induced map in K-theory:

$$\pi_! : K(\widetilde{X}) \to K(X) \quad .$$

Recall that the induced bundle construction determines a map $\pi^!$: $K(X) \to K(\widetilde{X})$. The following lemma describes the connection between $\pi_!$ and $\pi^!$.

LEMMA 3.3. Let $a \in K(X)$, and $b \in K(\widetilde{X})$.

(a) $\pi_!(\pi^! a \cdot b) = a \cdot \pi_! b$;

(b) $\pi_! \pi^! a = a \cdot \pi_! 1$;

(c) Let t: $\widetilde{X} \to \widetilde{X}$ be the map which interchanges the two elements of each fibre. Then $\pi^! \pi_! b = b + t^! b$;

(d) the map $\pi_!$ has finite cokernel. (I.e., $K(X)/\pi_! K(\widetilde{X})$ is finite.)

PROOF (a). We may assume that $a = [\xi]$, and $b = [\eta]$; here ξ is a vector bundle on X, and η is a vector bundle on $\widetilde{X}$. It suffices to show that

$$\pi_*(\pi^* \xi \otimes \eta) \cong \xi \otimes \pi_* \eta \quad . \tag{15}$$

Let $x \in X$, and let y_1, y_2 be the points of X lying over X. Both sides of (15) have fibres canonically isomorphic to $\xi_x \otimes (\eta_{y_1} \oplus \eta_{y_2})$; in this way we get the isomorphism (15). The continuity of (15) is easily checked using local charts.

(b): This follows from (a) by taking $b = 1$.

(c): Again we may assume that $b = [\eta]$; we have to show that

$$\pi^*(\pi_*\eta) \cong \eta \oplus t^*\eta \quad . \tag{16}$$

If $y \in \tilde{X}$, then the fibre of both sides of (16) at y is $\eta_y \oplus \eta_{t(y)}$. Therefore (16) holds.

(d): Let 0^1 be the trivial complex line bundle on $\tilde{X}$; $[0^1] = 1$. Since $\pi_*(0^1)$ is two-dimensional, we have

(17) $\quad ch(\pi_!(1)) = 2$ plus positive dimensional terms.

It follows formally from (17) that $K(X) \cdot \pi_! 1$ has finite index in $K(X)$. (Cf. the proof of XV, Theorem 3.) But $K(X) \cdot \pi_!(1) \subseteq \operatorname{im} \pi_!$ by (b). This proves (d).

3.4. We shall also need the relative version of $\pi_!$. Let X, $\tilde{X}$ be as in 3.2. Let Y be a subset of X such that (X, Y) admits the structure of a finite CW pair; let $\tilde{Y} = \pi^{-1}(Y)$. (For example, take $Y = \partial X$, and $\tilde{Y} = \partial\tilde{X}$.) We shall define a map

$$\pi_!: K(\tilde{X}, \tilde{Y}) \to K(X, Y) \quad . \tag{18}$$

Let $\alpha \in K(\tilde{X}, \tilde{Y})$. By II, Theorem 2, we have

$$\alpha = d(\xi, \eta, \sigma)$$

for certain vector bundles ξ, η on $\tilde{X}$ and $\sigma\colon \xi|\tilde{Y} \cong \eta|\tilde{Y}$. We put

$$\pi_!\alpha = d(\pi_*\xi, \pi_*\eta, \pi_*\sigma) \quad , \tag{19}$$

here $\pi_*\sigma\colon \pi_*\xi|Y \cong \pi_*\eta|Y$ is induced by σ. Using II, Theorem 2, one checks easily that (19) is a valid definition.

The following lemma is the relative version of Lemma 3.3 (parts (c) and (d)):

LEMMA 3.5. The map (18) has finite cokernel. Let $a \in K(\tilde{X}, \tilde{Y})$. Then $\pi^!\pi_! a = a + t^! a$. (Here $t\colon (\tilde{X}, \tilde{Y}) \to (\tilde{X}, \tilde{Y})$.)

3.6. Now let X be a closed C^∞-Riemannian manifold, not necessarily orientable; let $\widetilde{X}$ be an oriented double covering of X. We give $\widetilde{X}$ the Riemannian structure that makes $\pi\colon \widetilde{X} \to X$ a local isometry. It follows that π induces a double covering

$$\pi\colon \; B(\widetilde{X}) \to B(X)$$

which is a local isomorphism of almost-complex manifolds.

Let ξ be a complex vector bundle on X. If $\varphi \in C^\infty(X)$, let $M_\varphi\colon C^\infty(\xi) \to C^\infty(\xi)$ be multiplication by φ.

The following lemma gives a criterion for checking that an operator lies in Int_k.

LEMMA 3.6. Let ξ, η be complex vector bundles on X, and let $S\colon C^\infty(\xi) \to C^\infty(\eta)$. Suppose that the following two conditions hold:

(1) Let $\varphi, \psi \in C^\infty(X)$ have disjoint supports. Then

$$M_\varphi S M_\psi \in \mathrm{Op}_{k-1}(\xi, \eta) \quad .$$

(2) For each $p \in X$, there exists $\varphi \in C^\infty(X)$ such that $\varphi(p) = 1$, and $M_\varphi S M_\varphi \in \mathrm{Int}_k(\xi, \eta)$. Then

$$S \in \mathrm{Int}_k(\xi, \eta) \quad .$$

PROOF. Essentially the same as the proof of XVI, §3, Corollary to Theorem 3.

LEMMA 3.7. Let ξ, η be complex vector bundles on $\widetilde{X}$, and let $S \in E_k(\xi, \eta)$. Let $\pi_* S\colon C^\infty(\pi_*\xi) \to C^\infty(\pi_*\eta)$ be the map which makes the diagram

(20)
$$\begin{array}{ccc} C^\infty(\xi) & \xrightarrow{\quad S \quad} & C^\infty(\eta) \\ \wr\wr\wr & & \wr\wr\wr \\ C^\infty(\pi_*\xi) & \xrightarrow{\quad \pi_* S \quad} & C^\infty(\pi_*\eta) \end{array}$$

commutative. Then $\pi_* S \in E_k(\pi_*\xi, \pi_*\eta)$; moreover

(21)
$$\gamma(\pi_* S) = \pi_!(\gamma(S)),$$

and

(22) $$i_a(\pi_* S) = i_a(S) \quad .$$

PROOF. 1. The isomorphism (11) induces isomorphisms

$$H^j(\xi) \cong H^j(\pi_*\xi), \qquad Op_j(\xi, \eta) = Op_j(\pi_*\xi, \pi_*\eta) \quad ;$$

it follows that $\pi_* S \in Op_k$. If φ in $C^\infty(X)$, we define $\tilde{\varphi}$ in $C^\infty(\tilde{X})$ by $\tilde{\varphi}(\tilde{x}) = \varphi(\pi(\tilde{x}))$. Then if $\varphi, \psi \in C^\infty(X)$, we have

(23) $$\pi_*(M_{\tilde{\varphi}}\, SM_{\tilde{\psi}}) = M_\varphi\, \pi_* SM_\psi \quad .$$

If φ and ψ have disjoint supports, then $\tilde{\varphi}$ and $\tilde{\psi}$ do also. Thus $M_{\tilde{\varphi}}\, SM_{\tilde{\psi}} \in Op_{k-1}(\xi, \eta)$, so by (23), $M_\varphi \pi_* SM_\psi$ lies in $Op_{k-1}(\pi_*\xi, \pi_*\eta)$. Thus $\pi_* S$ satisfies (1) of Lemma 3.6.

2. Now let $p \in X$. Let U be a small neighborhood of p diffeomorphic to $\mathbf{R}^n$. Let $j_1, j_2 \colon U \to \tilde{X}$ be the two sections of $\tilde{X}$ over U. We put $U_i = j_i(U)$. Let $\varphi \in C^\infty(X)$ have support in U, and $\varphi(p) = 1$. We write $\tilde{\varphi} = \varphi_1 + \varphi_2$, where φ_i has support in U_i. By (14), we have canonical isomorphisms

(24) $$\pi_*\xi | U \cong j_1{}^*\xi \oplus j_2{}^*\xi \; ; \qquad \pi_*\eta | U \cong j_1{}^*\eta \oplus j_2{}^*\xi$$

which we treat as identifications.

It will be convenient in the following to identify U_1 and U_2 with U. In this way, we get identifications

$$\xi | U_i \cong j_i{}^*\xi \quad ; \qquad \eta | U_i \cong j_i{}^*\eta \quad .$$

If follows that $M_{\varphi_i}\, SM_{\varphi_k}$ becomes an operator

$$M_{\varphi_i}\, SM_{\varphi_k} : \; C^\infty(j_k{}^*\xi) \to C^\infty(j_i{}^*\eta) \quad .$$

In terms of (24), $M_\varphi \pi_* SM_\varphi$ $(= \pi_*(M_{\tilde{\varphi}} SM_{\tilde{\varphi}}))$ has the matrix

(25) $$\begin{pmatrix} M_{\varphi_1} SM_{\varphi_1} & M_{\varphi_1} SM_{\varphi_2} \\ M_{\varphi_2} SM_{\varphi_1} & M_{\varphi_2} SM_{\varphi_2} \end{pmatrix}$$

Thus $M_\varphi \pi_* S M_\varphi$ lies in Int_k. Since p was arbitrary,

$$\pi_* S \in \mathrm{Int}_k(\pi_* \xi, \pi_* \eta)$$

by Lemma 3.6.

3. We now compute the symbol of $\pi_* S$. Since φ_1 and φ_2 have disjoint supports, the off-diagonal terms of (25) lie in Op_{k-1}. It follows now from (25) that

$$\sigma_k(\pi_* S) = \pi_* \sigma_k(S) \quad . \tag{26}$$

This shows that $\pi_* S$ is elliptic. Moreover, in view of the definition of the relative $\pi_!$, (21) follows directly from (26). Finally, since (20) is commutative, we have isomorphisms

$$\ker(S) = \ker(\pi_* S) \;; \quad \mathrm{coker}(S) = \mathrm{coker}(\pi_* S) \quad .$$

From this, (22) follows immediately.

3.8. If $S\colon C^\infty(\xi) \to C^\infty(\eta)$ is an elliptic operator on X, then we set

$$i_t(S) = \mathrm{ch}(\gamma(S)) \cdot \mathscr{T}(B(X))[B(X)] \quad . \tag{27}$$

If X is orientable, this agrees with the previous definition of $i_t(X)$ (by the orientable case of Theorem 2).

We keep the notation of Lemma 3.7.

LEMMA 3.9. $i_t(S) = i_t(\pi_* S)$.

PROOF. Since $\pi\colon B(\tilde{X}) \to B(X)$ is an orientation-preserving double covering, we have $\pi_*[B(\tilde{X})] = 2[B(X)]$. Equivalently,

$$\alpha[B(X)] = \tfrac{1}{2}\, \pi^* \alpha[B(\tilde{X})] \qquad (\alpha \in H^*(B(X))) \quad . \tag{28}$$

Since $\pi\colon B(\tilde{X}) \to B(X)$ is a local isomorphism of almost-complex manifolds, we have

$$\mathscr{T}(B(\tilde{X})) = \pi^* \mathscr{T}(X) \quad . \tag{29}$$

Since $\pi t = \pi$, it follows from (29) that $t^* \mathscr{T}(\tilde{X}) = \mathscr{T}(\tilde{X})$.

Finally,

(30) $\pi^* ch(\gamma(\pi_* S)) = ch(\pi^! \pi_! \gamma(S)) = ch(\gamma(S) + t^! \gamma(S))$,

(by (21) and Lemma 3.5).

From (27)-(30) we get:

$$\begin{aligned} i_t(\pi_* S) &= \tfrac{1}{2}(ch(\gamma(S) + t^* ch(\gamma(S))) \cdot \mathscr{T}(B(\tilde{X}))[B(\tilde{X})] \\ &= \tfrac{1}{2}(1^* + t^*)(ch(\gamma(S)\,\mathscr{T}(B(\tilde{X})))[B(\tilde{X})] \\ &= (\tfrac{1}{2} ch(\gamma(S))\,\mathscr{T}(B(\tilde{X})))\,((1_* + t_*)[B(\tilde{X})]) \\ &= i_t(S) \quad . \end{aligned}$$

(We have used here the fact that since t preserves the almost-complex structure of $B(\tilde{X})$, $t_*([B(\tilde{X})]) = [B(\tilde{X})]$.)

3.10. PROOF of Theorem 2

Let X be a closed C^∞-manifold. Let $\tilde{X}$ be the orientable double cover of X. Since the index theorem is known for orientable X, if $S\colon\ C^\infty(\zeta) \to C^\infty(\eta)$ is an elliptic operator on $\tilde{X}$, we have

(31) $$i_a(S) = i_t(S) \quad .$$

By (31), (22) and Lemma 3.9, we get

(32) $$i_a(\pi_*(S)) = i_t(\pi_*(S)) \quad .$$

We now consider i_a and i_t as homomorphisms from $K(B(X), S(X))$ to $\mathbf{Q}$. (Cf. the proof of Theorem 1.) By (32), (21), and the fact that γ is surjective, we get $i_a = i_t$ on $\operatorname{im} \pi_!$.

But by Lemma 3.5, this is a subgroup of finite index of $K(B(X), S(X))$. It follows (since i_a, i_t map into $\mathbf{Q}$) that $i_a = i_t$ on all of $K(B(X), S(X))$. This completes the proof.

§4. The Riemann-Roch-Hirzebruch theorem

4.1. Let X be a compact complex manifold of complex dimension ℓ. Let η be a holomorphic vector bundle over X. We denote the sheaf of germs of holomorphic cross-sections of η by $\Omega(\eta)$. Let

$$\chi(X, \eta) = \Sigma(-1)^i \dim H^i(X, \Omega(\eta)) \quad ;$$

$\chi(X, \Omega(\eta))$ is the Euler characteristic of X with coefficients in the sheaf $\Omega(\eta)$.

4.2. We review some notation from IV, 6 d). The bundle $\xi = \Lambda(T^*(X)) \otimes C$ has a direct sum decomposition $\xi = \bigoplus_{p,q} \xi^{p,q}$: $\xi^{p,q}$ is the sub-bundle of differential forms of type (p, q). Put

$$\zeta = \bigoplus_q \eta \otimes \xi^{0,q} \quad .$$

Then $C^\infty(\zeta)$ is a graded vector space; $C^\infty(\eta \otimes \xi^{0,q})$ is the subspace of elements of grading q. There is a canonical differential operator $\bar\partial\colon C^\infty(\zeta) \to C^\infty(\zeta)$ which is homogeneous of degree $+1$. Its formal adjoint is denoted by υ. We put $\Box = \upsilon\bar\partial + \bar\partial\upsilon$; $\Box$ is the complex analogue of the operator Δ discussed in §1 of V. Note that υ and $\Box$ are homogeneous of degrees -1 and 0 respectively.

4.3. We now recall the complex analogues of the theorems of de Rham and Hodge. For references for this material we refer the reader to Hirzebruch's monograph [2, pp. 115-118].

The complex analogue of de Rham's theorem is the theorem of Dolbeault: We consider $C^\infty(\zeta)$ as a cochain complex with the differential $\bar\partial$. *The cohomology groups of this complex are canonically isomorphic,* (preserving gradings), *to the sheaf-theoretic cohomology groups* $H^*(X, \Omega(\eta))$. Thus if $\phi \in C^\infty(\eta \otimes \xi^q)$ and $\bar\partial\phi = 0$, ϕ represents some element of $H^q(X, \Omega(\eta))$.

We say that $\phi \in C^\infty(\zeta)$ is harmonic iff $\Box\phi = 0$. Then for $\phi \in C^\infty(\zeta)$ we have:

$$\Box\phi = 0 \longleftrightarrow (\bar\partial + \upsilon)\phi = 0 \longleftrightarrow \bar\partial\phi = \upsilon\phi = 0 \quad . \tag{33}$$

In view of this, if ϕ is harmonic, ϕ represents an element of $H^*(X, \Omega(\eta))$. *Conversely, every element of* $H^*(X, \Omega(\eta))$ *has a unique harmonic representative.*

Now let $\zeta^e = \oplus_q \eta \otimes \xi^{0,2q}$ and let $\zeta^o = \oplus_q \eta \otimes \xi^{0,2q+1}$. Since $\bar\partial$ and υ have degrees $+1$ and -1, $\bar\partial + \upsilon$ maps $C^\infty(\zeta^e)$ into $C^\infty(\zeta^o)$.

PROPOSITION 4.4. The operator

(34) $$\bar{\partial} + \upsilon: \quad C^{\infty}(\zeta^{e}) \to C^{\infty}(\zeta^{o})$$

is elliptic. The analytical index of (34) is the Euler characteristic of X with coefficients in the sheaf $\Omega(\eta)$.

The proof uses the results recalled in Section 4.3; it is quite similar to the proof of Proposition 1, in V, §1.

COROLLARY 4.5. We keep the previous notation and let $\mathcal{T}(X)$ be the Todd class of the complex tangent bundle of X. Then the Riemann-Roch-Hirzebruch formula

(35) $$\mathcal{T}(X)\mathrm{ch}(\eta)[X] = \chi(X, \Omega(\eta))$$

is valid.

PROOF. The index theorem asserts that the topological and analytical indices of an elliptic operator are equal. By Proposition 3, the right hand side of (14) is the analytical index of the operator (34). Proposition 5.2 of Chapter III shows that the topological index of (34) is equal to the left hand side of (14).

q.e.d.

Remark. Previous to the index theorem, (35) was known only for X a *projective* algebraic variety.

§5. Generalities on integrality theorems.

In this and the following paragraph, we deduce the known integrality theorems of algebraic topology from the index theorem.

5.1. Let X be a compact oriented manifold and $\alpha \in K(B(X), S(X))$. By XV, there exists at least one elliptic integro-differential operator D_{α} such that $\gamma(D_{\alpha}) = \alpha$. Its analytical index is an integer by definition. Therefore, the index theorem and the surjectivity of the map $D \to \gamma(D)$ imply the following

COROLLARY 5.2. Let $\alpha \in K(B(X), S(X))$. Then

$$i_t(\alpha) = ch(D_\alpha) \cdot \mathscr{T}(X)[X]$$

is an integer.

We shall assume that the reader is familiar with the notation of a G-structure on X (cf. III, §§2, 4). We shall deduce from 5.2 the following

PROPOSITION 5.3 Let G be a compact Lie group, V a real oriented 2ℓ-dimensional G-module. We suppose that G is transitive on the unit sphere of V. Let $v \in S(V)$, and let H be the subgroup of G leaving v fixed: $S(V) \cong G/H$. Suppose that M and N are two G-modules which are isomorphic as H-modules. Let $\widetilde{M}$ and $\widetilde{N}$ be the vector bundles over B_G associated to M and N respectively. (Thus $\widetilde{M} = E_G \times_G M$.)

If X is a manifold with a G-structure (associated to the G-module V), and $f: X \to B_G$ is a classifying map for the G-structure on X, then

$$f^{**}\left(\frac{ch(\widetilde{M}) - ch(\widetilde{N})}{\chi(V^*)}\right) \mathscr{T}(X)[X] \tag{36}$$

is an integer.

PROOF. Let $\phi: M \to N$ be an isomorphism as H-modules. Thus $\phi(hx) = h\phi(x) (h \in H)$ or equivalently

$$h\phi(h^{-1}x) = \phi(x) \quad . \tag{37}$$

Let $Iso(M, N)$ be the set of isomorphisms of M with N as complex vector spaces. We define $\sigma_1: G \to Iso(M, N)$ by $\sigma_1(g)(x) = g \circ \phi(g^{-1}x)$. Using (37), one verifies that σ_1 induces a map $\sigma_2: G/H \to Iso(M, N)$ by passage to quotients. On the other hand G/H is clearly isomorphic (as G-space) to $S(V)$. A G-invariant inner product on V sets up an isomorphism of G-modules $V \cong V^*$ and thus an isomorphism $S(V) \cong S(V^*)$ of G-spaces. Thus σ_2 gives rise to a G-equivariant map $\sigma: S(V^*) \to Iso(M,N)$.

As discussed in III, §4, σ can be used to construct elements $\alpha \in K(B(X), S(X))$ which are associated to the G-structure and to the G-modules M and N. The result now follows from III, Theorem 1 and Corollary 5.2.

5.4. The result of Proposition 13 can sometimes be improved by a factor of 2, as follows. Let $\mathbf{H}$ denote the field of quaternions.

PROPOSITION 5.4. Let X, G, M, N and V be as in Proposition 5.3. We make the following two additional assumptions:

1) M and N are quaternionic G-moldues.
2) There is a map $\sigma_1 : S(V^*) \to \mathrm{Hom}_{\mathbf{H}}(M, N)$ which
   a) is G-equivariant,
   b) is a homogeneous polynomial map of degree k,
   c) has the property

$$\sigma_1(v) \in \mathrm{Iso}_{\mathbf{H}}(M, N) \quad \text{for} \quad v \in V, \quad v \neq 0.$$

Then (36) is an even integer.

PROOF. Let P be the principal bundle for the G-structure on X. Let

$$\zeta = P \times_G M, \quad \eta = P \times_G N \quad ;$$

by a) and c) we may construct from σ an elliptic symbol $\sigma_P \in \mathrm{Symb}^k(\zeta, \eta)$ (cf. III, §4). In fact, b) shows that σ_P lies in $\mathrm{Symb}^d_k(\zeta, \eta)$ (cf. IV, §1). It follows from IV, Theorem 2 that there is a kth-order elliptic differential operator

$$D: \ C^\infty(\zeta) \to C^\infty(\eta)$$

such that $\sigma(D) = \sigma_P$.

Since M and N are quaternionic G-modules, ζ and η are quaternionic vector bundles. Moreover, for $v \in T^*(X)_x$, $\sigma(D)(v): \zeta_x \cong \eta_x$ is quaternion linear. (Since $\sigma_1: V^* \to \mathrm{Hom}_{\mathbf{H}}(M, N)$.) Let j be the quaternionic unit, and let

$$J: \zeta \to \zeta, \quad J: C^\infty(\zeta) \to C^\infty(\zeta), \text{ etc.}$$

be left-multiplication by j. Thus J is an anti-linear automorphism.

We put

$$D_1 = 1/2(D+J^{-1}DJ) \quad .$$

Then the following assertions are easy to verify:

1) D_1 is a kth order differential operator. (I.e., D_1 is complex linear; if the k-jet of ϕ vanishes at x, $D_1\phi$ vanishes at x.)

2) $D_1J = JD_1$ (use $J^{-1} = -J$). It follows that D_1 is quaternion-linear.

We now show $\sigma(D_1) = \sigma(D)$. In fact, let $v \in T^*(X)_x$, $e \in \xi_x$. Pick $g \in C^\infty(X, \mathbf{R})$ and $f \in C^\infty(\xi)$ such that

$$g(x) = 0, \quad dg_x = v, \quad f(x) = e \quad .$$

Then $Jf(x) = je$. By definition

$$\begin{aligned}\sigma_k(D_1)(v)(e) &= D_1(\tfrac{1}{k!}\, g^k f)(x) \\ &= 1/2(D(\tfrac{1}{k!}\, g^k f)(x) + j^{-1}(D(\tfrac{1}{k!}\, g^k(jf))(x)) \\ &= 1/2[\sigma_k(D)(v)(e) + j^{-1}\sigma_k(D)(v)(je)] \\ &= \sigma_k(D)(v)(e) \quad .\end{aligned}$$

(The last equality follows from the fact that $\sigma_k(D)(v)$ is quaternion-linear.)

Now $i_t(D_1)$ may be computed by III, Theorem 1; its value is (36). On the other hand, $\ker D_1$ and $\operatorname{coker} D_1$ are vector spaces over $\mathbf{H}$ since D_1 is $\mathbf{H}$-linear. It follows that as vector spaces over $\mathbf{C}$ they are even-dimensional. Thus

$$i_a(D_1) = \dim \ker D_1 - \dim \operatorname{coker} D_1$$

is even.

q.e.d.

§6. The integrality theorems

6.1. Let X^{2n} be an even dimensional manifold. The mixed cohomology class $\hat{\mathscr{A}}(X) \in H^*(X, \mathbf{Q})$ is defined by the formula

$$\hat{\mathscr{A}}(X) = \prod_{i=1}^{n} \left(\frac{y_i/2}{\sinh y_i/2} \right)$$

where the Pontrjagin classes of X are the elementary symmetric functions of $y_1^2, \ldots, y_n^2$.

6.2. The following theorem is a known consequence of the differentiable Riemann-Roch Theorem (cf. [3]). In this section we shall deduce it from the general integrality theorem of 5.3.

THEOREM. Let X^m be an even-dimensional manifold. Let $z \in H^2(X, \mathbf{Z})$. Let $\rho_2\colon H^*(X, \mathbf{Z}) \to H^*(X, \mathbf{Z}_2)$ be reduction mod 2. Let $w_2(X) \in H^2(X, \mathbf{Z}_2)$ be the second Stiefel Whitney class of X. We suppose that

$$\rho_2(z) = w_2(X) \quad .$$

Finally, let W be a complex vector bundle over X, of dimension n. Then

$$\hat{\mathscr{A}}(X)e^{z/2} \operatorname{ch}(W)[X]$$

is an integer.

6.3. Using the real form of the differential Riemann-Roch Theorem, Theorem 6.2 can sometimes be improved by a factor of 2. We shall deduce the improved theorem from Proposition 5.4.

THEOREM. Let X be a manifold of dimension m, where $m \equiv 4(8)$. We suppose that $w_2(X) = 0$ (i.e., that X admits the structure of a Spin manifold). Let W be a real vector bundle of dimension n. We write $\operatorname{ch}(W)$ for $\operatorname{ch}(W \otimes_{\mathbf{R}} \mathbf{C})$. Then

$$\operatorname{ch}(W)\hat{\mathscr{A}}(X)[X]$$

is an even integer.

6.4. An outline of the proofs goes as follows. We first recall the definition of the group $Sc(m)$. It will turn out that the hypotheses of Theorem 6.2 allow one to impose an $Sc(m)$-structure on X. We then recall results on the representation theory of $Sc(m)$ which will serve as input to §5.3. The output will be Theorem 6.2. For §6.3, the situation is similar. One puts a Spin-structure on X, and uses results about the quaternionic representations of Spin(n) together with §5.4.

6.5 Let $SO(2) \times SO(n)$ be considered as a subgroup of $SO(2+n)$ in the obvious way. (Here $n \geq 2$.) Let $\pi: Spin(n+2) \to SO(n+2)$ be the covering map. Put

$$Sc(n) = \pi^{-1}(SO(2) \times SO(n)) \quad .$$

If P is a principal Spin(k)-bundle, then $P \times_{Spin(k)} SO(k) = Q$ is a principal SO(k)-bundle.

Conversely, it is well-known that if Q is a principal SO(k)-bundle, a necessary and sufficient condition that Q be isomorphic to a bundle of the form

$$P \times_{Spin(k)} SO(k) \quad ,$$

where P is a principal Spin(k)-bundle, is that $w_2(Q) = 0$.

Now let Q be an $SO(2) \times SO(k)$-bundle over X. For all practical purposes, Q may be considered as an ordered pair (Q_1, Q_2) where Q_1 is a principal SO(2)-bundle over X and Q_2 is a principal SO(k)-bundle over X. (Here Q_1, for example, is associated to Q via the projection map: $SO(2) \times SO(k) \to SO(2)$.) A necessary and sufficient condition that Q be isomorphic to a bundle of the form $P \times_{Sc(k)} (SO(2) \times SO(k))$, where P is a principal Sc(k)-bundle, is that

$$w_2(Q_1) + w_2(Q_2) = 0 \quad .$$

6.6. The two-sheeted covering $Sc(k) \to SO(2) \times SO(k)$ induces an isomorphism of rational cohomology rings:

$$H^*(B_{Sc(k)}; \mathbf{Q}) \cong H^*(B_{SO(2)}; \mathbf{Q}) \otimes H^*(B_{(SO(k)}; \mathbf{Q}) \quad .$$

We denote by χ the universal Euler class (with either integral or rational coefficients): $\chi \in H^2(B_{SO(2)})$. Thus $H^2(B_{SO(2)}, A) = A[\chi]$ (where $A = \mathbf{Z}$ or $\mathbf{Q}$). As usual, we consider $H^*(B_{SO(k)}, \mathbf{Q})$ as a subring of $\mathbf{Q}[y_1, \ldots, y_n]$ where $n = [k/2]$. Thus $H^*(B_{Sc(k)}, \mathbf{Q})$ is identified with a subring of $\mathbf{Q}[\chi, y_1, \ldots, y_n]$. We shall also use χ to denote the characteristic class for $Sc(k)$-bundles determined by $\chi \in H^2(B_{Sc(k)}, \mathbf{Q})$.

6.7. PROPOSITION. Let X, $z \in H^2(X, \mathbf{Z})$ be as in Theorem 6.2. Then X admits an $Sc(m)$-structure (with principal bundle, P, say) such that $\chi(P) = z$. (Here V is $\mathbf{R}^m$, and the action of $Sc(m)$ on V is given by the composition

$$Sc(m) \xrightarrow{\pi} SO(2) \times SO(m) \xrightarrow{\pi_2} SO(m).)$$

PROOF. We give X a Riemannian structure with principal $SO(m)$-bundle Q_2. Recall that the integral Euler class sets up a 1-1 correspondence between principal $SO(2)$-bundles over X and $H^2(X, \mathbf{Z})$. Let Q_1 be an $SO(2)$-bundle over X with $\chi(Q_1) = z$. Now by hypothesis, $w_2(Q_1) + w_2(Q_2) = \rho_2(\chi(Q_1)) + w_2(X) = \rho_2(z) + w_2(X) = 0$. Let Q' be the $SO(2) \times SO(m)$-bundle corresponding to the ordered pair (Q_1, Q_2). According to §6.5, there is an $Sc(m)$-bundle P such that $P \times_{Sc(m)} (SO(2) \times SO(m)) \cong Q'$. It follows that $\chi(P) = \chi(Q_1) = z$ (rational cohomology) and that $P \times_{Sc(m)} SO(m) \cong Q_2$. Since Q_2 is the frame bundle of X, this isomorphism gives rise to an isomorphism $\psi\colon P \times_{Sc(m)} V \cong T(X)$. Thus (P, ψ) is the desired $Sc(m)$-structure on X.

6.8. Let $\iota\colon Sc(k) \to Sc(k+1)$ be the "inclusion" map that covers the "inclusion" map $SO(2) \times SO(k) \to SO(2) \times SO(k+1)$. Then $Sc(k+1)$ acts transitively on $S^k \subset \mathbf{R}^{k+1}$, and $Sc(k)$ is the subgroup fixing e_{k+1}.

The following Proposition summarizes the remarks of [3] on the representations of $Sc(m)$. (In [3], $Sc(m)$ is referred to as G_m.)

PROPOSITION. There are complex $Sc(2n)$-modules M' and N' such that

(1) M' and N' are isomorphic as $Sc(2n-1)$-modules.

(2) In $H^*(B_{Sc(2n)}, \mathbf{Q})$, we have

$$ch(\widetilde{M}') - ch(\widetilde{N}') = e^{\chi/2} \prod_{i=1}^{n} (e^{y_i/2} - e^{-y_i/2}) .$$

6.9. The following paragraph summarizes the results we will need on quaternionic spin-representations (cf. [1, 4]).

$\mathbf{H}$ is the field of quaternions; A_m the Clifford algebra on $\mathbf{R}^m$ (cf. IV, §10). We suppose $m \equiv 4(8)$. Then there is, up to isomorphism, a unique irreducible $A_m \otimes \mathbf{H}$-module, S_m. (S_m is, in fact, an irreducible A_m-module.) As $A_m^+ \otimes \mathbf{H}$-module, S_m splits uniquely, $S_m = S_m^+ \oplus S_m^-$, into irreducible modules. Moreover, $A_m^- S_m^{\pm} \subseteq S_m^{\mp}$.

Since $\mathrm{Spin}(m) \subseteq A_m^+$, $S_m^{\pm}$ is a quaternionic Spin(m)-module.

Consider $S_m^{\pm}$ as a complex Spin(m)-module (via the inclusion $\mathbf{C} \subset \mathbf{H}$). Let $\tilde{S}_m^{\pm}$ be the vector bundle on $B_{\mathrm{Spin}(m)}$ associated to $S_m^{\pm}$. Then, with appropriate labeling of $S_m^{\pm}$,

$$\mathrm{ch}(\tilde{S}_m^+) - \mathrm{ch}(\tilde{S}_m^-) = \prod_{i=1}^{m/2} (e^{y_i/2} - e^{-y_i/2}) \quad .$$

(We are identifying $H^*(B_{\mathrm{Spin}(m)}; \mathbf{Q})$ with $H^*(B_{SO(m)}; \mathbf{Q})$ via the map induced from the canonical map $p\colon B_{\mathrm{Spin}(m)} \to B_{SO(m)}$.

PROOF of Theorem 6.2. We may assume, by Proposition 6.7, that X has an Sc(m)-structure, with associated principal Sc(m)-bundle P_1. Give W a hermitian structure. The principal bundle of W is then a U(n)-bundle P_2. The ordered pair (P_1, P_2) corresponds to an $Sc(m) \times U(n)$-bundle P, and X may thus be viewed as a manifold with an $Sc(m) \times U(n)$-structure.

For brevity, let G be $Sc(m) \times U(n)$. Then G acts, via the projection $G \to Sc(m)$, on the Sc(m)-module $\mathbf{R}^m$ and G is transitive on the unit sphere of $\mathbf{R}^m$ since Sc(m) is. Moreover the subgroup, H, of G that leaves e_m fixed is precisely $Sc(m-1) \times U(n)$.

Let M' and N' be as in Proposition 6.8. Put $M = M' \otimes \mathbf{C}^n$, $N = N' \otimes \mathbf{C}^n$. From the actions of Sc(m) on M' and of U(n) on $\mathbf{C}^n$, we get an action of G on M. Similarly, G acts on N. From Proposition 6.8, it follows that M and N are isomorphic as H-modules. We can apply the results of §5.3 to M, N and G. The result is that

$$\mathrm{ch}(W)e^{X/2}\prod_i \frac{(e^{y_i/2}-e^{-y_i/2})\cdot y_i}{(1-e^{y_i})(1-e^{-y_i})}[X]$$

is integral. (As usual, the Pontrjagin classes of X are viewed as the elementary symmetric functions in $y_1^2, \ldots, y_r^2$ where $r = m/2$.)

The result now follows from the identity

$$\frac{e^{y_i/2}-e^{-y_i/2}}{(1-e^{y_i})(1-e^{-y_i})} = -\frac{1}{e^{y_i/2}-e^{-y_i/2}} = \frac{-1}{2\sinh y_i/2}$$

PROOF of Theorem 6.3. The proof is, for the most part, quite similar to that of Theorem 6.2; we omit many details. Let $G = \mathrm{Spin}(n) \times O(m)$. Then, using the hypothesis $w_2(X) = 0$, we give X a suitable G-structure (cf. first paragraph of the proof of Theorem 6.2).

Let $M = S_m^+ \otimes_R R^n$ and $N = S_m^- \otimes_R R^n$ (cf. §6.9). Then M and N are quaternionic G-modules. Let $V = \mathbf{R}^m$. (We identify V with V^* by means of the natural inner product of $\mathbf{R}^m$.) We are going to apply Proposition 14. Thus we need a map

$$\sigma_1 : S(V^*) \to \mathrm{Hom}_{\mathbf{H}}(M, N).$$

Since $R^m \subseteq A_m^-$, and $A_m^- S_m^+ \subseteq S_m^-$, there is a bilinear pairing $\psi: \mathbf{R}^m \otimes_{\mathbf{R}} S_m^+ \to S_m^-$. If $v \in S(V^*)$, $s \in S_m^+$, $w \in \mathbf{R}^n$, we put

$$\sigma_1(v)(s \otimes w) = \psi(v \otimes s) \otimes w \quad .$$

Then σ_1 satisfies the hypotheses of Proposition 5.4.

The remainder of the proof follows the last two paragraphs of the proof of Theorem 6.2. The interested reader will be able to reconstruct the details.

REFERENCES

[1] M. F. Atiyah, R. Bott and Arnold Shapiro, *Clifford modules*, Topology, vol. 3, supp. 1 (1964) pp. 3-38.

[2] F. Hirzebruch, *Neue Topologische Methoden in der Algebraischen Geometrie*, Springer-Verlag, 1956.

[3] F. Hirzebruch, *A Riemann-Roch theorem for differentiable manifolds*, Séminaire Bourbaki, Février, 1959.

[4] John Milnor, *The Representation Rings of Some Classical Groups*, mimeographed notes, Princeton, 1963.

APPENDIX I

THE INDEX THEOREM FOR MANIFOLDS WITH BOUNDARY

M. F. Atiyah

Introduction

In this appendix we shall indicate briefly how the index theorem may be extended to manifolds with boundary. If X is a smooth compact manifold with boundary Y and d is an elliptic differential operator on X then there is a definition of an "elliptic boundary condition" (or boundary operator) b. This definition, due originally to Lopatinski, imposes an algebraic restriction on the symbol of b relative to the symbol of d. In §1 we shall give this definition, taking care to state everything intrinsically. Such a pair (d, b) then has an index and the problem is to express this index in terms of the topological data provided by the symbols $\sigma(d)$ and $\sigma(b)$.

In the case when the boundary is empty then $\sigma(d)$ defines a difference element $[\sigma(d)] \in K(B(X), S(X))$ and hence a cohomology class $\operatorname{ch} d \in H^*(X; \mathbf{Q})$ by the formula

$$\operatorname{ch} d = (-1)^{n(n+1)/2} \varphi_* \operatorname{ch}[\sigma(d)] \quad ,$$

φ_* being the Thom isomorphism.

In the general case we shall show in §2 that the pair $\sigma(d)$, $\sigma(b)$ defines a difference element

$$[\sigma(d, b)] \in K(B(X), B(X)|Y \cup S(X)) \quad ,$$

and hence a relative cohomology class

$$\operatorname{ch}(d, b) \in H^*(X, Y; \mathbf{Q})$$

by the formula

$$ch(d, b) = (-1)^{n(n+1)/2}\,\varphi_*\,ch[\sigma(d, b)] \quad ,$$

φ_* being now the relative Thom isomorphism

$$H^*(B(X), B(X)|Y \cup S(X); \mathbf{Q}) \to H^*(X, Y; \mathbf{Q}) \quad .$$

The *topological index* $i_t(d, b)$ is then defined, in analogy with the closed case, by

$$i_t(d, b) = (ch(d, b)\,\mathcal{T}(X))[X].$$

Note that $\mathcal{T}(X) \in H^*(X; \mathbf{Q})$ but that

$$ch(d, b) \cdot \mathcal{T}(X) \in H^*(X, Y; \mathbf{Q})$$

and so this can be evaluated on the fundamental homology class of X (which is an element of $H_n(X, Y; \mathbf{Q})$).

If $i_a(d, b)$ denotes the analytical index of the pair (d, b) then we have *

THEOREM. Let (d, b) be an elliptic differential operator on (X, Y). Then we have $i_a(d, b) = i_t(d, b)$.

In §3 we shall make a few brief remarks on the method of proof.

§1. Ellipticity for manifolds with boundary

Throughout we shall be concerned with a smooth manifold X with boundary Y. Let E, G be smooth complex vector bundles on X, Y respectively. A differential boundary operator from E to G is a linear map

$$b: C^\infty(E) \to C^\infty(G)$$

which is given locally by a composition $\tau \circ \tilde{b}$ where $\tilde{b}$ is a matrix of partial derivatives on X and τ is the restriction mapping from X to Y. In the jet terminology of Section IV we can give a more formal definition as follows. A differential boundary operator from E to G of order ℓ is a map $b: C^\infty(E) \to C^\infty(G)$ of the form $b = T_* r j_\ell$, where $j_\ell: C^\infty(E) \to C^\infty(J^\ell(E))$ is the jet map, $r: C^\infty(J^\ell(E)) \to C^\infty(J^\ell(E)|Y$ is the restriction from X to Y and

* This theorem is the result of joint work of Atiyah, Bott and Singer.

$$T_*: \quad C^\infty(J^\ell(E)|Y) \to C^\infty(G)$$

is induced by $T \in \mathrm{Hom}(J^\ell(E)|Y, G)$. It is easy to see that $T \mapsto b$ defines an isomorphism

$$\mathrm{Hom}(J^\ell(E)|Y, G) \to \mathrm{Biff}_\ell(E, G)$$

where $\mathrm{Biff}_\ell(E, G)$ denotes the vector space of all differential boundary operators from E to G of order ℓ.

From the jet bundle exact sequence [IV, Theorem 1] we deduce therefore an exact sequence

$$0 \to \mathrm{Biff}_{\ell-1}(E, G) \to \mathrm{Biff}_\ell(E, G) \xrightarrow{\sigma_\ell} \mathrm{Hom}(L_s^\ell(T(X), E)|Y, G) \to 0 \quad .$$

The image of an element of $\mathrm{Biff}_\ell(E, G)$ under σ_ℓ is called its symbol.

If* $G = G_1 \oplus \ldots \oplus G_r$ and $b = (b_1, b_2, \ldots, b_r)$ with

$$b_i : \quad C^\infty(E) \to C^\infty(G_i)$$

a differential boundary operator from E to G_i of order ℓ_i, we shall say that b is a differential boundary operator from E to G of order $\ell = (\ell_1, \ell_2, \ldots, \ell_r)$. The symbol $\sigma_\ell(b)$ of b is then defined to be $\sigma_{\ell_1}(b_1) \oplus \ldots \oplus \sigma_{\ell_r}(b_r)$.

By a differential operator on (X, Y) we shall mean a pair (d, b) where

$$d: \quad C^\infty(E) \to C^\infty(F)$$

is a differential operator on X and

$$b: \quad C^\infty(E) \to C^\infty(G) = C^\infty(G_1) \oplus \ldots \oplus C^\infty(G_r)$$

is a differential boundary operator. We proceed now to describe the appropriate definition of ellipticity for a pair (d, b). More precisely, if d is of order k and b is of order $\ell = (\ell_1, \ldots, \ell_r)$ we shall define what we mean by an elliptic operator (d, b) of order (k, ℓ). As for the case when Y is empty, the definition will be a condition on the symbol

$$\sigma(d, b) = (\sigma_k(d), \sigma_\ell(b)) \quad .$$

---

* For full generality we should of course consider the case when $E = E_1 \oplus E_2 \oplus \ldots \oplus E_s$. For simplicity of exposition we leave this extension to the reader. The decomposition of G however, is much more important since even the simplest boundary operators tend to be inhomogeneous.

At a point $y \in Y$ we have a natural epimorphism

$$p_y: \ T^*(X)_y \to T^*(Y)_y$$

with a one-dimensional kernel N_y (the co-normal at y). For each $v \in T^*(Y)_y$, $v \neq 0$, let $L_v = p^{-1}(v)$. Thus L_v is an affine line in the vector space $T^*(X)_y$. Let Λ_v denote the algebra of "polynomial" or regular maps $L_v \to \mathbf{C}$: if we choose an isomorphism $L_v \cong \mathbf{R}$, then we get an isomorphism $\Lambda_v \cong \mathbf{C}[t]$ (the ring of polynomials in one variable t). Suppose now

$$f: \ T^*(X)_y \to W$$

is a homogeneous polynomial map of $T^*(X)_y$ into some complex vector space W. Then the restriction of f to L_v defines a regular map

$$L_v \to W$$

or, equivalently, an element of $W \otimes_{\mathbf{C}} \Lambda_v$. Thus we obtain a homomorphism

$$L_s^k(T^*(X)_y, W) \to W \otimes_{\mathbf{C}} \Lambda_v \quad .$$

In particular, taking $W = \mathrm{Hom}(E_y, F_y)$, and using the natural isomorphism (essentially the λ_k of IV, §1),

$$\mathrm{Hom}(L_s^k(T(X)_y, E_y), F_y) \cong L_s^k(T^*(X)_y, \mathrm{Hom}(E_y, F_y))$$

we obtain finally a homomorphism

$$\rho_v: \ \mathrm{Hom}(L_s^k(T(X)_y, E_y), F_y) \to \Lambda_v \otimes \mathrm{Hom}(E_y, F_y) \quad .$$

Hence from the symbol $\sigma_k(d)$ we obtain an element

$$\rho_v\sigma_k(d)(v, y) \ \in \ \Lambda_v \otimes \mathrm{Hom}(E_y, F_y) \quad ,$$

and similarly from the symbol $\sigma_\ell(b)$ we obtain elements

$$\rho_v\sigma_{\ell_i}(b_i)(v, y) \ \in \ \Lambda_v \otimes \mathrm{Hom}(E_y, (G_i)_y) \quad .$$

For brevity let us put

$$\tau(d)(v, y) = \rho_v\sigma_k(d)(v, y)$$

$$\tau(b)(v, y) = \bigoplus_i \rho_v\sigma_{\ell_i}(b_i)(v, y) \in \Lambda_v \otimes \mathrm{Hom}(E_y, G_y) \quad .$$

Identifying $\Lambda_v \otimes \mathrm{Hom}(E_y, F_y)$ with $\mathrm{Hom}_{\Lambda_v}(E_y \otimes_{\mathbf{C}} \Lambda_v, F_y \otimes_{\mathbf{C}} \Lambda_v)$ we may regard $\tau(d)(v, y)$ as a Λ_v-homomorphism

$$E_y \otimes_{\mathbf{C}} \Lambda_v \to F_y \otimes_{\mathbf{C}} \Lambda_v$$

and similarly $\tau(b)(v, y)$ may be regarded as a Λ_v-homomorphism

$$E_y \otimes_{\mathbf{C}} \Lambda_v \to G_y \otimes_{\mathbf{C}} \Lambda_v \quad .$$

It is convenient now to dualize* and to consider instead

$$\tau(d)^*(v, y): \; F_y^* \otimes_{\mathbf{C}} \Lambda_v \to E_y^* \otimes_{\mathbf{C}} \Lambda_v \quad ,$$
$$\tau(b)^*(v, y): \; G_y^* \otimes_{\mathbf{C}} \Lambda_v \to E_y^* \otimes_{\mathbf{C}} \Lambda_v \quad .$$

Let $M(v, y) = \mathrm{Coker}\, \tau(d)^*(v, y)$. Suppose now that d is elliptic of order k. This implies that, for all (v, y),

$$\mathrm{Supp}(M(v, y)) \cap L_v = \emptyset \tag{1.1}$$

where $\mathrm{Supp}(M(v, y) \subset \mathrm{Spec}(\Lambda_v)$ is the set of maximal primes of Λ_v at which $\tau(d)^*(v, y)$ is not invertible. In particular, $M(v, y)$ is a torsion-module and so

$$M(v, y) = \bigoplus_\lambda M_\lambda(v, y), \qquad \lambda \in \mathrm{Supp}(M(v, y))$$

where M_λ is M localized at λ. Now L_v has a natural orientation coming from the "inward orientation" of the co-normal N_y: if $(x_1, \ldots, x_n)$ are local coordinates for X at y with $x_n = 0$ defining Y and $x_n \geq 0$ defining X then dx_n is a basis of N_y and defines its orientation. Thus, $L_v \to \mathrm{Spec}\, \Lambda_v$ is the inclusion of a real oriented affine line in a complex affine line and so we can distinguish between the two components of $\mathrm{Spec}\, \Lambda_v - L_v$ as the *upper* and *lower* half-planes: denoted as usual by $\mathrm{Im}\, \lambda > 0$, $\mathrm{Im}\, \lambda < 0$ respectively. Because of (1.1) it follows that we get a decomposition

$$M(v, y) = M^+(v, y) \oplus M^-(v, y)$$

where

$$M^+ = \bigoplus_\lambda M_\lambda \qquad \mathrm{Im}\, \lambda > 0 \quad ,$$
$$M^- = \bigoplus_\lambda M_\lambda \qquad \mathrm{Im}\, \lambda < 0 \quad .$$

---

* It can be argued that all symbols should be dualized, but to avoid confusion we shall not change the convention at this stage.

Let $\pi^+(v, y): E_y^* \otimes_{\mathbf{C}} \Lambda_v \to M^+(V, y)$ denote the composition of the natural map $E_y^* \otimes_{\mathbf{C}} \Lambda_v \to M(v, y)$ and the projection $M \to M^+$. Finally let

$$j(v, y): \quad G_y^* \to G_y^* \otimes_{\mathbf{C}} \Lambda_v$$

be induced by the natural inclusion $\mathbf{C} \to \Lambda_v$ (as the constant functions on L_v) and let

$$\beta(v, y): \quad G_y^* \to M^+(v, y)$$

be defined as the composition

$$\beta(v, y) = \pi^+(v, y) \circ \tau(b)^*(v, y) \circ j(v, y) \quad .$$

With this notation established we can now give the definition of ellipticity.

DEFINITION 1.2. An elliptic differential operator on (X, Y) of order (k, ℓ) is a pair (d, b) such that

(i) d is elliptic of order k

(ii) for all $y \in Y$ and $v \in T^*(Y)_y$, $v \neq 0$, the map

$$\beta(v, y): \quad G_y^* \to M^+(v, y)$$

is an isomorphism.

We proceed now to show that this definition is essentially the same as that given in [Hörmander: Linear Partial Differential Operators Chapter X]. Hörmander starts by considering the case of homogeneous constant coefficient operators in the half-space $x_n \geq 0$ of $\mathbf{R}^n$. Let P be an $m \times m$ matrix whose entries are homogeneous polynomials of degree k in n variables, and let p_j be $m_j \times m$ matrices $(j = 1, \ldots, r)$ whose entries are homogeneous of degree ℓ_j $(j = 1, \ldots, r)$. Then Hörmander defines $\{P(\frac{\partial}{\partial x_1}, \ldots, \frac{\partial}{\partial x_n}); p_j(\frac{\partial}{\partial x_1}, \ldots, \frac{\partial}{\partial x_n}) \ j=1, \ldots, r\}$ to be an elliptic boundary system if

(i) P is elliptic

(ii) $mk = 2 \sum m_j$

(iii) the boundary problem

$$P\left(\frac{\partial}{\partial x_1}, \ldots, \frac{\partial}{\partial x_n}\right) f = 0$$

$$p_j\left(\frac{\partial}{\partial x_1}, \ldots, \frac{\partial}{\partial x_n}\right) f|_{x_n=0} = 0 \qquad (j=1, \ldots, r)$$

has no solution, bounded for $x_n \geq 0$, which is of the form

$$f(x_1, \ldots, x_{n-1}) = \exp(ix_1\xi_1 + \ldots + ix_{n-1}\xi_{n-1})h(x_n)$$

with $(\xi_1, \ldots, \xi_{n-1}) \neq 0$ (and real) and $h \neq 0$.

First let us observe that (ii) and (iii) may be reformulated as

(ii)' for each $(\xi_1, \ldots, \xi_{n-1}) \neq 0$ and real, and for every set of vectors $g_j \in \mathbf{C}^{m_j}$, the boundary problem

$$(*) \qquad P(\xi_1, \ldots, \xi_{n-1}, -i\frac{d}{dx_n}) h = 0$$

$$(**) \qquad p_j(\xi_1, \ldots, \xi_{n-1}, -i\frac{d}{dx_n}) h|_{x_n=0} = g_i \qquad (j=1, \ldots, r)$$

has a unique solution h which is bounded for $x_n \geq 0$.

In fact, writing $v = (\xi_1, \ldots, \xi_{n-1})$, let $\mathscr{M}_v$ denote the vector space of solutions of (*). We have $\dim \mathscr{M}_v = km$. Since P is elliptic we can decompose

$$\mathscr{M}_v = \mathscr{M}_v^+ \otimes \mathscr{M}_v^-$$

where $\mathscr{M}_v^+$ consists of exponential polynomials involving $\exp(i\lambda x_n)$ with $\operatorname{Im}\lambda > 0$ and $\mathscr{M}_v^-$ involves those with $\operatorname{Im}\lambda < 0$. Thus $\mathscr{M}_v^+$ consists of the solutions of (*) which are bounded for $x_n \geq 0$. The equation (**) then defines a mapping

$$\mathscr{M}_v^+ \rightarrow \bigoplus_j \mathbf{C}^{m_j} \quad .$$

If (ii)' is satisfied, this is an isomorphism so that $\dim \mathscr{M}_v^+ = \Sigma\, m_j$. Replacing v by $-v$ we also have

$$\dim \mathscr{M}_{-v}^+ = \Sigma\, m_j$$

But $M_{-v}^+ \cong \mathscr{M}_v^-$ and so

$$\dim \mathscr{M}_v^+ = \dim \mathscr{M}_v^- = \Sigma\, m_j \quad .$$

Hence

$$\Sigma\, m_j = \frac{1}{2} \dim \mathscr{M}_v = \frac{1}{2}\, km \quad .$$

Thus (ii)' implies (ii) and also (iii) (taking $g = 0$). Conversely, (iii) implies that

$$\dim \mathscr{M}_v^+ \leq \Sigma\, m_j$$

and, replacing v by $-v$, that

$$\dim \mathscr{M}_v^- \leq \Sigma\, m_j \quad .$$

Hence, from (ii), these must be equalities, and so injectivity of the map

$$\mathscr{M}_y^+ \to \bigoplus_j \mathbf{C}^{m_j}$$

implies surjectivity. Thus (ii) and (iii) imply (ii)'.

In the general case when the coefficients are variable and the operators not homogeneous, we impose the above conditions on the constant coefficient problems obtained by fixing the values of the coefficients at each point of the boundary and taking the highest order terms (and in the interior we continue to require ellipticity of P of course). In other words we impose conditions (i) and (ii)' on the *symbols* of the operators. We want to show that this will give Definition 1.2. To do this we shall express Definition 1.2 in the local coordinates around the point $y \in Y$. Then v will have coordinates $(\xi_1, \ldots, \xi_{n-1})$ and we can identify Λ_v with $\mathbf{C}[x_n]$. For brevity, since (y, v) are now fixed, we shall omit all the symbols (y, v) and write $\Lambda = \Lambda_v$, $E = E_y$ etc.

Let $\mathbf{D}$ denote the smooth functions of x_n (with values in $\mathbf{C}$) and turn this into a Λ-module in the usual way by

$$x_n(f) = -i\, \frac{df}{dx_n} \quad .$$

Now apply the functor $\mathrm{Hom}_\Lambda(\ , \mathbf{D})$ to the diagram

$$\begin{array}{ccccccc} F^* \otimes \Lambda & \xrightarrow{\tau(d)^*} & E^* \otimes \Lambda & \longrightarrow & M & \longrightarrow & 0 \\ & & \Big\downarrow \tau(b)^* & & & & \\ & & G^* \otimes \Lambda & & & & \end{array}$$

and we get

$$\begin{array}{ccccccc} 0 & \to & \mathrm{Hom}_\Lambda(M, \mathbf{D}) & \to & E \otimes \mathbf{D} & \xrightarrow{\theta} & F \otimes \mathbf{D} \\ & & & & \Big\downarrow \varphi & & \\ & & & & G \otimes \mathbf{D} & & \end{array}$$

where θ, φ are precisely the ordinary differential operators occurring in (*), (**). Thus

$$\mathrm{Hom}_\Lambda(M, \mathbf{D}) \cong \mathscr{M}$$

as Λ-modules, so that

$$\mathrm{Hom}_\Lambda(M^+, \mathbf{D}) \cong \mathscr{M}^+$$

From the composition

$$G^* \longrightarrow G^* \otimes \Lambda \xrightarrow{\pi^+\tau(b)^*} M^+$$

we obtain the commutative diagram

$$\begin{array}{ccccc}
\mathrm{Hom}_{\mathbf{C}}(G^*, \mathbf{D}) & \xleftarrow{\cong} & \mathrm{Hom}_\Lambda(G^* \otimes \Lambda, \mathbf{D}) & \longleftarrow & \mathrm{Hom}_\Lambda(M^+, \mathbf{D}) \\
\downarrow & & \downarrow & & \downarrow \alpha \\
\mathrm{Hom}_{\mathbf{C}}(G^*, \mathbf{C}) & \xleftarrow{\cong} & \mathrm{Hom}_{\mathbf{C}}(G^* \otimes \Lambda, \mathbf{C}) & \longleftarrow & \mathrm{Hom}_{\mathbf{C}}(M^+, \mathbf{C})
\end{array}$$

where the vertical arrows are induced by the map $\mathbf{D} \to \mathbf{C}$ given by $f \mapsto f(0)$. Condition (ii)' asserts precisely that the dotted arrow is an isomorphism. The composition on the bottom line is precisely β^*, the dual of

$$\beta: \ G^* \to M^+ .$$

Hence, the equivalence of (ii)' and Definition 2.1 (ii) will follow if we can show that

$$\alpha: \ \mathrm{Hom}_\Lambda(M^+, \mathbf{D}) \to \mathrm{Hom}_{\mathbf{C}}(M^+, \mathbf{C})$$

is an isomorphism. Since both spaces have the same dimension it is sufficient to prove α injective. Suppose therefore, $\psi \in \mathrm{Hom}_\Lambda(M^+, \mathbf{D})$ with $\alpha(\psi) = 0$. Then for any $m \in M^+$, we have

$$\psi(f(x_n)m) = f\left(-i \frac{d}{dx_n}\right) \psi(m) \Big|_{x_n=0} = 0$$

for all polynomials f. But M^+ is a torsion module so that $\psi(m)$ is an exponential polynomial and in particular is analytic. Since all its derivatives vanish for $x_n = 0$ we must have $\psi(m) = 0$. Hence $\psi = 0$ and so α is injective. This completes the identification of our definition with that of Hörmander. Essentially Definition 2.1 is just a translation of Hörmander's condition into intrinsic algebraic terms.

Suppose now that (d, b) is an elliptic operator on (X, Y).

The operator d itself defines for each (v, y) (with $v \neq 0$) a vector space $M^+(v, y)$. The set M^+ of all these has a natural bundle structure over $T'(Y)$, the complement of the zero-section in $T^*(Y)$. We write $M^+(d)$ when we want to show the dependence of M^+ on d. The boundary operator b then defines a vector bundle isomorphism

$$\beta: \pi_Y^* G^* \to M^+$$

where $\pi_Y: T'(Y) \to Y$ is the projection. Thus an elliptic operator on (X, Y) has associated with it two vector bundle isomorphisms, namely the isomorphism

$$\sigma(d): \pi_X^* E \to \pi_X^* F$$

on $T'(X)$ and the isomorphism β on $T'(Y)$. In the next section we shall show how to combine these two isomorphisms to obtain a more convenient invariant.

An elliptic operator (d, b) on (X, Y) is a mapping

$$C^\infty(E) \to C^\infty(F) \oplus C^\infty(G) \quad .$$

It is shown in Hörmander (*loc. cit.*) that this mapping has finite-dimensional kernel and cokernel, and hence an index. This is the *analytical index* of (d, b) and is denoted by $i_a(d, b)$.

§2. The difference element $[\sigma(d, b)]$

To simplify notation we shall adopt the following general convention. If $f_i: Y \to X_i$ are fixed maps $(i=1, 2)$ and E_i are vector bundles on X_i, then we write $\mathrm{Hom}_Y(E_1, E_2)$ instead of $\mathrm{Hom}(f_1^* E_1, f_2^* E_2)$.

Now let X be a compact manifold with boundary Y. We choose a Riemannian metric on X and take the induced metric on Y. This defines for us $B(X)$, $S(X)$, $B(Y)$, $S(Y)$ the unit ball and unit sphere bundle of $T^*(X)$ and $T^*(Y)$ respectively. Moreover, the metric enables us to identify $B(Y)$ with a subspace of $B(X)|Y$. The inward unit normal along Y defines a section of $S(X)|Y$ which we denote by ν. The outward normal is denoted by $-\nu$.

Let (d, b) be an elliptic operator on (X, Y) as in §1. Then

$$\sigma(d) \in \mathrm{ISO}_{S(X)}(E, F)$$

and $\sigma(b)$ defines

$$\beta \in ISO_{S(Y)}(G^*, M^+)$$

where M^+ is the bundle on $T'(Y)$ defined by $\sigma(d)$ as explained in §1. What we want to show is that β defines in a natural way an element mapping into $[\sigma(d)]$ under the homomorphism

$$K(B(X), B(X)|Y \cup S(X)) \to K(B(X), S(X)) \quad .$$

The direct construction of this element is rather intricate since it depends essentially on the proof of the Bott periodicity theorem. It seems best, therefore, to characterize the element we are looking for axiomatically and then to state an existence theorem.

For each point $\eta \in S(Y)_y$ we consider the semi-circle C_η joining it to $\pm \nu_y$. A point on it is described parametrically by an angle θ, the point (η, θ) corresponding to θ being

$$\eta \operatorname{Sin} \theta - \nu_y \operatorname{Cos} \theta \quad .$$

Thus $0 \leq \theta \leq \pi$, $\theta = 0$ corresponds to $-\nu$ and $\theta = \pi$ to $+\nu$. We put $z = \exp(2i\theta)$. Let r be a fixed integer. Given vector bundles E, F over X we consider elements

$$\alpha \in ISO_{S(X)}(E, F)$$

with the property that for each $y \in Y$ and $\eta \in S(Y)_y$ the restriction of α to the semi-circle C_η is of the form

$$\alpha(\eta, \theta) = \exp(ri\theta)p_\eta(z)$$

where $p_\eta(z)$ is a polynomial in z with values in $\operatorname{Hom}(E_y, F_y)$. The set of all such α (E, F being allowed to vary) is denoted by $\mathcal{Q}_r(X)$. Note that if $\alpha = \sigma(d)$ is the symbol of an elliptic differential operator of order k, then the restriction of α to C_η is a homogeneous polynomial of degree k in $\operatorname{Cos} \theta, \operatorname{Sin} \theta$ and hence $\alpha \in \mathcal{Q}_{-k}(X)$.

Let $\alpha \in \mathcal{Q}_r(X)$ and let $p_\eta(z)$ be the associated polynomial in z defined above. Then since $\alpha(\eta, \theta)$ is an *isomorphism* for all (η, θ) it follows that $p_\eta(z)$ is also an isomorphism for all η and all z with $|z| = 1$. Hence if we put $\Lambda = \mathbf{C}[z]$ and define M_η by the exact sequence of Λ-modules:

$$F_y^* \otimes \Lambda \xrightarrow{p_\eta^*} E_y^* \otimes \Lambda \to M_\eta \to 0$$

then M_η is a torsion module with

$$\mathrm{Supp}(M_\eta) \cap \{|z| = 1\} = \emptyset \quad .$$

Thus we get a decomposition

$$M_\eta = M_\eta^+ \oplus M_\eta^-$$

where M_η^+ is obtained by localizing inside the unit circle and M_η^- by localizing outside. Then $M^+ = \cup_\eta M_\eta^+$ has a natural structure of vector bundle over $S(Y)$. We write $M^+(\alpha)$ to show the dependence of M^+ on α.

If $\alpha = \sigma(d)$ where d is an elliptic differential operator of order k then the bundle $M^+(\alpha)$ is naturally isomorphic to the bundle denoted by $M^+(d)$ in §1. In fact, the line L_v of §1, with $v = \eta$, is just the line $\eta + t\nu$ so that $\Lambda_v = \mathbf{C}[t]$. Hence putting

$$(*) \qquad t = -\mathrm{Cot}\ \theta = i \cdot \frac{1+z}{1-z}$$

we see that

$$\tau(d)(t) = \alpha(\eta, \theta) = \exp(-ki\theta)p_\eta(z)$$

and the conformal transformation (*) takes the upper half t-plane into the interior of the unit circle in the z-plane. If we let Λ_1, Λ_2 be the rings defined by

$$\Lambda_1 \subset \mathbf{C}(z) \ \text{ with no poles in } |z| < 1$$

$$\Lambda_2 \subset \mathbf{C}(t) \ \text{ with no poles in } \mathrm{Im}\ t > 0$$

then * induces an isomorphism $\Lambda_1 \cong \Lambda_2$. But by definition of $M_\eta^+(d)$ and $M_\eta^+(\alpha)$ we have the exact sequences

$$F^* \otimes \Lambda_1 \xrightarrow{p_1} E^* \otimes \Lambda_1 \to M_\eta^+(d) \to 0$$

$$F^* \otimes \Lambda_2 \xrightarrow{\tau_2} E^* \otimes \Lambda_2 \to M_\eta^+(\alpha) \to 0$$

where p_1, τ_2 denote the homomorphisms obtained by extending $\mathbf{C}[z]$ to Λ_1 and $\mathbf{C}[t]$ to Λ_2 respectively. Hence we have a natural isomorphism

$$M_\eta^+(d) \cong M_\eta^+(\alpha)$$

and so a vector bundle isomorphism

$$M^+(d) \cong M^+(\alpha)$$

as asserted.

We shall denote by $\mathcal{Q}_r(X, Y)$ the set of all pairs (α, β) where

(i) $\alpha \in \mathcal{Q}_r(X)$;

(ii) $\beta \in \mathrm{ISO}_{S(Y)}(H, M^+(\alpha))$ for some vector bundle H on Y.

By what we have seen in §1 it follows that an elliptic differential operator (d, b) on (X, Y) of order (k, ℓ) defines an element of $\mathcal{Q}_{-k}(X, Y)$ (where $H = G^*$ in the notation of §1). By a slight abuse of language we shall refer to this element as the symbol of (d, b) and denote it by $\sigma(d, b)$.

We shall denote by $\mathcal{Q}_r^*(X)$ the subset of $\mathcal{Q}_r(X)$ consisting of those α with the property that, for each $\eta \in S(Y)_y$, the associated polynomial $p_\eta(z)$ depends only on y. For such an α the vector space M_η^+ depends only on y and so $M^+(\alpha)$ is, in a natural way, a vector bundle on Y. Hence, taking $H = M^+(\alpha)$ the identity map of $M^+(\alpha)$ gives a natural choice for β. We shall identify $\mathcal{Q}_r^*(X)$ with its image in $\mathcal{Q}_r^*(X, Y)$ under the map

$$\alpha \mapsto (\alpha, \mathrm{Id}(M^+(\alpha))) .$$

If $\alpha \in \mathrm{ISO}_{S(X)}(E, F)$ is an element of $\mathcal{Q}_r^*(X)$ then by definition its value on the semi-circles C_η, for $\eta \in S(Y)_y$, depends only on y and not on η. Thus for fixed y, θ the value of α on the circle $(\eta, \theta) \subset S(X)_y$ is constant, and so α can be extended trivially to the interior. This extension then defines an element

$$\bar{\alpha} \in \mathrm{ISO}_{\partial B(X)}(E, F)$$

where $\partial B(X) = S(X) \cup B(X)|Y$. Explicitly, if $y \in Y$, $\eta \in S(Y)_y$, $0 \leq \theta \leq \pi$, $\rho > 0$

$$\bar{\alpha}(\rho\eta \operatorname{Sin} \theta - \nu_y \operatorname{Cos} \theta) = \alpha(\eta \operatorname{Sin} \theta - \nu_y \operatorname{Cos} \theta) .$$

Isomorphism and direct sums in $\mathcal{Q}_r(X, Y)$ are defined in the obvious way.

If E, F are vector bundles over $X \times I$, an element $\alpha \in \mathrm{ISO}_{S(X)\times I}(E, F)$ with the property that its restriction to $S(X) \times \{t\}$ is an element of $\mathcal{Q}_r(X)$, for each $t \in I$, will be called a *homotopy* in $\mathcal{Q}_r(X)$. If α is such a homotopy then we can define $M^+(\alpha)$ as a vector bundle over $S(Y) \times I$ so that

$$M^+(\alpha)|S(Y) \times \{t\} = M^+(\alpha_t) \quad .$$

If now H is a vector bundle over $Y \times I$ and $\beta \in ISO_{S(Y)\times I}(H, M^+(\alpha))$ the pair (α, β) will be called a homotopy in $\mathcal{Q}_r(X, Y)$. Two elements ξ, $\eta \in \mathcal{Q}_r(X, Y)$ are called *homotopic* if there is a homotopy (α, β) in $\mathcal{Q}_r(X, Y)$ so that ξ is isomorphic to (α_0, β_0) and η is isomorphic to (α_1, β_1).

We are now in a position to state the main topological result which is needed.

PROPOSITION 2.1. There exists one and only one function $f\colon \mathcal{Q}_r(X, Y) \to K(B(X), \partial B(X))$ satisfying the following conditions:

(i) $f(\xi) = f(\eta)$ if ξ, η are homotopic;

(ii) $f(\xi \oplus \eta) = f(\xi) + f(\eta)$;

(iii) $f(\alpha) = [\bar{\alpha}]$ if $\alpha \in \mathcal{Q}_r^*(X)$.

If f is the unique function given by Proposition 2.1 we shall put, for $\xi \in \mathcal{Q}_r(X, Y)$

$$[\xi] = f(\xi) \quad .$$

In particular, if (d, b) is an elliptic differential operator on (X, Y) we have an element

$$[\sigma(d, b)] \in K(B(X), \partial B(X)).$$

From this $ch(d, b)$ and $i_t(d, b)$ are then defined as explained in the Introduction.

Remark. The proof of Proposition 2.1 will contain an explicit construction for $f(\xi)$. In principle therefore, the topological index $i_t(d, b)$ can be calculated explicitly.

§3. Comments on the proof

We discuss first Proposition 2.1. The idea of the proof is to show that, given any $\xi \in \mathcal{Q}_r(X, Y)$, we can construct $\eta \in \mathcal{Q}_r^*(X)$ with $[\bar{\eta}] = 0$ and a homotopy of $\xi \oplus \eta$ to another $\zeta \in \mathcal{Q}_r^*(X)$. If this can be done then, for any f satisfying (i), (ii), and (iii) we must have

$$f(\xi) = f(\xi \oplus \eta) - f(\eta) = f(\zeta) - f(\eta) = [\bar{\zeta}] \quad .$$

Thus *uniqueness* of f will follow. To prove the *existence* of such an f we need a reasonably canonical construction of ζ from ξ, that is to say, we need a construction which may depend on some choices but should have the property that $[\zeta]$ is independent of all the choices. A construction with these properties can be deduced quite easily from the elementary proof of the periodicity theorem [Atiyah and Bott: on "The periodicity theorem for complex vector bundles," Acta Mathematica 112 (1964)]. See also the lectures by Atiyah-Bott in the Proceedings of the International Colloquium on Differential Analysis (Tata Institute, 1964).

The relevance of the periodicity theorem to Proposition 2.1 is quite clear if we consider the symbol $\sigma(d)$ of an elliptic differential operator at a point $y \in Y$. On the one hand, $\sigma_y(d)$ defines a difference element $[\sigma_y(d)] \in K(B(X)_y, S(X)_y) \cong \widetilde{K}(S^n)$ where $n = \dim X$. On the other hand, $\sigma_y(d)$ also defines a vector bundle M_y^+ on $S(Y)_y = S^{n-2}$. These two objects, defined by $\sigma_y(d)$, turn out to correspond essentially under the periodicity map

$$\beta: \quad \widetilde{K}(S^{n-2}) \to \widetilde{K}(S^n) \quad .$$

The precise formula is actually,

$$[\sigma_y(d)] = -\beta(M_y^+ - \dim M_y^+)^*$$

where $*$ is the duality operator[†] on K. In fact this is not only true locally but along the whole of Y so that one obtains:

PROPOSITION 3.1. A necessary condition for an elliptic differential operator d on X to admit an elliptic boundary condition is that $[\sigma(d)]$ should lie in the kernel of the restriction homomorphism

$$K(B(X), S(X)) \to K(B(X)|Y, S(X)|Y) \quad .$$

However Proposition 2.1 is essentially more precise than Proposition 3.1 since it shows how a particular choice of elliptic boundary condition leads to an element of $K(B(X), S(X) \cup B(X)|Y)$ which of course, is the third term in the exact sequence to which the homomorphism of Proposition 3.1 belongs. That is why the proof of Proposition 2.1 requires not only the periodicity theorem itself but also its proof.

† Cf. footnote on page 341.

APPENDIX II

NON-STABLE CHARACTERISTIC CLASSES AND THE TOPOLOGICAL INDEX OF CLASSICAL ELLIPTIC OPERATORS

Weishu Shih

In this appendix we give another computation of the topological index of an elliptic operator associated to a G-structure, thus obtaining those for the classical ones on Riemannian or complex manifolds. We begin in §1 with an introduction of characteristic classes, in H^* and K, which are not necessarily invariant by the addition of trivial bundles. This will be used in §2 to define an endomorphism τ of the semi-group of characteristic classes which gives a unified approach to the Todd class, A- and L-genus. We deduce in §3 a formula relating the character of an operator and the characteristic classes of the base manifold which implies the desired result for the index. In particular, we remark that the character of an operator associated to a G-structure depends only on the image, by the canonical homomorphism $K(B(X), S(X)) \to K(X)$, of its symbol.

§1. Characteristic classes

We recall that a semi-group (abelian) is a set with an operation which satisfies all the axioms of a group except the existence of inverse elements. The following semi-groups are useful for our purpose.

1. Let X ba a CW-complex and denote by $\mathcal{E}_{\mathbf{C}}(X)$ the semi-group (resp. semi-ring) of isomorphism classes of complex vector bundles over X with respect to the Whitney sum (resp. and the tensor product). Similarly, $\mathcal{E}^+_{\mathbf{R}}(X)$ the semi-group of even-dimensional oriented real vector bundles over X.

2. Let Λ be a fixed integral domain, and consider $\Lambda[[t]]$,

the ring of formal power series with coefficients in Λ. Then the following subsets of $\Lambda[[t]]$ defined by

$$\Lambda^{+}[[t]] = \{f \mid f(-t) = f(t)\}$$
$$\Lambda^{\pm}[[t]] = \{f \mid f(-t) = f(t) \quad \text{or} \quad f(-t) = -f(t)\}$$
$$\Lambda^{+}[[t]]^{*} = \{f \mid f(t) = f(1/(1+t) -1)\}$$
$$\Lambda^{\pm}[[t]]^{*} = \{f \mid f(t) = f(1/(1+t) -1) \quad \text{or} \quad f(t) = -f(1/(1+t) -1\}$$

are sub semi-groups of the semi-group $\Lambda[[t]]$ with respect to the multiplication of power series.

3. For each CW-complex X the even-dimensional product

$$H^{2*}(X, \Lambda) = \prod_{i} H^{2i}(X, \Lambda)$$

of its cohomology is a semi-group with respect to the cup-product.

Now we recall that if $\mathscr{E}$ and H are two functors

$$\mathscr{E}, H : \mathscr{F} \rightsquigarrow \mathscr{G}$$

from the category F of finite CW-complexes into that of semi-groups $\mathscr{G}$, then the set of natural transformations from $\mathscr{E}$ into H, which we shall denote by $\mathscr{H}om(\mathscr{E}, H)$, is again a semi-group. If $f \in \mathscr{H}om(\mathscr{E}, H)$, $X \in \mathscr{F}$ we write f_X (or simply f) for the morphism from $\mathscr{E}(X)$ into H(X) defined by f. Now if we associate to each $X \in \mathscr{F}$ the semi-group $\mathscr{E}_{\mathbf{C}}(X)$ etc. we obtain contravariant functors

$$\mathscr{E}_{\mathbf{C}}, \mathscr{E}^{+}_{\mathbf{R}}, K, KO, H^{2*}$$

from $\mathscr{F}$ into $\mathscr{G}$ and we use

$$\mathscr{H}om(\mathscr{E}, H)_{\mu} \quad \text{where } \mu = (+, \times), \quad (+, +) \quad \text{ring}$$

to indicate the semi-group of natural transformations, for example $\mu = (+, \times)$ if the first functor $\mathscr{E}$ is the semi-group with respect to the Whitney sum and the second with respect to the cup or tensor product. Any element of the semi-group $\mathscr{H}om(\mathscr{E}, H)$ may be called a *characteristic class* (or cohomology operation if $\mathscr{E} = H$) and it is said to be *stable* if it is in the image of the canonical monomorphism: $\mathscr{H}om(K, H)_{\mu} \to \mathscr{H}om(\mathscr{E}_{\mathbf{C}}, H)_{\mu}$. The composition of natural transformations induces a map

$$\mathscr{H}om(K, H)_{\mu} \times \mathscr{H}om(\mathscr{E}, K)_{\nu} \to \mathscr{H}om(\mathscr{E}, H)_{\delta}$$

which is denoted by $(f, g) \to f \circ g$, and when μ, ν, δ are suitably chosen " $\circ$" is bilinear.

Example 1.1. Consider the *alternate exterior algebra* (resp. exterior algebra) defined for each complex vector bundle ξ by the virtual bundle

$$\Lambda'(\xi) = \sum_i (-1)^i \Lambda^i\xi \quad (\text{resp. } \Lambda(\xi) = \sum_i \Lambda^i\xi)$$

where $\Lambda^i\xi$ is the i-th exterior power of ξ. This gives two elements

$$\Lambda', \Lambda \in \mathscr{H}om(\mathscr{E}_{\mathbf{C}}, K)_{+,\times} \quad .$$

Example 1.2. Let η be a real oriented plane bundle over X and consider the elements of K(X) given by the virtual bundles

$$\tilde{\Lambda}^+(\eta) = \xi + \bar{\xi} \qquad \tilde{\Lambda}^-(\eta) = \xi - \bar{\xi}$$

where ξ is the unique (within isomorphism) complex line bundle which is isomorphic to η as an oriented real bundle, $\bar{\xi}$ its conjugate. We shall see later that this gives rise to unique elements

$$\tilde{\Lambda}^+, \tilde{\Lambda}^- \in \mathscr{H}om(\mathscr{E}^+_{\mathbf{R}}, K)_{+,\times}$$

Now let $P_\infty(\mathbf{C})$ denote the infinite-dimensional complex projective space which may be considered as a classifying space for U(1) and SO(2). Its cohomology ring is a polynomial ring with a distinguished generator α of dimension 2. Hence, for each complex line bundle ξ (resp. oriented plane bundle η) over $X \in \mathscr{F}$, there exists a unique class, namely the fundamental class of ξ (resp. η), denoted by

$$\alpha_\xi \in H^2(X, \Lambda) \qquad (\text{resp. } \alpha_\eta \in H^2(X, \Lambda)) \quad ,$$

which is the image of α under a classifying map from X into $P_\infty(\mathbf{C})$ inducing ξ (resp. η). Moreover, remark that given a power series $g(t) \in \Lambda[[t]]$ then

$$g(\alpha_\xi) \in H^{2*}(X, \Lambda)$$

(resp. $g(\alpha_\eta)$) is well defined. Then we have

THEOREM 1.1. There exist unique isomorphisms of semigroups

$$\varphi: \mathcal{H}om(\mathcal{E}_{\mathbf{C}}, H^{2*})_{+,\times} \xrightarrow{\approx} \Lambda[[t]]_{\times}$$

$$\psi: \mathcal{H}om(\mathcal{E}_{\mathbf{C}}, H^{2*})_{+,\times} \xrightarrow{\approx} \Lambda[[t]]_{+}$$

such that for each complex line bundle ξ we have

$$f(\xi) = \varphi(f)(\alpha_\xi) \qquad f \in \mathcal{H}om(\mathcal{E}_{\mathbf{C}}, H^{2*})_{+,\times}$$
$$g(\xi) = \psi(g)(\alpha_\xi) \qquad g \in \mathcal{H}om(\mathcal{E}_{\mathbf{C}}, H^{2*})_{+,+}$$

If Λ is a field of characteristic zero then there is a bijective map

$$\delta: \mathcal{H}om(\mathcal{E}_{\mathbf{C}}, H^{2*})_{ring} \xrightarrow{\approx} \Lambda$$

from the set of "non zero ring homomorphisms" to Λ, such that the canonical inclusion $\mathcal{H}om(\mathcal{E}_{\mathbf{C}}, H^{2*})_{ring} \subseteq \mathcal{H}om(\mathcal{E}_{\mathbf{C}}, H^{2*})_{+,+}$ is given by

$$\beta \to e^{\beta t} = 1 + \beta t + \ldots + \frac{\beta^n}{n!} t^n + \ldots \qquad \beta \in \Lambda$$

under the identifications δ and ψ.

THEOREM 1.2. If the coefficient ring Λ of H^{2*} contains $1/2$, then we have unique isomorphisms of semi-groups

$$\varphi: \mathcal{H}om(\mathcal{E}^+_{\mathbf{R}}, H^2)_{+,\times} \xrightarrow{\approx} \Lambda^{\pm}[[t]]_{\times}$$

$$\psi: \mathcal{H}om(\mathcal{E}^+_{\mathbf{R}}, H^2)_{+,+} \xrightarrow{\approx} \Lambda^{+}[[t]]_{+}$$

such that for each oriented plane bundle η, we have

$$f(\eta) = \varphi(f)(\alpha_\eta) \qquad f \in \mathcal{H}om(\mathcal{E}^+_{\mathbf{R}}, H^{2*})_{+,\times}$$
$$g(\eta) = \psi(g)(\alpha_\eta) \qquad g \in \mathcal{H}om(\mathcal{E}^+_{\mathbf{R}}, H^{2*})_{+,+}$$

If the coefficients of H^{2*} are the rationals (or the real numbers) then there is a bijective map

$$\delta: \mathcal{H}om(\mathcal{E}^+_{\mathbf{R}}, H^2)_{ring} \xrightarrow{\approx} \mathbf{Q}^+$$

(where $\mathbf{Q}^+$ = non negative rationals) such that the inclusion $\mathcal{H}om(\mathcal{E}^+_{\mathbf{R}}, H^2)_{ring} \subseteq \mathcal{H}om(\mathcal{E}^+_{\mathbf{R}}, H^{2*})_{+,+}$ is given by

$$\beta \to e^{\beta t} + e^{-\beta t} \qquad \beta \in \mathbf{Q}^+$$

Under the identification δ and ψ .

Remark 1.1. We write $\Lambda[[t]]_\times$ to indicate the multiplication of power series is used as the structure of the semi-group, similarly for $\Lambda[[t]]_+$. By definition of K, we may replace $\mathscr{E}_{\mathbf{C}}$ by K in the case (+, +) and ring, e.g. $\mathscr{H}om(\mathscr{E}_{\mathbf{C}}, H^{2*})_{ring} = \mathscr{H}om(K, H^{2*})_{ring}$.

We shall denote by

$$ch: \mathbf{Q} \to \mathscr{H}om(K, H^{2*})_{ring}$$

the inverse of δ and write $ch^\beta = ch(\beta)$ for $\beta \in \mathbf{Q}$. This is reasonable because $ch^1 = ch$ is just the Chern character, and ch^0 may be identified with the augmentation in K-theory. We shall see later that ch^{-1} and $ch^{1/2}$ will be also useful. Several operations of power series can be transported by the bijection φ (resp. ψ) hence *give a new interesting characteristic class*, e.g. derivative, addition, substitution etc. We shall simply write f^λ for the substitution of λt in f.

COROLLARY 1.1. (Atiyah-Hirzebruch[3]) A characteristic class in $\mathscr{H}om(\mathscr{E}, H^2)_{+,\times}$ is stable iff its corresponding power series by φ has leading coefficient an invertible element of Λ , and the identification map given by Hirzebruch's multiplicative sequence[8] commutes with φ.

We recall that if ξ is a complex line bundle over a finite CW-complex X and $f(t) \in \mathbf{Z}[[t]]$ a power series with integer coefficients then

$$f(\xi-1) \in K(X)$$

is a well defined element of K(X): obtained by substituting the virtual bundle $\xi-1$ (where 1 is the trivial complex line bundle) into f(t). This is possible, because the Chern character of $\xi-1$ has evidently vanishing zero-dimensional component, hence is nilpotent in K(X). Similarly, if Λ is an integral domain, and $f(t) \in \Lambda[[t]]$ then $f(\xi-1) \in K(X) \otimes_{\mathbf{Z}} \Lambda$, is also well defined.

THEOREM 1.3. There exist unique isomorphisms of semi-groups

$$\varphi: \mathcal{H}om(\mathcal{E}_{\mathbf{C}}, K \otimes_{\mathbf{Z}} \Lambda)_{+,\times} \xrightarrow{\approx} \Lambda[[t]]_{\times}$$

$$\psi: \mathcal{H}om(\mathcal{E}_{\mathbf{C}}, K \otimes_{\mathbf{Z}} \Lambda)_{+,+} \xrightarrow{\approx} \Lambda[[t]]_{+} \quad ,$$

such that for each complex line bundle ξ we have

$$f(\xi) = \varphi(f)(\xi-1) \qquad f \in \mathcal{H}om(\mathcal{E}_{\mathbf{C}}, K \otimes_{\mathbf{Z}} \Lambda)_{+,\times}$$

$$g(\xi) = \psi(g)(\xi-1) \qquad g \in \mathcal{H}om(\mathcal{E}_{\mathbf{C}}, K \otimes_{\mathbf{Z}} \Lambda)_{+,+} \quad .$$

In the case $\Lambda = \mathbf{Z}$, there is a unique bijective map

$$\delta: \mathcal{H}om(\mathcal{E}_{\mathbf{C}}, K)_{ring} \xrightarrow{\approx} \mathbf{Z}$$

such that the inclusion $\mathcal{H}om(\mathcal{E}_{\mathbf{C}}, K)_{ring} \subseteq \mathcal{H}om(\mathcal{E}_{\mathbf{C}}, K)_{+,\times}$ is given by

$$n \mapsto (1+t)^n \qquad n \in Z \quad ,$$

under the identification δ and ψ.

THEOREM 1.4. There exist unique isomorphisms of semi-groups

$$\varphi: \mathcal{H}om(\mathcal{E}^+_{\mathbf{R}}, K \otimes_{\mathbf{Z}} \Lambda)_{+,\times} \xrightarrow{\approx} \Lambda^{\pm}[[t]]^*_{\times}$$

$$\psi: \mathcal{H}om(\mathcal{E}^+_{\mathbf{R}}, K \otimes_{\mathbf{Z}} \Lambda)_{+,+} \xrightarrow{\approx} \Lambda^{+}[[t]]^*_{+}$$

such that for each oriented plane bundle η we have

$$f(\eta) = \varphi(f)(\xi-1) \qquad f \in \mathcal{H}om(\mathcal{E}^+_{\mathbf{R}}, K \otimes_{\mathbf{Z}} \Lambda)_{+,\times}$$

$$g(\eta) = \psi(g)(\xi-1) \qquad g \in \mathcal{H}om(\mathcal{E}^+_{\mathbf{R}}, K \otimes_{\mathbf{Z}} \Lambda)_{+,+}$$

where ξ is the unique (within isomorphism) complex line bundle isomorphic to η as real bundle. In the case $\Lambda = \mathbf{Z}$, there is a unique bijective map

$$\delta: \mathcal{H}om(\mathcal{E}^+_{\mathbf{R}}, K)_{ring} \xrightarrow{\approx} \mathbf{Z}^+$$

(where $\mathbf{Z}^+$ is the non-negative integers), such that the inclusion $\mathcal{H}om(\mathcal{E}^+_{\mathbf{R}}, K)_{ring} \subseteq \mathcal{H}om(\mathcal{E}^+_{\mathbf{R}}, K)_{+,+}$ is given by

$$n \mapsto (1+t)^n + (1+t)^{-n} \qquad n \in \mathbf{Z}^+$$

under the identification δ and ψ.

From Remark 1.1 it follows:

COROLLARY 1.2. (T.tom Dieck[6]) The Adams' operations[1] are the only non-trivial cohomology operations of rings in K-theory.

COROLLARY 1.3. Under the identification $\mathcal{H}om(\mathcal{E}_{\mathbf{C}}, K)_{+,\times} \approx \mathbf{Z}[[t]]$, the alternate exterior algebra (resp. exterior algebra) defined in Example 1.1. corresponds to $-t$ (resp. $2+t$).

COROLLARY 1.4. Under the identification $\mathcal{H}om(\mathcal{E}^{+}_{R}, K)_{+,\times} \approx \mathbf{Z}^{\pm}[[t]]^{*}$ the power series

$$(1+t) - (1+t)^{-1},\ (1+t) + (1+t)^{-1}$$

correspond respectively to the characteristic classes

$$\tilde{\Lambda}^{-} \text{ and } \tilde{\Lambda}^{+}$$

introduced in Example 1.2. The image of $\tilde{\Lambda}^{-}$ on an even-dimensional oriented real vector bundle is exactly the one obtained by the construction given in Chapter III, §6, by using Riemann metrics.

COROLLARY 1.5. Let the coefficients in H^{2*} be the rationals $\mathbf{Q}$. Then under the identification of φ and δ, the canonical compositions

$$\mathcal{H}om(K, H^{2*})_{ring} \times \mathcal{H}om(\mathcal{E}_{\mathbf{C}}, K)_{+,\times} \xrightarrow{\circ} \mathcal{H}om(\mathcal{E}_{\mathbf{C}}, H^{2*})_{+,\times}$$

$$\mathcal{H}om(K, H^{2*})_{ring} \times \mathcal{H}om(\mathcal{E}^{+}_{R}, K)_{+,\times} \xrightarrow{\circ} \mathcal{H}om(\mathcal{E}^{+}_{R}, H^{2*})_{+,\times}$$

are given by

$$(ch^{\beta} \circ f)(t) = f(e^{\beta t} - 1)$$

the substitution of the power series $e^{\beta t} - 1$ into f, where β in $\mathbf{Q}$, $f \in \mathbf{Z}[[t]]$ or $\mathbf{Z}^{\pm}[[t]]^{*}$.

Remark. 1.2. All the operations in vector bundles may be interpreted by power series, e.g. complexification, dual etc. Other kinds of compositions can be obtained also, e.g. $\mathcal{H}om(K, H^{2*})_{+,\times} \times \mathcal{H}om(\mathcal{E}_{\mathbf{C}}, K)_{+,+} \to \mathcal{H}om(\mathcal{E}_{\mathbf{C}}, H^{2*})_{+,\times}$ which gives in particular, the *Chern class of the image of a bundle under the Adams' operation. The cocycle condition of Bott*[5] follows also from composition. Similar results for other kinds of bundles are obtained, e.g. the KO case follows from Anderson[2].

§2. τ-homomorphism

We shall give another interpretation of Todd class (resp. $\hat{A}$-, L-genus) which is more closely related to the Λ', $\tilde{\Lambda}^-$, and $\tilde{\Lambda}^+$ elements of $\mathcal{H}om(\mathcal{E}, K)_{+,\times}$. Consider first the sub-semi-group of $\mathcal{H}om(\mathcal{E}, H)_{+,\times}$ defined in the following way: denoting by k a non-negative integer, ξ (resp. η) any complex line bundle (resp. oriented real plane bundle)

$$\mathcal{H}om^*(\mathcal{E}_{\mathbf{C}}, K \otimes_{\mathbf{Z}} \Lambda)_{+,\times} = \{f \mid \exists\, \tilde{f}, k, \text{ such that } (f \cdot \tilde{f})(\xi) = (\xi - 1)^k, \ \forall \xi\}$$

$$\mathcal{H}om^*(\mathcal{E}_{\mathbf{C}}, H^{2*})_{+,\times} = \{f \mid \exists\, \tilde{f}, k, \text{ such that } (f \cdot \tilde{f})(\xi) = (\alpha_\xi)^k, \ \forall \xi\}$$

$$\mathcal{H}om^*(\mathcal{E}_{\mathbf{R}}, H^{2*})_{+,\times} = \{f \mid \exists\, \tilde{f}, k, \text{ such that } (f \cdot \tilde{f})(\eta) = (\alpha_\eta)^k, \ \forall \eta\}$$

where α_ξ (resp. α_η) is the fundamental class of ξ (resp. η) and we use the multiplication for the semi-group operation of $\mathcal{H}om$.

LEMMA 2.1. For each $f \in \mathcal{H}om^*$, there is a unique $\tilde{f}$ in $\mathcal{H}om^*$ which gives the minimum value of k, and, therefore, we obtain an endomorphism of semi-groups

$$\tau\colon \mathcal{H}om^*(\mathcal{E}_{\mathbf{C}}, K \otimes_{\mathbf{Z}} \Lambda)_{+,\times} \to \mathcal{H}om^*(\mathcal{E}_{\mathbf{C}}, K \otimes_{\mathbf{Z}} \Lambda)_{+,\times}$$

$$\tau\colon \mathcal{H}om^*(\mathcal{E}, H^{2*})_{+,\times} \to \mathcal{H}om^*(\mathcal{E}, H^{2*})_{+,\times}$$

where $\mathcal{E} = \mathcal{E}_{\mathbf{C}}, \mathcal{E}^+_{\mathbf{R}}$. The minimum k is called *the order* $\omega(f)$ *of* f. Moreover, the image "τf" is stable, and $\tau^2 f \cdot \tau f = 1$, where $\tau^2 f = \tau(\tau f)$ and 1 is the unit of the semi-group $\mathcal{H}om^*$.

This follows immediately from the fact that $\mathcal{H}om^*$ corresponds to those power series whose first vanishing coefficient is an invertible element of Λ, in particular if Λ is a field $\mathcal{H}om^*$ and $\mathcal{H}om$ coincide. If we define the *Euler class in* K-*theory*

$$\chi \in \mathcal{H}om(\mathcal{E}_{\mathbf{C}}, K)_{+,\times}$$

to be the one which corresponds to the power series "t", then for any $f \in \mathcal{H}om^*(\mathcal{E}_{\mathbf{C}}, K)_{+,\times}$ and any complex vector bundle ξ, we have

$$\chi^{\omega(f)} \cdot \tau^2 f = f, \quad (f \cdot \tau f)(\xi) = \chi(\xi)^{\omega(f)}, \quad \omega(f) \text{ the order of } f.$$

Similarly, if $f \in \mathcal{H}om^*(\mathcal{E}_{\mathbf{C}}, H^{2*})_{+,\times}$ then we have

$$(f \cdot \tau f)(\xi) = (\text{the top Chern class of } \xi)^{\omega(f)}$$

Finally, the complexification "$\otimes\, \mathbf{C}$" and τ are anti-commutative, i.e., the following diagram is commutative

$$\begin{array}{ccc} \mathcal{H}om^*(\mathcal{E}_{\mathbf{C}}, H^{2*})_{+,\times} & \xrightarrow{\ \otimes\, \mathbf{C}\ } & \mathcal{H}om^*(\mathcal{E}^{\pm}_{\mathbf{R}}, H^{2*})_{+,\times} \\ \downarrow \tau & & \downarrow (-1)^{[\omega(f)/2]} \cdot \tau \\ \mathcal{H}om^*(\mathcal{E}_{\bar{\mathbf{C}}}, H^{2*})_{+,\times} & \xrightarrow{\ \otimes\, \mathbf{C}\ } & \mathcal{H}om^*(\mathcal{E}^{+}_{\mathbf{R}}, H^{2*})_{+,\times} \end{array}$$

Recalling that "$\circ$" denotes the canonical composition

$$\circ : \mathcal{H}om(K, H^{2*})_{ring} \times \mathcal{H}om(\mathcal{E}_{\mathbf{C}}, K)_{+,\times} \to \mathcal{H}om(\mathcal{E}_{\mathbf{C}}, H^{2*})_{+,\times}$$

and when the rational numbers $\mathbf{Q}$ are taken for coefficients in H^{2*}, $ch^{\beta} \in \mathcal{H}om(K, H^{2*})_{ring}$, $\beta \in \mathbf{Q}$, being an arbitrary element. We propose to give the following

DEFINITION 2.1. For each pair of elements $ch^{\beta} \in \mathcal{H}om(K, H^{2*})_{ring}$, $f \in \mathcal{H}om(\mathcal{E}_{\mathbf{C}}, K)_{+,\times}$, their τ-class is defined to be $\tau(ch \circ f)$, the image of the composition by τ.

And the definition is justified by the

THEOREM 2.1. The following equalities hold in $\mathcal{H}om(\mathcal{E}_{\mathbf{C}}, H^{2*})_{+,\times}$

(1) $$\tau(ch^{-1} \circ \Lambda') = \mathcal{T}$$

(2) $$\tau(ch \circ \Lambda') = -\bar{\mathcal{T}}$$

where $\mathcal{T}$ the Todd class and $\bar{\mathcal{T}}$ its conjugate, Λ' the alternate exterior algebra. And in $\mathcal{H}om(\mathcal{E}^{+}_{\mathbf{R}}, H^{2})_{+,\times}$

(3) $$2\tau(ch \circ \tilde{\Lambda}^{-}) = A\text{-genus}$$

(4) $$\tau(ch \circ \tilde{\Lambda}^{-} \cdot \tau\tilde{\Lambda}^{+}) = L\text{-genus}$$

where $\tilde{\Lambda}^{-}$, $\tilde{\Lambda}^{+}$ are defined in Example 1.2.

Remark 2.1. We may replace ch by ch^β, e.g.,

$$\tau(ch^\beta \circ \tilde{\Lambda}^- \cdot \tau\tilde{\Lambda}^+) = 1/\beta\ L^\beta \qquad \beta \neq 0, \quad \beta \in \mathbf{Q}$$

but the present statement is convenient for later use. Now it follows from the definition of τ, that in $\mathcal{H}om(\mathcal{E}_{\mathbf{C}}, H^{2*})_{+,\times}$

$$(ch^{-1} \circ \Lambda') \cdot \mathcal{T} = \text{top Chern class},$$

similar equality for A-, L-genus. Moreover the relation between "$\circ$" and "τ" can be obtained; in particular, if f is stable then $\tau(ch^\beta \circ f) = ch^\beta \circ \tau f$. And, in $\mathcal{H}om(\mathcal{E}^+_{\mathbf{R}}, H^{2*})_{+,\times}$ we have

$$2L^{\beta/2} = -\tau^2(ch^\beta \circ \tilde{\Lambda}^-) \cdot \tau(ch^{-\beta} \circ \Lambda' \otimes C) \quad .$$

Finally, the "τ" can be defined for other kinds of characteristic classes.

§3. The character of classical elliptic operators

Given a $\mathcal{E}^+_{\mathbf{R}}$-pair (resp. $\mathcal{E}_{\mathbf{C}}$-pair): (X, η) where η is a 2n-dimensional oriented real vector bundle (resp. complex vector bundle) over a finite CW-complex X, we shall denote by

$$t(\eta) \quad \text{and} \quad \varphi = \varphi_\eta: \ H^*(t(\eta)) \xrightarrow{\approx} H^*(X)$$

the Thom space (i.e., $B(\eta)/S(\eta)$ as defined in Chapter I) and isomorphism (resp. decomplexification of η), and

$$p: \ K(t(\eta)) \to K(X)$$

the homomorphism induced by the zero section of η. We shall define a subset of $K(t(\eta))$

$$U(t(\eta)) \subseteq K(t(\eta))$$

namely the *universal elements of the pair* (X, η) as follows: Consider those representations

$$\rho: \ G \to SO(2n)$$

(resp. $U(n)$), where G is a compact connected Lie group such that

(1) the image $\rho(G)$ has the maximum rank n

(2) ρ induces η, i.e., in $\mathcal{E}^+_{\mathbf{R}}(X)$, $\eta = h^*_\rho(\rho^*\eta_0)$ for some map h_ρ from X to the classifying space B_G, with η_0 the universal 2n-oriented (resp. n-complex) bundle over $B_{SO(2n)}$ (resp. $B_{U(n)}$).

Then we take the union

$$U(t(\eta)) = \bigcup h_\rho^* K(t(\rho^* \eta_0))$$

over all ρ and h_ρ, of the image of h_ρ^*. Remark that $U(t(\eta))$ is non-empty, because one can take $G = SO(2n)$ or a maximal torus of $SO(2n)$. Now let

$$\theta \in \mathscr{H}om(\mathscr{E}_{\mathbf{R}}^{+}, K)_\mu$$

(resp. $\mathscr{H}om(\mathscr{E}_{\mathbf{C}}, K)_\mu$), then the subset of $U(t(\eta))$

$$U_\theta(t(\eta)) = \bigcup h_\rho^* K_\theta(t(\rho^* \eta_0))$$

is called *θ-universal elements*, where $K_\theta = p^{-1}(\theta(\rho^* \eta_0)) \subseteq K(t(\rho^* \eta_0))$. Similarly we may replace K by $K \otimes_{\mathbf{Z}} \Lambda$ or KO etc.

DEFINITION 3.1. An elliptic operator D on a manifold X, is said to be *θ-universal* if its symbol $[\sigma(D)]$ is in $U_\theta(t(\eta)) \subseteq K(t(\eta)) \cong K(B(X), S(X))$ where $\eta = T^*(X)$ is the cotangent bundle of X. (Cf. Chapter I, §1).

It is easy to see that

(1) For an even-dimensional oriented Riemann manifold, the operator "d+δ", defined in Chapter V, §2, is $\Lambda' \otimes \mathbf{C}$-universal.

(2) For a complex analytic manifold the operator "$\bar{\partial} + \vartheta$" (cf. Chapter III) is Λ'-universal.

(3) For an even-dimensional oriented Riemann manifold the operator defined in Chapter V, Lemma 6, is $\tilde{\Lambda}^-$-universal.

Now given a characteristic class f in $\mathscr{H}om(K, H^{2*})$ and a $\mathscr{E}$-pair (X, η) we want to compute the composite

$$\varphi \cdot f\colon\ K(t(\eta)) \xrightarrow{f} H^{2*}(t(\eta)) \xrightarrow{\varphi} H^{2*}(X)$$

of f with Thom's isomorphism. For θ-universal elements, this can be done by finding another $f^{(\theta)} \in \mathscr{H}om(\mathscr{E}, H^{2*})$ which gives the required value on $\mathscr{E}(X)$ without passing to the Thom space; more precisely, we need:

(*) for each $\mathscr{E}$-pair (X, η) and each $\delta \in U_\theta(t(\eta))$

$$\varphi \cdot f(\delta) = f^{(\theta)}(\eta) \quad ,$$

i.e., on universal elements $\varphi \cdot f$ is constant, as one might have expected.

For simplicity, we suppose that the coefficients are the rationals $\mathbf{Q}$ in the rest of this paragraph.

PROPOSITION 3.1. Let $\theta \in \mathcal{H}om(\mathcal{E}, K)_{\mu}$ and $f \in \mathcal{H}om(K, H^{2*})_{\nu}$ be such that their composition $f \circ \theta$ is in $\mathcal{H}om(\mathcal{E}, H^{2*})_{+,\times}$ and of order greater than one: $\omega(f \circ \theta) \geq 1$. Then there exists a unique $f^{(\theta)} \in \mathcal{H}om(\mathcal{E}, H^{2*})_{+,\times}$ satisfying the condition (*). In fact, it is given by

$$f^{(\theta)} = \chi^{\omega-1} \cdot \tau^{2}(f \circ \theta) \qquad \omega = \omega(f \circ \theta)$$

where χ is the *Euler class* in $\mathcal{H}om(\mathcal{E}, H^{2*})_{+,\times}$; $\tau^2 = \tau \circ \tau$, the endomorphism in Lemma 2.1. and $\mathcal{E} = \mathcal{E}_{\mathbf{C}}, \mathcal{E}^{+}_{\mathbf{R}}$.

Now remark that each $\theta \in \mathcal{H}om(E, K)_{+,\times}$ determines a *unique element* in $\mathcal{H}om(\mathcal{E}, H^{2*})_{+,\times}$, namely

$$ch(\theta) = -\chi^{\omega-1} \cdot \tau(\tau(ch \circ \theta) \cdot ch \circ \Lambda' \otimes \mathbf{C}) \qquad \omega = \omega(\theta)$$

where $\mathcal{E} = \mathcal{E}_{\mathbf{C}}, \mathcal{E}^{+}_{\mathbf{R}}$. On the other hand, for each elliptic operator D on a manifold X we denote by c(D) the class

$$c(D) = ch(D) \cdot \mathcal{T}(T(X) \otimes \mathbf{C}) \in H^{2*}(X, \mathbf{Q})$$

where T(X) the tangent bundle of X. Then the above proposition implies

PROPOSITION 3.2. Let $\theta \in \mathcal{H}om(\mathcal{E}^{+}_{\mathbf{R}}, K)_{+,\times}$ (resp. $\mathcal{H}om(\mathcal{E}_{\mathbf{C}}, K)_{+,\times}$ and D a θ-universal elliptic operator on a C^{∞}-manifold (resp. complex analytic manifold). Then the class c(D) is equal to the value of $ch(\theta)$ on the cotangent bundle $T^{*}(X)$, (resp. the complex dual of the tangent bundle) of X:

$$c(D) = ch(\theta)(T^{*}(X)) \quad .$$

In particular, when $\theta = \Lambda' \otimes \mathbf{C}$, we have $\omega(\theta) = 2$, and the Lemma 2.1 implies

$$\tau(\tau(ch \circ \Lambda' \otimes \mathbf{C})(ch \circ \Lambda' \otimes \mathbf{C}) = 1 \quad ,$$

hence the Proposition 3.2 implies

THEOREM 3.1. If X is an even-dimensional oriented manifold and D a $\Lambda' \otimes \mathbf{C}$-universal elliptic operator e.g., "$d+\delta$", then the class $c(D)$ is equal to the negative Euler class of X, and in particular, its topological index is given by

$$i_t(D) = \chi(T(X))[X] \quad .$$

Similarly, we have (cf. Theorem 2.1.)

THEOREM 3.2. If X is an even-dimensional oriented manifold and D a $\widetilde{\Lambda}^-$-universal elliptic operator e.g., the one defined in Chapter V, Lemma 6, then the class $c(D)$ is equal to the "$-2L^{1/2}$", in particular

$$i_t(D) = L(T(X))[X] \quad .$$

Now we remark that it is sufficient to study the case "without coefficient bundle" for the Riemann-Roch-Hirzebruch formula(cf. Chapter XIX, §4.5) in fact

PROPOSITION 3.3. Let D be an elliptic operator of order 1 from a complex vector bundle to an-other, and F is a coefficient bundle. Then the character of "$D \hat{\otimes} 1_F$" (cf. notation in Chapter IV, §8) is given by

$$ch(D \hat{\otimes} 1_F) = ch(D) \cdot ch(F) \quad .$$

THEOREM 3.3. If X is a complex analytic manifold and D a Λ'-universal elliptic operator e.g., "$\bar{\partial} + \vartheta$", then the class $c(D)$ is equal to the "$-\mathcal{T}$", of the complex dual of its tangent bundle $T(X)$, in particular

$$i_t(D) = \mathcal{T}(T(X))[X] \quad .$$

Remark 3.1. Generalizations and details will appear elsewhere, the proofs are analogous to those in Borel [4].

REFERENCES

[1] J. F. Adams, "Vector fields on spheres," Ann. of Math., vol. 75, No. 3, 1962.

[2] D. W. Anderson, "A new cohomology theory," (to appear).

[3] M. F. Atiyah and F. Hirzebruch, "Cohomologie Operationen und characterische Klassen," Math. Zeitschr, vol. 77, 1961.

[4] A. Borel, "Sur la cohomologie des espaces fibrés principaux et des espaces homogènes de groupes de Lie compacts," Ann. of Math. vol. 57, 1953.

[5] R. Bott, "Lectures on K(X)," Harvard University, 1962.

[6] T. tom Dieck, "Tagungsbericht Topologie," Math. Forschungsinstitut, Oberwolfach, Germany, 1963.

[7] F. Hirzebruch, "Neue topologische Methoden in der algebraischen Geometrie," Ergebnisse der Math., Springer, 1956.

[8] J. Milnor, "Lectures on characteristic classes," Princeton University, 1957.

PRINCETON MATHEMATICAL SERIES

Edited by Marston Morse and A. W. Tucker

1. The Classical Groups, Their Invariants and Representations
By HERMANN WEYL ....314 pp. $6.00
3. An Introduction to Differential Geometry
By LUTHER PFAHLER EISENHART ....316 pp. $7.50
4. Dimension Theory
By WITOLD HUREWICZ and HENRY WALLMAN ....174 pp. $4.50
5. Analytical Foundations of Celestial Mechanics
By AUREL WINTNER ....460 pp. $9.00
6. The Laplace Transform
By DAVID VERNON WIDDER ....416 pp. $7.50
7. Integration
By EDWARD J. MCSHANE ....400 pp. $7.50
8. Theory of Lie Groups: I
By CLAUDE CHEVALLEY ....229 pp. $5.00
9. Mathematical Methods of Statistics
By HARALD CRAMER ....570 pp. $10.00
10. Several Complex Variables
By S. BOCHNER and W. T. MARTIN ....216 pp. $6.00
11. Introduction to Topology
By S. LEFSCHETZ ....226 pp. $6.00
12. Algebraic Geometry and Topology
Edited by R. H. FOX, D. C. SPENCER, and A. W. TUCKER ....408 pp. $10.00
14. The Topology of Fibre Bundles
By NORMAN STEENROD ....232 pp. $5.00
15. Foundations of Algebraic Topology
By SAMUEL EILENBERG and NORMAN STEENROD ....342 pp. $9.00
16. Functionals of Finite Riemann Surfaces
By MENAHEM SCHIFFER and DONALD C. SPENCER ....464 pp. $10.00
17. Introduction to Mathematical Logic, Vol. I
By ALONZO CHURCH ....384 pp. $9.00
18. Algebraic Geometry
By S. LEFSCHETZ ....242 pp. $7.50
19. Homological Algebra
By H. CARTAN and S. EILENBERG ....408 pp. $9.00
20. The Convolution Transform
By I. I. HIRSCHMAN and D. V. WIDDER ....280 pp. $6.50
21. Geometric Integration Theory
By HASSLER WHITNEY ....396 pp. $10.00
22. Qualitative Theory of Differential Equations
By V. V. NEMICKII and V. V. STEPANOV ....530 pp. $15.00
23. Topological Analysis, REVISED EDITION
By GORDON T. WHYBURN ....132 pp. $5.00
24. Analytic Functions
By AHLFORS, BEHNKE and GRAUERT, BERS, *et al.* ....204 pp. $5.00
25. Continuous Geometry
By JOHN VON NEUMANN ....296 pp. $7.50
26. Riemann Surfaces
By L. AHLFORS and L. SARIO ....393 pp. $10.00
27. Differential and Combinatorial Topology
Edited by S. S. CAIRNS ....273 pp. $8.50

PRINCETON UNIVERSITY PRESS
PRINCETON, NEW JERSEY